DIGITAL PLL FREQUENCY SYNTHESIZERS

Theory and Design

DIGITAL PLL
FREQUENCY
SYNTHESIZERS

Theory and Design

ULRICH L. ROHDE, Ph.D., Sc.D.

Partner of Rohde & Schwarz, Munich, West Germany
Adjunct Professor, Department of Electrical Engineering,
George Washington University, Washington, D.C.
President, Communications Consulting Corp., Upper
Saddle River, New Jersey

Prentice-Hall, Inc., Englewood Cliffs, N. J., 07632

Library of Congress Cataloging in Publication Data

Rohde, Ulrich L.
   Digital PLL frequency synthesizers.

   Bibliography: p.
   Includes index.
   1. Frequency synthesizers.   2. Phase-locked
loops.   3. Digital electronics.   I. Title.
TK7872.F73R63 1983   621.3815′33   82-11216
ISBN 0-13-214239-2

Neither the author nor the publisher assumes any responsibility regarding the operating performance of the schematics used in this text.

Editorical/production supervision by Barbara Bernstein
Manufacturing buyer: Gordon Osbourne

Printed in the United States of America

10 9 8 7 6 5 4 3

ISBN   0-13-214239-2

PRENTICE-HALL INTERNATIONAL, INC., *London*
PRENTICE-HALL OF AUSTRALIA PTY. LIMITED, *Sydney*
EDITORA PRENTICE-HALL DO BRAZIL, LTDA, *Rido de Janeiro*
PRENTICE-HALL CANADA LTD., *Toronto*
PRENTICE-HALL OF INDIA PRIVATE LIMITED, *New Delhi*
PRENTICE-HALL OF JAPAN, INC., *Tokyo*
PRENTICE-HALL OF SOUTHEAST ASIA PTE. LTD., *Singapore*
WHITEHALL BOOKS LIMITED, *Wellington, New Zealand*

Contents

Preface

Practically all modern signal generators and radio communication equipment make heavy use of digital frequency synthesizers. Information about the design of those synthesizers is scattered in various articles, and most books place emphasis on theoretical description and mathematics.

The objective of this book is to provide as much practical circuit information as possible while presenting only the necessary mathematical background and formulas. The book, therefore, addresses itself to college students who have to get acquainted with phase-locked loops (PLLs) or have to build certain projects, to practicing engineers who are designing synthesizers for various applications, and to senior engineers and people in management functions to be able to evaluate new trends and techniques. Whereas most books on this matter show no detailed circuits, I acquaint the reader with practical and reliable circuits that can be used as starting tools.

Most design engineers, technicians, and students have access to small desktop calculators or computers, probably in BASIC. Programs for the solution of digital PLL systems are provided. Results are tabulated, and Bode diagrams determined by the computer's graphic capabilities are shown. In addition, a number of small programs for hand-held calculators are given.

A number of novel techniques and approaches are shown in this book, and special attention is paid to nonlinear effects and tracking behavior of phase/frequency comparators. The book is divided into seven chapters, starting with Chapter 1 on loop fundamentals. Chapter 2 outlines the noise and spurious response of loops and Chapter 3 deals with special loops, most of them having been developed fairly recently. Chapter 4 discusses analyzing PLL components.

Many practical details will be found in this section for low-noise oscillators, the influence of tuning diodes, frequency standard design, and nonlinear effects in digital tri-state comparators. In addition, a section on wideband high-gain amplifiers deals with the requirements of loops with sampling frequencies above 100 kHz and other requirements of special amplifiers.

Chapter 5 goes into the details of multiloop synthesizers, starting with such earlier design principles as mix and divide, triple mix, or drift canceling loops. The ground rules for setting up complex loops are then laid out, and the use of micro-processors in frequency synthesizers and their use in communication equipment is then dealt with.

Chapter 6 consists of the analysis and schematic details of three practical synthesizers as a design guide.

Finally, the Appendix is divided into a mathematical review and into a list of useful computer programs.

Most of the practical information given in this book is a result of my work as Head of the R&D Military Communications Division of AEG Telefunken, Ulm West Germany; as a consultant to various companies, such as RCA Astro Division; and my activities as a Professor of Electrical Engineering at the University of Florida, Gainesville.

It should be noted that no single person can design or create all these things alone. Therefore, I would like to take this opportunity to thank all my friends and colleagues, especially those of Rohde & Schwarz, who have helped me and provided me with up-to-the-minute information on circuits for this book. The computer-aided design analysis programs were developed and tested together wirh Mr. Bruno Binggeli of Laboratory RCA, Zurich, Switzerland. The PLL high-order phase-locked loop analysis program was put together by Mr. Krause of Rohde & Schwarz, Munich. All of the programs in this book were carefully tested and used as design tools in the work of frequency synthesizers in the past. Dr. Jack Smith of the University of Florida, Gainesville, contributed substantially to the theoretical part of this book with a number of new ideas and practical examples that were used in classes. Many com-panies helped me in providing essential detailed material, and I am grateful to have received permission from Adams Russell, Anzac Division, to use their latest informa-tion on mixers; from KVG Company (West Germany) for information on crystal and crystal oscillator design; from ITT (Intermetall, West Germany) for information on switching diodes and tuning diodes application; from Hewlett-Packard for information on low-noise designing and measuring techniques, as well as on fractional division N principles; from California Microwave for information on UHF synthesizer design; from Motorola Semiconductor Products for information on integrated circuits; from Rohde & Schwarz, Munich, for being allowed to publish details of current frequency synthesizer design; from Dr. Roland Best and Fachschriftenverlag, Aargauer Tagblatt AG, Aarau/Schweiz, for using his unique design describing the pull-in method for the tri-state phase/frequency comparator; from Philips Semiconductor, England, for information on LSI synthesizer ICs; and last but not least, *MicroWaves, Electronics, Electronic Design, r.f. design, EDN Magazine*, and *ham radio magazine*, for permis-sion to use excerpts from selected papers. I am especially grateful to Mr. David Boelio of Prentice-Hall for allowing me to update the manuscript right up to the last minute; to Mrs. Lynne Peterson, who spent endless hours typing and correcting the manuscript; and to my family for their understanding of the time I devoted to this project.

ULRICH L. ROHDE, PH.D., SC.D.

Upper Saddle River, New Jersey

Important Notations

Symbol	Meaning
a_i $(i = 1, 2, \ldots, n)$	Loop parameters of nth-order PLL
a_n, a_k	Digital data values
A	Amplifier gain
$A(s)$	Open-loop gain
$A(\omega)$	Amplitude of transfer function
	Amplitude response of network
B_i	Bandwidth of input bandpass filter (Hz)
B_L	Noise bandwidth of PLL (Hz)
$B(s)$	Closed-loop gain of PLL
$E(s)$	Error function
F	Noise figure
f, f_i	Frequency (Hz)
f_c	Corner frequency of flicker noise
f_m	Fourier frequency (sideband, offset, modulation, baseband frequency)
f_o	Carrier frequency
$f(t)$	Instantaneous frequency
Δf	Peak frequency deviation (Hz)
$\Delta f(t)$	Instantaneous frequency fluctuation

Δf_{peak}	Peak deviation of sinusoidal frequency modulation
Δf_{res}	Residual FM
$F(s), F(j\omega)$	Transfer function of loop filter
$G(s), G(j\omega)$	Feedforward function (rad/s)
$G_n(s)$	Transfer characteristic of a divider
$H(s), H(j\omega)$	Feedback transfer function
K	Loop gain (rad/s)
K_d'	Phase detector gain before lock (V/rad)
K_θ	Phase detector gain factor (V/rad)
K_m	Multiplier gain
K_o	VCO gain factor (rad/s V)
K_s	Shapter constant
K_v	Dc gain of PLL
	Velocity error coefficient (rad/s)
k	An integer
	An integer index on a sequence
k	1.4×10^{-23} W s/°K
$L(x)$	Laplace transform of x
$\mathcal{L}(f_m)$	Single-sideband phase noise to total signal power in a 1-Hz bandwidth
m	An integer
$m(t)$	Modulation waveshape
M	An integer denoting frequency multiplication or division
n	An integer
n	Loop order
$n(t)$	Noise voltage (V)
$\overline{n(t)}$	Time average of noise
N, N_i	An integer representing frequency division or multiplication
$P(j\omega)$	Fourier transform of pulse waveshape
P_s	Signal power (W)
P_{ssB}	Power of single sideband
P_{sav}	Available signal power
Q_{unl}	Quality factor of unloaded resonator
$s = \sigma + j\omega$	Laplace transform complex variable
SNR	Signal-to-noise ratio
SNR_L	Signal-to-noise ratio in loop bandwidth $2B_L$
S_o	One-sided spectral density of white noise (dB/Hz)
$S_{\Delta f}(f_m)$	Spectral density of frequency fluctuations

$S_y(f_m)$	Spectral density of fractional frequency fluctuations
$S_{\Delta\theta}(f_m)$	Spectral density of phase perturbation
$S_{\Delta\phi}(f_m)$	Spectral density of phase noise
t	Time (s)
t_{acq}	Acquisition time of a loop
t_{lock}	Lock-in time for phase lock
T	Symbol interval of digital data stream (s)
T_{AV}	Average time to first cycle slip (s)
T_o	Degrees Kelvin
T_p	Pull-in time (s)
v_c, V_c	VCO control voltage (V)
v_d, V_d	Phase detector output voltage (V)
$v(t)$	Instantaneous voltage
V_o	Peak amplitude of VCO voltage (V)
V_s	Peak amplitude of signal voltage (V)
V_{sL}	Peak amplitude of sinusoidal signal at limiting port
$V_{n\,rms}$	Equivalent noise voltage (1-Hz bandwidth)
V_{sav}	Available signal voltage
W_e	Maximum energy stored in capacitor
W_i	Spectral density of white noise (W/Hz)
$y(t)$	Instantaneous fractional frequency offset from nominal frequency
θ	Phase angle (rad)
θ_i	Phase angle of input signal (rad)
$\theta_e = \theta_i - \theta_o$	Phase error between input signal and VCO (rad)
θ_o	VCO phase (rad)
θ_p	Loop phase error caused by oscillator noise (rad)
θ_v	Steady-state phase error (static phase error, loop stress) due to offset of input frequency (rad)
$\Delta\theta$	Phase deviation (rad)
$\Delta\theta$	Amplitude of phase step (rad)
$\Delta\theta$	Peak deviation of phase modulation (rad)
$\Delta\theta(t)$	Instantaneous fluctuation of phase perturbation
ζ	Damping factor of second-order loop
ρ	Signal-to-noise ratio
ρ_{sav}	Input signal-to-noise ratio
σ_n	Standard deviation (rms value) of noise $n(t)$ (V)
$\sigma_y^2(\tau)$	Allan variance

τ	Time constant (s)
τ_1, τ_2, τ_L	Time constants in loop filter (s)
τ_p	Pull-in time constant
$\Delta\phi(t)$	Instantaneous phase fluctuation
$\Delta\phi_{peak}$	Peak deviation of sinusoidal phase modulation, also modulation index
ϕ	Loop phase error reduced modulo 2π (rad)
ϕ_{N_o}	Phase fluctuation internal to an oscillator
$\phi(\omega)$	Phase of transfer function of a network
ψ	Phase of a transfer function (rad)
$\omega = 2\pi f$	Angular frequency (rad/s)
$j\omega$	Fourier transform variable
ω_i	Radian frequency of input signal (rad/s)
ω_m	Modulating frequency (rad/s)
ω_n	Natural frequency of second-order loop (rad/s)
$\Delta\omega$	Amplitude of frequency step or of frequency offset (rad/s)
$\Delta\omega$	Peak deviation of frequency modulation (rad/s)
$\Delta\dot{\omega}$	Rate of change of frequency (rad/s²)
$\Delta\omega_H$	Hold-in limit of PLL (rad/s)
$\Delta\omega_L$	Lock-in limit of PLL (rad/s)
$\Delta\omega_P$	Pull-in limit of PLL (rad/s)
$\Omega(s)$	Laplace transform $L[\Delta\omega(t)]$

DIGITAL PLL
FREQUENCY
SYNTHESIZERS
Theory and Design

1

Loop Fundamentals

1-1 INTRODUCTION TO LINEAR LOOPS

The majority of the new frequency synthesizers utilize the phase-locked loop (PLL). Indeed, it was the realization of the PLL in an integrated circuit that led to the inexpensive frequency synthesizer. Because an understanding of PLLs is necessary for the design of frequency synthesizers, they are discussed in detail in this chapter. The emphasis here is on the PLL as used in a frequency synthesizer rather than on the PLL as used for signal detection. For the latter problem, the PLL input is a relatively low-level signal embedded in noise, and the PLL serves to detect the noisy signal. For PLL applications in frequency synthesizers, the input signal-to-noise ratio is high, and the PLL serves to lock out the output frequency on a multiple of the input frequency.

Although the PLL is a nonlinear device, it can be modeled as a linear device over most of its operating range. This chapter first presents the linearized analysis of the PLL, including its stability characteristics. The design of compensating filters to improve PLL performance is then discussed.

PLLs include a phase detector, low-pass filter, and voltage-controlled oscillator, as illustrated in Figure 1-1. The phase detector is a nonlinear device, and its characteristics determine loop performance. The various types of phase detectors are described in Chapter 3. The loop transient performance is discussed in Section 1-10. No generalized results are available for transient performance, but the discussion illustrates one analysis approach that can be used.

Several books have been published on this matter, and for those involved in

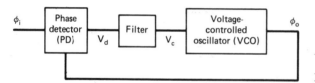

ϕ_i

ϕ_o

Figure 1-1   Block diagram of a PLL.

research or interested in a more theoretical approach of the PLL principle, the following books are recommended:

BEST, ROLAND, *Theory and Application of Phase-Locked Loops* (Theorie und Anwendungen des phase-locked Loops), Fachschriftenverlag Aargauer Tagblatt AG, Aarau, Switzerland, 1976 (Order No. ISBN 3–85502–011–6).

BLANCHARD, ALAIN, *Phase-Locked Loops*, Wiley, New York, 1976.

EGAN, WILLIAM F., *Frequency Synthesis by Phase Lock*, Wiley, New York, 1981.

GARDNER, FLOYD M., *Phaselock Techniques*, 2nd ed., Wiley, New York, 1980.

GORSKI-POPIEL, JERZY, *Frequency Synthesis Techniques and Applications*, IEEE Press, New York, 1975.

KLAPPER, JACOB, and JOHN T. FRANKLE, *Phase-Locked and Frequency Feedback Systems*, Academic Press, New York, 1972.

KROUPA, VENCESLAV F., *Frequency Synthesis Theory, Design and Applications*, Griffin, London, 1973.

MANASSEWITSCH, VADIM, *Frequency Synthesizers Theory and Design*, 2nd ed., Wiley, New York. 1980.

The term *phase-locked loop* refers to a feedback loop in which the input and feedback parameters of interest are the relative phases of the waveforms. The function of a PLL is to track small differences in phase between the input and feedback signal. The phase detector measures the phase difference between its two inputs. The phase detector output is then filtered by the low-pass filter and applied to the voltage-controlled oscillator (VCO). The VCO input voltage changes the VCO frequency in a direction that reduces the phase difference between the input signal and the local oscillator. The loop is said to be in *phase lock* or *locked* when the phase difference is reduced to zero.

Although the PLL is nonlinear since the phase detector is nonlinear, it can be accurately modeled as a linear device when the loop is in lock. When the loop is locked, it is assumed that the phase detector output voltage is proportional to the difference in phase between its inputs; that is,

$$V_d = K_\theta(\theta_i - \theta_o) \tag{1-1}$$

where θ_i and θ_o are the phases of the input and VCO output signals, respectively. K_θ is the phase detector gain factor and has the dimensions of volts per radian. It will also be assumed that the VCO can be modeled as a linear device whose output frequency deviates from its free-running frequency by an increment of frequency

$$\Delta\omega = K_o V_e \tag{1-2}$$

where V_e is the voltage at the output of the low-pass filter and K_o is the VCO gain factor, with the dimensions of rad/s per volt. Since frequency is the time derivative of phase, the VCO operation can be described as

$$\Delta\omega = \frac{d\theta_o}{dt} = K_o V_e \tag{1-3}$$

With these assumptions, the PLL can be represented by the linear model shown in Figure 1-2. $F(s)$ is the transfer function of the low-pass filter. The linear transfer function relating $\theta_o(s)$ and $\theta_i(s)$ is

$$B(s) = \frac{\theta_o(s)}{\theta_i(s)} = \frac{K_\theta K_o F(s)/s}{1 + K_\theta K_o F(s)/s} \tag{1-4}$$

If no low-pass filter is used, the transfer function is

$$B(s) = \frac{\theta_o}{\theta_i} = \frac{K_\theta K_o}{s + K_\theta K_o} = \frac{K}{s + K} \tag{1-5}$$

which is equivalent to the transfer function of a simple low-pass filter with unity dc gain and bandwidth equal to K.

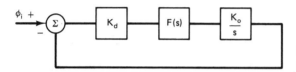

Figure 1-2 Block diagram of a PLL using a linearized model.

This is really the minimum configuration of a PLL. Since there is no divider in the chain, the output frequency and the reference frequency are the same. The first PLL built probably used a ring modulator as a phase detector. The ring modulator or diode bridge is electrically the same as a four-quadrant multiplier and operates from $-\pi$ to $+\pi$ of phase range.

Since the VCO probably has a sine-wave output and the reference frequency also has a sine wave, it is referred to as a *sinusoidal phase detector*. This does not really mean that the phase detector is sinusoidal; it means that the waves applied to the phase detector are sinusoidal.

Since there are no digital components in this basic loop, it is correctly called an *analog phase-locked loop* and, as stated above, is the minimum form of a phase-locked loop. To model it correctly, a number of assumptions are required.

We have already stated that, for our initial consideration, the loop is locked and that the transfer characteristic of the phase frequency detector is linear in the area of operation. A four-quadrant multiplier or diode quad has a sinusoidal output voltage as shown in Figure 1-3, and is only piecewise linear for $\theta = 0$ or in the center of operation.

This minimum configuration of a PLL has several drawbacks. The absence of a filter does not allow one to choose parameters for optimized performance; the diode ring has only several hundred millivolts output, and an additional loop amplifier will add noise to the system. Therefore, for frequency synthesizer applications, a simple

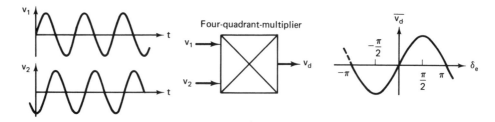

Figure 1-3 Waveform and transient characteristic of a linear phase detector.

analog loop without any filter is rarely used. Such a loop would be called a first-order type 1 loop, and we will deal with it later.

There are some applications for a 1:1 loop, as we will see. The 1:1 loop is used to clean up an existing frequency, whereby the loop bandwidth is kept narrow enough to allow fast locking, and wide enough to permit fast acquisition. However, the loop bandwidth is more narrow than the spurious frequencies present at the reference input. The attenuation of the loop filter of such a loop, which should be a second-order loop, will clean up the output signal relative to the reference.

1-2 CHARACTERISTICS OF A LOOP

We have met the minimum-configuration analog PLL and already learned that there are several limitations to this loop. The first step in increasing the output voltage delivered from the diode quad and avoiding an operational amplifier is to use a different phase detector.

If the diode bridge arrangement is changed and the diodes are overdriven by the reference signal and the input signal from the VCO remains sufficiently small relative to the reference, the phase detector is still in a linear operation mode, and the output signal of the phase detector is no longer a sinusoidal curve but rather has a linear sawtooth form. The range over which the phase detector operates is still from $-\pi$ to $+\pi$, and the circuit is called *quasi-digital*. Later, when dealing with ring modulators, we will learn that it is a major requirement that the reference or LO signal must have a specified range, with a minimum typically 0.5 V for hot carrier diodes, and the VCO voltage should be substantially smaller for linear operation.

As the amplitude of the VCO signal is increased, the diode bridge or double-balanced modulator is overdriven, and a large number of harmonics occur. In a 1:1 loop, this is not very dangerous because all harmonics are phase and frequency coherent and do not generate unwanted signals. If a double-balanced mixer is used in a conversion scheme inside a loop, as we will see later, it is of utmost importance to operate the double-balanced mixer in its linear range and use a double-balanced mixer that has sufficient isolation between all ports.

In the case of the double-balanced mixer, whether overdriven from the LO or not, we refer to it as an analog linear phase-locked loop. If the VCO signal also overdrives the double-balanced mixer, we call it quasi-digital.

4

The digital equivalent of a double-balanced mixer is the exclusive-OR gate. The exclusive-OR gate, when built in CMOS logic, can be operated at 12 V, and therefore the dc output voltage can now be from almost 0 to +12 V, obtained from the integrator. We now have found a way to increase our dc control voltage without the noise sacrifice of an additional operational amplifier.

Both the double-balanced mixer and the exclusive-OR gate are only phase sensitive. The exclusive-OR gate also operates from $-\pi$ to $+\pi$, and the VCO has to be pretuned to be within the capture range.

Both phase detectors can be used for harmonic locking.

When we analyze the various loop components in Chapter 4 we will find some drawbacks that limit the use of the exclusive-OR gate.

The edge-triggered JK master/slave flip-flop can be used as a phase/frequency comparator. It operates from -2π to $+2\pi$. The edge-triggered JK master/slave flip-flop has two outputs. One output supplies pulses to charge a capacitor, and the other can be used to discharge a capacitor.

To use this phase/frequency detector requires an active loop filter or active integrator, commonly referred to as a *charge pump*. This type of phase detector generates a beat frequency at the output, and the average dc voltage generated in the integrator is either negative or positive, relative to half the power supply voltage, depending on whether the signal frequency is higher or lower than the reference. This is a useful feature and explains why we can state that this circuit is not only phase sensitive but also frequency sensitive. Unfortunately, the frequency sensitivity for this type of phase/frequency discriminator is useful only for large differences. For very small differences in frequency, there is very little advantage in choosing this circuit over the exclusive-OR gate or the double-balanced mixer. We will learn more about this circuit in Chapter 4.

The most important circuit for phase/frequency comparators is probably an arrangement of two flip-flops and several gates. This particular circuit will be called a *tri-state phase/frequency comparator*, for reasons we will see later. It has several advantages:

1. The operating range is linear, from -2π to $+2\pi$.
2. It has the best possible locking performance and best frequency and phase difference detection.
3. Regardless of the amount of frequency error, the average output voltage is always above or below half the operating voltage. This results in good locking.

The last two types of phase/frequency detectors, because of their charge/discharge capability, require active filters or summation circuits. It is theoretically possible to avoid the amplifier and use purely resistive circuits, but as we will soon learn, this has disadvantages. So far, we still have only used a loop that has no frequency divider.

The introduction of a frequency divider requires that the input to the divider be a square wave (TTL), and we will now define all loops that use digital dividers and phase/frequency comparators as digital loops. This should not be confused with digital synthesizers. A digital frequency synthesizer is most likely a direct synthesizer in which the output frequency is digitally generated with the help of a computer and is not available anywhere in analog or sine-wave form. The output frequency is then the summation of several digital signals in a quasi-sine wave at the output generated only by means of digital circuitry. There are several methods besides the one currently used, which employs a lookup table for sine or cosine functions. For very low frequency application, a complicated arrangement of diodes can be used to generate sine waves out of triangular waveshapes. Table 1-1 shows a comparison of the various phase/frequency detectors.

We have learned that because of its wider operating range, the phase-locked loop using digital phase/frequency comparators offers significant advantages over the analog PLL, and that is the main reason it is used in frequency synthesizers.

A closed loop is really a feedback system, and the various rules for feedback systems apply. We have already written down without further justification the formula that applies for a closed loop:

$$B(s) = \frac{\text{forward gain}}{1 + (\text{open-loop gain})} \tag{1-6}$$

Before we continue, let us take a look at some of the abbreviations and definitions that are used in feedback control systems. Figure 1-4 shows the equivalent block diagram of a feedback system. The gain is equal to the multiplication of the VCO gain K_o times the phase/frequency comparator K_θ and will be abbreviated by K:

TABLE 1-1 COMPARISON OF VARIOUS PHASE/FREQUENCY COMPARATORS

Type	Operating range	Sensitivity
Diode ring	$-\pi$ to π	Phase only
Exclusive-OR gate	$-\pi$ to π	Phase only
Edge-triggered JK flip-flop	-2π to 2π $(-\pi$ to $\pi)$; see Table 1-2	Phase frequency; undefined for small errors
Tri-state phase/ frequency comparator	-2π to 2π	Phase frequency

$$K = K_o K_\theta \frac{\text{rad} \cdot S^{-1}}{V} \frac{V}{\text{rad}} \tag{1-7}$$

The feedforward function

$$G(s) = \frac{K}{s} F(s) \tag{1-8}$$

takes a filter function $F(s)$ into consideration, and the fact that the VCO itself is a perfect integrator is also taken into consideration.

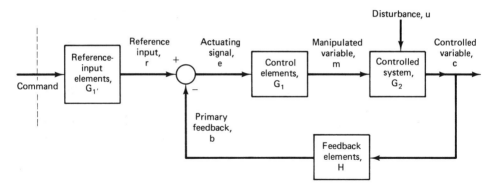

Figure 1-4   Equivalent diagram of a PLL using feedback control system analogy.

To close the loop, we have to describe the feedback transfer function

$$H(s) = \frac{1}{N} \tag{1-9}$$

which will describe the divider ratio N and assumes that there is no delay in the divider. If there is delay in the divider, $H(s)$ is expressed in the form

$$H(s)^* = \frac{e^{-T_n s}}{N} \tag{1-10}$$

Therefore, the open-loop gain of the system

$$A(s) = G(s)H(s) \tag{1-11}$$

This definition of open-loop gain must not be confused with the open gain K or the feedforward gain. From our definition above, the closed-loop gain

$$
\begin{aligned}
B(s) &= \frac{\text{forward gain}}{1 + (\text{open-loop gain})} \\[2mm]
&= \frac{\theta_o(s)}{\theta_i(s)} \\[2mm]
&= \frac{G(s)}{1 + G(s)H(s)} \\[2mm]
&= \frac{K(s)F(s)}{s + K(s)F(s)/N}
\end{aligned} \tag{1-12}
$$

It has become customary to incorporate the divider ratio N in the K, which means that K in most cases can be said to equal

$$\frac{K_o K_\theta}{N}$$

If this substitution is made, the formulas are generally valid, provided that the correct factor of K is selected, and the formulas are generally usable regardless of the actual division ratio. In synthesizer design it is interesting to determine the system's noise bandwidth, B_n, which is defined as

$$B_n = \frac{1}{2\pi} \int_0^\infty B(j\omega)\, d\omega \qquad (1\text{-}13)$$

The 3-dB bandwidth can be determined by solving the equation substituting $|B_n(j\omega)| = 0.707$; the resulting $j\omega$ would then be the 3-dB bandwidth, the complex variable j deleted. Another important piece of information in feedback control system performance is the *steady-state error*, that is, the error remaining after all transients have died out. The equation for the error function

$$E(s) = \frac{\theta_e}{\theta_i} = 1 - B(s) = \frac{1}{1 + G(s)H(s)} \qquad (1\text{-}14)$$

We will compute the steady-state error as a function of the various systems in Section 1-10 and make some predictions on loops of various orders. I have previously mentioned that we have classified the loops to be either analog or digital, referring to the phase/frequency detector, and in writing the initial equations, I have already indicated that the loop may or may not have a filter incorporated.

In analyzing the loop, we will find that to describe a loop, we can express it both in terms of the order of the loop and the type of loop. The expression "type of loop" refers to the number of integrators used. A PLL using no active integrator can really only be a type 1 loop. The phrase "order" refers to the order of the polynomial which is required to express the loop transfer characteristic.

The absolute minimum in a loop is a phase/frequency detector, a VCO, and no filter. By this definition, this would be a first-order type 1 loop. Another way of explaining this is by saying that the type of a system refers to the number of poles of the loop transfer function locked at the origin. The order of a system refers to the highest degree of the polynomial expression of the denominator that can be expanded into a polynomial expression. In this book we deal with loops of types 1 and 2 from first order up to fifth.

We have now learned that there are two classifications for loops:

1. Classification by phase detector, characterizing the loop to be analog or digital
2. Characterizing the loop by the type of loop filter and number of integrators

1-3 DIGITAL LOOPS

Using our previous definition, a digital PLL is a PLL system in which the phase/ frequency comparator is built from digital components such as gates or flip-flops to form either an exclusive-OR gate, an edge-triggered JK master/slave flip-flop, or what I call a tri-state phase/frequency comparator. In addition, digital PLLs use frequency dividers, and although some circuits using the principle of subharmonic locking for dividers are known, this generally refers to the use of asynchronous or synchronous dividers. Asynchronous dividers are usually ripple counters, and synchronous dividers are counters that are being clocked by a common reset line.

The basic difference between an analog and a digital phase/frequency loop is in the possible delay introduced by the frequency divider and the nonlinear effects of the phase/frequency comparator, and the question of ultimate resolution of the phase/frequency comparator. The phase/frequency comparator using active filters shows some highly nonlinear performance during zero crossings at the output or under perfectly locked conditions. As there is no output from a tri-state phase/frequency comparator under locked conditions, the gain of the loop is zero until there is a requirement to send correcting pulses from the digital phase/frequency comparator, which then results in a jump of loop gain.

We will prove that digital phase/frequency comparators, especially tri-state phase/frequency comparators, have two ranges for acquisition. One is called *pull-in* range, and the other is called *lock-in* range. The acquisition time is the time for both. This total time to acquire both frequency and phase lock is sometimes called *capture time* or *digital acquisition time*. Depending on the loop filter and the phase/frequency comparator, we will have different time constants.

For reasons of convenience and linearity, we have, so far, assumed that the loop is in locked condition. Initially, when the loop is switched on for the first time, it is far from being locked, and the VCO frequency can be anywhere within tuning range. *Tuning range* is defined as the frequency range over which the voltage-controlled oscillator (VCO) can be tuned with the available control voltage.

There are, however, limitations because of the tuning diodes. The minimum voltage that can be applied is determined by the threshold voltage of the diode itself before it becomes conductive. This voltage is typically 0.7 V, and the maximum voltage is the voltage determined by the breakdown voltage of the tuning diode. Even in the case where the familiar back-to-back diode arrangement is used, these are the two limits for the voltage range. In practice, however, this range is even more narrow because the voltage sensitivity of the tuning diode is excessive at the very low end and very small at the extreme high end. Even before the breakdown voltage is reached, the noise contribution from the diode already increases because of some zener effects.

As the loop currently is not in locked condition, we have to help it to acquire lock. Very few loops acquire locking by themselves, a process called *self-acquisition*. Generally, the tuning range is larger than the acquisition range. Self-acquisition is a slow, unreliable process. If the loop is closed for the first time, the process called "pull-in" will occur. The oscillator frequency, together with the reference frequency, will generate a beat note and a dc control voltage of such phases that the VCO is pulled in a direction of frequency lock. As the oscillator itself generates noise in the form of a residual FM, the oscillator is constantly trying to break out of lock, and the loop is constantly monitoring the state and reassuring lock. This results, under normal circumstances, in constant charging and discharging of the holding capacitor responsible for the averaging process.

There is one other phase/frequency comparator that is really more a switch than anything else; it is called a *sample/hold comparator*. The sample/hold comparator, which we will deal with later, has the advantage of very good reference frequency suppression, introduces a phase shift which reduces the phase margin, and is really useful only up to several hundred kilohertz of frequency. For frequencies higher than this, there is too much leakage. The sample/hold comparator, which has been very popular for several years, is described in Chapter 4. Modern frequency synthesizers, however, prefer digital phase/frequency comparators because the sample/hold comparator is only a phase comparator and does not recognize frequency offsets. It is too slow to be used for harmonic sampling and, in my opinion, has only limited use.

The sample/hold comparator is used mostly with T networks for additional reference suppression, and although these circuits provide good reference suppression, the phase margin has to be so high that the loops are generally slow in their response.

The switching speed of the loop and its general performance to noise are covered in detail in Section 1-10.

Now let us take a look at a numerical example. Consider a frequency synthesizer using a PLL to synthesize a 1-MHz signal from a 25-kHz reference frequency. To realize an output frequency of 1 MHz, a division of 1 MHz/25 kHz = 40 is necessary.

Let us assume that there is no filtering included, and therefore the closed-loop transfer function will be

$$B(s) = \frac{K}{s + K/N} \tag{1-15}$$

A typical value for K_θ is 2 V/rad and a typical value for the VCO gain factor K_o is 1000 Hz/V. With these values the closed-loop transfer function is

$$B(s) = \frac{K_\theta K_o}{s + K_\theta K_o/N} = \frac{1000 \times 2\pi \times 2}{s + [(1000 \times 2\pi \times 2)/40]} = \frac{4000\pi}{s + 100\pi} \tag{1-16}$$

The 3-dB frequency of the system by definition is

$$\omega_{3dB} = \frac{K_\theta K_o}{N} \tag{1-17}$$

and therefore

$$\omega_n = 100\pi$$

If this is solved to determine f, we obtain $f = 50$ Hz.

As the reference frequency is 25 kHz, the reference suppression of the simple system can be determined from

$$A = 20 \log_{10} \left(\frac{25{,}000}{50}\right) = 20 \log_{10} (500)$$

$$= 54 \text{ dB}$$

The loop bandwidth of the system by itself is 50 Hz.

We have, with very little effort, calculated a first-order type 1 loop. We deal more with these loops in Chapter 2.

Table 1-2 shows the input waveforms and the output average voltage of:

1. A four-quadrant multiplier or double-balanced mixer being driven either by a sine wave or a squarewave.
2. The input and output voltages for an exclusive-OR gate.
3. The input and output voltages after the integrator of an edge-triggered JK master/slave flip-flop.

4. The input and output voltages of a tri-state phase/frequency comparator after the integrator. Notice that the extended operating range is linear from -2π to $+2\pi$.

TABLE 1-2 CIRCUIT DIAGRAMS AND INPUT AND OUTPUT WAVEFORMS OF VARIOUS PHASE/FREQUENCY COMPARATORS[a]

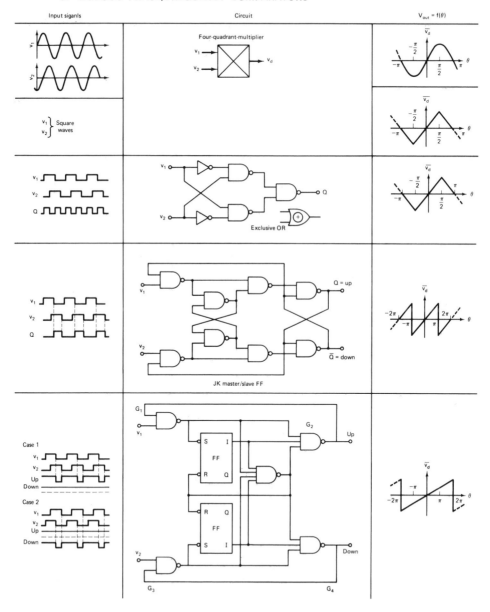

| Input siganls | Circuit | $V_{out} = f(\theta)$ |

[a]Courtesy of Fachschriftenverlag, Aargauer Tagblatt AG, Aarau/Switzerland.

1-4 TYPE 1 FIRST-ORDER LOOPS

The type 1 first-order loop contains a digital phase/frequency comparator and a digital divider, and throughout the rest of this book we will deal only with digital loops. This is done on the assumption that the phase/frequency comparator can be modeled as a linear device over the operating range, which is certainly not true. However, as most of the formulas and deviations that deal with PLLs have certain assumptions which have finite accuracy, it is permissible to do so. I realize that a purist will be offended by this statement. However, as many PLLs have been designed by rule of thumb and the final results were within a few percent accurate, I assume that the reader will permit this simplification.

The analog loop, as mentioned before, does not provide enough dc output, and for reasons of sideband noise, there is no advantage in using the linear loop in digital frequency synthesizers. Therefore, the phase-locked loop without a loop filter, $F(s) = 1$, is called a type 1 first-order loop because it has only one integrator, and the highest power (s) in the denominator of the system transfer function is 1.

The open-loop gain of a type 1 first-order PLL is equal to the forward gain divided by N, $K_\theta K_o/s/N$. The transfer function is

$$B(s) = \frac{N}{1 + s[1/(K_\theta K_o/N)]} \qquad (1\text{-}18)$$

The loop noise bandwidth can be determined from the integration to be

$$B_n = \frac{K_\theta K_o}{4N} \qquad (1\text{-}19)$$

It should be noted that the noise bandwidth changes as a function of the division ratio N. If there is a large change in the division ratio, the noise bandwidth will change substantially. This is another reason why the type 1 first-order loop is not very popular.

Let us assume that the loop is not in locked condition. The phase/frequency comparator receives two different frequencies at the two inputs. For digital phase/frequency comparators we will use an exclusive-OR gate, which requires an active integrator.

Because of the limits of the operating range, presteering is required for the VCO to be within the range $-\pi$ to $+\pi$ for a locking condition. It is known that the maximum difference between the VCO free-running frequency and the desired final frequency at which phase lock is possible can be equal to

$$\Delta\omega_{\text{capture}} = \Delta\omega_H = \frac{K_\theta K_o}{N} \qquad (\text{rad/s}) \qquad (1\text{-}20)$$

It is important to keep the steady-state phase error small; therefore, high dc loop gain is required. As the increase in loop gain would require an amplifier, this makes the loop noisy and eventually unstable.

I have explained previously that the VCO gain is limited because of the tuning range of the diodes, and we will learn later that it is desirable to keep the VCO gain as low as possible. The input line to the VCO is a high-impedance line, and pick up on this line will result in spurious output at the VCO. To keep the spurious frequencies small, the VCO gain must be kept as small as possible.

The phase detector sensitivity depends mainly on the operating voltage. We recall that the double-balanced modulator with four diodes supplies only several hundred millivolts; instead, the exclusive-OR gate was chosen, as this can be operated from 12 V or even higher if CMOS logic is used.

There are several estimates regarding the acquisition time for the type 1 first-order PLL. Using the exclusive-OR gate, the acquisition time is approximately

$$T_A = \frac{2}{K_\theta K_o / N} \ln \frac{2}{\theta_e} \qquad (1\text{-}21)$$

where ln refers to the natural logarithm and θ_e refers to the final phase error in radians.

From our previous example, the acquisition time T_A would be determined to be

$$T_A = \frac{2}{50} \ln \frac{2}{0.2}$$

$$= 9.2 \times 10^{-2} \text{ s}$$

Assuming that the initial offset was less than 50 Hz, the loop locks in frequency without skipping cycles. In practice, it is impossible to presteer the loop within 50 Hz; therefore, this formula has only limited use.

We have just determined the acquisition time, but we have to ask ourselves: What does it really mean? Does it mean that the frequency from the initial offset is now the same as the reference frequency? Does it mean that we have reached a certain percentage of final frequency or gotten very close to the final frequency or final phase? Will we ever reach the final value, or is there a residual error?

The *error function*, which we met earlier, provides us with information and insight.

$$E(s) = \frac{\theta_e}{\theta_i} = 1 - B(s) = \frac{1}{1 + G(s)H(s)} \qquad (1\text{-}14)$$

It has been shown that, depending on the type of change of input, we get different results. These results are determined by the use of a transformation from the frequency into the time domain. Section A-1-4 of the Appendix presents the mathematical background for the Laplace transform and discusses how it is applied. Here, we use only the results. Inserting the known factors into Eq. (1-14), we obtain

$$E(s) = \frac{s\theta_e(s)}{s + K} \qquad (1\text{-}22)$$

with $K = K_\theta K_o / N$. It is customary to analyze the performance of the loop for three different conditions:

1. To apply a step to the input and see what the output response is
2. A ramp voltage
3. A parabolic input

Case 1, the step input, means an instantaneous jump with zero rise time to which the output will respond with a delay. The steady-state phase error resulting from this step change of input phase of magnitude $\Delta\theta$ for a ramp,

$$\theta(s) = \frac{\Delta\theta}{s} \tag{1-23}$$

is

$$\epsilon = \lim_{s \to 0} \frac{s\,\Delta\theta}{s + K} = 0 \tag{1-24}$$

Case 2, the steady-state error resulting from a ramp of input phase which is the same as a step change in reference frequency in the amount $\Delta\omega[\theta(s) \times \Delta\omega/s^2]$, is

$$\epsilon = \lim_{s \to 0} \frac{\Delta\omega}{s + K} = \frac{\Delta\omega}{K} \tag{1-25}$$

It is apparent from those two equations that after a certain time, a type 1 first-order loop will track out any step change in input phase within the system hold-in range and will follow a step change in frequency with a phase error that is proportional to the magnitude of the frequency steps and inversely proportional to the dc loop gain. The loop will show the same performance if phase or frequency of the VCO changes rather than the reference.

In case 3, for the type 1 first-order PLL, it is of interest to examine a ramp change in frequency, the case in which the reference frequency is linearly changed with a time rate of $\Delta\omega/dt$ rad s^2 and $\theta(s) = 2\Delta\omega/dt/s^3$. Why is this so important? Let us assume that we sweep a PLL at a constant rate, as is done in some modern spectrum analyzers, and we have to find the final condition for the steady-state phase error. The final phase error

$$\epsilon = \lim_{s \to 0} \frac{2\Delta\omega/dt}{s^2 + sK} = \infty \tag{1-26}$$

What does this mean for us? It means that, as there is no infinite value for K in a type 1 first-order loop, this loop is not very attractive for tracking, and it also means that above a certain and critical rate of change of reference frequency or VCO frequency, the loop will no longer stay in locked condition. Therefore, if the loop is swept above a certain rate, it will not maintain lock.

1-5 TYPE 1 SECOND-ORDER LOOPS (see Figure 1-5)

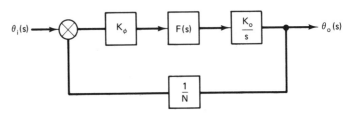

Figure 1-5 Block diagram of the second-order PLL.

If we insert in our PLL a simple low-pass filter

$$F(s) = \frac{1}{\tau_s + 1} \tag{1-27}$$

the closed-loop transfer function using

$$K = \frac{K_o K_\theta}{N} \tag{1-28}$$

$$B(s) = \frac{\theta_o(s)}{\theta_i(s)} = \frac{NK}{s(\tau s + 1) + K} = \frac{N}{(s^2/\omega_n^2) + (2\zeta/\omega_n)s + 1}$$

where

$$\omega_n = \sqrt{\frac{K}{\tau}} \tag{1-29}$$

and

$$2\zeta = \frac{\omega_n}{K} = \sqrt{\frac{1}{\tau K}} \tag{1-30}$$

The magnitude of the steady-state frequency response is

$$|B(s)| = \left| \frac{\theta_o}{\theta_i}(j\omega) \right| = \frac{1}{[(1 - \omega^2/\omega_n^2)^2 + (2\zeta\omega/\omega_n)^2]^{1/2}} \tag{1-31}$$

and the phase shift

$$\arg \frac{\theta_o}{\theta_i}(j\omega) = \arctan \frac{2\zeta\omega}{\omega_n(1 - \omega^2/\omega_n^2)^2} \tag{1-32}$$

The frequency response of this second-order transfer function determined in Eq. (1-28) is plotted in Figure 1-6 for selected values of ζ. For $\zeta = 0.707$, the transfer

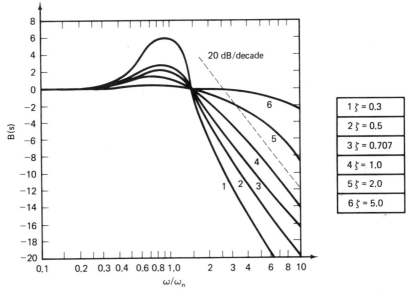

1	$\zeta = 0.3$
2	$\zeta = 0.5$
3	$\zeta = 0.707$
4	$\zeta = 1.0$
5	$\zeta = 2.0$
6	$\zeta = 5.0$

Figure 1-6   Frequency response of the type 2 second-order loop as a function of ζ.

function becomes the second-order "maximally flat" Butterworth response. For values of $\zeta < 0.707$, the gain exhibits peaking in the frequency domain. The maximum value of the frequency response M_p can be found by differentiating the magnitude of Eq. (1-28) (with $s = j\omega$). M_p is found to be

$$M_p = \frac{1}{2\zeta\sqrt{1 - \zeta^2}} \tag{1-33}$$

and the frequency ω_p at which the maximum occurs is

$$\omega_p = \omega_n\sqrt{1 - 2\zeta^2} \tag{1-34}$$

The 3-dB bandwidth B can be derived by solving for the frequency ω_h at which the magnitude of Eq. (1-28) (with $s = j\omega$) is equal to 0.707. B is found to be

$$B = \omega_n(1 - 2\zeta^2 + \sqrt{2 - 4\zeta^2 + 4\zeta^4})^{1/2} \tag{1-35}$$

The time it takes for the output to rise from 10 to 90% of its final value is called the *rise time t_r*. Rise time is approximately related to the system bandwidth by the relation

$$t_r = \frac{2.2}{B} \tag{1-36}$$

which is exact only for the first-order system described by Eq. (1-5).

The error signal θ_e, defined as $\theta_i - \theta_o$, can be expressed (in unity feedback systems) as

$$\theta_e(s) = \frac{\theta_i(s)}{1 + KG(s)} = \frac{\theta_i(s)}{1 + KF(s)/s} \tag{1-37}$$

If the system is stable, the steady-state error for polynomial inputs $\theta_i(t) = t^n$ can be obtained from the final value theorem,

$$\lim_{t\to\infty} \theta_e(t) = \lim_{s\to 0} s\theta_e(s)$$
$$= \lim_{s\to 0} \frac{2\theta_i}{KF(s)} \tag{1-38}$$

If $\theta_i(t)$ is a step function representing a sudden increase in phase, $\theta_i(s) = 1/s$ and

$$\lim_{t\to\infty} \theta_e(t) = \lim_{s\to 0} \frac{s}{KF(s)} \tag{1-39}$$

$F(s)$ is either a constant or a low-pass filter which may include poles at the origin. That is,

$$\lim_{s\to 0} F(s) = \frac{K^*}{s^n} \neq 0 \tag{1-40}$$

Therefore, Eq. (1-39) can be written

$$\lim_{t\to\infty} \theta_e(t) = \lim_{s\to 0} \frac{s^{n+1} K^*}{KK^*} = 0 \tag{1-41}$$

That is, a PLL will track step changes in phase with zero steady-state error.

If there is a constant-amplitude change in the input frequency of A rad/s,

$$\theta_i(s) = \frac{A}{s^2} \tag{1-42}$$

Equation (1-39) becomes

$$\lim_{t\to\infty} \theta_\epsilon(t) = \lim_{s\to 0} \frac{A}{KF(s)} = \frac{A}{KF(0)} \tag{1-43}$$

If $F(0) = 1$, the steady-state phase error will be inversely proportional to the loop gain K. Recall that the larger the K is, the larger will be the closed-loop bandwidth and thus the faster the loop response. To increase the response speed and reduce the tracking error, the loop gain should be as large as possible. If $F(0)$ is finite, there will be a finite steady-state phase error. The frequency error,

$$f_\epsilon(t) = \frac{d}{dt}\,\theta_\epsilon(t) \tag{1-44}$$

will be zero in the steady state. That is, the input and VCO frequencies will be equal $(\omega_i = \omega_o)$.

Table 1-3 shows the popular loop filters for the type 2 second-order loop. We have now dealt with case 1, a simple RC filter. The performance obtained with this loop filter is relatively restricted, mainly because the advantage over the loop with no filter was that we only got one additional parameter, a time constant τ_1.

Let us look at the table and the various filters. The passive filter type 2 uses two resistors and one capacitor, which allows compensation of phase.

The active filter, with which we will be dealing shortly, will add an additional integrator and therefore change this loop from a type 1 second-order to a type 2 second-order. The second-order loops we are currently dealing with are of type 1 because there is only one integrator involved, the VCO.

As we have only the time constant available as the additional parameter, which as we saw previously determines both the natural loop frequency ω_n and the damping factor ζ, we have not made much progress toward improving the loop and choosing independent parameters. If we add a resistor in series with the capacitor and obtain the loop filter shown in Table 1-3, type 2, the transfer function $F(s)$ is

$$F(s) = \frac{1 + \tau_2 s}{1 + \tau_1 s} \tag{1-45}$$

or as it is sometimes defined,

$$F(s) = \frac{1 + j\omega\tau_2}{1 + j\omega(\tau_1 + \tau_2)} \tag{1-46}$$

What is the difference? In the first case, we use the abbreviation

$$\tau_1 = (R_1 + R_2)C \tag{1-47}$$

and

$$\tau_2 = R_2 C \tag{1-48}$$

whereas in the second case, and as listed in Table 1-3,

$$\tau_1 = R_1 C \tag{1-49}$$

TABLE 1-3 CIRCUIT AND TRANSFER CHARACTERISTICS OF SEVERAL PLL FILTERS

Type	Passive		Active	
	1	2	3	4
Circuit				
Transfer characteristic				
$F(j\omega) =$	$\dfrac{1}{1+j\omega\tau_1}$	$\dfrac{1+j\omega\tau_2}{1+j\omega(\tau_1+\tau_2)}$	$\dfrac{1+j\omega\tau_2}{j\omega\tau_1}$	$\dfrac{1}{j\omega\tau_1}$

$$\tau_1 = R_1C \qquad \tau_2 = R_2C$$

and

$$\tau_2 = R_2 C \tag{1-50}$$

This fact should be pointed out, as it may cause confusion to the reader. This results in the transfer function of the type 1 second-order PLL using the first-case definition,

$$B(s) = \frac{K(1 + \tau_2 s/1 + \tau_1 s)}{s + K(1 + \tau_2 s/1 + \tau_1 s)}$$
$$= \frac{K(1/\tau_1)(1 + \tau_2 s)}{s^2 + (1/\tau_1)(1 + K\tau_2)s + (K/\tau_1)} \tag{1-51}$$

To be consistent with our previous abbreviations, we now insert the terms of the loop damping factor ζ and the natural frequency ω_n and obtain

$$B(s) = \frac{s\omega_n[2\zeta - \omega_n/K] + \omega_n^2}{s^2 + 2\zeta\omega_n s + \omega_n^2} \tag{1-52}$$

where

$$\omega_n = \sqrt{\frac{K}{\tau_1}} \qquad \text{rad/s} \tag{1-53}$$

and

$$\zeta = \frac{1}{2}\sqrt{\frac{1}{\tau_1 K}}(1 + \tau_2 K) \tag{1-54}$$

We remember our abbreviation used previously, $K = K_\theta K_o/N$. The magnitude of the transfer function of the phase-lag filter magnitude

$$|F(j\omega)| = \sqrt{\frac{1 + (\omega R_2 C)^2}{1 + [\omega C(R_1 + R_2)]^2}} \tag{1-55}$$

and the phase

$$\theta(j\omega) = \arctan(\omega\tau_2) - \arctan(\omega\tau_1) \quad \text{degrees}$$

When we use the other definition of τ_1 and τ_2 and insert the abbreviation

$$\omega_n = \sqrt{\frac{K}{\tau_1 + \tau_2}} \tag{1-56}$$

$$\zeta = \frac{1}{2}\sqrt{\frac{K}{\tau_1 + \tau_2}}\left(\tau_2 + \frac{1}{K}\right) \tag{1-57}$$

we obtain the expression

$$B(s) = \frac{s\omega_n(2\zeta - \omega_n/K) + \omega_n^2}{s^2 + 2\zeta(\omega_n^s + \omega_n^2)} \tag{1-58}$$

which turns out to give the same result.

As we were interested in the 3-dB bandwidth of the type 1 first-order loop, we now determine the 3-dB bandwidth of the type 1 second-order loop to be

$$B_{3dB} = \frac{\omega_n}{2\pi}(a + \sqrt{a^2 + 1})^{1/2} \qquad \text{Hz} \tag{1-59}$$

with the substitution

$$a = 2\zeta^2 + 1 - \frac{\omega_n}{K}\left(4\zeta - \frac{\omega_n}{K}\right) \tag{1-60}$$

The noise bandwidth of the type 1 second-order loop

$$B_n = \frac{\omega_n}{2}\left(\zeta + \frac{1}{4\zeta}\right) \qquad \text{Hz} \tag{1-61}$$

Again, we are interested in the final phase error and information we can gain from the phase error function

$$E(s) = \frac{s(1 + \tau_1 s)\theta(s)}{\tau_1 s^2 + (1 + K\tau_2)s + K} \tag{1-62}$$

As we are still dealing with a type 1 system, we obtain zero steady phase error, for a step in phase, and constant error for a ramp input in phase. One of these cases is shown in Figure 1-7, where the transient phase error due to a step in phase has been plotted with the Tektronix 4052 computer and a special program.

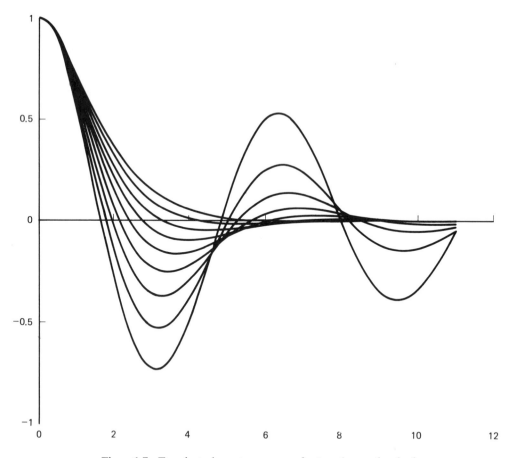

Figure 1-7 Transient phase step response for type 1 second-order loop.

For the loop to stay in lock, the following critical values have to be considered. The maximum rate of change of reference frequency $d \, \Delta\omega/dt$ should satisfy the equation

$$\left(\frac{d \, \Delta\omega}{dt}\right)_{\text{max}} = \omega_n^2 \tag{1-63}$$

The maximum rate at which the VCO can be swept must satisfy the condition

$$\left(\frac{d \, \Delta\omega}{dt}\right)_{\text{max}} < \frac{\omega_n^2}{2}$$

to achieve lock. The hold-in range of this loop

$$\Delta\omega_H = K \qquad \text{rad/s} \tag{1-64}$$

and the capture range

$$\Delta\omega_C = K\left(\frac{\tau_1}{\tau_2}\right) \qquad \text{rad/s} \tag{1-65}$$

An approximate time required for this type 1 second-order loop to obtain frequency lock is

$$T_{\text{acq}} \simeq \frac{4(\Delta f)^2}{B_n^3} \qquad \text{seconds} \tag{1-66}$$

A simple numerical example may give some additional insight. Let us assume that we have an oscillator operating at 45 MHz, using a reference frequency of 1 kHz. The tuning range of the oscillator is 5 MHz, which means that the frequency of the VCO in the beginning can be either at 40 or 50 MHz, as an extreme value. If we take the Δf offset worst-case condition of 5 MHz, and to get adequate reference suppression we use a 50-Hz natural loop frequency and a damping factor ζ of 0.7, the noise bandwidth

$$B_n = \frac{50}{2}\left(0.7 + \frac{1}{0.7 \times 4}\right)$$

$$= 25(0.7 + 0.3571)$$

$$= 25 \times 1.0571$$

$$= 26.4 \text{ Hz}$$

For a 5-MHz offset,

$$T_{\text{acq}} = \frac{4(5 \times 10^6)^2}{26.4^3} = 5.4 \times 10^9 \text{ s}$$

This is a ridiculous value. Unless the loop gets acquisition help, we would lose patience before it has ever acquired lock. Let us assume for a moment that we have a Δf of only 1 kHz or one step size. This still results in an acquisition time of 380 s, much too long for practical values. In Section 1-10 we will learn some acquisition aids that can speed up the otherwise lengthy procedure. For now it is sufficient to know that in cases where we do not use a phase/frequency comparator it generates a beat note that is capable of switching and, therefore, aiding acquisition. Externally switched oscillators can be used, or automatic circuits can be incorporated that change the loop bandwidth before acquisition occurs and therefore can speed up the circuit substantially.

We end our discussion of the type 1 second-order loop here and concentrate on the more popular type 2 second-order loop. Why is the type 2 second-order loop so much more popular?

We found out previously that the freedom of choice of parameters was limited.

1. In the type 1 first-order loop with no filter, K determined everything.
2. In the type 1 second-order loop, we had one time constant (τ_1) available, which restricted us in the choice of ω_n and ζ, as these values were related. The type 1 second-order loop has finite dc gain and therefore it is questionable whether the term "PLL" is really justified. By this definition we really should not call it a true PLL system because from the assumptions made previously, zero phase error requires infinite dc gain.

How do we accomplish the infinite dc gain, and how do we accomplish zero phase error?

If it is necessary to have zero phase error in response to step changes in the input frequency, $\lim_{s \to 0} F(s)$ must be infinite. That is, the dc gain of the low-pass filter must be infinite. This can be realized by including in $F(s)$ a pole at the origin. In this case $F(s)$ will be of the form

$$F(s) = \frac{1}{s} \frac{\tau_2 s + 1}{\tau_1} \tag{1-67}$$

The addition of the pole at the origin creates difficulties with the loop stability. In fact, the system will now be unstable unless a lead network is included in $F(s)$. With a passive filter, therefore resulting in a type 1 second-order loop, the condition is generally that we start with specified values for ω_n and ζ and want to determine the time constants τ_1 and τ_2. This has rarely been shown in the literature, and for those interested, here is the result. We start off with $K_\theta K_o / N = K$ and

$$\omega_n = \sqrt{\frac{K}{\tau_1 + \tau_2}} \tag{1-56}$$

$$\zeta = \frac{1}{2} \left(K + \frac{1}{\tau_1 + \tau_2} \right)^{1/2} \left(\tau_2 + \frac{1}{K} \right) \tag{1-68}$$

By squaring ζ and inserting the value for ω_n, after some manipulation we obtain

$$\tau_2^2 K^2 + \tau_2 2K + 1 - 4\zeta^2 \frac{K^2}{\omega_n^2} = 0 \tag{1-69}$$

This equation can be solved with

$$\tau_1 = \frac{K}{\omega_n^2} - \tau_2 \tag{1-70}$$

$$\tau_2 = \frac{-2K + \sqrt{4K^2 - 4K^2[1 - 4\zeta^2(K^2/\omega_n^2)]}}{2K^2} \tag{1-71}$$

and

$$R_1 = \frac{\tau_1}{C} \tag{1-72}$$

and

$$R_2 = \frac{\tau_2}{C} \tag{1-73}$$

1-6 TYPE 2 SECOND-ORDER LOOP

The type 2 second-order loop uses a loop filter in the form

$$F(s) = \frac{1}{s} \frac{\tau_2 s + 1}{\tau_1} \tag{1-67}$$

The multiplier $1/s$ indicates a second integrator, which is generated by the active amplifier. In Table 1-3, this is the type 3 filter. The type 4 filter is mentioned there as a possible configuration but is not recommended because, as stated previously, the addition of the pole of the origin creates difficulties with loop stability and, in most cases, requires a change from the type 4 to the type 3 filter. One can consider the type 4 filter as a special case of the type 3 filter, and therefore it does not have to be treated separately. Another possible transfer function is

$$F(s) = \frac{1}{R_1 C} \frac{1 + \tau_2 s}{s} \tag{1-74}$$

with

$$\tau_2 = R_2 C \tag{1-50}$$

Under these conditions, the magnitude of the transfer function

$$|F(j\omega)| = \frac{1}{R_1 C \omega} \sqrt{1 + (\omega R_2 C)^2} \tag{1-75}$$

and the phase

$$\theta = \arctan (\omega \tau_2) - 90 \text{ degrees}$$

Again, as if for a practical case, we start off with the design values ω_n and ζ, and we have to determine τ_1 and τ_2. Taking an approach similar to that for the type 1 second-order loop, the results are

$$\tau_1 = \frac{K}{\omega_n} \tag{1-76}$$

and

$$\tau_2 = \frac{2\zeta}{\omega_n} \tag{1-77}$$

and

$$R_1 = \frac{\tau_1}{C} \tag{1-72}$$

and

$$R_2 = \frac{\tau_2}{C} \tag{1-73}$$

The closed-loop transfer function of a type 2 second-order PLL with a perfect integrator is

$$B(s) = \frac{K(R_2/R_1)[s + (1/\tau_2)]}{s^2 + K(R_2/R_1)s + (K/\tau_2)(R_2/R_1)} \tag{1-78}$$

By introducing the terms ζ and ω_n, the transfer function now becomes

$$B(s) = \frac{2\zeta\omega_n s + \omega_n^2}{s^2 + 2\zeta\omega_n s + \omega_n^2} \tag{1-79}$$

with the abbreviation

$$\omega_n = \left(\frac{K}{\tau_2}\frac{R_2}{R_1}\right)^{1/2} \qquad \text{rad/s} \tag{1-80}$$

and

$$\zeta = \frac{1}{2}\left(K\tau_2\frac{R_2}{R_1}\right)^{1/2} \tag{1-81}$$

and $K = K_\theta K_o/N$.

The 3-dB bandwidth of the type 2 second-order loop is

$$B_{3dB} = \frac{\omega_n}{2\pi}[2\zeta^2 + 1 + \sqrt{(2\zeta^2 + 1)^2 + 1}]^{1/2} \qquad \text{Hz} \tag{1-82}$$

and the noise bandwidth is

$$B_n = \frac{K(R_2/R_1) + 1/\tau_2}{4} \qquad \text{Hz} \tag{1-83}$$

Again, we ask the question of the final error and use the previous error function,

$$E(s) = \frac{s\theta(s)}{s + K(R_2/R_1)\{[s + (1/\tau_2)]/s\}} \tag{1-84}$$

or

$$E(s) = \frac{s^2\theta(s)}{s^2 + K(R_2/R_1)s + (K/\tau_2)(R_2/R_1)} \tag{1-85}$$

As a result of the perfect integrator, the steady-state error resulting from a step change in input phase or change of magnitude of frequency is zero.

If the input frequency is swept with a constant range change of input frequency $(\Delta\omega/dt)$, for $\theta(s) = (2\Delta\omega/dt)/s^3$, the steady-state phase error is

$$E(s) = \frac{R_1}{R_2}\frac{\tau_2(2\Delta\omega/dt)}{K} \qquad \text{rad} \tag{1-86}$$

The maximum rate at which the VCO frequency can be swept for maintaining lock

$$\frac{2\Delta\omega}{dt} = \frac{N}{2\tau_2}\left(4B_n - \frac{1}{\tau_2}\right) \qquad \text{rad/s} \tag{1-87}$$

The introduction of N indicates that this is referred to the VCO rather than to the phase/frequency comparator. In the previous example of the type 1 first-order loop, we referred it only to the phase/frequency comparator rather than the VCO.

1-6-1 Transient Behavior of Digital Loops Using Tri-State Phase Detectors

Pull-in characteristic.   The type 2 second-order loop is used with either a sample/hold comparator or a tri-state phase/frequency comparator.

We will now determine the transient behavior of this loop. Figure 1-8 shows the block diagram.

Very rarely in literature is a clear distinction between pull-in and lock-in characteristics or frequency and phase acquisition made as a function of the digital phase/frequency detector. Somehow, all the approximations or linearizations refer to a sinusoidal phase/frequency comparator or its digital equivalent, the exclusive-OR gate.

The tri-state phase/frequency comparator, which seems to be the most popular one and will be explored in greater detail in Chapter 4, follows slightly different mathematical principles.

The phase detector gain

$$K'_d = \frac{V_d}{\omega_o} = \text{phase detector supply voltage/loop idling frequency}$$

is explained fully in Chapter 4, and we only use the result here. This phase detector gain is valid only in the out-of-lock state and is a somewhat coarse approximation to the real gain, which, due to nonlinear differential equations, is very difficult to calculate. However, practical tests show that this approximation is still fairly accurate.

Definitions:

$$\Omega_1(s) = \mathcal{L}[\Delta\omega_1(t)] \qquad \text{Reference input to } \delta/\omega \text{ detector}$$

$$\Omega_2(s) = \mathcal{L}[\Delta\omega_2(t)] \qquad \text{Signal VCO output frequency}$$

$$\Omega_e(s) = \mathcal{L}[\omega_e(t)] \qquad \text{Error frequency at } \delta/\omega \text{ detector}$$

$$\Omega_e(s) = \Omega_1(s) - \frac{\Omega_2(s)}{N}$$

$$\Omega_2(s) = [\Omega_1(s) - \Omega_e(s)]N$$

From the circuit above,

$$A(s) = \Omega_e(s)K'_d$$

$$B(s) = A(s)F(s)$$

$$\Omega_2(s) = B(s)K_o$$

The error frequency at the detector

$$\Omega_e(s) = \Omega_1(s)N\frac{1}{N + K_oK'_dF(s)} \tag{1-88}$$

The signal is stepped in frequency:

$$\Omega_1(s) = \frac{\Delta\omega_1}{s} \qquad (\Delta\omega_1 = \text{magnitude of frequency step}) \qquad (1\text{-}89)$$

Active Filter of First Order. If we use an active filter

$$F(s) = \frac{1 + s\tau_2}{s\tau_1} \qquad (1\text{-}90)$$

and insert this in Eq. (1-88), the error frequency

$$\Omega_e(s) = \Delta\omega_1 N \frac{1}{s\left(N + K_o K_d' \dfrac{\tau_2}{\tau_1}\right) + \dfrac{K_o K_d'}{\tau_1}} \qquad (1\text{-}91)$$

Utilizing the Laplace transformation, we obtain

$$\omega_e(t) = \Delta\omega_1 \frac{1}{1 + K_o K_d'(\tau_2/\tau_1)(1/N)} \exp\left[-\frac{t}{(\tau_1 N/K_o K_d') + \tau_2}\right] \qquad (1\text{-}92)$$

and

$$\lim_{t\to 0} \omega_e(t) = \frac{\Delta\omega_1 N}{N + K_o K_d'(\tau_2/\tau_1)} \qquad (1\text{-}93)$$

$$\lim_{t\to\infty} \omega_e(t) = 0 \qquad (1\text{-}94)$$

Passive Filter of First Order. If we use a passive filter

$$F(s) = \frac{1 + s\tau_2}{1 + s(\tau_1 + \tau_2)} \qquad (1\text{-}95)$$

for the frequency step

$$\Omega_1(s) = \frac{\Delta\omega_1}{s} \qquad (1\text{-}96)$$

the error frequency at the input becomes

$$\Omega_e(s) = \Delta\omega_1 N \left\{ \frac{1}{s} \frac{1}{s[N(\tau_1 + \tau_2) + K_o K_d'\tau_2] + (N + K_o K_d')} \right.$$

$$\left. + \frac{\tau_1 + \tau_2}{s[N(\tau_1 + \tau_2) + K_o K_d'\tau_2] + (N + K_o K_d')} \right\} \qquad (1\text{-}97)$$

For the first term we will use the abbreviation A, and for the second term we will use the abbreviation B.

$$A = \frac{1/[N(\tau_1 + \tau_2) + K_o K_d'\tau_2]}{s\left[s + \dfrac{N + K_o K_d'}{N(\tau_1 + \tau_2) + K_o K_d'\tau_2}\right]} \qquad (1\text{-}98)$$

$$B = \frac{\dfrac{\tau_1 + \tau_2}{N(\tau_1 + \tau_2) + K_o K_d'\tau_2}}{s + \dfrac{N + K_o K_d'}{N(\tau_1 + \tau_2) + K_o K_d'\tau_2}} \qquad (1\text{-}99)$$

After the inverse Laplace transformation, our final result becomes

$$\mathcal{L}^{-1}(A) = \frac{1}{N + K_o K_d'} \left\{ 1 - \exp\left[-t\, \frac{N + K_o K_d'}{N(\tau_1 + \tau_2) + K_o K_d' \tau_2} \right] \right\} \qquad (1\text{-}100)$$

$$\mathcal{L}^{-1}(B) = \frac{\tau_1 + \tau_2}{N(\tau_1 + \tau_2) + K_o K_d' \tau_2} \exp\left(-t\, \frac{N + K_o K_d'}{N(\tau_1 + \tau_2) + K_o K_d' \tau_2} \right) \qquad (1\text{-}101)$$

and finally

$$\omega_e(t) = \Delta\omega_1 N[\mathcal{L}^{-1}(A) + (\tau_1 + \tau_2)\mathcal{L}^{-1}(B)] \qquad (1\text{-}102)$$

What does the equation mean? We really want to know how long it takes to pull the VCO frequency to the reference. Therefore, we want to know the value of t, the time it takes to be within equal or less of 2π of lock-in range.

The PLL can, at the beginning, have a phase error from -2π to $+2\pi$, and the loop, by accomplishing lock, then takes care of this phase error.

We can make the reverse assumption for a moment and ask ourselves, as we have done earlier, how long the loop stays in phase lock. This is called the *pull-out* range. Again, we apply signals to the input of the PLL as long as the loop can follow and the phase error does not become larger than 2π. Once the error is larger than 2π, the loop jumps out of lock.

We will learn more about this in Section 1-10, but as already mentioned with regard to the condition where the loop is out of lock, a beat note occurs at the output of the loop filter following the phase/frequency detector.

The tri-state phase/frequency comparator, however, works on a different principle, and the pulses generated and supplied to the charge pump do not allow the generation of an ac voltage. The output of such a phase/frequency detector is always unipolar, but, relative to the value of $V_{batt}/2$, the integrator voltage can be either positive or negative. If we assume for a moment that this voltage should be the final voltage under a locked condition, we will observe that the resulting dc voltage is either more negative or more positive relative to this value, and because of this, the VCO will be "pulled in" to this final frequency rather than swept in, which had been mentioned previously. The swept-in technique applies only in cases of phase/frequency comparators, where, this beat note is being generated. A typical case would be the exclusive-OR gate or even a sample/hold comparator. This phenomenon is rarely covered in the literature, and is probably discussed in detail for the first time in Ref. 1.

Let us assume now that the VCO has been pulled in to final frequency to be within 2π to the final frequency, and the time t is known. The next step is to determine the lock-in characteristic. The computer program for the type 2 second-order PLL in Section A-2-4 will determine those two values independently, and the acquisition time is equal to the sum of both values.

Lock-in characteristic.   We will now determine lock-in characteristic, and this requires the use of a different block diagram. Figure 1-8 shows the familiar block diagram of the PLL, and we will use the following definitions:

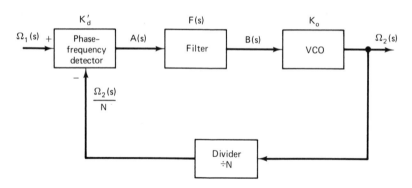

Note: The frequency transfer const. of the VCO = K_o

(not $\dfrac{K_o}{s}$, which is valid for phase transfer only.)

Figure 1-8 Block diagram of a digital PLL before lock is acquired.

$\theta_1(s) = \mathcal{L}[\Delta\delta_1(t)]$ Reference input to δ/ω detector

$\theta_2(s) = \mathcal{L}[\Delta\delta_2(t)]$ Signal VCO output phase

$\theta_e(s) = \mathcal{L}[\delta_e(t)]$ Phase error at δ/ω detector

$\theta_e(s) = \theta_1(s) - \dfrac{\theta_2(s)}{N}$

From the block diagram, the following is apparent:

$$A(s) = \theta_e(s)K_d$$
$$B(s) = A(s)F(s)$$
$$\theta_2(s) = B(s)\frac{K_o}{s}$$

The phase error at the detector

$$\theta_e(s) = \theta_1(s)\frac{sN}{K_oK_dF(s) + sN} \tag{1-103}$$

In Section A-1-4 we will see that a step in phase at the input, with the worst-case error being 2π, results in

$$\theta_1(s) = 2\pi\frac{1}{s} \tag{1-104}$$

We will now treat the two cases using an active or a passive filter.

Active Filter.   The transfer characteristic of the active filter

$$F(s) = \frac{1 + s\tau_2}{s\tau_1} \tag{1-90}$$

This results in the formula for the phase error at the detector,

$$\theta_e(s) = 2\pi \frac{s}{s^2 + sK_oK_d\tau_2/\tau_1/N + K_oK_d/\tau_1/N} \tag{1-105}$$

The polynomial coefficients for the denominator are

$$a_2 = 1$$
$$a_1 = K_oK_d\tau_2/\tau_1/N$$
$$a_0 = K_oK_d/\tau_1/N$$

and we have to find the roots W_1 and W_2. Expressed in the form of a polynomial coefficient, the phase error

$$\theta_e(s) = 2\pi \frac{s}{(s + W_1)(s + W_2)} \tag{1-106}$$

After the Laplace transformation has been performed, the result can be written in the form

$$\delta_e(t) = 2\pi \frac{W_1e^{-W_1t} - W_2e^{-W_2t}}{W_1 - W_2} \tag{1-107}$$

with

$$\lim_{t \to 0} \delta_e(t) = 2\pi$$

and

$$\lim_{t \to \infty} \delta_e(t) = 0$$

The same can be done using a passive filter.

Passive Filter.   The transfer function of the passive filter

$$F(s) = \frac{1 + s\tau_2}{1 + s(\tau_1 + \tau_2)} \tag{1-95}$$

If we apply the same phase step of 2π as before, the resulting phase error is

$$\theta_e(s) = 2\pi \frac{[1/(\tau_1 + \tau_2)] + s}{s^2 + s\dfrac{N + K_oK_d\tau_2}{N(\tau_1 + \tau_2)} + \dfrac{K_oK_d}{N(\tau_1 + \tau_2)}} \tag{1-108}$$

Again, we have to find the polynomial coefficients, which are

$$a_2 = 1$$
$$a_1 = \frac{N + K_oK_d\tau_2}{N(\tau_1 + \tau_2)}$$
$$a_0 = \frac{K_oK_d}{N(\tau_1 + \tau_2)}$$

and finally, find the roots for W_1 and W_2. This can be written in the form

$$\theta_e(s) = 2\pi \left[\frac{1}{\tau_1 + \tau_2} \frac{1}{(s + W_1)(s + W_2)} + \frac{s}{(s + W_1)(s + W_2)} \right] \tag{1-109}$$

Now we perform the Laplace transformation and obtain our result:

$$\delta_e(t) = 2\pi \left(\frac{1}{\tau_1 + \tau_2} \frac{e^{-W_1t} - e^{-W_2t}}{W_2 - W_1} + \frac{W_1e^{-W_1t} - W_2e^{-W_2t}}{W_1 - W_2} \right) \tag{1-110}$$

with

$$\lim_{t \to 0} \delta_e(t) = 2\pi$$

and

$$\lim_{t \to \infty} \delta_e(t) = 0$$

I will show with the type 2 third-order loop how these roots are being determined, as the roots are going to be fifth order. I assume that determining the roots of a cubic equation is known and easy.

As a result of the last equation for the active as well as for the passive filter, Eqs. (1-107) and (1-110) have the dimension of radians. Although mathematically speaking it is not strictly accurate, it is permissible to multiply these values with the division ratio N and the reference frequency to obtain a final error in the dimension frequency. It has been shown in practical experiments that, if this final error is less than 0.1 Hz, the time (t) it takes to get there can be taken as the lock-in time. In Chapter 2, we will learn that any VCO has a certain residual FM. That means that even under locked condition, the output frequency moves within certain boundaries. Medium-quality synthesizers show a residual FM of 3 Hz, whereas a loop with dividers at the output and low division ratio can have a residual FM as low as 0.1 Hz or better. This is, at times, also called *incidental FM*, and similar expressions have been found in the literature.

In Table 1-2 we indicated that the exclusive-OR gate and the edge-triggered JK master/slave flip-flop have a different operation mode than that of the tri-state phase/frequency comparator.

We will go into the details in Section 1-10, since the tri-state phase/frequency comparator does not require any acquisition aid.

Let us take a look at a numerical example. We have a PLL with the following parameters:

Reference frequency	5000 Hz
K_o	$2\pi \times 1$ MHz
K_θ	2.1 V/rad
N	1000
ω_n	500 Hz
Phase margin	45°
ζ	0.7
R_1	1336 Ω
R_2	445 Ω
C_1	1E-6 F
Reference suppression	20 dB
Lockup time	8 ms

These values were determined for the type 2 second-order loop with the program presented in Section A-2-4. In Section 1-7 we will find that the type 2 third-order loop, although initially somewhat more difficult to treat mathematically, will show better reference suppression, faster lockup time, and really is better as far as reproducibility is concerned. This is due to the fact that there are always stray capacitors and some other elements in the circuit which can be incorporated in the type 2 third-order loop, whereas the type 2 second-order loop really does not exist in its pure form.

Some of the dynamics of the type 2 second-order loop and of the type 2 third-order loop are dealt with in Section 1-10. For reasons of consistency, however, the transient behavior of the type 2 second-order loop has already been treated, and the equivalent performance of the type 2 third-order loop will be discussed on the following pages.

1-7 TYPE 2 THIRD-ORDER LOOP

I have stated several times previously that low-order loops really do not exist. The reasons for this are the introduction of phase shift by the operational amplifier, stray capacitors, and other things in the loop.

The type 2 third-order loop is a very good approximation of what is actually happening and can easily be developed from the type 2 second-order loop by adding one more RC filter at the output. Most likely, the operational amplifier as part of the active filter has to drive a feed-through capacitor, and for reasons of spike decoupling or additional filtering, one resistor is put in series.

Figure 1-9 shows a loop filter for a type 2 third-order loop. Just a reminder: this loop has two integrators, one being the VCO and one being the operational amplifier and three time constants.

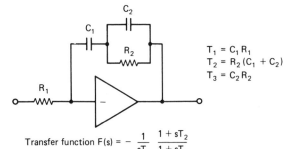

Transfer function $F(s) = -\dfrac{1}{sT_1} \dfrac{1 + sT_2}{1 + sT_3}$

$$T_1 = C_1 R_1$$
$$T_2 = R_2 (C_1 + C_2)$$
$$T_3 = C_2 R_2$$

Figure 1-9 Circuit diagram of the loop filter for the third-order loop.

This filter can be redrawn as shown in Figure 1-10. The transfer function for this filter

$$F(s) = \frac{-1}{s\tau_1}\frac{1 + s\tau_2}{1 + s\tau_3} \tag{1-111}$$

with

$$\tau_1 = C_1 R_1 \tag{1-112}$$

$$\tau_2 = R_2(C_1 + C_2) \tag{1-113}$$

$$\tau_3 = C_2 R_2 \tag{1-114}$$

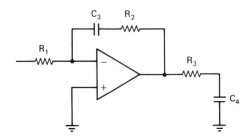

$$F(s) = -\frac{1}{C_3 R_1}\frac{1 + s/\omega_z'}{s(1 + s/\omega_p)} \qquad \omega_z = \frac{1}{R_2 C_3} \qquad j\omega_p = \frac{1}{R_3 C_4}$$

Figure 1-10 Circuit diagram of redrawn Figure 1-9. Note that this is the same type of loop filter as in the type 2 second-order loop with an additional RC time constant.

Let us now determine the transfer function for the type 2 third-order loop.

1-7-1 Transfer Function of Type 2 Third-Order Loop

The forward gain

$$K = K_\theta F(s)\frac{K_o}{s} \tag{1-115}$$

and for

$$H(s) = \frac{1}{N} \qquad N = \text{division ratio} \tag{1-116}$$

the open-loop gain

$$A(s) = K_\theta F(s)\frac{K_o}{s}\frac{1}{N} \tag{1-117}$$

and the system transfer function

$$B(s) = \frac{\theta_o(s)}{\theta_i(s)} = \frac{\text{forward gain}}{1 + (\text{open-loop gain})}$$

$$= \frac{K_\theta F(s)(K_o/s)}{1 + \frac{K_\theta F(s)(K_o/s)}{N}} \tag{1-118}$$

$$= \frac{K_\theta F(s)K_o}{s + \frac{K_\theta F(s)K_o}{N}}$$

If we insert our time constants τ_1, τ_2, and τ_3, we obtain

$$B(s) = \frac{\theta_o(s)}{\theta_i(s)} = \frac{1 + s\tau_2}{s\tau_1 + s^2\tau_1\tau_3}\frac{K_\theta K_o}{s + \frac{K_\theta K_o}{N}\frac{1 + s\tau_2}{s\tau_1 + s^2\tau_1\tau_3}} \tag{1-119}$$

and

$$B(s) = NK_\theta K_o(1 + s\tau_2)\frac{1}{s^3 N\tau_1\tau_3 + s^2 N\tau_1 + sK_\theta K_o\tau_2 + K_\theta K_o} \tag{1-120}$$

$$\text{polynomial } P = s^3 N\tau_1\tau_3 + s^2 N\tau_1 + sK_\theta K_o\tau_2 + K_\theta K_o \tag{1-121}$$

As we have done before, we have to determine the roots:

$$\frac{P}{N\tau_1\tau_3} = s^3 + s^2\frac{1}{\tau_3} + sK_\theta K_o\frac{\tau_2}{N\tau_1\tau_3} + K_\theta K_o\frac{1}{n\tau_1\tau_3} = 0 \qquad (1\text{-}122)$$

Therefore, the coefficients are

$$a_4 = 1 \qquad (1\text{-}123)$$

$$a_3 = \frac{1}{\tau_3} \qquad (1\text{-}124)$$

$$a_2 = K_\theta K_o\frac{\tau_2}{N\tau_1\tau_3} \qquad (1\text{-}125)$$

$$a_1 = K_\theta K_o\frac{1}{N\tau_1\tau_3} = \frac{a_2}{\tau_2} \qquad (1\text{-}126)$$

The polynomial is of the order of 3, and we can use a calculator routine to find the roots b_1, b_2, and b_3, and finally:

$$s_1 = 0 \qquad (1\text{-}127)$$

$$s_2 = -b_1 \qquad (1\text{-}128)$$

$$s_3 = -b_2 \qquad (1\text{-}129)$$

$$s_4 = -b_3 \qquad (1\text{-}130)$$

The next step is partial fraction forming:

$$\frac{1}{a_4s^4 + a_3s^3 + a_2s^2 + a_1s}$$

$$= \frac{1}{a_4s(s + b_1)(s + b_2)(s + b_3)} \qquad (1\text{-}131)$$

$$= \left(\frac{c_1}{s + b_1} + \frac{c_2}{s + b_2} + \frac{c_3}{s + b_3} + \frac{c_4}{s}\right)\frac{1}{a_4}$$

Now we have to determine C_i, for $i = 1$ to 4, and multiply the equation above,

$$\frac{c_1(s + b_2)(s + b_3)s + c_2(s + b_1)(s + b_3)s + c_3(s + b_1)(s + b_2)s + c_4(s + b_1)(s + b_2)(s + b_3)}{(s + b_1)(s + b_2)(s + b_3)s}$$

which is equal to

$$\frac{1}{(s + b_1)(s + b_2)(s + b_3)s} \qquad (\text{numerator} = 1)$$

Rearranging yields

$$s^3(c_1 + c_2 + c_3 + c_4)$$

$$+ s^2[c_1(b_2 + b_3) + c_2(b_1 + b_3) + c_3(b_1 + b_2) + c_4(b_1 + b_2 + b_3)]$$

$$+ s[c_1b_2b_3 + c_2b_1b_3 + c_3b_1b_2 + c_4(b_1b_2 + b_1b_3 + b_2b_3)]$$

$$+ c_4b_1b_2b_3$$

and since

$$c_1 + c_2 + c_3 = 0 \qquad (1\text{-}132)$$

$$c_1(b_2 + b_3) + c_2(b_1 + b_3) + c_3(b_1 + b_2) = 0 \qquad (1\text{-}133)$$

$$c_1 b_2 b_3 + c_2 b_1 b_3 + c_3 b_1 b_2 = \frac{1}{N\tau_1\tau_3} \qquad (1\text{-}134)$$

our final result is

$$c_3 = -c_1 - c_2 \qquad (1\text{-}135)$$

$$c_2 = -c_1 \frac{b_3 - b_1}{b_3 - b_2} \qquad (1\text{-}136)$$

$$c_1 = \frac{1}{N\tau_1\tau_3} \frac{1}{(b_3 - b_1)(b_2 - b_1)} \qquad (1\text{-}137)$$

Let us test this equation with a step function

$$\theta_i(s) = \frac{1}{s} \qquad (1\text{-}138)$$

We obtain

$$
\begin{aligned}
\theta_o(s) &= NK_\theta K_o \frac{1 + s\tau_2}{s} \frac{1/N\tau_1\tau_3}{s^3 + \dfrac{1}{\tau_3}s^2 + \dfrac{\tau_2 K_\theta K_o}{N\tau_1\tau_3}s + \dfrac{K_\theta K_o}{N\tau_1\tau_3}} \\[2mm]
&= NK_\theta K_o \left[\tau_2 \left(\frac{c_1}{s + b_1} + \frac{c_2}{s + b_2} + \frac{c_3}{s + b_3} \right) \right. \\[2mm]
&\quad \left. + \frac{c_1}{b_1}\left(\frac{1}{s} - \frac{1}{s + b_1} \right) + \frac{c_2}{b_2}\left(\frac{1}{s} - \frac{1}{s + b_2} \right) + \frac{c_3}{b_3}\left(\frac{1}{s} - \frac{1}{s + b_1} \right) \right] \quad (1\text{-}139) \\[2mm]
&= NK_\theta K_o \left[\frac{(\tau_2 - 1/b_1)c_1}{s + b_1} + \frac{(\tau_2 - 1/b_2)c_2}{s + b_2} + \frac{(\tau_2 - 1/b_3)c_3}{s + b_3} \right. \\[2mm]
&\quad \left. + \frac{(c_1/b_1) + (c_2/b_2) + (c_3/b_3)}{s} \right]
\end{aligned}
$$

If we perform a Laplace transformation, our final result is

$$
\begin{aligned}
\theta_o(t) = NK_\theta K_o \left[\left(\tau_2 - \frac{1}{b_1} \right) c_1 e^{-b_1 t} + \left(\tau_2 - \frac{1}{b_2} \right) c_2 e^{-b_2 t} \right. \\[2mm]
\left. + \left(\tau_2 - \frac{1}{b_3} \right) c_3 e^{-b_3 t} + \left(\frac{c_1}{b_1} + \frac{c_2}{b_2} + \frac{c_3}{b_3} \right) \right]
\end{aligned}
\qquad (1\text{-}140)
$$

To plot the Bode diagram, the open-loop gain equation for $A(j\omega)$ must be determined and plotted in magnitude and phase. We obtain

$$
\begin{aligned}
A(j\omega) &= -\frac{K_\theta K_o}{Nj\omega}\left(\frac{1}{j\omega\tau_1} \right) \frac{1 + j\omega\tau_2}{1 + j\omega\tau_3} \\[2mm]
&= \frac{K_\theta K_o}{N\omega^2}\left(\frac{1 + j\omega\tau_2}{1 + j\omega\tau_3} \right) \frac{1}{\tau_1}
\end{aligned}
\qquad (1\text{-}141)
$$

We will then abbreviate

$$\frac{K_\theta K_o}{N\omega^2} = \tau_9 \tag{1-142}$$

The phase is determined from

$$\frac{(1 + j\omega\tau_2)(1 - j\omega\tau_3)}{1 + \omega^2\tau_3^2} = \frac{1 + \omega^2\tau_2\tau_3 + j\omega(\tau_2 - \tau_3)}{1 + \omega^2\tau_3^2} \tag{1-143}$$

and

$$\tan\phi = \frac{\omega\tau_2}{1 + \omega^2\tau_2\tau_3} - \frac{\omega\tau_3}{1 + \omega^2\tau_2\tau_3} \tag{1-144}$$

The magnitude

$$|A(j\omega)| = \frac{\tau_9}{\tau_1}\frac{\sqrt{1 + \omega^2\tau_2^2}}{\sqrt{1 + \omega^2\tau_3^2}} \tag{1-145}$$

with

$$|A(j\omega)| = 1 \qquad \text{(crossover point)} \tag{1-146}$$

We finally obtain

$$\tau_1 = \tau_9\sqrt{\frac{1 + \omega^2\tau_2^2}{1 + \omega^2\tau_3^2}} \tag{1-147}$$

and

$$A_1 = 1 + \omega^2\tau_2^2 \tag{1-148}$$
$$A_2 = 1 + \omega^2\tau_3^2 \tag{1-149}$$

The phase margin

$$\phi = \arctan\omega\tau_2 - \arctan\omega\tau_3 + \pi \tag{1-150}$$

assuming that

$$\omega^2\tau_2\tau_3 \ll 1$$

Let us determine the natural loop frequency ω_o from the point of zero slope of the phase response,

$$\frac{d\phi(\omega)}{d\omega} = 0 \tag{1-151}$$

$$\frac{d\phi}{d\omega} = \frac{\tau_2}{1 + (\omega\tau_2)^2} - \frac{\tau_3}{1 + (\omega\tau_3)^2} = 0 \tag{1-152}$$

and therefore

$$\omega_o = \sqrt{\frac{1}{\tau_2\tau_3}} \tag{1-153}$$

If we set

$$\alpha = \arctan\omega\tau_2 \tag{1-154}$$
$$\beta = \arctan\omega\tau_3 \tag{1-155}$$
$$\phi = \alpha - \beta + \pi \tag{1-156}$$

and

$$\tan \phi = \tan [(\alpha - \beta) + \pi]$$
$$= \frac{\tan (\alpha - \beta) + 0}{1 - 0} = \tan (\alpha - \beta) \tag{1-157}$$

$$\tan (\alpha - \beta) = \frac{\tan \alpha - \tan \beta}{1 + \tan \alpha \tan \beta} = \frac{\omega \tau_2 - \omega \tau_3}{1 + \omega^2 \tau_2 \tau_3} = \tan \phi \tag{1-158}$$

If we set

$$\omega = \omega_o = \sqrt{\frac{1}{\tau_2 \tau_3}} \tag{1-159}$$

then

$$\tan \phi_o = \frac{(1/\sqrt{\tau_2 \tau_3})(\tau_2 - \tau_3)}{1 + 1} = \frac{\tau_2 - \tau_3}{2\sqrt{\tau_2 \tau_3}} \tag{1-160}$$

and

$$\sqrt{\tau_2 \tau_3} = \frac{1}{\omega_o} \tag{1-161}$$

$$\omega_o^2 \tau_2 \tau_3 = 1 \tag{1-162}$$

$$\tau_2 = \frac{1}{\omega_o^2 \tau_3} \tag{1-163}$$

Using this value, we can determine the time constant τ_3 from

$$\tan \phi_o = \frac{(1/\omega_o^2 \tau_3) - \tau_3}{2(1/\omega_o)} = \frac{(1/\omega_o^2 \tau_3) - \omega_o \tau_3}{2} \tag{1-164}$$

and

$$2 \tan \phi_o \omega_o \tau_3 = 1 - \omega_o^2 \tau_3^2 \tag{1-165}$$

$$\omega_o^2 \tau_3^2 + 2 \tan \phi_o \omega_o \tau_3 - 1 = 0 \tag{1-166}$$

The time constant τ_3 is determined from

$$\begin{aligned}
\tau_3 &= \frac{-2 \tan \phi_o \omega_o + \sqrt{4 \tan^2 \phi_o \omega_o^2 + 4\omega_o^2}}{2\omega_o^2} \\
&= \frac{-2 \tan \phi_o \omega_o + 2\omega_o \sqrt{\tan^2 \phi_o + 1}}{2\omega_o^2} \\
&= \frac{\tan \phi_o + \sqrt{(\cos^2 \phi_o + \sin^2 \phi_o)/\cos^2 \phi_o}}{\omega_o} \\
&= \frac{-\tan \phi_o + 1/\cos \phi_o}{\omega_o}
\end{aligned} \tag{1-167}$$

τ_3 is now determined independent of the other parameters, τ_1 and τ_2, by setting the value for ω_o and the phase margin ϕ to begin with. Once τ_3 is determined, the values for τ_2 and τ_1 can be computed by inserting them in the necessary equations.

These equations were somewhat lengthy, but they were spelled out in great detail to show the approach taken. A computer program based on these equations is presented in the Appendix and can be used for Bode diagram plottings.

1-7-2 FM Noise Suppression

In drawing the Bode plot, it is also convenient to show the suppression of noise of the VCO that is provided by the phase-locked loop. Using

$$E_n = \text{VCO noise voltage}$$

and

$$E = \text{noise voltage with loop closed}$$

we can write

$$E(s) = E_n(s)\frac{1}{1 + (\text{open-loop gain})}$$

$$= \frac{1}{1 + G(s)H(s)} = \frac{1}{1 + A(s)} \qquad (1\text{-}168)$$

or

$$\left|\frac{E(\omega)}{E_n(\omega)}\right| = \frac{1}{\dfrac{K_\theta K_o}{N\omega^2 \tau_1}\left|\dfrac{1 + j\omega\tau_2}{1 + j\omega\tau_3}\right| + 1} \qquad (1\text{-}169)$$

The type 2 third-order loop is really the most important but was not used that often in the past. This may be a lack of understanding or not realizing that, by proper combination of the time constants, the unavoidable feed-through capacitors and some series capacitors can be incorporated to obtain this type of a loop. The advantages of the third-order loop over the second-order loop are in the higher reference suppression for a given loop frequency, or if a certain loop frequency has to be chosen because of lockup time, the reference suppression is higher than we would find in the case of a type 2 second-order loop.

Let us take a case where we have the following parameters:

Reference frequency	5000 Hz
K_o	$2\pi \times 1$ MHz
K_θ	2.1
Division ratio N	10,000
ω_n	500 Hz
Phase margin	45°

The resulting values for the loop filter are determined from the computer program:

R_1	5600 Ω
R_2	1105 Ω
C_1	5.7E-7 F
C_2	1.19E-7 F
Reference suppression	32 dB
Lockup time	3 ms

The same loop in a type 2 second-order system would show reference suppression of 20 dB for the same loop bandwidth and 8-ms lockup time. These last two figures clearly indicate the advantage of the type 2 third-order loop.

Many applications require an even higher reference suppression. In the following analysis, we will deal with higher-order loops that are capable of additional suppression. However, the lockup time and the phase stability now may become a trade-off, as we will soon find out.

1-8 HIGHER-ORDER LOOPS

1-8-1 Fifth-Order Loop Transient Response

The fifth-order loop consists of a type 2 third-order loop with a second-order low-pass filter. The integrator is described by

$$F(s) = -\frac{1}{s\tau_1}\frac{1+s\tau_2}{1+s\tau_3} \tag{1-111}$$

and the second-order low-pass filter is described by

$$K(s) = \frac{1}{s^2(1/\omega_n^2) + s(2d/\omega_n) + 1} \tag{1-170}$$

The transfer function of the filters

$$T(s) = \frac{-(1+s\tau_2)}{s^2\tau_1\tau_3 + s\tau_1}\frac{1}{s^2(1/\omega_n^2) + s(2d/\omega_n) + 1}$$

$$= -\frac{1+s\tau_2}{s^4\dfrac{\tau_1\tau_3}{\omega_n^2} + s^3\dfrac{\tau_1}{\omega_n}\left(2d\tau_3 + \dfrac{1}{\omega_n}\right) + s^2\tau_1\left(\tau_3 + \dfrac{2d}{\omega_n}\right) + s\tau_1} \tag{1-171}$$

We use the familiar block diagram, Figure 1-11, which shows the phase detector, the low-pass filter, the active integrator [both condensed in $T(s)$], the VCO, and the divider. The forward gain now becomes $(K_\theta K_o/s)T(s)$, and the open-loop gain

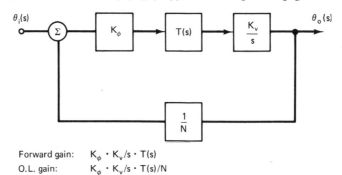

Forward gain: $K_\phi \cdot K_v/s \cdot T(s)$
O.L. gain: $K_\phi \cdot K_v/s \cdot T(s)/N$

Figure 1-11 Block diagram of the type 2 fifth-order loop. Note that the low-pass filter and active integrator are combined in $T(s)$.

$$A(s) = \frac{K_\theta K_o}{s} \frac{T(s)}{N} \tag{1-172}$$

The closed-loop transfer function

$$B(s) = \frac{\theta_o(s)}{\theta_i(s)} = \frac{\text{forward gain}}{1 + (\text{open-loop gain})} \tag{1-173}$$

or

$$\frac{\theta_o(s)}{\theta_i(s)} = \frac{(K_\theta K_o/s)T(s)}{1 + (K_\theta K_o/Ns)T(s)} = \frac{K_\theta K_o T(s)}{s + K_\theta K_o T(s)/N} \tag{1-174}$$

Rearranging yields

$$\theta_o(s) = \theta_i(s)K_\theta K_o \frac{T(s)}{s + K_\theta K_o T(s)/N} \tag{1-175}$$

The output phase, which is the same as the VCO phase, is now assumed to be disturbed by a step of magnitude S_v. The amount S_v would be in the maximum case $N \times 2\pi$, using phase detector operating ranges of $\pm 2\pi$.

If this step is referred to the input of the phase detector, it has to be divided by N, and in Laplace notation, we have

$$\theta_i(s) = \frac{S_v}{Ns} \tag{1-176}$$

from which results

$$\theta_o(s) = \frac{S_v K_\theta K_o}{N} \frac{T(s)}{s^2 + (K_\theta K_o/N)sT(s)} \tag{1-177}$$

with $K_\theta K_o/N = U$. Applying a partial fraction, we obtain

$$\theta_o(s) = \frac{S_v}{s} - \frac{S_v s}{s^2 + UsT(s)} = \frac{S_v}{s} - \frac{S_v}{s + UT(s)} \tag{1-178}$$

After some manipulations which are deleted, it can be shown that

$$\Delta\theta_o(s) = -S_v \frac{s^4 + s^3 \dfrac{2d\tau_3\omega_n + 1}{\tau_3} + s^2\left(\omega_n^2 + \dfrac{2d\omega_n}{\tau_3}\right) + s\dfrac{\omega_n^2}{\tau_3}}{s^5 + s^4 \dfrac{2d\tau_3\omega_n + 1}{\tau_3} + s^3\left(\omega_n^2 + \dfrac{2d\omega_n}{\tau_3}\right) + s^2\dfrac{\omega_n^2}{\tau_3} + s\dfrac{U\tau_2\omega_n^2}{\tau_1\tau_3}\dfrac{U\omega_n^2}{\tau_1\tau_3}} \tag{1-179}$$

We now factorize a denominator polynomial of the form

$$s^5 a_5 + s^4 a_4 + s^3 a_3 + s^2 a_2 + s a_1 + a_o$$

and therefore obtain the following coefficients:

$$a_5 = 1 \tag{1-180}$$

$$a_4 = \frac{2d\tau_3\omega_n + 1}{\tau_3} \tag{1-181}$$

$$a_3 = \omega_n^2 + \frac{2d\omega_n}{\tau_3} \tag{1-182}$$

$$a_2 = \frac{\omega_n^2}{\tau_3} \tag{1-183}$$

$$a_1 = U\tau_2 \frac{\omega_n^2}{\tau_1 \tau_3} \tag{1-184}$$

$$a_o = U \frac{\omega_n^2}{\tau_1 \tau_3} \tag{1-185}$$

The next task is to determine the roots W_i and rewrite the denominator polynomial in the form

$$P_{\text{denominator}} = (s - W_5)(s - W_4)(s - W_3)(s - W_2)(s - W_1) \tag{1-186}$$

For the Laplace transform, we need the residues

$$K_s = W_t = e^{ts} \frac{\text{numerator}}{\text{denominator without containing } W_t} \tag{1-187}$$

The next step is to calculate the binomial residues:

$$K_k = e^{tP_k} \frac{A_{k1} + A_{k2} + A_{k3} + A_{k4}}{B_{k1}B_{k2}B_{k3}B_{k4}} \tag{1-188}$$

$$K_1 = e^{tP_1} \frac{A_{16} + A_{15} + A_{14} + A_{13}}{B_{12}B_{13}B_{14}B_{15}} \tag{1-189}$$

$$K_2 = e^{tP_2} \frac{A_{26} + A_{25} + A_{24} + A_{23}}{B_{21}B_{23}B_{24}B_{25}} \tag{1-190}$$

$$K_3 = e^{tP_3} \frac{A_{36} + A_{35} + A_{34} + A_{33}}{B_{31}B_{32}B_{34}B_{35}} \tag{1-191}$$

$$K_4 = e^{tP_4} \frac{A_{46} + A_{45} + A_{44} + A_{43}}{B_{41}B_{42}B_{43}B_{45}} \tag{1-192}$$

$$K_5 = e^{tP_5} \frac{A_{56} + A_{55} + A_{54} + A_{53}}{B_{51}B_{52}B_{53}B_{54}} \tag{1-193}$$

As

$$A_{ij} = P_i \uparrow (j - 2)Qj \tag{1-194}$$

$$i = 1, 2, 3, N_2; \tag{1-195}$$

$$j = 3, 4, 5, N_2 + 1 \tag{1-196}$$

and

$$B_{ij} = P_i - P_j \tag{1-197}$$

$$i = 1, 2, 3, \ldots, N_2; \tag{1-198}$$

$$j = 1, 2, 3, \ldots, N_2 \tag{1-199}$$

it is apparent that

$$A_{1ij} \triangleq \text{real } A_{ij} \tag{1-200}$$

$$A_{2ij} \triangleq \text{imaginary } A_{ij} \tag{1-201}$$

$$B_{1ij} \triangleq \text{real } B_{ij} \tag{1-202}$$

$$B_{2ij} \triangleq \text{imaginary } B_{ij} \qquad (1\text{-}203)$$

$$K_{1i} \triangleq \text{real } K_i \qquad (1\text{-}204)$$

$$K_{2i} \triangleq \text{imaginary } K_i \qquad (1\text{-}205)$$

Using the results, we can rewrite

$$\Delta\theta_o(s) = \frac{s^4 Q_6 + s^3 Q_5 + s^2 Q_4 + s Q_3}{s^5 Q_6 + s^4 Q_5 + s^3 Q_4 + s^2 Q_3 + s Q_2 + Q_1} \qquad (1\text{-}206)$$

Finally, we obtain the roots P_1 to P_5 in terms of Q_1 to Q_6; then the partial fraction expansion gives the residues:

$$\underset{s=P_1}{K_1} = e^{tP_1} \frac{P_1^4 Q_6 + P_1^3 Q_5 + P_1^2 Q_4 + P_1 Q_3}{(P_1 - P_2)(P_1 - P_3)(P_1 - P_4)(P_1 - P_5)} \qquad (1\text{-}207)$$

$$\underset{s=P_2}{K_2} = e^{tP_2} \frac{P_2^4 Q_6 + P_2^3 Q_5 + P_2^2 Q_4 + P_2 Q_3}{(P_2 - P_1)(P_2 - P_3)(P_2 - P_4)(P_2 - P_5)} \qquad (1\text{-}208)$$

$$\underset{s=P_3}{K_3} = e^{tP_3} \frac{P_3^4 Q_6 + P_3^3 Q_5 + P_3^2 Q_4 + P_3 Q_3}{(P_3 - P_1)(P_3 - P_2)(P_3 - P_4)(P_3 - P_5)} \qquad (1\text{-}209)$$

$$\underset{s=P_4}{K_4} = e^{tP_4} \frac{P_4^4 Q_6 + P_4^3 Q_5 + P_4^2 Q_4 + P_4 Q_3}{(P_4 - P_1)(P_4 - P_2)(P_4 - P_3)(P_4 - P_5)} \qquad (1\text{-}210)$$

$$\underset{s=P_5}{K_5} = e^{tP_5} \frac{P_5^4 Q_6 + P_5^3 Q_5 + P_5^2 Q_4 + P_5 Q_3}{(P_5 - P_1)(P_5 - P_2)(P_5 - P_3)(P_5 - P_4)} \qquad (1\text{-}211)$$

$$\Delta\theta(t) = \left[\sum_{n=1}^{5} Kn \right] \qquad (1\text{-}212)$$

In Section A-2 we present a computer program that calculates the type 2 fifth-order loop. These calculations are incorporated in the program and may be useful for those who want to go through different steps and use it. The program contains all the necessary transformations, root finders, and other subroutines required.

What is the practical use of higher-order loops? Higher-order loops are really useful only in frequency synthesizers if the reference frequency is substantially higher than the loop frequency. A typical example would be a reference frequency of as high as 5 or 10 MHz down to as low as 25 kHz, which has to be suppressed more than 90 dB. The phase shift introduced by the additional filtering, as can be seen by the computer program in the Appendix and the example shown here, can be allowed only if the cutoff frequency of the loop is small relative to the additional poles of the filter. What is a typical example? Let us assume that we have a reference frequency of 25 kHz, and our loop frequency is set at 1 or 2 kHz. The resulting reference suppression with the simple loop filter would be approximately 20 times log (25 kHz/2 kHz), or roughly 20 dB. This is totally insufficient, of course.

The third-order loop, because of its deeper filtering, will increase this to roughly 33 dB, but this is still not enough. The insertion of a steep filter, such as an active filter or an LC elliptic filter, with poles at 25 kHz, will have very little phase shift at 2 kHz, the cutoff frequency of the loop filter, and a substantial suppression of reference becomes possible. However, these high-order systems are useful only if there is enough difference between the reference frequency and the loop frequency. The higher the ratio between the two values, the easier it becomes to design a high-order system.

To get high suppression, not too much phase shift, and to be able to work close to the reference frequency, special detectors are generally required. The phase shift introduced by using a sample/hold comparator is fairly small, and it is possible to set the loop filter at about half of the reference. If properly designed, the dual sampler combines good reference suppression with low noise. The phase shift can be adjusted and compensated. The drawback of the sample/hold comparator, as we will see in Chapter 4, is its limits as to what is the highest frequency of operation.

If properly designed, the tri-state phase/frequency comparator, also discussed in Chapter 4, may have 60 to 70 dB inherent reference suppression without the filter and may ease the requirement on the loop filter. Only recent developments, as will be described later, which compensate the spikes at the output of the tri-state phase/ frequency comparator, will reduce the phase jitter and incidental FM introduced by this somewhat noisy discriminator. As the tri-state comparator is somewhat noisier than the sample/hold, the particular loop with its cutoff frequency and its noise requirements will determine which sample to use. The computer programs in Section A-2 allow the interested reader to design several type 2 third-order loops, and by changing the cutoff frequency of the active filter, one can observe the impact the addition of the low-pass filter has on stability and lockup time, making it a high-order loop, in this case a fifth-order loop.

1-9 DIGITAL LOOPS WITH MIXERS

The single-loop synthesizer has a number of restrictions. One immediate restriction is the fact that the step size is the same as the reference frequency, unless special techniques are used, which are described in Chapter 3.

In addition, as we have frequency dividers that work only up to about 2000 MHz, it becomes difficult, if not impossible, to build a PLL at a much higher frequency unless some mixing techniques are used. These techniques are also sometimes referred to as *heterodyning techniques*. Figure 1-12 shows a single-loop synthesizer that has a mixer incorporated which heterodynes the VCO frequency down to a lower frequency at which we have dividers available. The auxiliary frequency that is injected in the loop for down-conversion is generated from the reference oscillator, and we will not go into the problems of noise generated because of this up-multiplication, as it is dealt with in Chapter 2. For now we are concerned only with the question of loop stability as a function of the introduction of this mixer, and its possible effects as far as unwanted sidebands are concerned. Let us assume the numerical example shown in Figure 1-13. This synthesizer is intended for use in an amateur transceiver operating from 144 to 148 MHz, a frequency range that is well within the capabilities of current dividers.

However, since we want to minimize power consumption, we find that it requires less power to generate an auxiliary frequency of 140 MHz from our 5-MHz standard

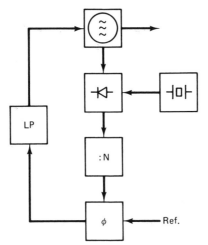

Figure 1-12 Block diagram of a digital PLL using the heterodyne technique.

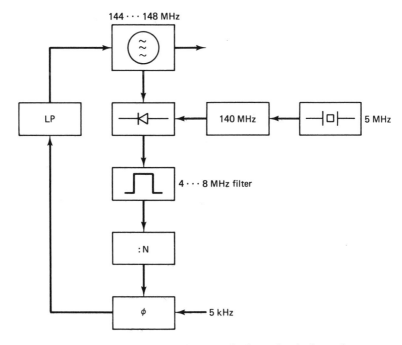

Figure 1-13 Block diagram of a 144–148 MHz synthesizer using the heterodyne technique, resulting in an internal IF of 4 to 8 MHz.

(synchronizing a 70-MHz crystal and doubling it). The output frequency of this mixer then is 4 to 8 MHz, and this frequency range can be handled by a programmable divider in CMOS. Between the mixer and the divider we will insert a bandpass filter of 4-MHz bandwidth. The divider in CMOS now has to operate between 4 and 8 MHz. For such amateur applications it is frequently required that the same synthesizer be used to transmit and receive.

For transmit applications, frequency modulating the synthesizer is required, and the modulation can be inserted in the loop filter, as the loop bandwidth probably is restricted to a few hundred hertz, while the step size will be 5 kHz, in accordance with the channels available. The modulation could also be done if the 140 MHz was generated from a free-running 70-MHz crystal, which is then modulated.

At 70 MHz we will probably have to use a third- or fifth-overtone crystal, which cannot be pulled very well, probably not enough to accommodate a maximum of 3-kHz deviation. More information on pulling of crystals is presented in Chapter 4.

What does the insertion of the mixer do to our system? The division ratio without mixing would have been 28,800 to 29,600, or a ratio of 1:1.0278. After inserting the mixing stage, the division ratio now is 800 to 1600, and the absolute ratio is 1:2.

The loop gain, assuming that the VCO gain is constant over the tuning range, is now changing by the amount 1:2. In some loops we will find that the introduction of such a mixer results in a much larger change of division ratios, and if the frequencies are not selected properly, a change of 1:10 will occur. This will cause two difficulties:

1. If the multiplication changes so much, the sideband of the reference being multiplied at the output will change substantially as a function of frequency setting, while the percentage change of the frequency at the output is very small. Therefore, at the higher frequency, in our case 148 MHz, the noise sideband inside the loop bandwidth will be twice as high as the 144 MHz. In a case where the loop gain changes more dramatically, such as 1:10, the noise will change by this amount.

2. If the loop gain changes with all other parameters remaining constant, this may cause a stability problem. The net result is that, in the case of a type 2 second-order loop, our damping factor ζ can range from 0.1 to 1, and the transient performance of the loop will vary substantially; therefore, stability will become an issue. We have to find a method to compensate for the change of loop gain, and we will show a method of dealing with this phenomenon in Section 1-10. Right now it is only important to know that it does occur and that it can present a problem.

The next effect the mixer produces is the consequence of phase shift of the IF filter following the mixer, in our case a filter ranging from 4 to 8 MHz. As a result, we have to modify our block diagram of the loop, as shown in Figure 1-14. The additional box represents the low-pass equivalent of the bandpass filter, and the delay of this filter has to be determined. There are a number of good books available that

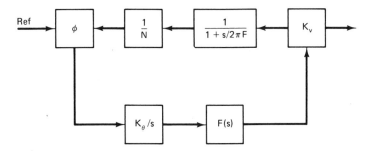

Figure 1-14 Linearized equivalent circuit of a PLL with the heterodyne technique, including delay information introduced by the IF filter.

provide the necessary computation aids for these filters and information about the delay. The best book, which is by Anatol Zverev [4], will be mentioned herein several times and is really an absolute must for the library of any design engineer who handles RF and filter design. The phase shift of the equivalent low-pass filter of the IF filter is

$$\theta_{\text{low pass}} = \arctan \frac{G_1(f_m) \sin \theta(f_m) - G_1(-f_m) \sin \theta(-f_m)}{G_1(f_m) \cos \theta(f_m) - G_1(-f_m) \cos \theta(-f_m)} \qquad (1\text{-}213)$$

In some cases, we will have to use loops with conversions, where the resulting IF filter is very narrow. The use of a crystal filter will introduce a group delay in addition to the phase shift. These delays have to be added to the block diagram and added or subtracted from the actual phase. Since this can be done fairly easily and has a substantial impact on the stability, it is recommended that the interested reader analyze such an example mathematically, where it is assumed that the loop bandwidth is 2 kHz, the IF bandwidth is 100 kHz, and the loop bandwidth is increased to 50 kHz. We also have to take into consideration the effect of the phase shift of the low-pass filter equivalent of the bandpass filter. As the output signal from the mixer is passing the IF filter, which will be assumed to be symmetrical, the amplitude of the carrier $G_1(f_m)$ will change relative to the input signal. The losses of the filter and the sidebands will be shifted in phase equal to the phase shift generated by the filter. As is known from the literature, it is possible to convert the bandpass performance of this filter into an equivalent low-pass filter and deal with it. These details and examples are beyond the scope of this book and should be studied in the literature, such as in the book by Zverev already mentioned.

There are a number of unpleasant effects in addition to the one mentioned, such as ringing, as a result of nonequalized group delay, and if the IF filter bandpass is not symmetrical relative to the carrier frequency, AM-to-FM conversion occurs and has to be calculated. These special effects are an interesting topic, and the reader should not only be made aware of them but encouraged to calculate some numerical examples. In the rest of the book, we will assume that we know how to deal with these effects. The result of the calculations will be that a higher phase margin than the 45° recommended for higher-order loops has to be allowed to compensate for the additional delay. As a result of this higher phase margin, the settling time of the loop will become larger. In analyzing loops and in determining what frequency arrangements to use, one has to be aware of these trade-offs and optimize the loop by calculating a number of examples and finding the best solution by iteration.

The next effect we will analyze is the number of spurious signals introduced by the mixer. The double-balanced mixer, the best for such application, is still a highly nonlinear device that generates harmonics of the two frequencies applied, and those frequencies will mix with each other, resulting in a wide spectrum at the output. In Section A-2 a computer program is provided that determines the combination of such products as they appear at the output of the double-balanced mixer. This method is preferred over the graphics method simply because the graphics method does not provide enough resolution. To keep the number of unwanted frequencies at the output at an acceptable level, we should observe two design rules:

1. To obtain an IF, the two input frequencies should be as high and as close together as possible; the lower image is then used. A fairly simple low-pass filter at the output minimizes the possibility of feed-through and unwanted products.

2. The power ratio between the RF and the LO should meet certain requirements. A design engineer is well advised to have about a 30-dB difference in level. Let us assume that the LO drive is $+17$ dBm, a typical drive level for a medium-level double-balanced mixer; the RF input should then be -13 dBm or less. A further reduction in RF input may have the disadvantage of requiring too many amplifiers following at the output of the mixer and therefore generating additional noise from the postamplifiers.

In cases such as that of our previous example, where we are mixing a fixed frequency of 140 MHz with a 144- to 148-MHz band, this requirement may be relaxed, and a drive level of 5 or 6 dBm may still be permissible. A decision on this matter depends on the particular case, and the best way of solving it is to take measurements in an actual circuit.

A spectrum analyzer connected at the output of the mixer operating at the range of interest with enough dynamic range should provide the necessary information. If these theoretical guidelines are followed, the design should be fairly trouble-free.

In Chapter 6 you will find several examples where double-balanced mixers are incorporated and IF frequencies inside the synthesizer are being used. In many cases, I have provided level information, and the particular synthesizers shown are spurious-free, at least 90 dB down relative to the carrier.

1-10 ACQUISITION

In order to understand the acquisition performance of the digital PLL, we must first look at the linearized model. As mentioned previously, we have several ranges in

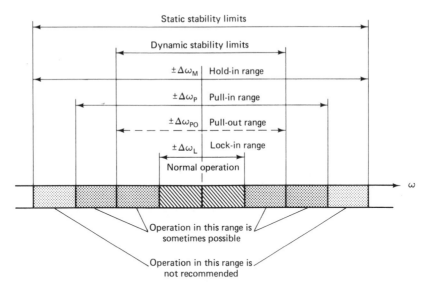

Figure 1-15 Possible operating ranges of a PLL.

which the loop can operate, and Figure 1-15 shows a plot of these ranges. The closest range around the center is the normal operating range and also the capture range, frequently called the *lock-in range*. Once a PLL has acquired lock, it maintains the locked condition within the hold-in range, and the borderline between the hold-in range and instability is fairly narrow. From our previous calculation and Laplace transform, applying

$$\theta_1(s) = \frac{\Delta\omega}{s^2} \tag{1-214}$$

to the input of the PLL, we can determine the maximum error using the final value theorem,

$$\lim_{t\to\infty} \theta_e(t) = \lim_{s\to 0} s\theta_e(s) = \frac{\Delta\omega}{K_o K_\theta F(o)} \tag{1-215}$$

With the assumption $\theta \approx \sin\theta$, the maximum amount this can be is 1 and therefore

$$\Delta\omega_H = K_o K_\theta F(o) \tag{1-216}$$

For the active filter $F(o)$ is infinite and therefore

$$\Delta\omega_H = \infty \tag{1-217}$$

and for the passive filter $F(o) = 1$ and

$$\Delta\omega_H = K_o K_\theta = \langle\!\langle\text{loop gain}\rangle\!\rangle \tag{1-218}$$

We have just calculated the hold-in range of the analog linear PLL. It is apparent that the use of an active loop filter guarantees a wider hold-in range.

Now let us go back and assume that the loop has not yet acquired lock. In the beginning we have two different frequencies applied to the phase detector. It is important to understand that, as the loop will acquire lock, we have to deal with two different ranges. One is the area in which we acquire frequency lock, and only after frequency lock has been accomplished can phase lock occur. There are several requirements necessary to make frequency lock possible.

1. The tuning range of the VCO has to be wide enough to cover the desired range of operation.
2. The VCO itself has to be able to oscillate through this required range without disruption of oscillation, a jump phenomenon frequently called "discontinuities."
3. The tuning diodes have to be operated in a range where they do not become conductive (see Chapter 4) since leakage current from the diodes into the phase detector causes difficulty.
4. Depending on the phase detector used, we either have a pull-in phenomenon, which we will discuss later, or sweeping, where the generated beat note at the output will sweep the oscillator from one end of the range to the other as an aid to acquire lock. In some instances, especially with pure phase detectors, an external frequency lock device may be necessary.

Figure 1-16 shows the two popular techniques used to help obtain frequency lock. The first one is the use of an additional frequency comparator, and an electronic device switches over from this to the phase detector. This technique is also currently used in the Philips HEF4750/51 LSI PLL integrated circuits. To obtain frequency lock, we first use a digital tri-state phase/frequency comparator which has a dead zone in the middle of its operating range where it is locked, and the system then switches over to a sample/hold comparator offering low-noise operation.

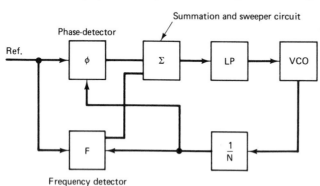

Figure 1-16 Block diagram of a PLL using a phase detector and frequency detector for acquisition aids in addition to the sweeper circuit.

Another technique used in the past is an external sweeping device. Figure 1-17 shows the schematic of such an arrangement. We find a phase detector that operates into an NPN transistor. The loop filter is at the output of the phase detector, and the gain of the following dc amplifier is defined as the ratio of R_L/R_E.

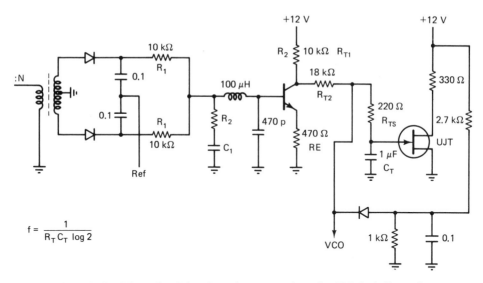

Figure 1-17 Schematic of the phase detector section of a PLL including a dc amplifier and a sweeping circuit.

A unijunction, or double-base transistor, is used to generate a sweeping signal. As the dc output voltage from this circuit reaches a certain level, the unijunction transistor ignites and starts its sweeping action. The frequency of oscillation of this circuit can be determined with the equation

$$f = \frac{1}{R_T C_T \log 2} \qquad (1\text{-}219)$$

Note that R_T has to be derived from adding $R_{T1} + R_{T2} + R_{T3}$ in the starting condition, whereby we can assume that the amplifier draws no current. For the values taken here, we obtain a frequency of

$$f = \frac{1}{(18 \text{ k}\Omega + 10 \text{ k}\Omega + 220 \text{ }\Omega)10^{-6} \log 2} = 118 \text{ Hz}$$

The circuit will be swept with this particular frequency.

We must now remember that there is a maximum frequency with which we can sweep the circuit to acquire lock. This is called the *pull-out range*. Pull-out range, defined $\Delta\omega_{PO}$, is determined by the equation

$$\Delta\omega_{PO} = 1.8\omega_n(\zeta + 1) \qquad (1\text{-}220)$$

which is an approximation that can be applied in most cases. In our particular case with the unijunction transistor, the maximum sweep rate for $\zeta = 0.7$ and $\omega_{PO} = 118(2\pi)$ results in 38 Hz for the loop frequency ω_n.

However, our system is currently not yet in lock; we still have to calculate the lock-in range. A similar formula can be found as a function of the type of filter. For the simple *RC* filter with no phase compensation, as shown previously, the lock-in range

$$\Delta\omega_L \approx \omega_n \tag{1-221}$$

and for the filter with phase compensation

$$\Delta\omega_L \approx 2\zeta\omega_n \tag{1-222}$$

We are interested in determining how long it takes to acquire lock. The following relation gives a good approximation of the lock-in time:

$$T_L \approx \frac{1}{\omega_n} \tag{1-223}$$

This is valid for all type 2 second-order linear PLLs. The calculation that we have just made referred to the phase lock. It becomes apparent from these equations that for $\zeta = 0.7$, the lock-in range is only equal to or slightly larger than the loop bandwidth. To move the VCO frequency within these limits, additional functions are required. This area is called *frequency lock*. We are now dealing with the pull-in range.

The pull-in range is the first range we have to deal with, as the phase-locked loop is about to acquire frequency, and later, phase lock. The explanation given here is somewhat backward, but it is easier to understand if one considers the ranges in this sequence, as the equations indicate the limitations. Pull-in is probably best understood by remembering that the system starts off with an offset in frequencies, and therefore a beat note appears at the output of the phase detector and of the loop filter. In the schematic using the sweeping technique shown previously, the loop bandwidth remains constant. Another way of helping the loop to acquire frequency lock is to widen the bandwidth of the loop filter, enabling phase lock with a larger frequency offset.

Figure 1-18 shows the schematic of a dual-time-constant loop filter which can

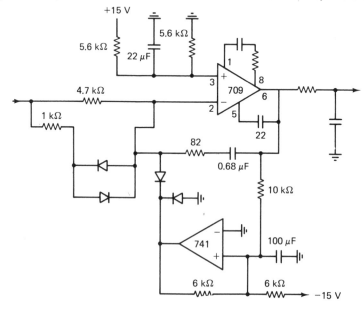

Figure 1-18 Schematic of a loop filter/integrator where the time constant is changed with the help of antiparallel diodes in the loop.

be used to explain the pull-in effect. Let us assume that initially we have a difference of several kilohertz between the two frequencies at the phase detector and are currently not considering the effect of a frequency divider.

The beat note generated at the output of the phase detector is an ac voltage together with a dc component. We also have to assume that in the initial condition the beat note is much larger in frequency than the bandwidth of the loop filter. As the output voltage of the loop filter either sweeps the oscillator to a higher or lower frequency, we have to see what the magnitude of the beat note as a function of sweeping is doing. It turns out that the difference in frequency becomes smaller if the VCO is swept toward higher values and becomes larger if the VCO is swept toward smaller frequency values. The output sweep frequency or beat note, therefore, is nonlinear and nonharmonic, and the average frequency at the output is no longer zero. The loop filter acting as an integrator will average the sweep.

The mathematical model for this pull-in is somewhat complicated and is given in the literature [2]. The *pull-in time*, defined as the time required for the average frequency error to decay from the initial condition to the locked limit, is

$$T_p \simeq \frac{(\Delta\omega)^2 \tau_2}{K^2} = \frac{(\Delta\omega)^2}{2\zeta\omega_n^3} \qquad (1\text{-}224)$$

This formula is valid only for the linear type 2 second-order loop. A model for the digital PLL will follow.

Example 1

Let us assume that our initial frequency offset is 1 MHz and that the loop bandwidth ω_n is 10 Hz. The time it requires for the pull-in range is

$$T_p = \frac{(2\pi \times 10^6)^2}{2\zeta(2\pi \times 10)^3} = 113.68 \times 10^6 \text{ s}$$

or 3.6 years. If we use the system that automatically increases the loop bandwidth with the two antiparallel diodes as previously shown, which results in a new loop bandwidth of 10 kHz prior to lock, the formula changes to

$$T_p = \frac{(2\pi \times 10^6)^2}{2\zeta(2\pi \times 10^4)^3} = 0.113 \text{ s}$$

The difference between both is dramatic, and with the simple trick of changing the loop bandwidth, we have speeded up the pull-in substantially.

Immediately after frequency lock has occurred, the switching diodes are no longer conductive. The remaining phase offset is handled by the lock-in function and the time it will now take to phase lock the loop:

$$T_L = \frac{1}{\omega_n} = \frac{1}{10(2\pi)} = 16 \text{ ms}$$

The time required for phase lock, therefore, is much smaller than the time required for frequency lock, and the total lock time would be 0.1296 s.

Lock-in performance of the digital PLL system that uses a tri-state digital phase/frequency comparator as shown in Chapter 4 can no longer be calculated using the linearized model as is frequently done in the literature. The output of the tri-state phase/frequency comparator behaves totally different from the linearized models.

We have to take a look at two different examples. First, we will look at a tri-state phase/frequency comparator where the loop filter is placed after the summation stage, and the RCA or Motorola CD4046 fits this description. When the system is switched on, first the two pulses that are combined through the CMOS switches will jam the output voltage up to the power supply voltage and the loop filter will delay this action, depending on the integration time constant. The dc voltage to the VCO, therefore, will slowly rise, the VCO will be swept, and pull-in will be accomplished.

It turns out that this particular example practically behaves as the linear analog phase detector version.

Now let us consider a phase/frequency comparator equal to the MC4044 which has two outputs, where pulses are available to charge or discharge a capacitor.

If the loop filter combination shown in Figure 1-19 is used, whereby each output of the phase/frequency comparator is applied to one input of an operational amplifier provided that the amplifier is fast enough to follow the input frequency, we now have

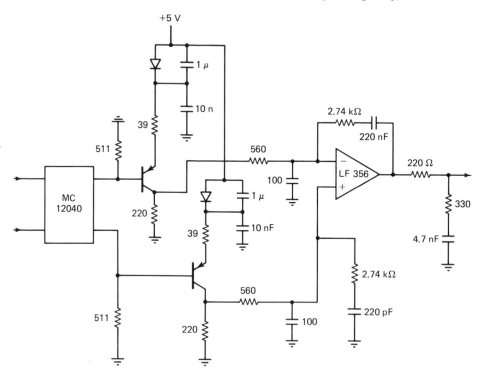

Figure 1-19 Schematic of an ECL phase/frequency comparator driving a high-frequency operational amplifier. The outputs to the inverting and noninverting input of the operational amplifiers are pulses which are charging and discharging the loop capacitor of 220 nF. Note the additional output filter following the operational amplifier.

to analyze the statistical average and determine from there what the output of the operational amplifier is showing.

The following mathematical mode, to the best of my knowledge, is the only one that ever assessed this effect correctly and was published by Roland Best in his book *Theory and Application of Phase-Locked Loops* [1]. The following discussion is published here with Dr. Best's permission.

1-10-1 Pull-in Performance of the Digital Loop

In the beginning of this chapter, when we were discussing the differences between the analog and digital PLL, we started with the digital phase/frequency comparators. The flip-flop-based digital phase/frequency comparators work on the principle that they analyze the rising edges of the input signals, edge-triggered flip-flops, and are insensitive to the duty cycle.

The output can be used to charge or discharge a capacitor and has to be combined with an active filter to take full advantage of its capabilities. Figure 1-19 showed the typical arrangement using this type of phase/frequency comparator.

Initially, when the loop is not in lock, we can assume that frequencies f_1 and f_2 have a random relation to each other, the phase of one to the other is random, and that the next edge of the following signal within the time interval $0 \leq t \leq T$ can occur with the same probability in any given time. We define $w(t) \, dt$ as the probability that the next rising edge of the signal f_2 will occur in the time $t \cdots t + dt$. Therefore, we can write

$$w(t) = \frac{1}{T_2} \qquad (t \leq T_2) \tag{1-225}$$

$$w(t) = 0 \qquad (t > T_2) \tag{1-226}$$

We now may have two principal cases:

1. f_2 is smaller than f_1 or $T_2 > T_1 = 1/f_1$, and the negative edge will occur: *case 1*: in the time interval $0 \leq t \leq T_1$; *case 2*: in the time interval $T_1 < t \leq T_2$.
2. In the case of f_1 being smaller than f_2, these conditions are reversed.

As the output signal of the phase/frequency comparator is a chain of pulses that are combined, the duty cycle $\delta(t)$ will change. The average duty cycle $\bar{\delta}$, according to probability theory, can be determined from

$$\bar{\delta} = \int_0^{T_2} w(t) \delta(t) \, dt \tag{1-227}$$

The integration of this can be done in two steps:

$$\bar{\delta} = \int_0^{T_1} w(t) \frac{t}{T_1} \, dt + \int_{T_1}^{T_2} w(t) \frac{t}{2T_1} \, dt \tag{1-228}$$

with

$$\delta(t) = \frac{t}{T_1} \quad \text{and} \quad \frac{t}{2T_1}$$

depending on the time area, as discussed previously.

   In reality, the time interval is not going to lie between T_1 and $2T_1$ but can be between T_1 and ∞. Therefore, our average duty cycle has to be written in the form of several integrals and

$$\bar{\delta} = \int_0^{T_1} w(t) \frac{t}{T_1} dt + \int_1^{T_1} w(t) \frac{t}{2T_1} dt + \cdots$$
$$+ \int_{T_1}^{T_2} w(t) \frac{t}{nT_1} dt \tag{1-229}$$

This can be converted into the final equation based on $f_1 > f_2$, and we obtain

$$\bar{\delta} = \frac{f_2}{2f_1} n - \sum_{i=1}^{n} \frac{1}{i} + \frac{f_1}{2nf_2} \tag{1-230}$$

with $n = \text{Int}(f_1/f_2) + 1$. Figure 1-20 shows the duty cycle for any combinations of $n\tau_1$, and Figure 1-21 shows the average duty cycle $\bar{\delta}$ as a function of the frequency ratio f_2/f_1. The straight-line approximation in this curve can be used to simplify the formula, as the lock-in will occur for the case $f_1 = f_2$. We will then obtain for the average duty cycle

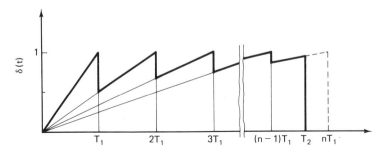

Figure 1-20 Change of duty cycle $\Delta(t)$ as a function of T. (Courtesy of Fachschriftenverlag, Aargauer Tagblatt AG, Aarau/Switzerland.)

$$\bar{\delta} = \frac{f_1 - f_2}{f_1} = \frac{\omega_1 - \omega_2}{\omega_1} \tag{1-231}$$

In this case, the average output voltage

$$\bar{v}_d = \bar{\delta} V_B = \frac{V_B}{\omega_o}(\omega_1 - \omega_2) \tag{1-232}$$

since

$$\bar{v}_d \approx K_d'(\omega_1 - \omega_2) \tag{1-233}$$

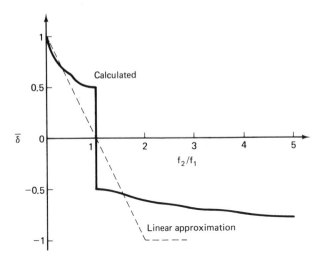

Figure 1-21   Average duty cycle $\bar{\delta}$ as a function of the frequency ratio f_2/f_1. (Courtesy of Fachschriftenverlag, Aargauer Tagblatt AG, Aarau/Switzerland.)

We finally obtain the previously used gain constant of the phase comparator of this particular type in the out-of-lock condition to be

$$K'_d \approx \frac{V_B}{\omega_o} \tag{1-234}$$

1-10-2 Coarse Steering of the VCO as an Acquisition Aid

We have learned so far that we can use a frequency detector or a sweep oscillator to steer or sweep the oscillator close to its final frequency.

In the case of the sweeping, we have to make sure that the sweeping speed is not too fast, because if it is, the oscillator will never acquire lock or it will skip cycles several times before it acquires lock. The phenomenon of cycle skipping is explained in Gardner's book [3], but generally not enough information is available about the particular loop to take full advantage of the theoretical evaluation.

Once the transfer characteristic of the VCO is known, it is possible to use a read-only memory (ROM) that receives frequency information, and with the help of a digital-to-analog (D/A) converter within very fine resolution, coarse steer the oscillator toward its desired final frequency. This method avoids the necessity of the additional external frequency comparator and the sweeping technique. The drawback is that if diodes are changed or the characteristic of the tuning diode as a function of age changes, the lookup table will become incorrect. This is true for extremely fine resolution. Let us assume the case where we have an oscillator operating from 70 to 80 MHz which we want to coarse steer. If we assume for a moment that the tuning diodes do not produce additional noise or that, under certain circumstances, the additional noise contribution of the coarse-steering tuning diodes can be neglected, it is possible to take an 8-bit D/A converter, as shown in Figure 1-22, that is getting its frequency information from the binary-coded decimal (BCD) commands to the

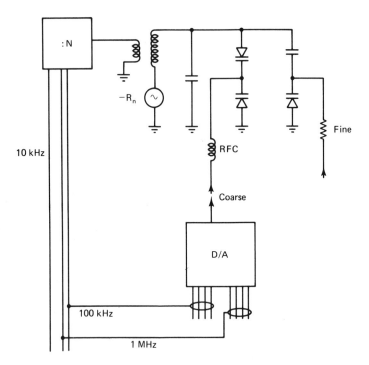

Figure 1-22   VCO coarse steering using a D/A converter.

frequency divider and generates within 100-kHz resolution an output that can be used to coarse steer the tuning diodes. Now the tuning diodes responsible for the fine tuning only have to work over a fairly narrow range, and as a result of this, the VCO gain is very small.

The output impedance of the D/A converter can be made very low, and as the coarse-tuning diodes are being driven from a low-impedance point rather than the typical high impedance the dc control line has, there is no pickup on the coarse-steering line from any hum of any significant amount. As the fine-control loop now has a voltage gain of 30 to 100 kHz/V at most, the pickup is reduced by at least 20 dB, if not more. Therefore, the amount of spurious signal because of pickup and hum is reduced by the same amount.

This technique has the advantage also that the loop gain for this narrow window remains fairly constant, regardless of the VCO's curvature, as the transfer characteristic in this narrow window does not change very much.

The D/A converter has to generate a dc voltage which is not linear but rather is the opposite of the transfer characteristic of the tuning diodes used for the wide tuning range. A larger voltage swing will be needed at the higher frequency, whereas less voltage is required at the low end of the VCO. A practical schematic where this technique is used is given in Chapter 6.

In dealing with mixers, we have learned that one of the drawbacks of a heterodyne loop is that the open-loop gain changes more dramatically as the division ratio
required becomes much larger. A typical loop without a heterodyne technique may
have 30 or 40% variation of loop gain due to change of N, and I have seen cases where
the division factor N, as a result of heterodyne technique, has changed by 20:1. How
do we cope with this problem? The best way of handling this is either to use a coarse-
steering technique with either tuning diodes or switching diodes and allow a very
narrow window in which the oscillator will operate or change the loop filter dc control
gain. Figure 1-23 shows an arrangement where, depending on the frequency setting
of the dividers, several CMOS switches change the dc loop gain following the loop
filter and, therefore, linearize the loop. The introduction of this amplifier after the
loop filter has the drawback that the noise is no longer limited by a following filter,
or if such an *RC* low-pass filter is used after the amplifier, the technique of analyzing
high-order loops has to be used, and inside the loop bandwidth, we still find the
additional noise contribution.

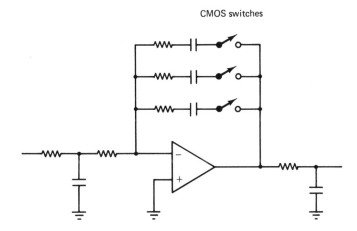

Figure 1-23 Linearizing of loop gain by changing loop components.

This approach is typically used in wideband loops where the output oscillator
operates from 200 to 300 MHz, as an example, and the reference frequency is between
100 kHz and several megahertz. The loop gain, because of the small division ratio, is
fairly high, while the loop gain variation due to some heterodyning may also be very
high. In an effort to linearize, the operational amplifiers are used to be either offset
with a dc control voltage, the loop filter is modified with additional capacitors in
parallel, or a dc amplifier following the loop filter is used, which changes the dc gain.
In some instances, all three techniques are used simultaneously, and it becomes very
tricky to avoid additional noise being brought into the loop and make all systems
track without difficulty. Figure 1-24 shows a combination of all of these techniques.
Table 1-4 shows the most important formulas for digital PLLs.

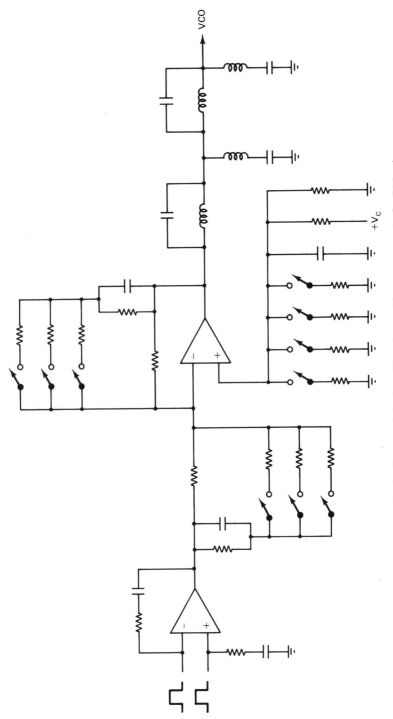

Figure 1-24 Circuit diagram of the loop filter dc amplifier arrangement of a PLL where the loop gain and dc offset is controlled by CMOS switches to linearize and coarse steer the VCO.

1-10-3 Loop Stability

The easiest way to analyze the loop stability is to plot the magnitude and phase of the open-loop transfer function $K_v F(s)/s$ as a function of frequency. First, consider the case where $F(s)$ is a simple low-pass filter described by Eq. (1-27). For this case the open-loop frequency response is

$$K_v G(j\omega) = \frac{K_v}{j\omega(j\omega\tau + 1)} \tag{1-235}$$

The straight-line approximation of the magnitude of this open-loop transfer function is plotted in Figure 1-25. The magnitude of the response decreases at the rate of 6 dB/octave until the frequency is equal to the -3-dB frequency of the low-pass filter $(\frac{1}{\tau})$; for higher frequencies the magnitude decreases at a rate of -12 dB/octave.

Several rules of thumb, developed by Bode for feedback amplifiers, are useful in selecting the loop parameters. The first has to do with selecting the filter bandwidth $\omega_L = 1/\tau$. The approximation is: If the open-loop frequency response crosses the 0-dB line with a slope of -6 dB/octave, the system is stable. If the slope is -12dB/octave or greater, the system is unstable. The second-order system under consideration is inherently stable, but the model is an approximation to a higher-order system. If the open-loop second-order model crosses the 0-dB line at -12 dB/octave, there is little room left for error. Additional phase shift from the VCO or phase detector could cause the loop to go unstable.

To have the open-loop gain cross the 0-dB line at -6 dB/octave, it is necessary that $\omega_L > K_v$. The larger ω_L is, the better will be the loop stability. From the filtering viewpoint, the smaller ω_L, the smaller the loop bandwidth and the less noise that

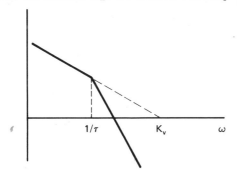

Figure 1-25 Magnitude of the open-loop gain of a PLL system.

will reach the VCO. K_v should be as small as possible to minimize the bandwidth. The larger the K_v, the smaller the steady-state error and the faster the loop response. Hence, in PLL design, compromises among noise performance, loop stability, steady-state error, and transient performance must be made.

Another rule of thumb that is helpful in PLL design is that the frequency ω_c at which the magnitude of the open-loop transfer function is unity,

$$\frac{K_v F(j\omega)}{j\omega_c} = 1 \tag{1-236}$$

TABLE 1-4 MOST IMPORTANT FORMULAS FOR DIGITAL PLLS (Second order only)

Phase frequency comparator	Exclusive-OR gate		Edge-triggered JK master/slave flip-flop	
	Active filter	Passive filter	Active filter	Passive filter
Hold-in range	$\Delta\omega_H \to \infty$	$\Delta\omega_H = \dfrac{\pi}{2}\dfrac{K_o K_d}{N}$	$\Delta\omega_H \to \infty$	$\Delta\omega_H = \pi\dfrac{K_o K_d}{N}$
Capture range				
$\tau_2 \neq 0$	$\Delta\omega_L \approx \pi\zeta\omega_n$		$\Delta\omega_L \approx 2\pi\zeta\omega_n$	
$\tau_2 = 0$	$\Delta\omega_L \approx \dfrac{\pi}{\sqrt{8}}\omega_n$		$\Delta\omega_L \approx \dfrac{\pi}{\sqrt{3}}\omega_n$	
Pull-in range	$\Delta\omega_P \approx \dfrac{\pi}{2}\sqrt{\dfrac{2\zeta\omega_n K_o K_d}{N}}$	$\Delta\omega_P \approx \dfrac{\pi}{2}\sqrt{\dfrac{2\zeta\omega_n K_o K_d}{N} - \omega_n^2}$	$\Delta\omega_P \approx \pi\sqrt{\dfrac{2\zeta\omega_n K_o K_d}{N}}$	$\Delta\omega_P \approx \pi\sqrt{\dfrac{2\zeta\omega_n K_o K_d}{N} - \omega_n^2}$
Pull-in time		$T_P \approx \dfrac{4}{\pi^2}\dfrac{\Delta\omega_0^2}{\zeta\omega_n^3}$		$T_P \approx \dfrac{\Delta\omega_0^2}{\pi^2\zeta\omega_n^3}$
Pullout range				
$\zeta < 1$	$\Delta\omega_{PO} \approx 1.8\omega_n(\zeta + 1)$		$\Delta\omega_{PO} = \pi\omega_n\exp\left(\dfrac{\zeta}{\sqrt{1-\zeta^2}}\arctan\dfrac{\sqrt{1-\zeta^2}}{\zeta}\right)$	
$\zeta > 1$			$\Delta\omega_{PO} = \pi\omega_n\exp\left(\dfrac{\zeta}{\sqrt{\zeta^2-1}}\arctan\dfrac{\sqrt{\zeta^2-1}}{\zeta}\right)$	

is approximately the closed-loop 3-dB bandwidth. This relation is exact for the case where $F(j\omega) = $ constant.

If $F(s)$ is a simple low-pass filter response and $\omega_L > K_v$, the open-loop frequency response will be as shown in Figure 1-26. In this case, the loop bandwidth is approximately equal to K_v.

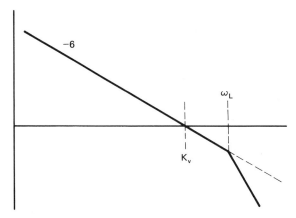

Figure 1-26 Open-loop frequency response in the case $\omega_L > K_v$.

If $\omega_L < K_v$, the straight-line approximation will cross the 0-dB line with a slope of -12 dB/octave, which is not good from the standpoint of loop stability. Thus the filter bandwidth should be greater than the open-loop crossover frequency ω_c; ω_c will be approximately equal to the closed loop bandwidth. Therefore, the filter bandwidth, for good loop stability, should be greater than the loop bandwidth for the simple type 1 system under discussion.

Another parameter that is useful in evaluating the response of second-order and higher systems is the phase margin, which is defined as

$$\phi_m = 180° + \arg KG(j\omega_c) \tag{1-237}$$

That is, the phase margin is equal to 180° plus the phase shift of the open-loop gain (a negative number) at the open-loop crossover frequency ω_c. The greater the phase margin, the more stable the system and the more phase lag from parasitic effects that can be tolerated.

Example 2

Consider a phase-locked loop which has $K_v = 10$ rad/s and which contains a low-pass filter with a corner frequency of 20 rad/s. The magnitude and phase of the open-loop transfer function are plotted in Figure 1-27. The system crossover frequency is approximately 10 rad/s. At this frequency, the phase shift of the open-loop transfer function is $-112.5°$, so the phase margin is 67.5°.

In this example, the complete phase plot was presented, but once one is familiar with phase plots, they no longer need to be included. One can simply calculate the phase shift after determining the open-loop crossover frequency from the magnitude plot.

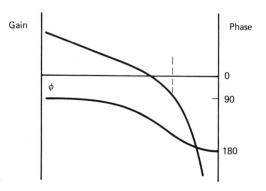

Figure 1-27 Magnitude and phase of the open-loop transfer function for $K_v = 10 \, \text{rad/s}$ and $\omega_L = 20 \, \text{rad/s}$.

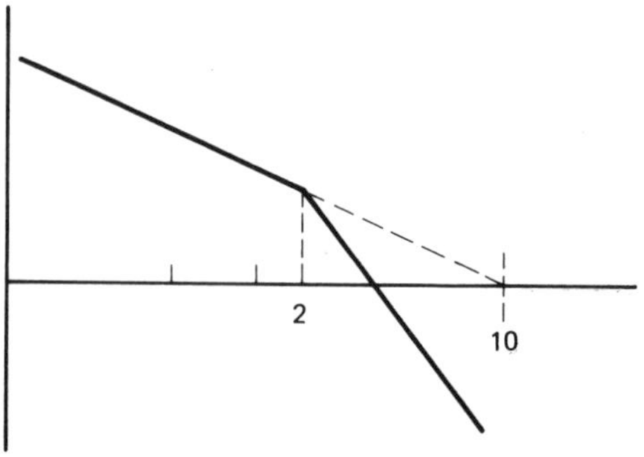

Figure 1-28 Magnitude of the open-loop gain of Example 3.

Example 3

In Example 2, if the filter corner frequency had been 2 rad/s rather than 20 rad/s, what would have been the system phase margin?

Solution. To determine the phase margin, first plot the magnitude of the open-loop gain and determine the crossover frequency. The straight-line approximation of the magnitude is plotted in Figure 1-28. ω_c is found to be approximately 4.4 rad/s. Thus the system phase margin is $180 - (90° + \arctan 2.2) = 23.40°$, which is too small for good loop stability. This is in agreement with the rule of thumb which states that if the magnitude of the open-loop response described crosses the 0-dB line with a slope of -12 dB/octave, the system is unstable. In this example, the straight-line approximation for the gain decreases at -12 dB/octave, but the actual response crosses the 0-dB line with a slope slightly more positive than -12 dB/octave: hence, the small phase margin.

Although the most important frequency-domain design parameters are the closed-loop bandwidth ω_h and the peak value M_p of the closed-loop frequency response, no design techniques exist that allow easy specification of B and M_p. It is relatively easy to design for specified open-loop parameters ω_c and ϕ_m. There are approximations that relate ω_c and ϕ_m to ω_n, M_p, ζ, and thus to the system rise time and overshoot. Fortunately, the conditions under which these approximations are valid are satisfied by most PLLs.

For the open-loop system (second-order loop),

$$K_v G(s) = \frac{K_v}{s(s/\omega_L + 1)} \tag{1-238}$$

Used with unity feedback, the closed-loop transfer function is given by Eq. (1-28), with

$$\omega_n^2 = K_v \omega_L \tag{1-239}$$

and

$$\zeta = \frac{1}{2} \sqrt{\frac{\omega_L}{K_v}} \tag{1-240}$$

The open-loop unity gain frequency is easily shown to be

$$\omega_c = \omega_L \left[\frac{\sqrt{1 + 4(K_v/\omega_L)^2} - 1}{2} \right]^{1/2} \tag{1-241}$$

Once ω_c is known, the phase margin

$$\phi_m = 90° - \arctan \frac{\omega_c}{\omega_L} = 90° - \arctan \left[\frac{\sqrt{1 + (1/2\zeta)^2} - 1}{2} \right]^{1/2} \tag{1-242}$$

can be calculated. This equation is plotted in Figure 1-29. The closed-loop system parameters of most importance are adequate stability (which is related to phase

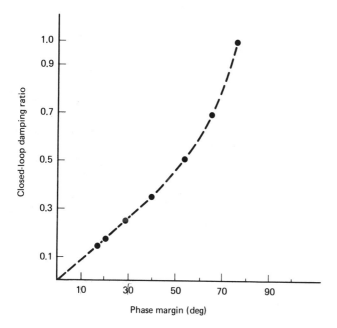

Figure 1-29 Closed-circuit damping ratio and phase margin relationship.

margin), system bandwidth (which determines the speed of the transient response), and system transient response (rise time and overshoot). For a low-pass transfer function, the bandwidth ω_n is defined as the frequency at which the gain is equal to 0.707 of its dc value. The bandwidth of the system represented by Eq. (1-28) is

$$\omega_h = \omega_n (1 - 2\zeta^2 + \sqrt{2 - 4\zeta^2 + 4\zeta^4})^{1/2} \tag{1-243}$$

which can be calculated using Eqs. (1-35), (1-239), and (1-240). For the underdamped second-order system given by Eq. (1-28) ($\zeta < 1$), the peak value of the time response to a unit step input can be shown to be

$$P_o = 1 + e^{-\pi\zeta/\sqrt{1-\zeta^2}} \tag{1-244}$$

The overshoot is determined solely by ζ. P_o as a function of ζ is plotted in Figure 1-30.

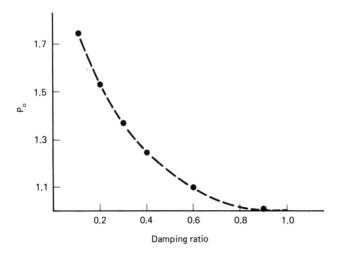

Figure 1-30   Peak overshoot as a function of damping ratio.

For high-order systems, the overshoot and bandwidth are not readily related to the open-loop system parameters, but a good first approximation is that Eq. (1-241) holds for higher-order systems. It is relatively easy to design a system to have a given phase margin. A design can then be evaluated using computer simulation. If the simulation indicates that the overshoot is too high (or too low) the phase margin can be increased (reduced), but the relations among phase margin, damping, and overshoot are amazingly accurate for higher-order systems. This implies that the response of most feedback systems can be described by a second-order model. Also, the closed-loop bandwidth can be related to the open-loop crossover frequency ω_c and the damping ratio, but it usually suffices to use the rule of thumb that the closed-loop bandwidth of underdamped systems is approximately 50% greater than the open-loop crossover frequency ω_c.

If it is desired to design for a peak transient overshoot, Eq. (1-240) can be used to determine the damping and then Eq. (1-241) is used to determine the required phase margin.

Example 4

For the phase-locked loop with open-loop transfer function

$$\frac{K_v}{s(s/\omega_L + 1)}$$

($K_v = 1000$), determine the low-pass filter corner frequency ω_L so that the system peak overshoot in response to a step input will be less than 20%.

Solution. Equation (1-242) or Figure 1-30 indicates that for $P_o < 1.2$, the damping ratio ζ must be greater than 0.45. For a ζ of 0.45, the corresponding phase margin is found [using Eq. (1-242)] to be about 50.

The low-pass filter can contribute $-40°$ phase lag 1 and the phase margin will be equal to 50%. Therefore, ω_L must be greater than ω_c (if $\omega_L = \omega_c$, the phase margin would be 45°), so ω_c is approximately 1000 rad/s $= K_v$. Thus arctan $1000/\omega L = 40°$ or $\omega_L = 1192$. (This is somewhat of an approximation, since adding the low-pass filter will slightly reduce the crossover frequency.) The desired open-loop transfer function becomes

$$\frac{1000}{s\left(\dfrac{s}{1.19 \times 10^3} + 1\right)} = KG(s) \qquad\qquad (1\text{-}245)$$

The step response is plotted in Figure 1-31. The overshoot is 13% and the rise time is 2.1 ms. The overshoot is considerably less than the specified maximum of 20% because of the straight-line approximations used to estimate the gain and cross-over frequency. Note that this second-order system is simple enough to be solved analytically since

$$\frac{K_vG}{1 + K_vG} = \frac{1}{(s^2/1000\omega_L) + (s/1000) + 1} = \frac{1}{(s^2/\omega_n^2) + (2\zeta s/\omega_n) + 1}$$

where $\omega_n^2 = 1000\,\omega_L$ and $2\zeta/\omega_n = 1/1000$, or

$$\zeta = \frac{\omega_n}{2000} = \frac{\sqrt{1000\omega_L}}{2000}$$

For $\zeta = 0.45$ (the design value),

$$\omega_L = \frac{(900)^2}{1000} = 810$$

The straight-line approximations resulted in a 32% error in the calculation of the low-pass corner frequency and the overshoot was 13% rather than 20% (for $\omega_L = 810$, the rise time is 2.28 ms). The differences between the two methods could have been reduced by accounting for the fact that the pole of the low-pass filter reduces the crossover frequencies and thus increases the actual phase margin over that estimated with the straight-line approximation.

In some instances it is also necessary to specify the loop bandwidth. In order to control both the loop damping and bandwidth, an amplifier can be added in series with the low-pass filter. If the filter is implemented using active components, the additional gain can be obtained without any additional components.

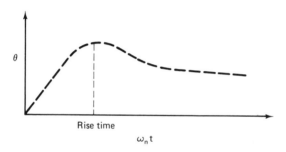

Rise time

$\omega_n t$

Figure 1-31 Overshoot and rise time of our example.

Example 5

Consider Example 4 with the additional specification that the rise time in response to a unit step input be less than 1 ms. Since the overshoot is to be less than 20%, the phase margin must be approximately 50°. To design for the rise-time specification, it is easiest to use the approximation

$$t_r = \frac{2.2}{B}$$

which is exact only for first-order systems, but provides a good design guideline for higher-order systems. Thus ω_c should be greater than $2.2/t_r = 2.2 \times 10^3$ rad/s.

The previous discussion has shown that

$$\omega_c = K_\theta K_o K = 1000K$$

Thus for an $\omega_c = 2.2 \times 10^3$ rad/s, an additional amplifier with a gain $K = 2.2$ needs to be added. With the increased ω_c, ω_L will have to be increased from Example 4 in order to meet the phase margin specification. For the second-order systems under discussion,

$$\frac{2\zeta}{\omega_n} = \frac{1}{K_v} \qquad (1\text{-}246)$$

The damping ζ is to be approximately 0.45 to meet the overshoot specification. It suffices to estimate the closed-loop bandwidth by assuming that it is approximately equal to ω_n, which is also approximately equal to the open-loop crossover frequency. Therefore, for $\zeta = 0.45$ and 1 ms rise time,

$$\omega_n = \frac{2.2}{10^{-3}} = 2.2 \times 10^3 = 2\zeta K_v = \sqrt{K_v \omega_L}$$

Therefore,

$$K_v = \frac{2.2 \times 10^3}{2 \times 0.45} = 2.44 \times 10^3$$

and

$$\omega_L = \frac{(2.2 \times 10^3)^2}{2.44 \times 10^3} = 1.98 \times 10^3$$

An additional gain K required is

$$K = 2.44$$

The complete open transfer function is then

$$K_v G(s) = \frac{2.44 \times 10^3}{s\left(\dfrac{s}{1.98 \times 10^3} + 1\right)}$$

and the closed-loop transfer function

$$\frac{K_v G}{1 + K_v G} = \frac{1}{\dfrac{s^2}{(2.2 \times 10^3)^2} + \dfrac{s}{2.44 \times 10^3} + 1}$$

A plot of the step response is shown in Figure 1-32. The peak overshoot is 10% and the rise time is 0.7 ms. The two specifications are now met. In general, two adjustable parameters, such as loop gain and filter bandwidth, are needed to independently specify overshoot and rise time.

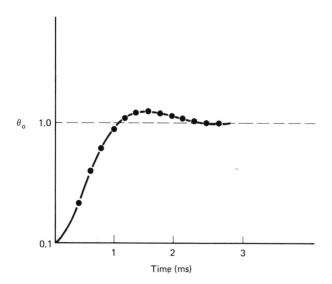

Figure 1-32 Plot of the step response of a 10% overshoot and 0.7 ms rise time.

An operational amplifier circuit to realize the low-pass filter with a gain of 2.4 is shown in Figure 1-33. Since the feedback impedance

$$Z_f = \frac{R_f}{R_f C_f s + 1} \tag{1-247}$$

the ideal voltage gain is

$$A_v = \frac{-Z_f}{Z_i} = \frac{-R_f/R_i}{R_f C_f s + 1} \tag{1-248}$$

which realizes the desired gain and filter provided that

$$\frac{R_f}{R_i} = 2.44 \quad \text{and} \quad R_f C_f = \frac{1}{1.98 \times 10^3}$$

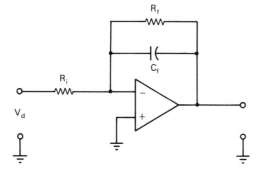

Figure 1-33 Loop filter with a gain of 2.2.

If the phase inversion resulting from this circuit is undesirable, phase inverting at the phase frequency discriminator can be performed.

REFERENCES

1. Roland Best, *Theorie und Anwendungen des phase-locked Loops*, Fachschriftenverlag Aargauer Tagblatt AG, Aarau, Switzerland, 1976, (Order No. ISBN-3-85502-011-6).

2. D. Richman, "Color Carrier Reference Phase Synchronization Accuracy in NTSC Color Television," *Proceedings of the IRE*, Vol. 42 (January 1954), pp. 106–133.

3. Floyd M. Gardner, *Phaselock Techniques*, 2nd ed., Wiley, New York, 1980.

4. Anatol I. Zverev, *Handbook of Filter Synthesis*, Wiley, New York, 1967.

5. A. Przedpelski, "Analyze, Don't Estimate Phase-Locked Loop Performance of Type 2 Third Order Systems," *Electronic Design*, May 10, 1978.

6. A. Przedpelski, "Optimized Phase Locked Loop to Meet Your Needs or Determine Why You Can't," *Electronic Design*, September 1978.

7. A. Przedpelski, "Suppress Phase Locked Loop Sidebands without Introducing Instability," *Electronic Design*, September 1978.

8. Alain Blanchard, *Phase-Locked Loops*, Wiley, New York, 1976.

9. C. R. Cahn, "Piecewise Linear Analysis of Phase-Locked Loops," *IRE Transactions on Space Electronics and Telemetry*, Vol. SET-8, No. 1 (March 1962), pp. 8–13.

10. J. A. Develet, Jr., "The Influence of Time Delay on Second-Order Phase-Lock Loop Acquisition Range," *Proceedings of the International Telemetering Conference*, Vol. 1, September 23–27, 1963, pp. 432–437.

11. W. F. Egan, "Phase-Locked Loop Simulation Program," *Proceedings of the 1976 GTE Symposium on Computer Aided Design*, Vol. 1, GTE Laboratories, Waltham, MA, June 1976, pp. 239–253.

12. J. Gibbs and R. Temple, "Frequency Domain Yields Its Data to Phase-Locked Synthesizer," *Electronics*, April 27, 1978, pp. 107–111.

13. L. J. Greenstein, "Phase-Locked Loop Pull-in Frequency," *IEEE Transactions on Communications*, Vol. COM-22 (August 1974), pp. 1005–1013.

14. U. Mengali, "Acquisition Behavior of Generalized Tracking Systems in the Absence of Noise," *IEEE Transactions on Communications*, Vol. COM-21 (July 1973), pp. 820–826.

15. E. N. Protonotarios, "Pull-in Performance of a Piecewise Linear Phase-Locked Loop," *IEEE Transactions on Aerospace and Electronic Systems*, Vol. AES-5, No. 3 (May 1969), pp. 376–386.

16. T. J. Rey, "Automatic Phase Control, Theory and Design," *Proceedings of the IRE*, October 1960, pp. 1760–1771.

17. R. G. Robson, "The Pull-in Range of a Phase-locked Loop," Conference on Frequency Generation and Control for Radio Systems, London, *Conference Publication No. 31*, May 1967, pp. 139–143.

18. J. Truxal, *Automatic Feedback Control System Synthesis*, McGraw-Hill, New York, 1955, pp. 38–41.

19. A. Viterbi, *Principles of Coherent Communication*, McGraw-Hill, New York, 1966.

20. C. S. Weaver, "A New Approach to the Linear Design and Analysis of Phase-Locked Loops," *IRE Transactions on Space Electronics and Telemetry*, Vol. SET-5 (December 1959), pp. 166–178.

2

Noise and Spurious Response of Loops

2-1 INTRODUCTION TO SIDEBAND NOISE

In the course of dealing with various synthesizer configurations, we will learn that the output noise of a synthesizer is an important design consideration. The main sources of noise are leakage of the reference frequency in phase-locked loops and the incomplete suppression of the unwanted component of mixer output (spurious). Another source of noise is the noise inherent in the oscillator.

If the spectral power density is measured at the output of an oscillator, a curve such as that of Figure 2-1 is observed. Rather than all of the power being concentrated at the oscillator frequency, some is distributed in frequency bands on both sides of the oscillator frequency.

As noise is a form of stability, it is useful to characterize frequency stability in the time domain in several areas. Short-term stability extends between a very small fraction of a second to 1 s, maybe under some considerations up to 1 min, and the value for the stability between 1 s and 1 min will be about the same. For longer time periods, we talk about long-term stability or aging. The aging is typically expressed in forms of how many parts in 10^{-10} or 10^{-11} per day the frequency changes. This information is in the time domain; in the frequency domain, we find terms like "random walk," "flicker," and "wide phase noise" which describe the slope of spectral density. The Fourier frequency, at times labeled f_m, is at times called sideband frequency, offset frequency, modulation frequency, or baseband frequency. In this book we will refer to it as *offset frequency*, describing the signal-to-noise ratio of an oscillator at a certain offset off the center frequency. The most common characterization

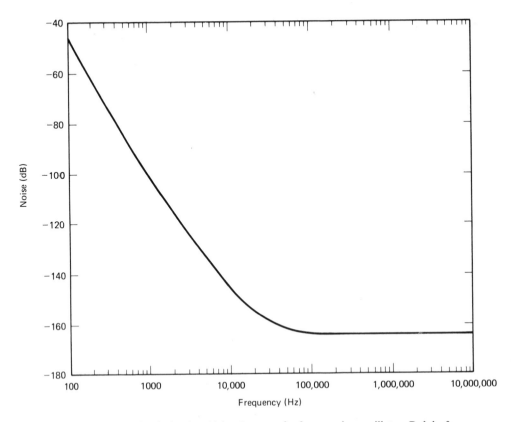

Figure 2-1 Typical noise sideband curve of a free-running oscillator, Rohde & Schwarz signal generator SMDU. (Courtesy of Rohde & Schwarz.)

of phase noise of a source is the frequency power density, and the probable reason for this is that it can be seen only as a spectrum analyzer when the AM noise contribution is insignificant. The spectrum analyzer display is then symmetrical.

Each one takes one side and by looking at sideband noise in a 1-Hz bandwidth leads to the definition of $\mathcal{L}(f_m)$. $\mathcal{L}(f_m)$ is defined as the ratio of the **single** sideband power of phase noise in a 1-Hz bandwidth f_m hertz away from the carrier frequency to the total signal power. This is plotted in Figure 2-1.

These unwanted frequency components are now referred to as *oscillator noise*. The oscillator output $S(t)$ can be expressed by the equation

$$S(t) = A(t) \cos [\omega_o t + \theta(t)] \tag{2-1}$$

where $A(t)$ describes the amplitude variation as a function of time and $\theta(t)$ is the phase variation. $\theta(t)$ is referred to as *phase noise*. A well-designed, high-quality oscillator is very amplitude stable and $A(t)$ can be considered constant. For a constant-amplitude signal, all oscillator noise is due to $\theta(t)$. Leeson has developed a model that describes the origins of phase noise in oscillators, and since it closely fits experimental

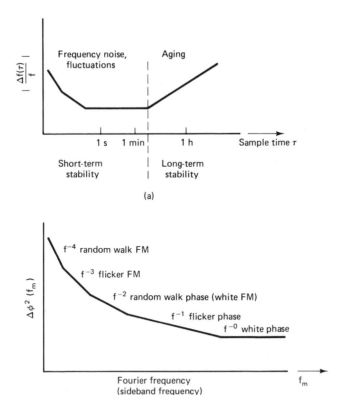

Figure 2-2   Characterization of noise sideband in the time and frequency domain and its contributions: (a) time domain; (b) frequency domain. (Courtesy of Hewlett-Packard Company.)

data, the model is widely used in describing the phase noise of oscillators and frequency synthesizers. Leeson's model will be described, but first a relation between the observed power spectral density function and $\theta(t)$ will be developed.

A carrier signal of amplitude V which is frequency modulated by a sine wave of frequency f_m can be represented by the equation

$$S(t) = V \cos \left(\omega_o t + \frac{\Delta f}{f_m} \sin \omega_m t \right) \tag{2-2}$$

where Δf is the peak frequency deviation and $\theta_p = \Delta f / f_m$ is the peak phase deviation, often referred to as the *modulation index* β. Equation (2-2) can be expanded as

$$S(t) = V[\cos (\omega_o t) \cos (\theta_p \sin \omega_m t) \\ - \sin \omega_o t \sin (\theta_p \sin \omega_m t)] \tag{2-3}$$

If the peak phase deviation is much less than 1 ($\theta_p \ll 1$),

$$\cos(\theta_p \sin \omega_m t) \approx 1$$

and

$$\sin(\theta_p \sin \omega_m t) \approx \theta_p \sin \omega_m t$$

Thus for $\theta_p \ll 1$, the signal $S(t)$ is approximately equal to

$$S(t) = V[\cos(\omega_o t) - \sin \omega_o t \, (\theta_p \sin \omega_m t)]$$
$$= V\left\{\cos(\omega_o t) - \frac{\theta_p}{2}[\cos(\omega_0 + \omega_m)t - \cos(\omega_0 - \omega_m)t]\right\} \tag{2-4}$$

That is, when the peak phase deviation is small, the phase deviation results in frequency components on each side of the carrier of amplitude $\theta_p/2$. This frequency distribution of a narrowband FM signal is useful for interpreting an oscillator's power spectral density as being due to phase noise. The phase noise in a 1-Hz bandwidth has a noise power-to-carrier power ratio of

$$\mathcal{L}(f_m) = \left(\frac{V_n}{V}\right)^2 = \frac{\theta_p^2}{4} = \frac{\theta_{rms}^2}{2} \tag{2-5}$$

The total noise is the noise in both sidebands and will be denoted by S_θ. That is,

$$S_\theta = 2\frac{\theta_{rms}^2}{2} = \theta_{rms}^2 = 2\mathcal{L}(f_m) \tag{2-6}$$

With this interpretation of the noise power, the noise can now be described in terms of its origin, see Figure 2-2.

Noise can be expressed in a number of ways; therefore, we want to try to cover the various methods of describing other forms of stability before we analyze the oscillator.

2-2 SPECTRAL DENSITY OF FREQUENCY FLUCTUATIONS, RELATED TO $S_{\Delta\theta}$ AND $\mathcal{L}$

Stability measurements with using frequency comparators give the *spectral density of frequency fluctuations*,

$$S_{\Delta f}(f_m) = \Delta f_{rms}^2 \tag{2-7}$$

To relate the spectral density of frequency fluctuations to the spectral density of phase noise, we recall that

$$\Delta f(t) = \frac{1}{2\pi}\frac{d\,\Delta\theta(t)}{dt} \tag{2-8}$$

Transformed into the frequency domain,

$$\Delta f(f_m) = f_m \,\Delta\theta(f_m) \tag{2-9}$$

$$S_{\Delta f}(f_m) = \Delta f_{rms}^2(f_m) = f_m^2 S_{\Delta\theta}(f_m) = 2f_m^2 \mathcal{L}(f_m) \tag{2-10}$$

NBS proposes to standardize the definition of the spectral density of fractional frequency fluctuations. The instantaneous frequency deviation is normalized to the carrier frequency f_o.

$$y(t) = \frac{\Delta f(t)}{f_o} \tag{2-11}$$

$$S_y(f_m) = \frac{1}{f_o^2} S_{\Delta f}(f_m) = \frac{f_m^2}{f_o^2} S_{\Delta\phi}(f_m) = \frac{2f_m^2}{f_o^2} \mathcal{L}(f_m) \tag{2-12}$$

Characterizing fractional frequency fluctuations allows better comparison between sources with different carrier frequencies.

2-3 RESIDUAL FM RELATED TO $\mathcal{L}(f_m)$

Residual FM, the total rms frequency deviation within a specified bandwidth, is another common way to specify the frequency stability of signal generators. Commonly used bandwidths are 50 Hz to 3 kHz, 300 Hz to 3 kHz, and 20 Hz to 15 kHz.

$$\Delta f_{\text{res}} = \sqrt{2}\sqrt{\int_a^b \mathcal{L}(f_m)f_m^2\, df_m} \tag{2-13}$$

Table 2-1 correlates Δf_{res} and $\mathcal{L}(f_m)$ for specific slopes of $\mathcal{L}(f_m)$ and $\mathcal{L}$ at 1 kHz = -100 dBc.

TABLE 2-1

$\mathcal{L}^{\text{a}}$ at 1 kHz (dBc)	Slope of $\mathcal{L}(f_m)$		Residual FM Δf_{res}		
	Exponent	dB/oct	50 Hz to 3 kHz	300 Hz to 3 kHz	20 Hz to 15 kHz
-100	0	0	1.34	1.34	15.0
-100	-1	-3	0.95	0.94	4.74
-100	-2	-6	0.77	0.73	1.73
-100	-3	-9	0.90	0.68	1.15

[a]For any $\mathcal{L}$ at 1 kHz different to -100 dBc, multiply Δf_{res} of the table by

$$\text{antilog}\frac{100 - |\mathcal{L} \text{ at 1 kHz/dBc}|}{20}$$

The table does not take into account any microphonic or spurious sidebands.

Example: $\mathcal{L}$ at 1 kHz = -88 dBc, slope -9 dB. For bandwidth 20 Hz to 15 kHz:

$$\Delta f_{\text{res}} = 1.15 \text{ Hz} \times \text{antilog}\frac{100 - 88}{20} = 4.6 \text{ Hz}$$

2-4 ALLAN VARIANCE RELATED TO $\mathcal{L}(f_m)$

For many applications, such as high-stability crystal oscillators or doppler radar systems, it is more relevant to describe frequency stability in the time domain. The characterization is based on the sample variance of fractional frequency fluctuations. Averaging differences of consecutive sample pairs with no deadtime in between yields the *Allan variance*, $\sigma_y^2(\tau)$, which is the proposed standard measure of frequency stability.

$$\sigma_y^2(\tau) \sim \frac{1}{2(M-1)} \sum_{K=1}^{M-1} (\bar{y}_{k+1} - \bar{y}_k)^2 \tag{2-14}$$

$\bar{y}_k$ is the average fractional frequency difference of the kth sample measured over sample time τ.

Conversions from frequency- to time-domain data and vice versa are possible but tedious. The power spectrum $\mathcal{L}(f_m)$ needs to be approximated by integer slopes of $0, -1, -2, -3, -4$. Then conversion formulas (see Table 2-2) can be applied. A good description of this procedure is given in Refs. 11 and 12.

TABLE 2-2 CONVERSION TABLE[a]

	Slope of $\sigma_y^2(\tau)$	$\sigma_y(\tau) =$	$\mathcal{L}(f) =$	Slope of $\mathcal{L}(f)$
White phase	-2	$\dfrac{\sqrt{\mathcal{L}(f)f_h}}{2.565f_o}\tau^{-1}$	$\dfrac{[\sigma_y(\tau)\tau f_o(2.565)]^2}{f_h}f^0$	0
Flicker phase	-1.9	$\dfrac{\sqrt{\mathcal{L}(f)f}[2.184 + \ln(f_h\tau)]}{2.565f_o}\tau^{-1}$	$\dfrac{[\sigma_y(\tau)\tau f_o(2.565)]^2}{2.184 + \ln(f_h\tau)}f^{-1}$	-1
White frequency	-1	$\dfrac{\sqrt{\mathcal{L}(f)f^2}}{f_o}\tau^{-1/2}$	$[\sigma_y(\tau)\tau^{1/2}f_o]^2 f^{-2}$	-2
Flicker frequency	0	$\dfrac{1.665\sqrt{\mathcal{L}(f)f^3}}{f_o}\tau^0$	$0.361[\sigma_y(\tau)f_o]^2 f^{-3}$	-3
Random walk frequency	$+1$	$\dfrac{3.63\sqrt{\mathcal{L}(f)f^4}}{f_o}\tau^{1/2}$	$[(0.276)\sigma_y(\tau)\tau^{-1/2}f_o]^2 f^{-4}$	-4

[a] τ = measurement time, $y = \Delta f_o/f_o$, f_o = carrier, f = sideband frequency, f_h = measurement system bandwidth.

We have covered the most frequently used measures of phase noise and have interrelated them. Before we take a look at the generation of phase noise in amplifiers and oscillators, let us take a look at the noise-conversion nomograph in Table 2-3. The example given there is self-explanatory.

As most of these relationships, for reasons of convenience, are expressed in decibels rather than absolute values, the following formulas are commonly used:

$$\mathcal{L}(f_m) = 10 \log_{10}\left(\frac{\Delta f_{peak}}{2f_m}\right)^2 \tag{2-15}$$

$$\mathcal{L}(f_m) = 10 \log_{10}\left(\frac{\Delta f_{rms}}{\sqrt{2}\,f_m}\right)^2 \tag{2-16}$$

$$\mathcal{L}(f_m) = 20 \log_{10}\frac{\Delta f_{rms}}{\sqrt{2}\,f_m} \tag{2-17}$$

$$\mathcal{L}(f_m) = 20 \log_{10}\frac{\theta_d}{2} \tag{2-18}$$

TABLE 2-3 NOISE-CONVERSION NOMOGRAPH: RELATIONSHIP AMONG MODULATING FREQUENCY (f_m), POWER SPECTRAL DENSITY OF PHASE (S_ϕ), MODULATION INDEX, SIDEBAND TO CARRIER RATIO (dBc), dBmO, AND FREQUENCY DEVIATION (Δf_{rms})[a]

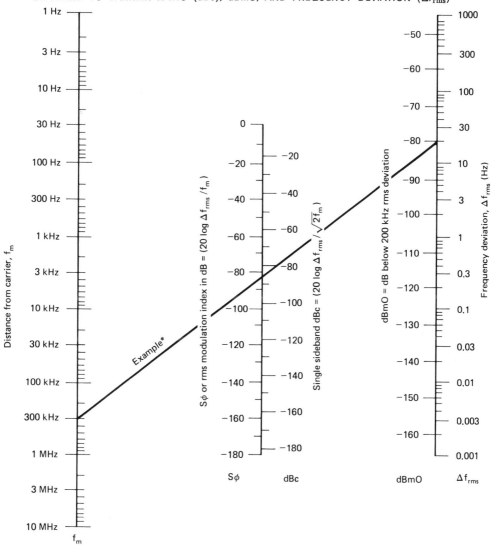

[a]Use consistent measurement bandwidth. Example: 20-Hz deviation in a 1-kHz band at 300 kHz from carrier = single-sideband dBc of −87 dB in a 1-kHz band.

2-5 CALCULATION OF OSCILLATOR NOISE

We will assume that the oscillator is composed of an amplifier with gain A and a high-Q resonant circuit, as illustrated in block diagram form in Figure 2-3. Since

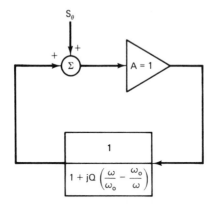

Figure 2-3 Block diagram of an oscillator with an amplifier and a high-Q resonator.

the gain of the resonant circuit has been normalized to unity at the resonant frequency f_o, the amplifier gain A must also be unity in order for the circuit to oscillate. Let S_θ represent the amplifier noise referred to the amplifier input. The white noise N per unit bandwidth at the amplifier input is given by

$$N = N_t + N_a = FkT \qquad (2\text{-}19)$$

where F is the amplifier noise figure. Therefore, the ratio of noise power per unit bandwidth to signal power P_s is FkT/P_s, which is a component of S_θ. In addition, amplifiers generate an additional *flicker*, or $1/f$ phase noise, about the carrier frequency due to carrier density fluctuations in the base resistance. A plot of S_θ for frequencies greater than the carrier frequency f_o is contained in Figure 2-3. For frequencies close to the carrier, S_θ has a $1/f$ spectrum. At high frequencies the spectrum is flat and equal to FkT/P_s. The frequency f below which the spectrum has a $1/f$ shape depends on the characteristic of the individual amplifiers. For the circuit of Figure 2-3 with positive feedback and $A = 1$, the closed-loop steady-state transfer function between the amplifier output and the amplifier input is given by

$$B(j\omega) = \frac{1}{1 - H(j\omega)} \qquad (2\text{-}20)$$

where

$$H(j\omega) = \frac{1}{1 + jQ\left(\dfrac{\omega}{\omega_o} - \dfrac{\omega_o}{\omega}\right)} \qquad (2\text{-}21)$$

Since $H(j\omega)$ is a high-Q filter and we are interested in describing the noise power distribution about the center frequency ω_o, $H(j\omega)$ can be replaced by its low-pass equivalent,

$$H_L(j\omega) = \frac{1}{1 + j\omega/\omega_L} \qquad (2\text{-}22)$$

where

$$\omega_L = \frac{\omega_o}{2Q} \tag{2-23}$$

is the equivalent bandwidth. Since the noise spectral density $S_o(\omega)$ at the output of a filter with a transfer function $G(j\omega)$, in terms of the spectral density $S_i(\omega)$ of the input noise, is given by

$$S_o(\omega) = S_i(\omega) |G(\omega)|^2 \tag{2-24}$$

the equivalent phase noise of the closed-loop system

$$
\begin{aligned}
S_o &= S_\theta \frac{1}{|1 - H(\omega)|^2} \\
&= \frac{S_\theta}{\left|1 - \dfrac{1}{1 + j\omega/\omega_L}\right|\left|1 - \dfrac{1}{1 - j\omega/\omega_L}\right|} \\
&= \frac{S_\theta(1 + \omega^2/\omega_L^2)}{\omega^2/\omega_L^2} \\
&= S_\theta\left(1 + \frac{\omega_L^2}{\omega^2}\right)
\end{aligned}
\tag{2-25}
$$

which can be written [using Eqs. (2-5), (2-19), and (2-23)]

$$S_o(\omega) = \frac{FkT}{P}\left(1 + \frac{\omega_o^2}{4Q^2\omega^2}\right) \tag{2-26}$$

which is the expression proposed by Leeson for describing the noise at the output of an oscillator.

As mentioned at the beginning of this chapter, there are various types of noise, and so far Leeson's model does not contain an allowance for the flicker noise. We will, therefore, modify our equation into

$$\mathcal{L}(f_m) = \frac{1}{2}\left[1 + \frac{1}{\omega_m^2}\left(\frac{\omega_o}{2Q_{\text{load}}}\right)^2\right]\frac{FkT}{P_{\text{sav}}}\left(1 + \frac{f_c}{f_m}\right) \tag{2-27}$$

This equation describes the phase noise at the output of the amplifier of the oscillator.

Earlier figures showed the difference depending on the Q of the oscillator. In accordance with Ref. 18, we will expand Leeson's equation further for an actual oscillator to show how the noise performance can be optimized. Q loaded can be expressed as

$$
\begin{aligned}
Q_{\text{load}} &= \frac{\omega_o W_e}{P_{\text{diss, total}}} = \frac{\omega_o W_e}{P_{\text{in}} + P_{\text{res}} + P_{\text{sig}}} \\
&= \frac{\text{reactive power}}{\text{total dissipated power}}
\end{aligned}
\tag{2-28}
$$

where W_e is the reactive energy stored in L and C,

$$W_e = \tfrac{1}{2}CV^2 \qquad P_{\text{res}} = \frac{\omega_o W_e}{Q_{\text{unl}}}$$

$$\mathcal{L}(f_m) = \frac{1}{2}\left[1 + \frac{\omega_o^2}{4\omega_m^2}\left(\frac{P_{in}}{\omega_o W_e} + \frac{1}{Q_{unl}} + \frac{P_{sig}}{\omega_o W_e}\right)^2\right]\left(1 + \frac{\omega_c}{\omega_m}\right)\frac{FkT_o}{P_{sav}} \qquad (2\text{-}29)$$

input power over reactive power

resonator Q

signal power over reactive power

flicker effect

phase perturbation

This equation is extremely significant because it contains most of the causes of phase noise in oscillators. To minimize the phase noise, the following design rules apply:

1. Maximize the unloaded Q.

2. Maximize the reactive energy by means of a high RF voltage across the resonator and obtain a low LC ratio. The limits are set by breakdown voltages of the active devices and the tuning diodes and the forward-bias condition of the tuning diodes.

3. Avoid saturation at all cost, and try to either have limiting or AGC without degradation of Q. Isolate the tuned circuit from the limiter or AGC circuit. Use anti-parallel tuning diode connections to avoid forward bias.

4. Choose an active device with the lowest noise figure. Currently, the best bipolar transistor is the Siemens BFT66 and the lowest noise field-effect transistors are U310 and 2N5397 up to 500 MHz. The noise figure of interest is the noise figure obtained at the actual impedance at which the device is operated. Using field-effect transistors rather than bipolar transistors, it is preferable to deal with the equivalent noise voltage and noise currents rather than with the noise figure, since they are independent of source impedance. The noise figure improves as the ratio between source impedance and equivalent noise resistance increases. In addition, in a tuning circuit, the source impedance changes drastically as a function of the offset frequency, and this effect has to be considered.

5. Phase perturbation can be minimized by using high-impedance devices such as field-effect transistors, where the signal-to-noise ratio of the signal voltage relative to the equivalent noise voltage can be made very high. This also indicates that in the case of a limiter, the limited voltage should be as high as possible.

6. Choose an active device with low flicker noise. The effect of flicker noise can be reduced by RF feedback. An unbypassed emitter resistor of 10 to 30 Ω in a bipolar circuit can improve the flicker noise by as much as 40 dB. In Chapter 4 we will study such an oscillator.

The proper bias point of the active device is important, and precautions should be taken to prevent modulation of the input and output dynamic capacitance of the active device, which will cause amplitude-to-phase conversion and therefore introduce noise.

7. The energy should be coupled from the resonator rather than another portion of the active device so that the resonator limits the bandwidth. A crystal oscillator using this principle is described later.

Equation (2-29) assumes that the phase perturbation and the flicker effect are the limiting factors, as practical use of such oscillators requires that an isolation amplifier be used.

In the event that the energy is taken directly from the resonator and the oscillator power can be increased, the signal-to-noise ratio can be increased above the theoretical limit of -174 dB, due to the low-pass filter effect of the tuned resonator. However, since this is mainly a theoretical assumption and does not represent the real world in a system, this noise performance cannot be obtained. In an oscillator stage, even a total noise floor of 170 dB is rarely achieved.

What other influences do we have that cause the noise performance to degrade?

So far, we have assumed that the Q of the tuned circuit is really determined only by the LC network and the loading effect of the transistor. In synthesizer applications, however, we find it necessary to add a tuning diode. The tuning diode has a substantially lower Q than that of a mica capacitor or even a ceramic capacitor. As a result of this, the noise sidebands change as a function of the additional loss. This is best expressed in the form of adjusting the value for the loaded Q in Eq. (2-27).

There seems to be no precise mathematical way of predetermining the noise influence of a tuning diode, but the following approximation seems to give proper results:

$$\frac{1}{Q_{T\,\text{load}}} = \frac{1}{Q_{\text{load}}} + \frac{1}{Q_{\text{diode}}} \tag{2-30}$$

The tuning diode is specified to have a cutoff frequency f_{max} which is determined from the loss resistor R_s and the value of the junction capacitance as a function of voltage (i.e., measured at 3 V). This means that the voltage determines the Q and, consequently, the noise bandwidth.

We will go into more detail in dealing with the mechanism and influence of tuning diodes in the oscillator section, where we will evaluate the various methods of building voltage tunable oscillators using tuning diodes and switching diodes. In this chapter we limit ourselves to practical results.

The loading effect of the tuning diode is due to losses, and these losses can be described by a resistor parallel to the tuned circuit.

It is possible to define an equivalent noise R_{aeq} that, inserted in Nyquist's equation

$$V_n = \sqrt{4KT_oR\,\Delta f} \tag{2-31}$$

where $KT_o = 4.2 \times 10^{-21}$ at about 300°K, R is the equivalent noise resistor, and Δf is the bandwidth, determines an open noise voltage across the tuning diode. Practical values of R equivalent for carefully selected tuning diodes are in the vicinity of 1000 Ω to 50 kΩ. If we now determine the noise voltage $V_n = \sqrt{4 \times 4.2 \times 10^{-21} \times 10{,}000}$, the resulting voltage value is 1.265×10^{-8} V$\sqrt{\text{Hz}}$.

This noise voltage generated from the tuning diode is now multiplied with the VCO gain, resulting in the rms frequency deviation

$$(\Delta f_{\text{rms}}) = K_o \times (1.265 \times 10^{-8}\ \text{V}) \text{ in 1-Hz bandwidth} \tag{2-32}$$

In order to translate this into the equivalent peak phase deviation,

$$\theta_d = \frac{K_o \sqrt{2}}{f_m}(1.265 \times 10^{-8} \text{ rad}) \text{ in 1-Hz bandwidth}$$

or for a typical oscillator gain of 100 kHz/V,

$$\theta_d = \frac{0.00179}{f_m} \text{ rad in 1-Hz bandwidth}$$

For $f_m = 25$ kHz (typical spacing for adjacent channel measurements for FM mobile radios), the $\theta_c = 7.17 \times 10^{-8}$. This can be converted now into the SSB signal-to-noise ratio

$$\mathcal{L}(f_m) = 20 \log_{10} \frac{\theta_c}{2} \tag{2-33}$$
$$= -149 \text{ dB/Hz}$$

This is the value typically achieved in the Rohde & Schwarz SMDU or with the Hewlett-Packard 8640 signal generator and considered state of the art for a free-running oscillator. It should be noted that both signal generators use a slightly different tuned circuit; the Rohde & Schwarz generator uses a helical resonator, whereas the Hewlett-Packard generator uses an electrically shortened quarter-wavelength cavity. Both generators are mechanically pretuned and the tuning diode with a gain of about 100 kHz/V is used for frequency-modulation purposes or for the AFC input. It is apparent that, because of the nonlinearity of the tuning diode, the gain is different for low dc voltages than for high dc voltages. The impact of this is that the noise varies within the tuning range. A detailed discussion of these phenomena is given in Chapter 4.

If this oscillator had to be used for a frequency synthesizer, the 1-MHz tuning range would be insufficient; therefore, a way had to be found to segment the band into the necessary ranges. In VCOs, this is typically done with switching diodes that allow the proper frequency bands to be selected. These switching diodes insert in parallel or series, depending on the circuit, or additional inductors or capacitors, depending on the design.

In low-energy-consuming circuits, the VCO frequently is divided into a coarse-tuning section using tuning diodes and a fine-tuning section with a tuning diode. In the coarse-tuning range, this results in very high gains, such as 1 to 10 MHz/V, for the diodes, and therefore the noise contribution of those diodes is very high and can hardly be compensated by the loop. For low-noise applications, which automatically mean higher power consumption, it is unavoidable to use switching diodes. More detailed information about the switching diodes and their applications is presented in Chapter 4.

Let us now examine some test results. If we go back to Eq. (2-27), Figure 2-4 shows the noise sideband performance as a function of Q, whereby the top curve with $Q_L = 100$ represents a somewhat poor oscillator and the lowest curve with $Q_L = 100,000$ probably represents a crystal oscillator where the unloaded Q of the crystal was in the vicinity of 3×10^6. Figure 2-5 shows the influence of flicker noise.

Corner frequencies of 10 Hz to 10 kHz have been selected, and it becomes apparent that around 1 kHz the influence is fairly dramatic, whereas the influence at

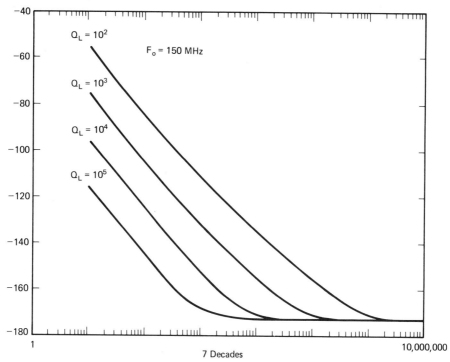

Figure 2-4 Noise sideband of an oscillator at 150 MHz as a function of the loaded Q of the resonator.

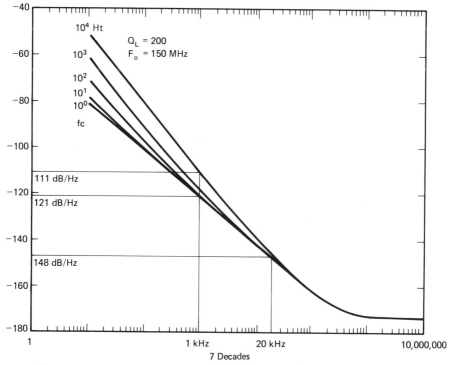

Figure 2-5 Noise sideband performance as a function of the flicker frequency ωC varying from 10 Hz to 10 kHz.

20 kHz off the carrier is not significant. Finally, Figure 2-6 shows the influence of the tuning diodes on a high-Q oscillator.

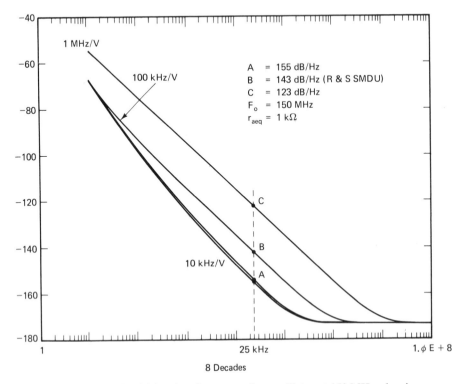

Figure 2-6 Noise sideband performance of an oscillator at 150 MHz, showing the influence of various tuning diodes.

Curve A uses a lightly coupled tuning diode with a K_o of 10 kHz/V; the lower curve is the noise performance without any diode. As a result, the two curves are almost identical, which can be seen from the somewhat smeared form of the graph. Curve B shows the influence of a tuning diode at 100 kHz/V and represents a value of 143 dB/Hz from 155 dB/Hz, already some deterioration. Curve C shows the noise if the tuning diode results at a 1-MHz/V VCO gain, and the noise sideband at 25 kHz has now deteriorated to 123 dB/Hz. These curves speak for themselves.

It is of interest to compare various oscillators. Figure 2-7 shows the performance of a 10-MHz crystal oscillator a 40-MHz LC oscillator, the 8640 cavity tuned oscillator at 500 MHz, the 310- to 640-MHz switched reactance oscillator of the 8662 oscillator, and a 2- to 6-GHz YIG oscillator at 6 GHz.

In the following paragraphs, we deal with the noise influence of other loop components, such as dividers, phase/frequency comparators and operational amplifiers, as well as examine the influence of the reference frequency on the loop noise sideband performance.

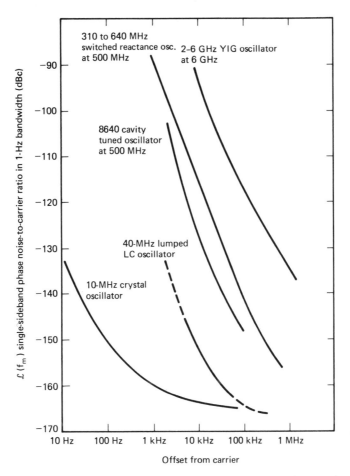

Figure 2-7 Comparison of noise sideband performances of a crystal oscillator, *LC* oscillator, cavity-tuned oscillator, switched reactance oscillator, and YIG oscillator. (Courtesy of Hewlett-Packard Company.)

2-6 *NOISE CONTRIBUTIONS IN PHASE-LOCKED SYSTEMS*

Figure 2-8 shows a block diagram of a phase-locked loop consisting of a phase detector, an integrator, a shaper-pretuned circuit, an additional attenuator as a second loop filter, the VCO, and finally the divider.

The reference has not been included. The reason for this is that we assume for a moment that the reference is ideal and noise-free, and take a look at the influence of the other elements of the loop.

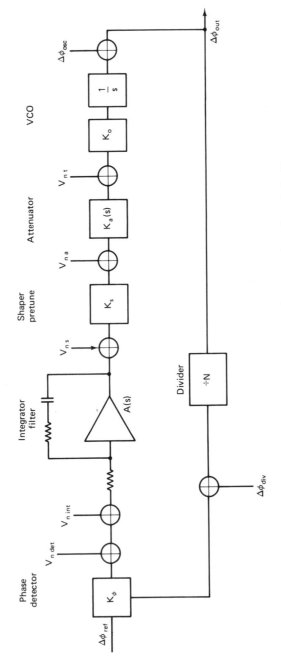

Figure 2-8 Block diagram showing the various noise sources in a phase-locked loop.

2-6-1 Phase Noise Characteristics of Amplifiers

As mentioned several times previously, it is an absolute necessity to provide an isolation amplifier between the VCO and the following circuits (e.g., the divider chain or others) to minimize any feedback or noise contribution because of periodic loading.

What does this do to our system noise? Unfortunately, if we assume that we generate our initial signal in a noise-free environment or at least start off with the theoretical minimum of −174 dBmHz, the spectral density of phase noise that is generated by a resistor at room temperature as a sideband noise floor, the signal will be degraded by the postamplifier. For example, a signal of 0 dBm passes through an amplifier with a 3-dB noise figure. The resulting spectral density of phase noise

$$S_{\Delta\theta} = -174 \text{ dBm} + 3 \text{ dB} - 0 \text{ dBm} = -171 \text{ dB/Hz} \qquad (2\text{-}34)$$

This theoretical floor can be observed only at a fairly large offset. With practical transistors, various noise sources have to be taken into consideration. As mentioned previously, the flicker noise is the major reason for the noise degradation, and its contribution is very device dependent and can range from a few hundred hertz to 1 MHz. It is caused by low-frequency device noise modulating the phase of the passing signal by modulating the transconductance and the input and output impedances of the amplifier (depletion layer and diffusion capacitance). There is very little one can do to reduce this effect on a large scale. One is limited to:

1. Some negative feedback at low frequency, such as an unbypassed emitter resistor
2. Some negative feedback at RF frequency to stabilize the transconductance
3. Designing the RF amplifier for a low noise figure, also at low frequency

Depending on the author, there are various speculations as to which device is best for low flicker noise. It appears to me that the first decision to make is to determine whether the device is being used in high- or low-power RF application. From recent experiments, it has been possible to prove that at medium levels, junction field-effect transistors show a significant advantage over bipolar transistors, as the modulation of the input and output impedances is less. The field-effect transistor shows a 10- to 20-dB better performance at drive levels of up to 1 V at the gate electrode in a frequency range from 50 to 500 MHz over the bipolar transistor. A plausible explanation is that the base spreading resistor and other loss resistors in the bipolar transistor have a significant influence at these high drive levels in addition to the effect of gain saturation, a nonlinear phenomenon in bipolar transistors that causes cross-modulation and intermodulation distortion.

However, these things are device dependent and may change as new devices are developed, and it is necessary to update this information periodically.

2-6-2 Phase Noise Characteristics of Dividers

Generally, the phase noise at the input of a divider appears at the divider output reduced by N. However, there are some limitations to this effect.

1. In accordance with Figure 2-9, the practical noise limit is in the vicinity of 170 dB
   for TTL dividers and 155 dB for ECL. CMOS dividers, up to an input frequency
   of 10 MHz, behave similar to TTL devices. However, the close-in noise or
   noise between 1 and 10 Hz off the carrier is slightly higher than that of TTL.
   TTL devices require higher shielding and better power supply decoupling to
   prevent external crosstalk between the various stages, which otherwise results
   in unwanted spurious outputs. Any unwanted sidebands are also reduced by
   the same amount of this ratio.

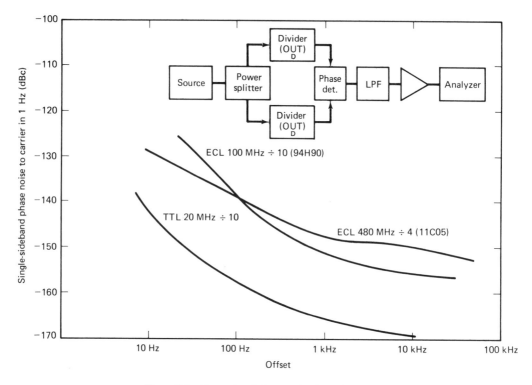

Figure 2-9   Example of phase noise introduced by dividers.

2. Most of these dividers, however, have another unpleasant effect, in the form
   of internal *crosstalk*. Crosstalk is defined as the amount of input frequency
   appearing at the output of the divider chain. In high-performance synthesizers
   it is necessary to use a low-pass filter after the reference or the programmable
   divider and a pulse shaper to translate the resulting sine wave back into a
   square wave in order to keep the output voltage at the input frequency sufficiently suppressed. Further details are given in Section 4-6.

Let us take a look at some of the mathematics involved. The instantaneous
phase $\theta_i(t)$ of a carrier frequency modulated by a sine wave of frequency f_m is given by

$$\theta_i(t) = \omega_o t + \frac{\Delta f}{f_m} \sin \omega_m t \qquad (2\text{-}35)$$

Instantaneous frequency is defined as the time rate of change of phase

$$\omega(t) = \frac{d\theta i(t)}{dt} = \omega_o + \frac{\Delta f}{f_m} \omega_m \cos \omega_m t$$

$$\leq \omega_o + \Delta \omega \qquad (2\text{-}36)$$

If this signal is passed through a frequency divider which divides the frequency by N, the output frequency/ω' will be given by

$$\omega' = \frac{\omega_o}{N} + \frac{\Delta \omega}{N} \qquad (2\text{-}37)$$

and the output phase by

$$\theta_i(t) = \frac{\omega_o t}{N} + \frac{\Delta f}{Nf_m} \sin \omega_m t \qquad (2\text{-}38)$$

The fundamental frequency at the divider output is

$$S(t) = V \cos \left(\frac{\omega_o t}{N} + \frac{\Delta f}{Nf_m} \sin \omega_m t \right) \qquad (2\text{-}39)$$

where V is the input peak voltage. The divider reduces the carrier frequency by N but does not change the frequency of the modulation signal. The peak phase deviation θ_p is reduced by the divide ratio N. Since it was shown that the ratio of the noise power to carrier power is

$$\frac{V_n^2}{V^2} = \frac{\theta_p^2}{4} \qquad (2\text{-}40)$$

frequency division by N reduces the noise power by N^2 for a perfect divider.

Example 1

The indirect frequency synthesizer shown in Figure 2-10 is used to generate a 5-GHz (5×10^9) signal. A 1-kHz reference signal is obtained from a 5-MHz reference oscillator ($M = 5000$) which is specified to have a single-sideband noise power of -140 dBc/Hz at a frequency separation of 0.5 kHz from the oscillator's operating frequency. If the loop bandwidth is assumed to be approximately 1 kHz, the noise from the reference oscillator will not be reduced by the low-pass filtering of the PLL. Although the

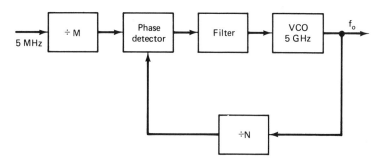

Figure 2-10 5-GHz YIG oscillator harmonic stabilized from a 5-MHz reference.

divider N will reduce the noise power by the factor N^2, the approximate loop transfer function is

$$\theta_o = \frac{\theta_r[K_vF(s)/s]}{1 + [K_vF(s)/sN]} = N\theta_r \qquad (2\text{-}41)$$

for reference frequencies below the loop bandwidth of 1 kHz. The net effect is that the output noise power is the reference oscillator noise power multiplied by $(N/M)^2$. N must be equal to 5×10^6 to obtain the specified output frequency of 5×10^9 Hz, and the output noise power due to the reference oscillator is

$$N_o = -140 \text{ dB/Hz} + 10 \log \left(\frac{5 \times 10^6}{5 \times 10^3}\right)^2 = -80 \text{ dB/Hz} \qquad (2\text{-}42)$$

at a frequency offset of 0.5 kHz.

Example 1 illustrates a problem inherent in PLL frequency synthesizers used to generate an output frequency much higher than the reference oscillator frequency. Although the reference oscillator noise power may be small, the same noise power appears on the output signal amplified by the factor N^2, where N is the output frequency/reference oscillator frequency ratio.

2-6-3 Phase Noise Characteristic of Phase/ Frequency Comparators

The phase/frequency comparator simplest form being a two-diode arrangement, a double-balanced mixer, exclusive-OR gate, flip-flop, or tri-state comparator, it is a highly nonlinear device despite the fact that we had linearized its performance for an easier understanding of the PLL performance. This means that radiation into any of the ports of this device is being transferred as a sideband spur, depending on the conversion loss of the system. Any hum reference radiation or outer signal somehow fed into the phase/frequency comparator up to a very high order of harmonics of the input signal can be detected. This has caused grief for many design engineers because it is normally not obvious that high orders of the reference can mix with some RF pickup.

There is another unpleasant effect related to digital and analog phase/frequency comparators. In an analog phase/frequency comparator, the dc output voltage is limited and has to be amplified up to 10 or 20 V, while the digital phase/frequency comparators, with their up-and-down pulse output, have to use a summation amplifier. In the first case, the additional amplifier introduces flicker noise and other sideband noise that will reduce the maximum signal-to-noise ratio, and in the case of the digital phase/frequency comparator under perfect locked condition is a range called the *zero gain area*. What does this mean? It means that if we assume that the loop is in locked condition and requires no pulses to update the holding capacitor, the phase/frequency comparator has zero gain. This causes loop instability at very low frequencies and degrades the close-in noise sideband performance by up to 20 dB. Cures for this dead-zone effect are described in Chapter 4.

2-6-4 Phase Noise Characteristics of Multipliers

In general, the reference oscillator operating at either 5 or 10 MHz is divided to 1 MHz, 100 kHz, or even down to 1 kHz to generate the reference frequency for the various loops.

The dividers have an ultimate noise floor depending on the offset from the center frequency from around 130 dB/Hz at 10 Hz to 160 dB/Hz at 10 kHz or maybe up to 170 dB/Hz for TTL dividers, and if necessary, shielding is used and ground loops are avoided. The PLL acts as a multiplier, as most likely the output frequency of the VCO is substantially higher than the reference frequency, and later we will analyze these effects inside and outside the loop.

Generally, in a multiplier the reverse result is found than is noticed in a frequency divider: the sideband noise and spurious response are increased by the multiplication factor. Let us assume that a 10-MHz reference frequency is divided down to 1 MHz, first with a noise floor of 170 dB/Hz, wideband, and then used as a reference frequency for a 10-MHz PLL. The noise performance is degraded by 20 dB because of this multiplication.

If the crystal oscillator is replaced by another synthesizer loop with some discrete spurs 80 dB below the carrier, they will maintain their 80-dB level, and if the VCO frequency is then increased to 100 MHz, they will deteriorate to 60 dB below the carrier.

In multiloop synthesizers, there is a frequent requirement for auxiliary frequencies that can be generated by one of the following:

1. Phase-locked loop as a multiplier
2. Transistor multiplier
3. Step recovery diode multiplier

In the case of the PLL multiplier, we have two choices:

1. Use a fixed divider.
2. Use harmonic sampling.

Harmonic sampling is generally used for frequencies above 2000 MHz because there are no dividers available that work reliably at higher frequencies. Attempts to use tunnel diodes for this purpose or parametric effects in tuning diodes have shown up in the literature from time to time but in production have failed to show reliable performance, due to component tolerances in temperature.

A harmonic sampler is typically a balanced modulator that uses hot carrier diodes which are being driven from a pulse or needle generator with extremely high harmonic contents. A typical application for such a circuit is in spectrum analyzers, where the input frequency and the YIG oscillator can be locked together. A similar application is where a harmonic comb is being generated from a 1-MHz reference, and locking can occur every 1 MHz to several gigahertz. These circuits require a pretuned mechanism to make sure that the desired harmonic is being selected and false locking is being prevented. This type of multiplication is used in systems where the frequency of the VCO is changed frequently and low spurious contents and high signal-to-noise ratio are required.

For fixed-frequency application, fixed-tuned frequency multipliers with transistors or step recovery diodes are used. The transistor multipliers work well up to several hundred megahertz, and the step recovery diodes or snap-off diodes can be used up to several gigahertz.

For higher frequency ranges, impatt diodes or other exotic devices can generate the necessary frequencies, and some of these multipliers are also built as *injection-lock oscillators*. An injection-lock oscillator can be considered as a frequency multiplier with a certain pulling range where the oscillator somehow locks up with the reference frequency. These are highly nonlinear phenomena, described in the literature from time to time, and the explanations and mathematical models are built primarily around experimental data and are not always very reliable. Low-frequency injection locking is a very convenient way of combining extremely high stability in certain types of crystal oscillators which are being used as a reference for extremely low noise crystal oscillators operating at the same frequency. In Section 4-2-5 we will see an example of a 10-MHz crystal oscillator being injection locked to an external reference. This method is also used now in many frequency synthesizers and frequency counters for the same reason: there is a major trade-off between the best operating mode for short-term stability versus long-term stability (aging).

For single-frequency applications, we find in synthesizer loops high-frequency crystal oscillators at discrete frequencies between 70 and 150 MHz which are locked against a frequency standard but with an extremely narrow loop so that the output noise sideband depends only on the crystal oscillator frequency, rather than on the input frequency. These loops have time constants of 1 Hz or less and therefore compensate only for temperature effects or aging.

If higher frequencies are required, such as 600 to 700 MHz, several choices are available. As the wideband noise floor is being multiplied, depending on the type of multiplier, different results can occur. Let us take a look at Figure 2-11, which shows three different multiplier chains. In scheme A, a 10-MHz crystal oscillator is multiplied directly up to 640 MHz. This system is bound to show a very high noise floor at 10 kHz and more off the carrier.

Scheme B uses the same multiplication scheme but incorporates two crystal filters, one at 40 MHz and one at 160 MHz. It should be noted that it is very difficult to build narrow-frequency crystal filters at these high frequencies. The 40-MHz crystal most likely is a third overtone crystal, and the 160-MHz crystal filter uses a ninth overtone crystal. These crystal filters are probably single-pole filters, and there is a trade-off between how narrow they can be made and how narrow the designer wants them to be. As aging, production, reproducibility, and temperature effects have

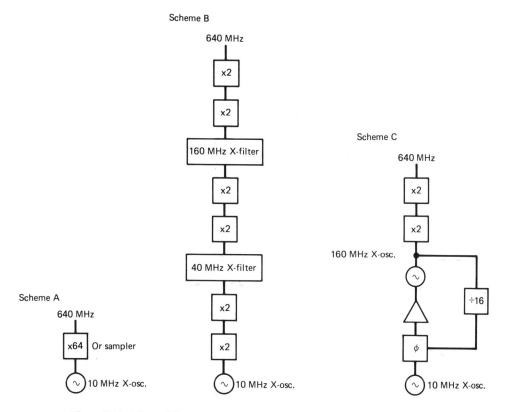

Figure 2-11   Three different ways of generating 640 MHz from a 10-MHz crystal oscillator. (Courtesy of Hewlett-Packard Company.)

to be taken into consideration, these crystal filters cannot be narrower than 1 kHz in a practical circuit.

Scheme C shows a phase-locked crystal oscillator at 160 MHz that is multiplied up to 640 MHz.

Schemes B and C both use a chain of times-2 multipliers. These can be built fairly conveniently with two diodes rather than transistors, and the advantage of these multipliers is the better noise performance, since the close-in noise of fast switching, hot carrier diodes is less than the noise found in bipolar transistors.

There is some merit in using a field-effect transistor as a frequency doubler since junction field-effect transistors, as well as MOS field-effect transistors, are square-law devices, and frequency multiplication becomes easy, as these devices have gain and a high output impedance, so they can operate into a tuned circuit for filtering purposes. Again, a decision has to be made regarding the frequency at which these multiplication stages should be operated. Above 300 or 400 MHz the diode multiplier would be preferred.

By now, we are curious to see the result of these different types of multiplication at the output frequency of 640 MHz. In Figure 2-12 we have plotted the noise performance of the 10-MHz crystal oscillator, which is very clean, and have shown the noise curves for cases A, B, and C.

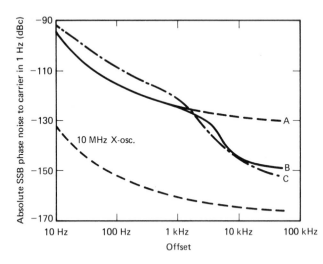

Figure 2-12 Noise sideband performance of the multipliers of Figure 2-11, cases A, B, and C. (Courtesy of Hewlett-Packard Company.)

Method A results in straight multiplication of the reference frequency; therefore, the reference oscillator noise is increased by 36 dB. Method B is also a straight multiplication, but the narrowband crystal filters have improved the noise sideband performance above 2 kHz off the carrier. Method C uses a 160-MHz overtone crystal oscillator. Because of the lower Q of this crystal compared to the 10-MHz crystal oscillator, the noise sideband performance is worse. In addition, because of the divider generating noise into the phase/frequency comparator, the close-in noise below 1 kHz of this method is higher than with any other method. It now becomes clear that method B is the preferred choice.

Method B is not without risks, however. The use of these crystal filters also means that the system has to be built mechanically to be extremely stable. Moving components can generate mechanical vibrations of the crystal, which in turn causes phase jumps. Several recently developed synthesizers using this scheme ran into difficulties with mechanical vibration from the built-in fan and minute oscillations from the power supply transformer generating line frequency spurs. There are other potential problems in this approach:

1. Additive noise in the first stages of multiplication
2. Low-frequency device noise and power supply noise, causing phase modulation in amplifiers, most sensitive again in the first stages of multiplication
3. Doubler noise
4. Crystal filter noise
5. Microphonic noise, inducing phase noise in crystal filters, already mentioned

2-6-5 Noise Contribution from Power Supplies

I have mentioned the effect of line frequency pickup several times so far, the most direct being ripple on the dc supply voltage.

Power supplies can generally be built in one of two ways:

1. Using a monolithic regulator
2. Using discrete components

The safe approach is generally to use two cascaded regulator systems, starting with a monolithic regulator, followed by a discrete postregulation.

In synthesizers, it is typical to find the following voltage requirements: $+5$ V, ± 12 V, $+9$ V, and $+24$ V. When using a power supply fed from a 110- or 220-V power line, the generation of these auxiliary voltages is fairly easy. As the 5 V probably has the highest current drain, this will be kept totally separate from the other voltages. The current consumption on the ± 12 V is in the order of several hundred milliamperes, and the 9 V is probably an auxiliary voltage that can be generated in a postregulator from the $+12$ V.

The $+24$ V requirement is generally of low power consumption and is required for the phase/frequency detector stages and the tuning diodes. If a dc amplifier translation stage is used following the phase/frequency comparators to drive the tuning diode, such a high voltage is necessary.

The dynamic regulation found in a regulator is typically 60 or sometimes 70 dB, which reduces the input ripple voltage to about 1 mV. This is insufficient for sensitive lines and a postregulator of at least the same amount must be added. Here a discrete circuit is the proper choice.

There are numerous regulators on the market, but the one with the lowest noise is probably the National LM723. The typical output noise of this regulator is in the vicinity of a few microvolts.

In battery-operated synthesizers, especially if they operate from 12 V dc, it is somewhat difficult to generate the higher voltage for the tuning diodes. One of the best approaches is to use a switching dc/dc converter stage that is being driven from the reference oscillator at a rate of 10 kHz to 1 MHz. As the power consumption on the tuning line is very small, no special power transistors are required, and regulators take care of reference suppression. As these stages are being driven from a square wave generated from a regulated power supply, extremely high values of regulation can be obtained, and the tuning voltage is therefore very clean and noise-free. Attempts to generate the auxiliary voltage from asynchronous dc/dc converters have generally resulted in poor performance, and this approach is not recommended.

2-7 OVERALL PHASE NOISE PERFORMANCE OF A SYSTEM

By now we are curious to see how the various stages of noise contribution affect the system. However, we have not yet taken into consideration the absolute reference frequency relative to the output frequency. It is apparent that a very narrow loop will show a different performance than a wide loop, and therefore the reference frequency plays an important role. From a system point of view, let us now take a look at the effects of reference frequency on the loop performance.

The expression for the output frequency of a single loop shows that in order to obtain fine frequency resolution the reference frequency must be small, equivalent to the step size. This creates conflicting requirements. One problem is that to cover a broad frequency range requires a large variation in N. Even if the hardware problems can be overcome, some method will normally be needed to compensate for the variations in loop dynamics which occur for widely varying values of N. The linearized loop transfer function is

$$B(s) = \frac{\theta_o(s)}{\theta_i(s)} = \frac{K_v F(s)/s}{1 + K_v F(s)/Ns} \qquad (2\text{-}43)$$

If N is to assume a large number of values, say from 1 to 1000, there will be a 60-dB variation in the open-loop gain and a correspondingly wide variation in the loop dynamics unless some means is used to alter the loop gain for different N values. A second problem encountered with a low reference frequency is that the loop bandwidth must be less than the reference frequency because the low-pass filter must filter out the reference frequency and its harmonics. It is explained in Section 1-10-3 that the loop bandwidth must be less than the filter bandwidth for adequate stability. Therefore, a low reference frequency results in a frequency synthesizer that will be slow to change frequency. Although the transient behavior is difficult to analyze, a rule of thumb often used in digital PLLs is that it takes approximately 25 cycles of the reference signal to change frequency. Thus if a 1-Hz reference frequency is used, it will take approximately 25 s to switch to a different frequency. Another problem introduced by a low reference frequency is its effect on noise introduced in the VCO. Figure 2-13 shows a linearized model of a PLL with the three main sources of noise. ϕ_{N_r} is the noise on the reference signal. ϕ_{N_θ} is the noise created in the phase detector; its largest components are at the reference frequency and the harmonics of this frequency. ϕ_{N_o} is the noise introduced by the VCO. VCO noise has most of its energy content near

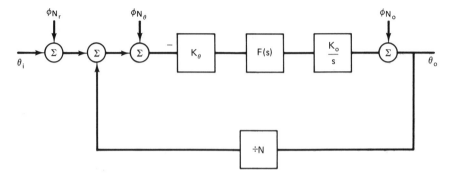

Figure 2-13 Linearized model of a PLL with the three main sources of noise.

the oscillator frequency; in the PLL model it can be interpreted as a low-frequency noise. The noise at the VCO output is given by

$$\phi = \frac{(\phi_{N_v} + \phi_{N_\theta})[K_v F(s)/s]}{1 + K_v F(s)/Ns} + \frac{\phi_{N_o}}{1 + K_v F(s)/Ns} \tag{2-44}$$

$$= G(s)(\phi_{N_r} + \phi_{N_\theta}) + Gr(s)\phi_{N_o}$$

$G(s)$ is a low-pass transfer function, and $Gr(s)$ is a high-pass transfer function. Since $F(s)$ is either unity or a low-pass transfer function, the PLL functions as a low-pass filter for phase noise arising in the reference signal and phase detector, and it functions as a high-pass filter for phase noise originating in the VCO. Since the VCO noise is a low-frequency noise, the output noise due to ϕ_{N_o} is minimized by having the loop bandwidth as wide as possible. At the same time, the loop bandwidth should be less than the reference frequency in order to minimize the effect of ϕ_{N_θ}, which is dominated by spurious frequency components at the reference frequency and its harmonics.

Therefore, the desire to have a low reference frequency f_r in order to obtain fine frequency resolution is offset by the need to have f_r large in order to reduce the loop settling time and also the amount of noise contributed by the VCO. One method frequently used to obtain fine frequency resolution and fast loop response is to use a multiple-loop synthesizer.

A *multiloop synthesizer* uses the various stages we have covered in this chapter as building blocks for a complete synthesizer. The particular example we will use is the Rohde & Schwarz SMPC signal generator, and we will look only at the synthesizer itself, not the entire generator. Without the modulation capability, the SMPC is also being sold under the name XPC. Figure 2-14 shows the block diagram of the synthesizer. A 10-MHz frequency standard is used to generate the auxiliary frequencies; it can be synchronized externally.

The main resolution of the synthesizer down to 1 Hz is achieved in a direct synthesizer where the frequencies are generated with the help of a lookup table of a sine-wave function, a principle explained in greater detail in Chapter 3.

This direct synthesizer operating from 2.2 to 2.3 MHz is mixed with the 10 MHz to generate a frequency of 12.2 to 12.3 MHz.

The 100-kHz reference frequency generated from the 10-MHz standard is used for the programmable divider and to phase lock a 135-MHz crystal oscillator in which the crystal acts as a narrow filter. This circuit has the advantage of combining the filter effects of two crystals in the multiplier loop, as mentioned earlier in this chapter. The loop also reduces some of the microphonic disturbances.

A third auxiliary frequency is generated by dividing the 135-MHz crystal oscillator output to 45 MHz.

The main oscillator is the 240- to 248-MHz phase-locked-loop oscillator system, which is locked by 240 to 248 MHz. Such a loop can be considered as a "cleanup" loop, where the loop bandwidth is kept narrow enough to clean up all the spurs and still allow a fast-enough switching time.

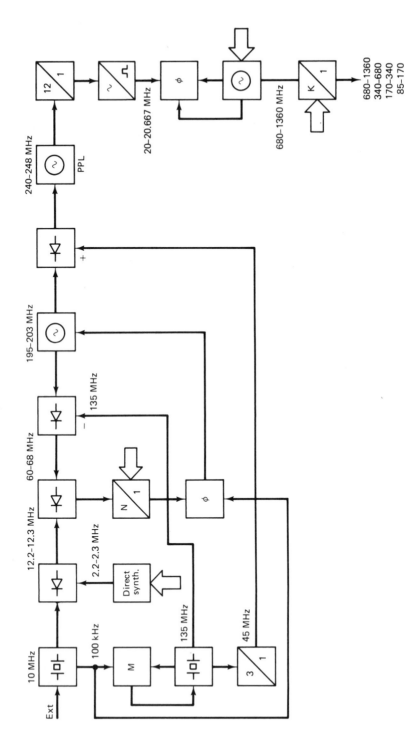

Figure 2-14 Rohde & Schwarz type XPC synthesizer. (Courtesy of Rohde & Schwarz.)

The output of this loop is then divided to 20 . . . 20.667 MHz and used to drive the output phase-locked loop, which covers 680 to 1360 MHz.

The programmable divider gets its information from the keyboard, and the microprocessor inside the synthesizer generates the necessary voltages to pretune the 680–1360-MHz oscillator. This is also called coarse steering. Therefore, the output oscillator will lock with the proper harmonic of the 20- to 20.667-MHz spectrum in a sampling-type phase/frequency comparator. This can be done without a frequency division under the harmonic lock principle, also described in this chapter.

In order to obtain the other frequency ranges, the output divider (K) divides the output range 680 to 1360 MHz into the subranges 340 to 680 MHz, 170 to 340 MHz, 85 to 170 MHz. It is obvious that the noise sideband at the lower range is therefore better than at the higher end; the noise performance therefore improves. The 135-MHz crystal oscillator is being used in an arrangement to generate the range 100 kHz to 100 MHz but is not shown in this block diagram.

As the microprocessor keeps track of all the various division ratios, it becomes apparent that the resolution for the direct synthesizer in the range 2 to 2.3 MHz has to be better than 1 Hz in order to get 0.1-Hz resolution up to 100 MHz at the final output frequency and 1 Hz from 100 to 1300 MHz.

How does this principle compare with other signal generators and synthesizers on the market? Figure 2-15 shows a comparison sheet in which the noise performance

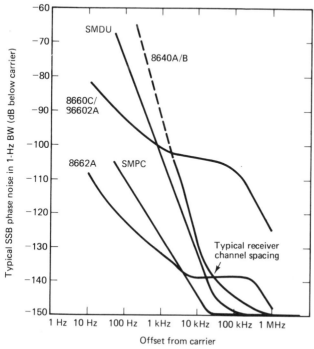

Figure 2-15 Comparison of phase noise of various signal generators and synthesizers.

of the Hewlett-Packard 8640A, B and the Rohde & Schwarz SMDU free-running signal generators are displayed. In addition, the older model HP8660C, 86602A, and the latest version, 8662A, are compared with the Rohde & Schwarz SMPC.

It becomes apparent that the close-in noise of the HP8662A from 1 Hz to about 3 kHz off the carrier is better than the SMPC, whereas the noise performance from 5 to 800 kHz of the SMPC is better. The reason for this is the different concept; the 8662A, being practically twice as expensive as the SMPC, is a much faster synthesizer, locking in less than $\frac{1}{2}$ ms while the SMPC has about 15 ms switching time. This indicates that the loop bandwidth of the SMPC is narrow, and therefore less cleanup can be achieved from the auxiliary circuits.

However, the far-out noise of the SMPC is better because it relies more heavily on the performance of the 680- to 1360-MHz oscillator that is locked against the 240- to 248-MHz oscillator with a fast divider of 12.

Special divider circuits were created to provide a low enough noise floor so that the total system's noise after the multiplication is not substantially degraded.

We can learn from this analysis that there is a speed and cost trade-off whereby the more complex system, especially using the fractional division synthesizer principle like that in the 8662A, can be made much faster and at higher cost, while in allowing a longer switching time and a somewhat more traditional approach, costs can be kept lower.

2-8 MEASUREMENT OF PHASE NOISE

The emphasis on low phase noise sources also guides the selection of test methods. Phase noise measurement techniques will be compared on the basis of minimum phase noise $\mathcal{L}$ measurable.

2-8-1 Heterodyne Frequency Measurement Technique

In the time domain, frequency stability is measured with period counters. Given a stable reference source, the resolution is greatly enhanced by heterodyning (Figure 2-16). Resolution:

$$\frac{\Delta f}{f_o} = \frac{f_D^2 \, \Delta \tau}{f_o} \tag{2-45}$$

where $\dfrac{\Delta f}{f_o}$ = minimum fractional frequency difference

$\quad f_D$ = difference frequency

$\quad \tau$ = sample time, minimum, $= 1/f_D$

$\quad \Delta \tau$ = least digit of period count

With computing counters the Allan variance σ_y can be obtained conveniently. Desktop computer-based systems such as the HP5390A frequency stability analyzer, convert time-domain data into spectral densities. The system noise floor is given by

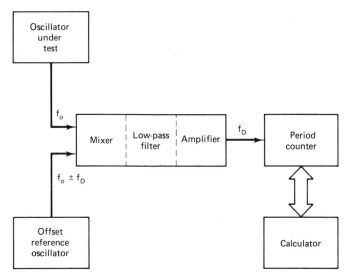

Figure 2-16 Noise measurements based on heterodyne technique.

$$\mathcal{L}_{\text{system}} = -174 + \log 10 \ \frac{f_D^2}{f_m^2} \qquad \text{dBc/Hz} \qquad (2\text{-}46)$$

For example: at $f_m = 1$ Hz with $f_D = 10$ Hz, the system can measure down to -154 dBc.

There are a number of other counters on the market which allow time-interval averaging or period-interval averaging, and the results may be processed by a computer used as a controller on the IEEE bus.

Compared with other methods, this technique loses its advantage quickly above Fourier frequencies greater than 100 Hz.

2-8-2 Phase Noise Measurement with Spectrum Analyzer

RF spectrum analyzers measure the spectral density $\mathcal{L}$ directly, provided that the phase noise of the source under test is significantly above its AM noise.

By down-converting with a clean reference source, AM noise of the source under test can be suppressed if it is used as the high-level LO drive for the mixer.

Limitations of this direct method are phase noise of the spectrum analyzer LO, dynamic range, and resolution.

An RF spectrum analyzer with a YIG oscillator as LO can measure $\mathcal{L}$ at 100 kHz down to approximately -120 dBc. Spectrum analyzers with synthesized LO allow phase noise measurements closer in. The various companies producing spectrum analyzers have so many new models under development that it is not possible to recommend certain types of analyzers, as new models may be available at the time of publication of this book.

However, the two most powerful spectrum analyzers currently available are the HP Model 8568A from 100 Hz to 1500 MHz, and the Model 8566A from 100 Hz to 22 GHz.

Both of these spectrum analyzers are synthesized rather than using a simple swept YIG oscillator. Hewlett-Packard uses a novel technique in the synthesizer portions of those spectrum analyzers which had been referred to as "rock-and-roll" technique, an expression borrowed from dance music rather than science. What it means is that at certain frequencies and at certain times the frequency is phase locked for a short period and then swept to the next lock point, a method that apparently combines precise frequency resolution and extremely low noise. The interested reader is referred to a brief discussion of this technique in Section 3-5 and in the details given in the instruction manuals for those analyzers. Figure 2-17 shows the two common test setups.

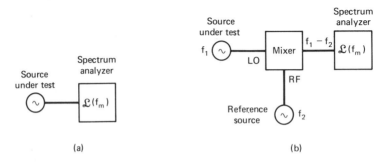

(a)   (b)

Figure 2-17   Two commonly used arrangements to determine noise sideband of a source.

2-8-3 Phase Noise Measurement with Frequency Discriminator

The spectral density of frequency fluctuations $S\Delta_f(f_m)$ of the source under test is obtained when the signal is applied to a frequency discriminator either directly or in a heterodyne fashion, shown in Figure 2-18.

$$\Delta f_{\text{rms}} = \frac{1}{K_F} \Delta V_{\text{rms}}$$

$$S_{\Delta f}(f_m) = \frac{1}{K_F^2}(\Delta V_{\text{rms}})^2(1\text{ Hz}) \tag{2-47}$$

$\mathcal{L}(f_m)$ is calculated from $S_{\Delta f}$:

$$\mathcal{L}(f_m) = \frac{1}{2}\frac{1}{f_m^2}S_{\Delta f}(f_m) \tag{2-48}$$

Assuming a noise floor of the discriminator represented by $\Delta V_{n\,\text{rms}}$, the system noise for $\mathcal{L}(f_m)$ is

$$\mathcal{L}_{\text{system}}(f_m) = \frac{1}{2}\frac{1}{K_F^2}\frac{1}{f_m^2}(\Delta V_{n\,\text{rms}})^2(1\text{ Hz}) \tag{2-49}$$

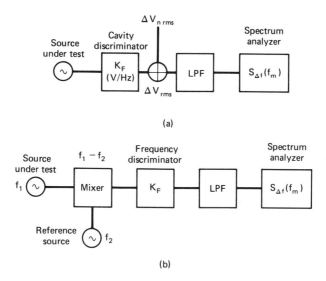

(a)

(b)

Figure 2-18 Phase noise measurement set up with cavity discriminator or frequency discriminator.

It indicates the basic drawback of the use of the frequency discriminator method in determining the phase noise $\mathcal{L}(f_m)$ of a source. The system's noise floor rises with f_m^{-2} toward low offsets. This assumes a white spectrum of ΔV_n.

Using the 8901A modulation analyzer ($\Delta_{fres} = 0.5$ Hz), for example, as the frequency discriminator, $\mathcal{L}_{system}$ at 1 kHz will be -105 dBc.

2-8-4 Delay Line and Mixer as Frequency Comparator

A mixer operating as a phase detector and a delay line has the combined effect of a frequency comparator, again yielding $S_{\Delta f}(f_m)$, as seen in Figure 2-19. Both inputs to the mixer have to be in quadrature to assure maximum phase sensitivity.

The output voltage ΔV of the mixer is proportional to the frequency deviation Δf of the source and to the phase detector constant K_θ and has a periodic, $(\sin x)/x$, dependence on $f_m \tau_d$.

$$\Delta V = K_\theta \Delta_\theta$$

$$\Delta V = K_\theta \tau_d \frac{\sin (\omega_m \tau_d/2)}{\omega_m \tau_d/2} \Delta \omega \qquad (2\text{-}50)$$

where τ_d = delay time
K_θ = phase detector constant
   $= V_{beat, peak}$ for sinusoidal beat signal
For $f_m \ll 1/2\tau_d$,

$$\Delta f_{rms} = \frac{\Delta V_{rms}}{2\pi k_\theta \tau_d}$$

$$\mathcal{L}(f_m) = \frac{1}{2f_m^2} S_{\Delta f}(f_m) = \frac{1}{2} \frac{(\Delta V_{rms})^2 (1 \text{ Hz})}{(2\pi)^2 K_\theta^2 \tau_d^2 f_m^2} \qquad (2\text{-}51)$$

$$S_{\Delta f}(f_m) = \frac{(\Delta V_{rms})^2 (1 \text{ Hz})}{(2\pi)^2 K_\theta^2 \tau_d^2}$$

101

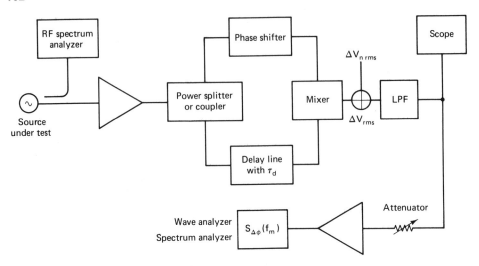

Figure 2-19   Noise sideband evaluation system using a delay line and a phase shifter.

The sensitivity of the system can again be evaluated by replacing ΔV_{rms}, caused by frequency fluctuations of the source, with $\Delta V_{n\,\text{rms}}$, representing mixer noise plus noise of the following amplifier.

$$\mathcal{L}_{\text{system}}(f_m) = \frac{1}{2}\frac{(\Delta V_{n\,\text{rms}})^2(1\text{ Hz})}{(2\pi)^2 K_\theta^2 \tau_d^2 f_m^2} \qquad (2\text{-}52)$$

With white mixer (plus amplifier) noise, the system sensitivity decreases with f_m^{-2}. The flicker characteristic of the mixer noise causes the noise floor to rise with f_m^{-3} toward low offsets.

   This method is also referred to as the *autocorrelation method* [19] and can be optimized toward two different goals. To determine the highest sensitivity for AM or spurious output at the input of the system, the delay should be set at $\tau_d = m(\pi/\omega_m)$, where the delay-line length is an integral number of even half-wavelengths. The system is optimized for maximum sensitivity of AM by varying the delay until a maximum dc level is obtained at the output of a mixer.

   The system has the maximum sensitivity to FM noise for $\tau_d = [(2m + 1)/\omega_m]\pi$. This time the system is tuned for maximum sensitivity to FM by adjusting the delay τ_d until a dc null is obtained by the output of the mixer.

   This principle can be reversed, which means that the output from the double-balanced mixer can be fed backward into the oscillator and can be used to stabilize the noise of the free-running oscillator.

   This method of feedback, described later for a signal generator, has been used in Germany since about 1968, together with a PAL delay line in a 5- to 5.5-MHz VFO. The method has been adapted lately by Fluke in its generator Model 6070A and Model 6071A synthesized signal generator. Reference 20 provides more details.

   References 15 and 16 explore this method extensively. $\mathcal{L}_{\text{system}}$ at 1 kHz can be as low as -115 dBc.

2-8-5 Phase Noise Measurement with Two Sources and Phase Comparator

The most direct and most sensitive method to measure the spectral density of phase noise $S\Delta\theta(f_m)$ requires two sources—one or both of them may be the device(s) under test—and a double-balanced mixer used as a phase detector. The RF and LO input to the mixer should be in phase quadrature, indicated by $0\ V_{dc}$ at the IF port. Good quadrature assures maximum phase sensitivity K_θ and minimum AM sensitivity. With a linearly operating mixer, K_θ equals the peak voltage of the sinusoidal beat signal produced when both sources are frequency offset (see Figure 2-20).

When both signals are set in quadrature, the voltage ΔV at the IF port is proportional to the fluctuating phase difference between the two signals.

$$\Delta\theta_{rms} = \frac{1}{K_\theta} V_{rms}$$

$$S_{\Delta\theta}(f_m) = \frac{(\Delta V_{rms})^2(1\ \text{Hz})}{V_{B\,peak}^2}\frac{1}{2}\frac{(\Delta V_{rms})^2(1\ \text{Hz})}{V_{B\,rms}^2} \tag{2-53}$$

$$\mathcal{L}(f_m) = \frac{1}{2}S_{\Delta\theta}(f_m) = \frac{1}{4}\frac{(\Delta V_{rms})^2(1\ \text{Hz})}{V_{B\,rms}^2}$$

where K_θ = phase detector constant
$\quad = V_{B\,peak}$ for sinusoidal beat signal

The calibration of the wave analyzer or spectrum analyzer can be read from the equations above. For a plot of $\mathcal{L}(f_m)$ the 0-dB reference level is to be set 6 dB above the level of the beat signal. The −6-dB offset has to be corrected by +1.0 dB for a wave analyzer and by +2.5 dB for a spectrum analyzer with log amplifier and average detector. In addition, noise bandwidth corrections may have to be applied.

Since the phase noise of both sources is measured in this system, the phase noise performance of one of them needs to be known for definite data on the other source. Frequently, it is sufficient to know that the actual phase noise of the dominant source cannot deviate from the measured data by more than 3 dB. If three unknown sources are available, three measurements with three different source combinations yield sufficient data to calculate accurately each individual performance.

Figure 2-20 indicates a narrowband phase-locked loop which maintains phase quadrature for sources that are not sufficiently phase stable over the period of the measurement. The two isolation amplifiers should prevent injection locking of the sources.

Residual phase noise measurements test one or two devices, such as amplifiers, dividers (Figure 2-9), or synthesizers (Figure 2-22), driven by one common source. Since this source is not free of phase noise, it is important to know the degree of cancellation as a function of Fourier frequency.

The noise floor of the system is established by the equivalent noise voltage ΔV_n at the mixer output. It represents mixer noise as well as the equivalent noise voltage of the following amplifier.

$$\mathcal{L}_{system}(f_m) = \frac{1}{4}\frac{(\Delta V_{n\,rms})^2(1\ \text{Hz})}{V_{B\,rms}^2} \tag{2-54}$$

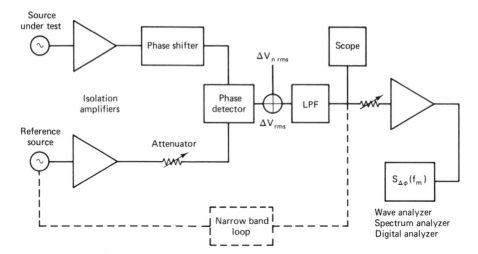

Figure 2-20   Phase noise system with two sources maintaining phase quadrature.

Noise floors close to -180 dBc can be achieved with a high-level mixer and a low-noise port amplifier. The noise floor increases with f_m^{-1} due to the flicker characteristic of ΔV_n. System noise floors of -166 dBc at 1 kHz have been realized.

In measuring low-phase-noise sources, a number of potential problems have to be understood to avoid erroneous data:

- If two sources are phase locked to maintain phase quadrature, it has to be ensured that the lock bandwidth is significantly lower than the lowest Fourier frequency of interest.
- Even with no apparent phase feedback, two sources can be phase locked (injection locked), resulting in suppressed close-in phase noise.
- AM noise of the RF signal can come through if the quadrature setting is not maintained sufficiently.
- Deviation from the quadrature setting will also lower the effective phase detector constant.
- Nonlinear operation of the mixer results in a calibration error.
- A nonsinusoidal RF signal causes K_θ to deviate from $V_{B\,\text{peak}}$.
- The amplifier or spectrum analyzer input can be saturated during calibration or by high spurious signals such as line frequency multiples.
- Closely spaced spurious signals such as multiples of 60 Hz may give the appearance of continuous phase noise when insufficient resolution and averaging is used on the spectrum analyzer.
- Impedance interfaces should remain unchanged going from calibration to measurement.

- In residual measurement systems phase, the noise of the common source might be insufficiently canceled due to improperly high delay-time differences between the two branches.

- Noise from power supplies for devices under test or the narrowband phase-locked loop can be a dominant contributor of phase noise.

- Peripheral instrumentation such as the oscilloscope, analyzer, counter, or DVM can inject noise.

- Microphonic noise might excite significant phase noise in devices.

Despite all of these hazards, automatic test systems have been developed and operated successfully [15]. Figure 2-21 shows a system that automatically measures

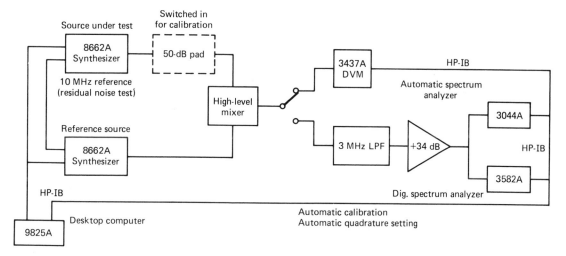

Figure 2-21 Automatic system to measure residual phase noise of two 8662A synthesizers. (Courtesy of Hewlett-Packard Company.)

the residual phase noise of the 8662A synthesizer. It is a residual test, since both instruments use one common 10-MHz reference oscillator. Quadrature setting is conveniently controlled by probing the beat signal with a digital voltmeter and stopping the phase advance of one synthesizer when the beat signal voltage is sufficiently close to zero.

The two plots of Figure 2-22 were done with the 3044A automatic spectrum analyzer covering 10 Hz to 13 MHz. The test system also measures spurious signals. On this chart the signals appear to be rather broad due to a limited number of data points per decade. Again, the older 8660C/86602A synthesized signal generator is compared with the new 8662A.

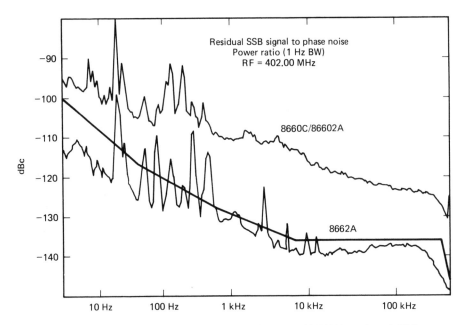

Figure 2-22 Signal-to-noise measurement of an 8660C/86602A and an 8662A Hewlett-Packard frequency synthesizer in an automated system. (Courtesy of Hewlett-Packard Company.)

REFERENCES

1. Jacques Rutman, "Characterization of Frequency Stability: A Transfer Function Approach and Its Application to Measure via Filtering of Phase Noise," *IEEE Transactions on Instrumentation and Measurement*, Vol. 22 (1974), pp. 40–48.

2. Chuck Reynolds, "Measure Phase Noise," *Electronic Design*, February 15, 1977, pp. 106–108.

3. J. A. Barnes, A. R. Chie, L. S. Cutter, et al., "Characterization of Frequency Stability," *IEEE Transactions on Instrumentation and Measurement*, Vol. IM-20, No. 2 (May 1971), pp. 105–120.

4. J. A. Barnes and R. C. Mockler, "The Power Spectrum and Its Importance in Precise Frequency Measurements," *IRE Transactions on Instrumentation*, 1960, pp. 149–155.

5. E. J. Baghdady, R. N. Lincoln, and B. D. Nelin, "Short-Term Frequency Stability: Characterization, Theory, and Measurements," *Proceedings of the IEEE*, 1965, pp. 704–722.

6. D. B. Leeson, "Short-Term Stable Microwave Sources," *Microwave Journal*, June 1970, pp. 59–69.

7. D. B. Leeson, "A Simple Model of Feedback Oscillator Noise Spectrum," *Proceedings of the IEEE*, 1966, pp. 329–330.

8. L. S. Cutler and C. L. Searle, "Some Aspects of the Theory and Measurement of Frequency Fluctuations in Frequency Standards," *Proceedings of the IEEE*, Vol. 54, (1966), pp. 136–154.

9. W. A. Edson, "Noise in Oscillators," *Proceedings of the IRE*, 1960, pp. 1454–1466.

10. Erich Hafner, "The Effects of Noise in Oscillators," *Proceedings of the IEEE*, Vol. 54 (1966), pp. 179–198.

11. M. C. Fischer, "Frequency Stability Measurement Procedures," Eighth Annual Precise Time and Time Interval Applications and Planning Meeting, December 1976.

12. D. A. Howe, "Frequency Domain Stability Measurements: A Tutorial Introduction," *NBS Technical Note 679*, March 1976.

13. D. J. Healey III, "Flicker of Frequency and Phase and White Frequency and Phase Fluctuations in Frequency Sources," *Proceedings of the 26th Annual Symposium on Frequency Control*, Fort Monmouth, NJ, June 1972, pp. 43–49.

14. Hewlett-Packard staff, "Understanding and Measuring Phase Noise in the Frequency Domain," *Application Note 207*, October 1976.

15. A. L. Lance, W. D. Seal, F. G. Mendozo, and N. W. Hudson, "Automating Phase Noise Measurements in the Frequency Domain," *Proceedings of the 31st Annual Symposium on Frequency Control*, June 1977.

16. A. L. Lance, W. D. Seal, N. W. Hudson, F. G. Mendozo, and Donald Halford, "Phase Noise Measurements Using Cross-Spectrum Analysis," Conference on Precision Electromagnetic Measurements, Ottawa, June 1978.

17. J. H. Shoaf, D. Halford, and A. S. Risley, "Frequency Stability Specification and Measurement: High Frequency and Microwave Signals," *NBS Technical Note 632*, January 1973.

18. Dieter Scherer, "Design Principles and Test Methods for Low Phase Noise RF and Microwave Sources," RF & Microwave Measurement Symposium and Exhibition, Hewlett-Packard.

19. A. Tykulsky, "Spectral Measurements of Oscillators," *Proceedings of the IEEE*, February 1966, p. 306.

20. Fred Telewski, Kingsley Craft, Eric Drucker, and Joe Martins, "Delay Lines Give RF generator Spectrum Purity, Programmability," *Electronics*, August 28, 1980, pp. 133–142.

21. Hewlett-Packard staff, "Timekeeping and Frequency Calibration," *Application Note 52–2* (Hewlett-Packard, Palo Alto, CA 94304, November 1975.)

22. David W. Allan, "Report on NBS Dual Mixer Time Difference System (DMTD) Built for Time-Domain Measurements Associated with Phase 1 of GPS," *NBSIR 750827*, National Bureau of Standards (U.S.) (NTIS, Springfield, VA 22151, January 1976).

23. Hewlett-Packard staff, "Measuring Warmup Characteristics and Aging Rates of Crystal Oscillators," *Application Note 174–11* (Hewlett-Packard, Palo Alto, CA 94394, November 1974).

24. David W. Allan, "The Measurement of Frequency and Frequency Stability of Precision Oscillators," *NBS Technical Note 669*, National Bureau of Standards, (U.S.) (SD Catalog No. C13.46: 669, U.S. Government Printing Office, Washington, DC 20402, May 1975).

25. Luiz Peregrino and David W. Ricci, "Phase Noise Measurement Using a High Resolution Counter with On-Line Data Processing," *Proceedings of the 30th Annual Symposium on Frequency Control*, U.S. Army Electronics Command, Fort Monmouth, NJ, 1976.

(Copies available from Electronic Industries Association, 2001 I Street, NW, Washington, DC 20006.)

26. Byron E. Blair, ed., *Time and Frequency: Theory and Fundamentals*, NBS Monograph 140, National Bureau of Standards (U.S.) (SD Catalog No. C13.44: 140, U.S. Government Printing Office, Washington, DC 20402, May 1974).

27. Hewlett-Packard staff, "Measuring Fractional Frequency Standard Deviation (sigma) versus Averaging Time (tau)," *Application Note 174–7* (Hewlett-Packard, Palo Alto, CA 94304, November 1974).

28. James E. Gray and David W. Allan, "A Method for Estimating the Frequency Stability of an Individual Oscillator," *Proceedings of the 28th Annual Symposium on Frequency Control*, US Army Electronics Command, Fort Monmouth, NJ, 1974, pp. 243–246. (Copies available from Electronic Industries Association, 2001 I Street, NW, Washington, DC 20006.)

29. *Reference Data for Radio Engineers*, 5th ed., (New York; Howard W. Sams, Indianapolis, IN, 1968, p. 21–7.

30. Hewlett-Packard staff, "Spectrum Analysis: Noise Measurements," *Application Note 150–4* (Hewlett-Packard, Palo Alto, CA 94304, January 1973).

31. Hewlett-Packard staff, "Spectrum Analysis: Signal Enhancement," *Application Note 150–7*, June 1975; and "Spectrum Analysis: Accuracy Improvement," *Application Note 150–8* (Hewlett-Packard, Palo Alto, CA 94304, March 1976).

32. Hewlett-Packard staff, "Spectrum Analysis: Noise Figure Measurement," *Application Note 150–9* (Hewlett-Packard, Palo Alto, CA 94304, April 1976).

33. Patrick Lesage and Claude Audoin, "Characterization of Frequency Stability: Uncertainty Due to the Finite Number of Measurements," *IEEE Transactions on Instrumentation and Measurement*, Vol. IM-22, No. 2 (June 1973), pp. 157–161.

3

Special Loops

Chapters 1 and 2 have familiarized us with the phase-locked loop, the fundamental building block of all modern frequency synthesizers. We now understand the various types and orders of loops, the performance of the loop, and the evaluation of the loop.

This chapter deals with special loops that are basically one-loop synthesizers. These systems can be combined, as we will see later, in multiloop synthesizers, or some of them can be used as stand-alone systems.

The resolution or step size of the synthesizer, as we have learned, is equal to the reference frequency. There is a conflict between speed and step size, and this chapter deals with ways of minimizing this conflict. First, we will take a look at a system generating frequencies digitally with the help of logic circuitry and/or a digital computer. As today's technology provides us with fast microprocessors, these systems, using microprocessors and lookup tables, are capable of ultrafine-resolution synthesizers.

Then we take a look at multiloop sampler loops, where the various samplers are being used to speed up the response of the very narrow loops commonly required in high-resolution systems. Loops with sequential phase shifters allow increased resolution at the expense of absolute accuracy.

Then we will see how a delay line can be used to improve noise performance. This is almost the reverse technique of what we saw in Chapter 2, where the delay line was used to measure the phase noise.

Finally, we acquaint ourselves with the fractional N phase-locked loop, a spin-off of the digiphase system.

3-1 DIRECT DIGITAL SYNTHESIS

Direct digital frequency synthesis (DDFS) consists of generating a digital representation of the desired signal, using logic circuitry and or a digital computer, and then converting the digital representation to an analog waveform using a digital-to-analog converter. Recent advances in microelectronics, particularly the microprocessor, make DDFS practical, at frequencies ≤ 100 kHz. Systems can be compact, low power, and can provide very fine frequency resolution with virtually instantaneous switching of frequencies. DDFS is finding increased application, particularly in conjunction with PLL synthesizers.

DDFS utilizes a single source frequency (clock) as a time reference. One method of digitally generating the values of a sine wave is to solve interactively the digital recursion relation

$$Yn = (2 \cos \omega t)Y_{n-1} - Y_{n-2} \tag{3-1}$$

There are at least two problems with this method. The noise can increase until a limit cycle (nonlinear oscillation) occurs. Also, the finite word length used to represent $2 \cos \omega t$ places a limitation on the frequency resolution. Another method of DDFS, direct table lookup, consists of storing the amplitude coefficients in memory. The continuing miniaturization in size and cost of read-only memory make this the most frequently used technique. One method of direct table lookup outputs the same N points for each cycle of the sine wave, and changes the output frequency by adjusting the rate at which the points are outputted. It is relatively difficult to obtain fine frequency resolution with this approach, so a modified table-lookup method is normally used. It is this method that will be described here.

The function $\cos \omega t$ is approximated by outputting the function

$$\cos \omega nT \qquad (n = 0, 1, 2, \dots)$$

where T is the rate at which digital words are converted in the D/A converter; $1/T$ is referred to as the sampling rate.

The lowest output frequency waveform contains N distinct points in its waveform, as illustrated in Figure 3-1. A waveform of twice the frequency can then be

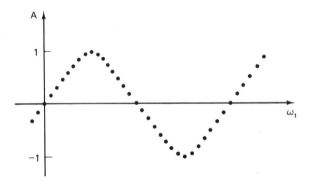

Figure 3-1 Synthesized waveform generated by direct digital synthesis.

110

generated, using the same sampling rate, but outputting every other data point; a waveform k times as fast is obtained by outputting every kth point at the same rate T. The frequency resolution is then the same as the lowest frequency f_L. The maximum output frequency f_u is selected so that it is an integral multiple of f_L:

$$f_u = kf_L \qquad (3\text{-}2)$$

If P points are used in the waveform of the highest-frequency f_u, then

$$N = kP \qquad (3\text{-}3)$$

points are used in the lowest-frequency waveform. The number N is limited by the amount of available memory. The minimum value that P can assume is usually taken to be $P = 4$. With this small value of P, the output waveform contains many harmonics of the desired output frequency, but the harmonics can be removed by low-pass filtering the D/A output. For $P = 4$, the period of the highest frequency,

$$T_u = \frac{1}{f_u} = 4T \qquad (3\text{-}4)$$

or

$$f_u = \frac{1}{4T} \qquad (3\text{-}4)$$

Therefore, the highest possible attainable frequency is determined by the fastest sampling rate possible.

So far in the design of the DDFS we have determined that:

1. The desired frequency resolution determines the lowest output frequency f_L.
2. The number of D/A conversions used to generate f_L is

$$N = 4k = 4\frac{f_u}{f_L} \qquad (3\text{-}5)$$

   provided that four D/A conversions are used to generate f_u.
3. The maximum output frequency f_u is limited by the maximum sampling rate of the DDFS:

$$f_u \leq \frac{1}{4T} \qquad (3\text{-}6)$$

   or conversely, the sampling rate $(1/T)$ is determined from

$$T = \frac{1}{4f_u} \qquad (3\text{-}7)$$

The architecture of the complete DDFS is shown in Figure 3-2. To generate the frequency nf_L, the integer 0 is addressing the register, and each clock cycle $k \times n$ is added to the contents of the accumulator so that the contents of the memory address register are increased by $k \times n$, each $(k \times n)$th point of memory is addressed], and the contents of this memory location are transferred to the D/A converter.

To complete the DDFS, memory size and the length (number of bits) of each

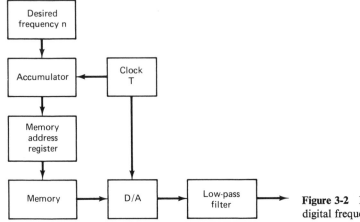

Figure 3-2 Block diagram of a direct digital frequency synthesizer.

word must be determined. Word length is determined by the system noise requirements. The D/A output samples are those of an exact sinusoid corrupted with deterministic noise due to the truncation caused by the finite length of the digital words. It can be shown that if a $(n + 1)$-bit word length is used (including one bit as the sign bit), the worst-case noise power due to the truncation will be

$$\sigma^2 = \frac{1}{2^n} \qquad (3\text{-}8)$$

or $-6n$ dB. For each bit added to the word length, the spectral purity improves by 6 dB.

Example 1

What word length will be required in a DDFS if the output spectral purity is to be at least 80 dB?

Solution. Since the noise power is $-6n$ dB, n must be at least 14. One additional bit is needed for the sign; therefore, the minimum word length needed is 15 bits for an 80 dB signal-to-noise ratio.

The memory size is determined from Eq. (3-5):

$$N = 4\frac{f_u}{f_L}$$

where N is the number of points in the lowest-frequency sinusoid. Clearly, N words of memory would be sufficient for storing the data. However, the amount of memory required can usually be markedly reduced. First, it is only necessary to store the values for the first quadrant (0 to 90°) of the sine wave, since the values for the other three quadrants can be computed directly from these values; so a maximum of

$$N = \frac{f_u}{f_L}$$

memory points are required. The amount of memory can also be reduced by including one or more multipliers, but since multiplication is relatively slow, particularly with microprocessors, and memory is small and inexpensive, multiplication is rarely used to reduce the memory requirements. The amount of memory may still be reduced from that specified by Eq. (3-5) when the spectral purity requirements are not too severe. This point is illustrated in the following example:

Example 2

Design a DDFS to cover the frequency range 0 to 10 kHz with a frequency resolution of 0.001 Hz. The spectral purity is to be at least 40 dB.

Solution. The use of 8-bit words, including the sign bit, will give a spectral purity of 42 dB, and this meets the noise specification. Since

$$N = \frac{f_u}{f_L} = \frac{10^4}{0.001} = 10^7 = 2^{24}$$

it appears at first inspection that a large amount of memory is required. However, only $2^8 = 256$ different words can be formed using 8-bit words, so 256 memory locations should suffice. The explanation of this apparent contradiction is that although 10^7 different points are specified, the phase increments $\Delta\theta = \omega t$ are so small that approximately

$$2^{24} \div 2^7 = 2^{17}$$

increments are needed before a change is registered in the 8-bit word (a 24-bit word would be required to represent all the 2^{24} words). The complete design is illustrated in Figure 3-3. A 24-bit accumulator is required, but only 7 bits are used to address the 128-word memory. The sign bit directly controls the polarity of the D/A output. Greater frequency resolution could be obtained simply by increasing the length of the accumulator.

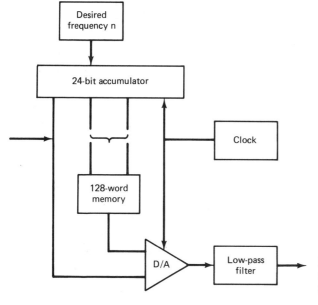

Figure 3-3 Direct digital frequency synthesizer with 24-bit accumulator and 128-word memory.

The main drawback of DDFS is that it is limited to relatively low frequencies. The upper frequency is directly related to the maximum possible clock frequency. An upper frequency limit of approximately 10 kHz can be realized with microprocessors and approximately 1 MHz with special-purpose logic. DDFS is also noisier than the other methods, but adequate spectral purity can be obtained if sufficient low-pass filtering is used at the output. DDFS systems are easily constructed using readily available microprocessors. The main advantages of the method are its flexibility, easy realization of very low frequencies, and virtually instantaneous switching time. The combination of DDFS for fine frequency resolution plus other synthesis methods to obtain high frequency performance is illustrated by the following example.

Synthesizer Design Example.   Consider the design of a frequency synthesizer to cover the range 198 to 200 MHz in 10-Hz increments with a frequency switching time of less than 100 ms. These specifications are typical of those imposed on a synthesizer to be contained in a satellite communications system. The fine frequency resolution and short settling time is required in a system that uses "frequency hopping" as a means of preventing unauthorized reception of the data transmission.

There are many systems that can meet the frequency range and resolution requirements. They include:

1. A single-loop indirect synthesizer
2. Multiple-loop indirect synthesizers
3. A PLL–DDFS combination
4. A direct frequency synthesizer
5. A combined DDFS and direct synthesizer

The single-loop indirect (PLL) synthesizer is not a good choice for several reasons. First, N must vary from 19.8×10^6 to 20×10^6, and programmable dividers are not yet available which operate at 198 MHz. Also, the 10-Hz frequency resolution specification requires that the reference frequency be 10 Hz. For a 10-Hz reference frequency, the loop settling time would be on the order of 2.5 s, which is much too slow.

A two-loop synthesizer that can cover the specified frequency spectrum is shown in Figure 3-4. The output frequency is the sum of the local oscillator frequency f_L and the frequency of VCO 1 (f_1). That is,

$$f_o = f_L + f_1 \tag{3-9}$$

The output f_1 is found from

$$f_r = \frac{f_1 - f_2/1000}{M} \tag{3-10}$$

and

$$f_r = \frac{f_2 - f_L/2}{N} \tag{3-11}$$

Therefore,

$$f_o = f_L + Mf_r + \frac{f_2}{1000} = f_L + Mf_r + N\frac{f_v}{1000} + \frac{f_L}{2000} \tag{3-12}$$

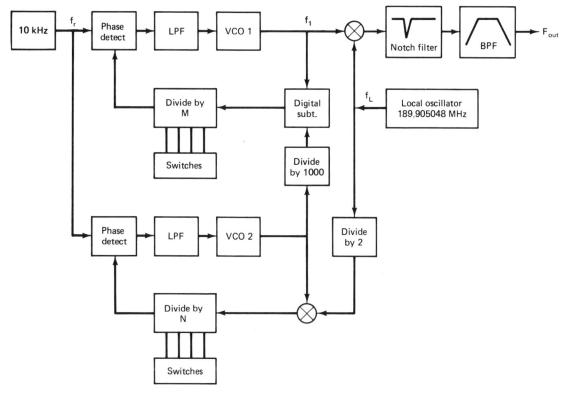

Two loop synthesizer: 198.000000 to 199.999990 MHz

Figure 3-4 Two-loop synthesizer to generate 198 to 199.9999 MHz in 1-Hz steps.

For a reference frequency,

$$f_r = 10 \text{ kHz}$$

$$f_o = 1.0005 f_L + 10^4 M + 10N$$

N could be a three-digit decimal number (1–999) to select the three least significant digits of the frequency, and M could vary between 1 and 200 to select the three most significant digits—but then the output bandpass filter requirements would be too stringent. Therefore, it is better to place a minimum value on M and then reduce f_L. For example, M could vary from 800 to 1000; then

$$1.0005 f_L = 198 \times 10^6 = 800 \times 10^4$$

or

$$f_L = 189.905048 \times 10^6 \text{ Hz}$$

For this synthesizer, the reference frequency for each loop is 10 kHz, so the settling time would be approximately

$$t_s = \frac{25}{10^4} = 2.5 \text{ ms}$$

which is a marked improvement over the single-loop system. If a shorter settling time is required, other alternatives should be considered. Although a direct frequency synthesizer could be designed to meet the specifications, it will not be discussed here because of the hardware complexity of such a system.

A DDFS cannot be used because of the high output frequency required, but a direct digital frequency synthesizer could be used to obtain the fine frequency resolution with very short settling times. The DDFS could then be combined with a direct or indirect synthesizer to obtain the high output frequency. Figure 3-5 illustrates another solution to the problem. The configuration is often referred to as a direct digital/direct/indirect hybrid synthesizer. In this system the DDFS generates the

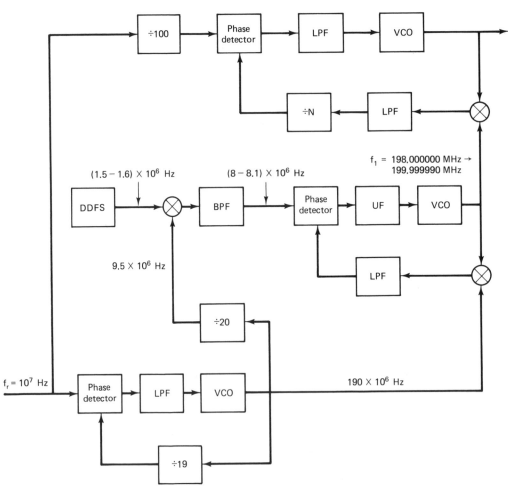

Figure 3-5 Hybrid synthesizer using direct digital frequency synthesis together with a phase-locked loop.

frequencies 1.5 to 1.6 MHz in 10-Hz increments. The minimum frequency of 1.5 MHz is selected to ease the filter requirements of BPF 1. The upper PLL uses a reference frequency of 100 kHz to generate the frequency increments of 100 kHz ($0 \leq N \leq 20$). Since the DDFS responds almost instantaneously, the overall settling time is determined primarily by the loop with the 100-kHz reference frequency; the settling time can be estimated to be approximately 25 μs.

We have drawn these multiloop synthesizer block diagrams without further justification. By "further justification" I mean we have not justified the combination of frequencies or what other considerations were taken into account. This is done in Chapter 5, where we deal with multiloop synthesizer system analysis and the use of microprocessors.

3-2 MULTIPLE SAMPLER LOOPS

In Chapter 2 we discussed the question of noise in great detail. We concluded that the output of the VCO also contains noise, and it is very clear that it is highly desirable to minimize this noise contribution.

In Chapter 1 we have seen the effect of the loop filter and that higher-order loop filters have better reference suppression.

The tri-state phase/frequency comparator allows us first to obtain frequency and then phase lock, and if it were an ideal circuit, it would provide total suppression of the reference. We go into the details of this circuit in Chapter 4, but it should already be clear that the ideal tri-state phase/frequency comparator, because of its complementary output stage under locked condition, should have no reference output.

It is obvious that such an ideal circuit does not exist. A better approximation is the sample/hold comparator. However, this circuit has a limited pull-in range, as it is a pure phase and not a phase/frequency comparator. The following shows a fairly simple circuit arrangement in which the use of several samplers will increase the pull-in range over the conventional circuit while maintaining low noise and high reference suppression. Figure 3-6 shows the block diagram of a multisampler loop. As can be seen, three samplers are used in a row. The first sampler is operated at 100 kHz, the second sampler at 10 kHz, and the final sampler at 100 Hz. This leads to a one-loop synthesizer arrangement with 100-Hz step size, where the capture range is largely extended.

Previously, such a circuit would have been built by using a frequency detector first. This frequency detector would coarse steer the VCO to a window in which phase lock is possible, and then the loop gain and all other parameters would have to be optimized for smooth phase lock and undisturbed VCO frequency when leaving the desired window.

Conventionally, this coarse tuning could have also been accomplished by tying digital-to-analog converters to the input of the frequency dividers to generate a dc voltage for coarse steering. The drawback here is the large amount of circuitry involved, the possible noise contribution of the coarse steering circuit, and the

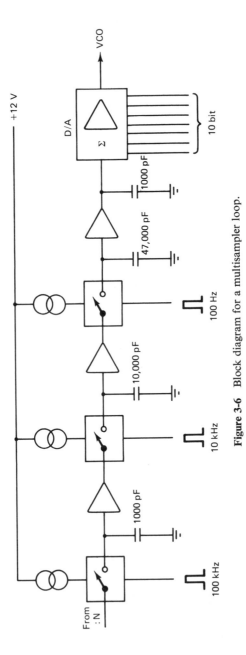

Figure 3-6 Block diagram for a multisampler loop.

temperature-compensating requirement for the voltage-controlled oscillator because over the entire operating temperature, the VCO has to track a predetermined voltage/ frequency curve. Cascading several sample/hold comparators has the advantage that the time constants or the low-pass filters for subsequent sections can be set to a lower frequency, and therefore the acquisition time for each portion can be optimized. To help acquisition further, a digital-to-analog converter can be used to superimpose a dc voltage on the dc output of the sample/hold comparator.

The advantage of this circuit again is that filtering can be applied at the output of the sample/hold comparator, whereby the voltage generated by the D/A converter is applied in a very smooth form, avoiding degradation of noise performance and, specifically, reference frequency suppression. This circuit has been used in the AEG Telefunken E1500 and E1700 shortwave receiver family with great success. The cost/performance ratio of such a loop is extremely attractive. The traditional difficulty of microphonic effects is minimized because of the update of the coarse loop, since the first two sample/hold comparators would detect a major offset of phase or frequency, consequently controlling at a higher speed than the final 100-Hz time constant would permit.

In this configuration, the step size is still limited by the reference frequency, and the following method of applying a sequential phase detector allows increase of resolution. In our example, this will be by a factor of 10. The final system described in this chapter, called the fractional divison N synthesizer, will have, theoretically, infinite resolution in a single-loop frequency synthesizer that uses a clever combination of analog and digital circuitry.

3-3 LOOPS WITH SEQUENTIAL PHASE SHIFTERS

From the discussion of frequency counters and frequency dividers, we remember that the resolution or lowest digit is determined by the first frequency divider.

If we divide at the input by the amount of P, the output frequency of the prescaler will be F_o/P. Rather than use digital division, we can use all-pass filters producing voltages with 90° mutual phase difference. Let us take a look at Figure 3-7, showing a sequential phase shifter. The two all-pass filters are driving two isolation amplifiers which are used for decoupling. The transformers at the output produce phases 180° and 270°. Ten phase angles with $N \times 36°$ are now produced in a summation network, and one phasing step at a time is selected by one of the diodes. Through sequenced continuous switching of these diodes, a frequency displacement is obtained, depending on the timing of the sequencer. It is apparent that 36° in 10 ms or 100 Hz gives 10-Hz displacement, $2 \times 36°$ gives 20 Hz, and up to $9 \times 36°$ in 10 ms gives 90 Hz. This continuous switching is controlled by feeding the output of the last frequency dividers in the programmable divider of the frequency synthesizer to a divide-by-10 ripple counter and using the BCD outputs to drive a BCD/decimal decoder that in turn provides the switching currents for the diodes. This is a very unique and fairly inexpensive way to increase the resolution, in this particular case, by 10. Depending on

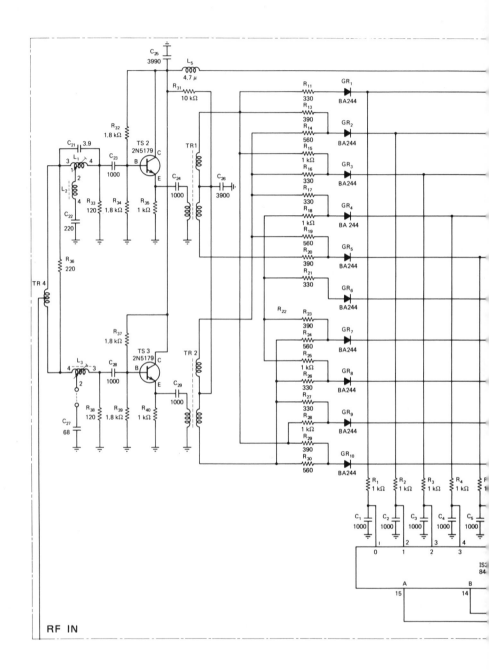

RF IN

120

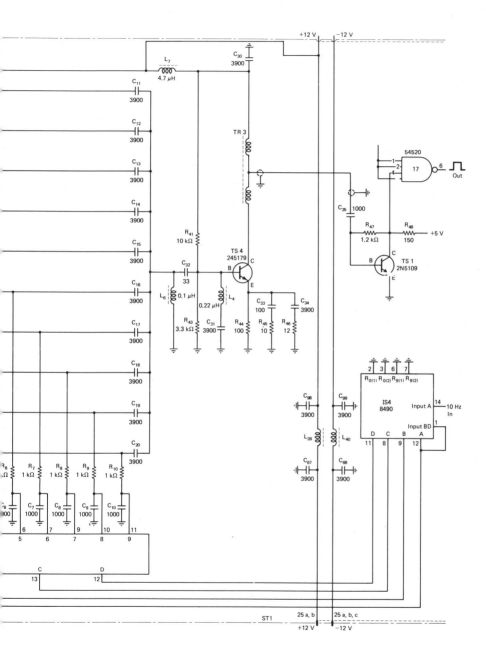

Figure 3-7 Schematic of a sequential phase shifter.

the quality and accuracy of the components used, it is possible to increase the frequency resolution another 10 times. If components of 1% accuracy would be used and two digits of increased resolution would be achieved, the final error would be equal to the last digit. In most applications for shortwave receivers or frequency synthesizers where the built-in frequency standard is of medium quality, such a circuit is permissible. Let us look at the resulting accuracy.

Let us assume that a shortwave receiver has a first IF of 60 MHz and the local oscillator, to convert an input frequency range from 10 kHz to 30 MHz up to 60 MHz. Then one has to cover a frequency range from roughly 60 to 90 MHz. If we use a particular frequency standard, a worst case would occur when the input frequency from the antenna would be 30 MHz and the LO frequency, 90 MHz. If the frequency standard accuracy is 1×10^7, this would mean that the frequency error would be 1 Hz in 10 MHz or 9 Hz in 90 MHz. If such a frequency resolution extension scheme as just described would have been used, the resolution is still 10 times better than the inherent accuracy. A time base of 1×10^8 is required for a 1-Hz frequency error, which then would be equal to the error with 1% components used in the sequential phase shifter.

In the case where the 10-Hz digit is set to zero, this circuit can be disabled, and therefore a suitable decoding should be included. This applies also if a 10-times-higher frequency extension is used. The advantage of doing this is that the absolute accuracy in 100-Hz steps is always equal to the built-in reference, as in most cases it is permissible to trade higher frequency resolution for last-digit accuracy.

3-4 LOOPS WITH DELAY LINE AS PHASE COMPARATORS

The circuit we have just studied, if absolutely ideal components without drift and tolerances were available, would theoretically enable us to come up with infinite resolution. However, the introduction of this circuit will introduce some switching noise, probably spikes, and the low-pass filter action of the phase/frequency comparator will cure part of it. However, it is a discontinuous arrangement, and we will now take a look at a system that allows continuous adjustment based on a principle that we have used earlier.

When measuring the phase noise of a frequency synthesizer (Figure 2-19), for all practical purposes we can assume that the delay time τ_d is a constant over time and change of environment, which, of course, is an assumption. We can, by making the phase shifter variable, measure a certain offset from the carrier.

The voltage that is obtained from the mixer was connected to the oscilloscope or the wave analyzer. By integrating this voltage and feeding it through an amplifier back to the VCO, we can close the loop. This arrangement is a noise feedback system. Figure 3-8 shows a circuit in which a PAL delay line and a variable phase shifter are used to stabilize an oscillator if the proper bandwidth and phase offset is chosen. According to Eqs. (2-50) to (2-52), the close-in noise sideband performance of the oscillator can be drastically improved. This circuit has actually been used in some

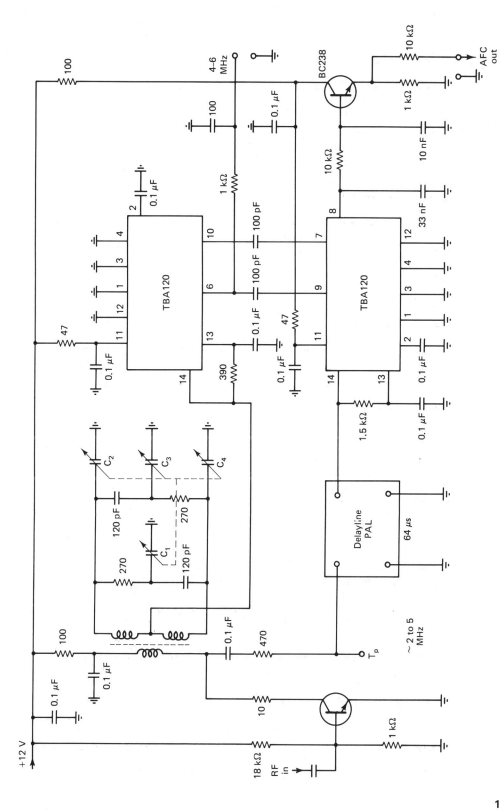

Figure 3-8 Schematic of a delay-line-stabilized oscillator system.

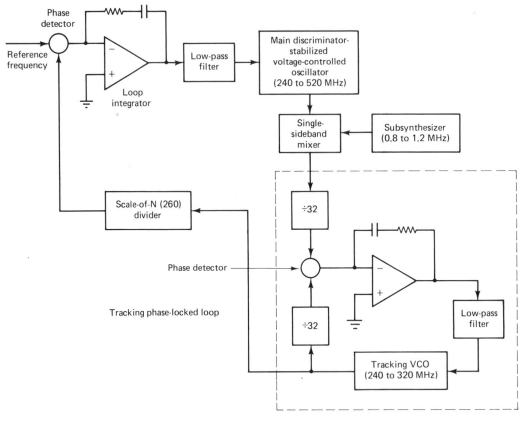

Figure 3-9 Block diagram of the Model 6070A delay-line-stabilized Fluke synthesizer. (Courtesy of *Electronics*.)

German ham equipment and in the Fluke synthesized signal generator Model 6070A and 6071A. In the case of Fluke, a SAW delay line is used, and as shown in Figure 3-9, by using a subsynthesizer system, a 240- to 520-MHz oscillator is improved by this technique, and the subsynthesizer from 0.8 to 1.2 MHz provides increased resolution down to 1 Hz. Further details on this new Fluke synthesizer can be found in Ref. 8.

The ultimate resolution of this system is determined by the subsynthesizer, which, as discussed earlier, might be a direct digital synthesizer.

The special loops we have seen so far showed an increase in resolution with the trade-off of losing accuracy.

The fractional division N synthesizer offers, theoretically, unlimited resolution and extremely fast settling time. We will learn more about this in the next section.

3-5 FRACTIONAL DIVISION N SYNTHESIZERS

Conventional single-loop synthesizers use frequency dividers where the division ratio N is an integer value between 1 and several hundred thousand, and the step size is equal to the reference frequency. Because of the loop filter requirements, the decrease of reference frequency automatically means an increase of settling time. It would be unrealistic to assume that a synthesizer with lower than 100-Hz reference can be built, because the large division ratio in the loop would reduce the loop gain so much that tracking would be very poor, and the settling time would be several seconds.

If it were possible to build a frequency synthesizer with a 100-kHz reference and fine resolution, this would be ideal because the VCO noise from 2 or 3 kHz off the carrier could determine the noise sideband, while the phase noise of frequencies from basically no offset from the carrier to 3 kHz off the carrier would be determined by the loop gain, the division ratio, and the reference. Because of the higher reference frequency, the division ratio would be kept smaller. Traditionally, this conflicting requirement resulted in multiloop synthesizers.

An alternative would be for N to take on fractional values. The output frequency could then be changed in fractional increments of the reference frequency. Although a digital divider cannot provide a fractional division ratio, ways can be found to accomplish the same task effectively. The most frequently used method is to divide the output frequency by $N + 1$ every M cycles and to divide by N the rest of the time. The effective division ratio is then $N + 1/M$, and the average output frequency is given by

$$f_o = \left(N + \frac{1}{M}\right) f_r \tag{3-13}$$

This expression shows that f_o can be varied in fractional increments of the reference frequency by varying M. The technique is equivalent to constructing a fractional divider, but the fractional part of the division is actually implemented using a phase accumulator. The phase accumulator approach is illustrated by the following example.

Example 3

Consider the problem of generating 455 kHz using a fractional N loop with a 100-kHz reference frequency. The integral part of the division $N = 4$ and the fractional part $1/M = 0.55$ or $M = 1.8$ (M is not an integer); the VCO output is to be divided by 5 ($N + 1$) every 1.8 cycles, or 55 times every 100 cycles. This can be easily implemented by adding the number 0.55 to the contents of an accumulator every cycle. Each time the accumulator overflows (the contents exceed 1) the divider divides by 5 rather than 4. Only the fractional value of the addition is retained in the phase accumulator.

Arbitrarily fine frequency resolution can be obtained by increasing the length of the phase accumulator. For example, with a 100-kHz reference a resolution of $10^5/10^5 = 1$ Hz can be obtained using a five-digit BCD accumulator.

This new method* which we will analyze now in greater detail is currently used in a number of instruments, such as Hewlett-Packard generators and spectrum analyzers, where it is called fractional N synthesizer, whereas the earlier version, called the digiphase system, is used in the Dana series 7000 synthesizers. A modifica-

*Part of this description is based on the Hewlett-Packard 3335A signal generator and reproduced with Hewlett-Packard's permission.

tion of the digiphase system that reduces the low-frequency content of the phase detector output is used in the Racal receiver RA6790. Racal has applied for a patent for this method.

We will now discuss the advantages and drawbacks of this system. At first it may appear that the fractional N loop has unlimited advantages. However, in reality, it is a compromise between resolution, spurious response, and lockup time. Reference 2 may help to clarify the applications further. In reality, the expression fractional N is not quite correct. The loop does not supply a fractional division ratio but rather changes the division ratio periodically over a certain period by the help of an adder driven by the fraction register.

The fractional N phase-locked loop (*NF loop*) is a modified divide-by-N loop. Its unique feature is that it can operate at fractional multiples of the reference signal instead of steps. In the NF loop, N refers to the integer part and F to the fractional part of the divide-by-N number. This number multiplied by the reference signal represents the loop frequency. The integer part is that of a divide-by-N loop. The fractional part represents the offset frequency of the VCO with respect to the integer component of frequency.

The description of the NF loop is divided into two parts. The first is a general discussion of the NF loop concept using example frequencies. The second describes the NF loop using simplified block diagrams.

Consider the divide-by-N loop phase detector output under open-loop condition. Assume a reference frequency of 100 kHz, $N = 10$, and VCO frequency of 1.01 MHz ($N = 1.0$ MHz; $F = 0.01$ MHz). The VCO operates at a fractional multiple (10.1) of the reference signal (10.1 × 0.1 MHz = 1.01 MHz). This configuration is shown in the block diagram of Figure 3-10. The phase detector compares the low-to-high transitions of the reference and divide-by-N signals. Since the VCO is not operating

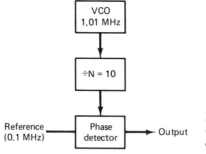

Figure 3-10 Basic diagram of an open-loop divide-by-N loop. (Courtesy of Hewlett-Packard Company.)

at N times the reference but with a fractional component ($F = 0.01$ MHz), the signal from the divide-by-N block advances on the reference signal. Each time the divide-by-N signal makes a low-to-high transition, the phase detector compares it with the reference and generates an output proportional to the period between the two low-to-high transitions. In the phase-locked condition of a divide-by-N loop, this period remains constant. In the open-loop example, where the VCO contains a fractional component, the period between low-to-high transitions continuously increases, resulting in an increasing phase detector output voltage.

When analyzing the open-loop divide-by-N loop, it is of interest to view the operation in terms of reference periods. A reference period is defined as the time required for the reference signal to complete one cycle. Each reference period the reference signal goes through one cycle while the VCO, which is operating 10.1 times as fast, goes through 10.1 cycles. We can say the VCO has advanced one-tenth of a cycle of phase on the integer part $N \times f_{ref}$ (f_{ref} = reference frequency) in one reference period. In two reference periods, the VCO has gone 20.2 cycles or advanced two-tenths of a cycle of phase on $N \times f_{ref}$. When the VCO operates with a fractional offset (F), it continually advances phase on $N \times f_{ref}$ each reference period. From the example of Figure 3-10, in 10 reference periods, the VCO signal will have gone 101 cycles, or advanced one cycle of phase (360°) with respect to $N \times f_{ref}$. Table 3-1 illustrates the phase relationship of $N \times f_{ref}$ and NF. While the VCO signal advances phase on $N \times f_{ref}$, the divide-by-N VCO signal applied to the phase detector advances phase on the reference frequency.

TABLE 3-1 PHASE RELATIONSHIP OF $N \times f_{ref}$ AND NF

Number of ref. periods ($f_{ref} = 100\,kHz = 0.1\,MHz$)	Number of completed cycles of:		Phase advancement of NF on $N \times f_{ref}$
	$N \times f_{ref} = 1\,MHz$ ($N = 10$)	NF $= 1.01\,MHz$	
1	10	10.1	0.1 cycle of phase
2	20	20.2	0.2 cycle of phase
3	30	30.3	0.3 cycle of phase
4	40	40.4	0.4 cycle of phase
.	.	.	.
.	.	.	.
.	.	.	.
9	90	90.9	0.9 cycle of phase
10	100	101.0	1 full cycle of phase (360°)

In a divide-by-N loop, the VCO is phase locked to a reference signal, and operates at a multiple N of the reference frequency ($N \times f_{ref}$). In an NF loop, the VCO operates at an integer-plus-fractional multiple of the reference frequency ($N \times f_{ref} + F = NF$). As previously illustrated in Figure 3-10, assume again that the VCO operates at 1.01 MHz, the reference is 0.1 MHz, and N equals 10. Each time the reference signal goes through one cycle, the VCO goes through 10.1 cycles. After 10 reference cycles (10 reference periods) the VCO has gone 101 cycles. The VCO has advanced one full cycle of phase (360°) on $N \times f_{ref}$. If a VCO cycle is removed from the VCO pulse train applied to the divide-by-N block at the point a full VCO cycle has advanced, the phase advancement on the average is canceled and the average frequency applied to the divide-by-N block is $N \times f_{ref}$ or, in this example, 1 MHz.

Because of the continual removal of a VCO cycle (removal of one cycle of phase) at each point the VCO advances one cycle on $N \times f_{\text{ref}}$, the phase detector output becomes a sawtooth waveform (see Figure 3-11). The waveform increases linearly due to the advancing phase of the VCO until the VCO has advanced one cycle of VCO phase (360°). At this point a cycle is removed from the VCO pulse train, canceling the previous advancement of a cycle of phase. The phase detector responds to this sudden one-cycle (360°) phase loss by returning to its initial output. The sequence is repetitive, generating the sawtooth waveform. The maximum amplitude reached represents one cycle of VCO phase. As the VCO frequency is increased, the time interval for the VCO to go through one cycle of phase is less. Therefore, the maximum phase detector amplitude is decreased. The phase detector maximum amplitude is inversely proportional to the VCO frequency.

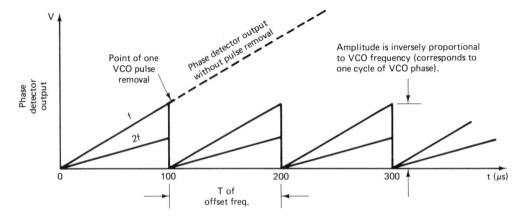

Figure 3-11   Phase detector sawtooth output. (Courtesy of Hewlett-Packard Company.)

The necessity to remove one VCO cycle from the VCO output each time the output advances one cycle of phase on $N \times f_{\text{ref}}$ requires that we use a pulse remover block in the divide-by-N loop block diagram (see Figure 3-12). If a VCO pulse is removed each time the VCO advances one cycle of phase, the average frequency applied to the divide-by-N block is $N \times f_{\text{ref}}$ and the average frequency applied to the phase detector is f_{ref}. The relationship of the phase detector sawtooth output and the pulse trains shown in Figure 3-12 is illustrated in Figure 3-13. A method of determining when the VCO has advanced one cycle of phase is required. Such information can then be used to trigger the pulse remover block and a VCO cycle removed at the appropriate time.

The fractional part of the VCO frequency determines the time required for the VCO to advance one cycle of phase on $N \times f_{\text{ref}}$. The time required is the period of the fractional offset frequency and corresponds to a certain number of reference periods. If the fractional part of the VCO is stored in a register added to a second register each reference period, the second register will contain a running total which represents the VCO phase advancement at any point in time. For this reason the

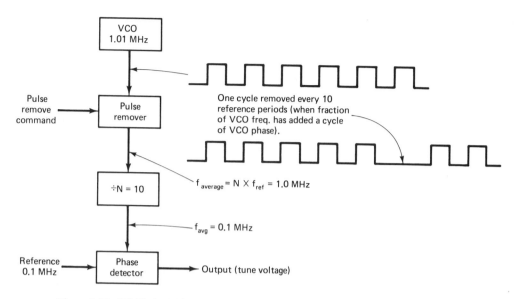

Figure 3-12   Divide-by-*N* loop with pulse remover block. (Courtesy of Hewlett-Packard Company.)

second register is called a *phase register* and the entire configuration, an *accumulator* (see Figure 3-14). The phase register will reach unity after the same reference period during which the VCO has advanced one full cycle of phase. (Recall the preceding example; in one reference period the VCO has gone 10.1 cycles, in two reference periods, the VCO has gone 20.2 cycles, and so on. The summing register will contain 0.1 after one reference period, 0.2 after the second, and so on). When unity is reached, the phase register overflows and transmits an overflow signal. This signal occurs at

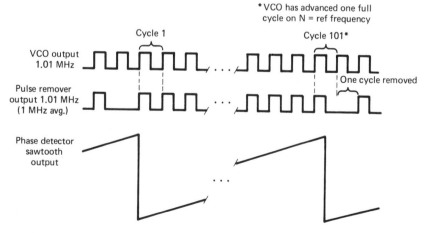

Figure 3-13   Phase detector sawtooth output with respect to pulse remover output. (Courtesy of Hewlett-Packard Company.)

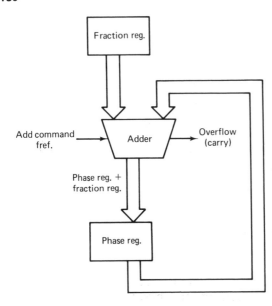

Figure 3-14 Accumulator. (Courtesy of Hewlett-Packard Company.)

the time the VCO has advanced one cycle of phase on $N \times f_{ref}$ and is applied to the pulse remover block as a pulse remove signal.

If the VCO operates with an offset frequency not evenly divisible into 1 (such as 0.03), a fractional overflow can result when the phase register reaches unity. For example, if the VCO operates at 1.03 MHz instead of 1.01 MHz, after one reference period it has gone 10.3 cycles, 20.6 after two, 30.9 after three, and 41.2 after the fourth reference period. Prior to the fourth reference period, the phase register has accumulated 0.9. The fourth reference period 0.3 is added to the 0.9 from the phase register and results in 1.2. This causes an overflow as the pulse remove signal and the fractional overflow of 0.2 is loaded into the phase register and the next sequence phase begins to accumulate from 0.2 instead of zero.

Up to this point, the discussion has developed the NF loop to include the pulse remove command section. Figure 3-15 is a block diagram of the NF loop with the pulse remove command section. This structure provides a means of automatically removing a VCO cycle whenever the VCO advances one full cycle of phase on the frequency $N \times f_{ref}$.

The open-loop phase detector output of Figure 3-15 is a sawtooth waveform superimposed on a dc voltage. Only the dc voltage of this output is of interest. A VCO requires a dc tune voltage to maintain a stable output signal. A sawtooth ac signal superimposed on the dc VCO tune voltage would cause VCO frequency modulation.

The ac component must be canceled or removed, leaving the dc component to tune the VCO to the proper frequency.

We know that the VCO output advances a fraction of a cycle of phase on $N \times f_{ref}$ each reference period. The fraction of a cycle of phase that the VCO is advanced at any one reference period is represented by the fractional sum in the phase register. (Recall that the phase register is incremented by the fractional VCO

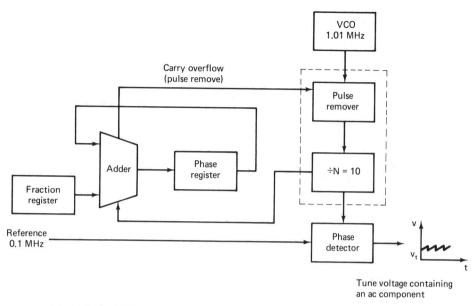

Figure 3-15 NF loop with pulse remove command section. (Courtesy of Hewlett-Packard Company.)

output each reference period.) For the example of Figure 3-15, the contents of the phase register when viewed with respect to time is a staircase resetting to zero once unity is reached (see Figure 3-16). The staircase approximates a sawtooth waveform (see dashed lines). The "front edge" of each step represents the phase detector output for that reference period. (Recall that the phase detector does not generate a ramp but samples the VCO with respect to the reference each reference period.)

If the contents of the summing register are applied to a digital-to-analog (D/A) converter, the D/A converter output will follow the steps of the summing register and approximate a sawtooth output. Inverting the D/A converter output and summing it with the phase detector output essentially cancels the ac component (sawtooth) of the phase detector output. This leaves the dc component required as a VCO control signal.

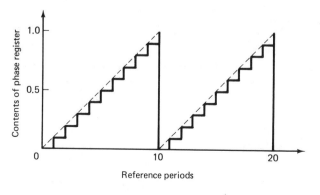

Figure 3-16 Phase register contents. (Courtesy of Hewlett-Packard Company.)

Two requirements exist for the waveform generated by the D/A converter to approximate the phase detector sawtooth output.

1. It must have a variable amplitude.
2. It must have a variable period.

The amplitude is inversely proportional to the frequency of the VCO and changes whenever the VCO frequency is changed. To demonstrate the amplitude dependency on the VCO frequency, refer to Figure 3-17.

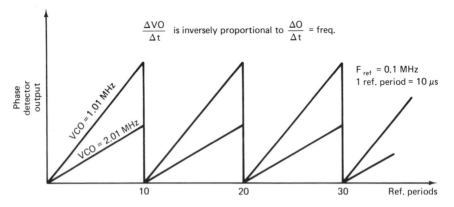

Figure 3-17 Phase detector output for two VCO frequencies with the same offset. (Courtesy of Hewlett-Packard Company.)

In the figure a reference of 0.1 MHz is used (horizontal axis plotted in reference periods) and plots of the phase detector output for VCO frequencies of 1.01 MHz and 2.01 MHz are shown. Note that each VCO frequency example contains a 0.01-MHz offset or fractional frequency. In terms of reference periods (10 μs), the period of the 0.01-MHz offset is 10 reference periods. At this point the offset frequency has completed one cycle and added a cycle of phase to the VCO signal. Since the period of 2 MHz is half the interval of 1 MHz, the phase detector output representing one cycle of phase at 2 MHz is half the amplitude of the output, representing one cycle of 1 MHz phase. When the VCO cycle is removed, a 360° phase loss is detected by the phase detector and it responds by returning to its initial output, causing the high-to-low transition of the sawtooth. If the offset or fractional part of the VCO frequency is changed, the period of the sawtooth changes for these two periods are the same. The sawtooth generated by the D/A converter must change amplitude and period as the phase detector output changes and must be superimposed on zero volts dc. It can then be inverted and summed with the phase detector output to remove the sawtooth from the tune voltage applied to the VCO.

A general block diagram of an NF loop is shown in Figure 3-18. The basic elements of a divide-by-N loop are present: the VCO, divide-by-N counter, phase detector, and low-pass filter. In addition to these, a fraction register, adder, and

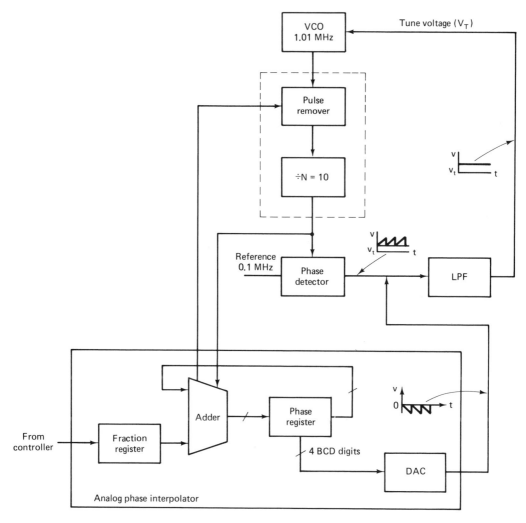

Figure 3-18   General block diagram of a NF loop. (Courtesy of Hewlett-Packard Company.)

phase register provide the "bookkeeping system" recording the phase advancement from reference period to reference period. This system is known as a *phase interpolator*, and in conjunction with a digital-to-analog converter the system is referred to as an *analog phase interpolator* (API). During each reference period it generates an analog voltage equal and opposite in polarity to the phase advancement voltage generated by the phase detector. The voltage applied to the LPF is then the net VCO tune voltage. Since the "bookkeeping system" must update each reference period (the phase detector output changes each reference period after the VCO/N and reference signal comparison), the system receives its add command (update command) at a VCO/N rate.

The NF loop is a modified divide-by-*N* loop. It contains all the basic elements of the divide-by-*N* loop with the addition to several other sections. Figure 3-19 illustrates

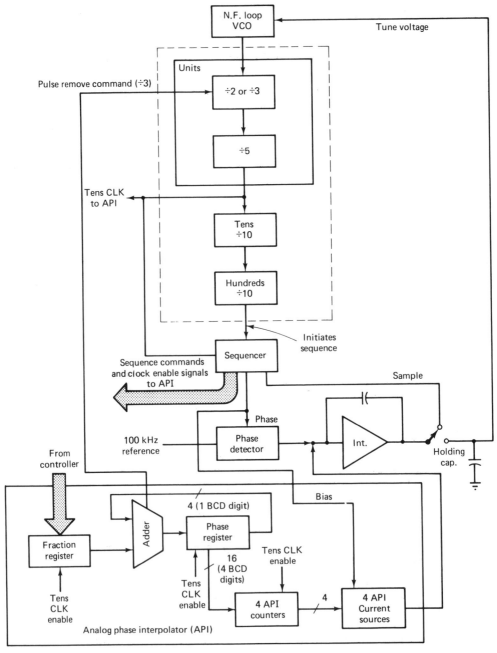

Figure 3-19 Basic block diagram of a NF loop. (Courtesy of Hewlett-Packard Company.)

the additions made to the "loop." These additions are a sequencer, an N counter that can be changed to an $(N + 1)$ counter, and an integrator and sample/hold which are used to develop the tune voltage. Compare this diagram to Figure 3-18.

The NF loop operates according to an established sequence of events which occur once each reference period. The sequence is initiated at a rate equal to the VCO/N signal. This is accomplished by initiating each sequence of events with the N counter output. The sequencer generates a number of enable and command signals which are summarized here.

1. *API Tens Clock Enable Signals.* These signals enable the Tens Clock to update the data in the API registers (bookkeeping system).

2. *API Counter Tens Clock Enable.* This signal enables the Tens Clock to clock the four API counters, which are preset each reference period by the four most significant digits of the phase register, which keeps a running total of the phase advancement.

3. *Bias Command.* This signal turns on the four API current sources to establish a current reference point.

4. *Phase Command.* This signal is the Bias command reclocked to the Tens Clock and again reclocked to the NF loop VCO. It is compared with the reference each reference period by the phase detector.

5. *Sample Command.* This signal initiates the sampling of the integrator output each reference period. Once the integrator has settled following the summation of the phase detector and API signals, the integrator voltage is transferred to the holding capacitor.

The rate of events is determined by the Tens Clock, which is the NF loop VCO divided by 10. The sequence of events is initiated once each reference period, but once initiated, the events occur at a rate determined by the VCO frequency.

Figure 3-20 illustrates the loop by a heavy line and separates between digital and analog halves of the loop. The basic structure is shown in Figure 3-21. The major sections of the loop structure are input, decode and data registers, divide by N with pulse remove, sequencer, phase detector, API, integrator, sample-and-hold, and VCO.

The input decode section interfaces the loop with the data transmitted by the controller. These data include the loop frequency and instructions that set up the operating modes of the data registers in the phase interpolator. Data register operation is controlled by a steering section.

The data registers comprise the bookkeeping scheme of the phase interpolator. There are three data registers:

1. f_1 frequency register
2. f_2 frequency register
3. Phase register

Only one of the frequency registers is active at a time. The frequency register

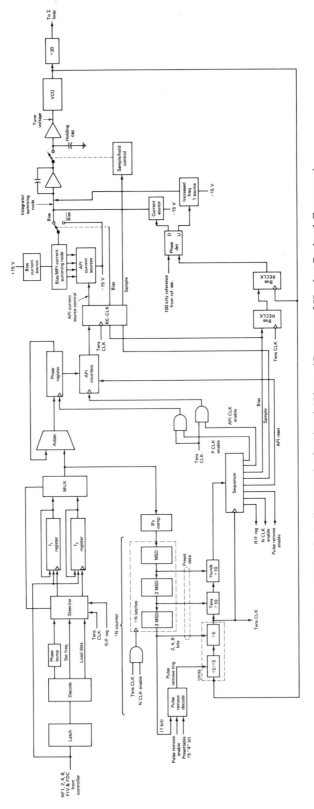

Figure 3-20 Block diagram of a fractional *N* loop. (Courtesy of Hewlett-Packard Company.)

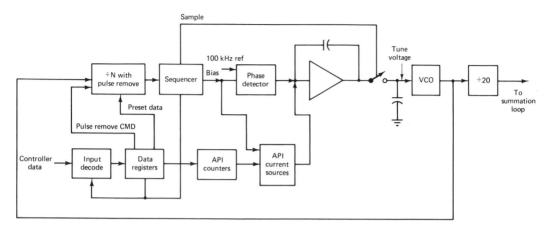

Figure 3-21 Basic structure of a NF loop. (Courtesy of Hewlett-Packard Company.)

will always contain the current frequency of operation and these data will be circulated (output connected to input and the data shifted until starting state is reached) once each reference period. The other frequency register contains the previous frequency of operation and rests idle but enabled to accept new data when a new output is programmed.

The data steering logic controls the operating modes of the f_1 and f_2 frequency registers. The Load Data command enables the idle frequency register to be clocked by the controller line LDC (Load Data Clock) to enter a new frequency. During this time the operation of the loop is not interrupted because the circulating frequency register continues operation while data are being loaded. Once the data are entered, the Set Freq command interchanges the functions of the f_1 and f_2 registers and the new data now circulate to operate the loop at the new frequency.

Frequency data in the f_1 or f_2 register consist of 16 BCD digits which are loaded least significant digit first. The 12 least significant digits represent the fractional portion of the frequency, and the next three digits contain the integer or N portion of the frequency. This accounts for 15 of the 16 digits in the f_1 or f_2 register. The sixteenth digit, which is the last digit loaded, is not required and therefore is always loaded as a zero. During circulation of the data in the f_1 or f_2 register, this digit is truncated and does not affect the operation of the loop.

During each reference period the divide-by-N counter initiates a sequence of events by triggering the sequencer. Part of the sequence is the enabling of the f_1 or f_2 register clock, the phase register clock, and the N register clock. The phase register is clocked for the first 12 digits circulated by the f_1 or f_2 register, the N register for the next three. When the sixteenth digit is circulated by the f_1 or f_2 register, neither phase register nor N register is clocked; therefore, this digit has no effect on the loop operation. As a result of the sequence of clocking the registers and N register, the phase register quantity has been increased by the fractional component of the f_1 or f_2 register. The N register contains the three N number digits used to preset the divide-by-N counter.

The phase register serves two purposes:

1. Records the total phase advancement of the VCO with respect to each reference period
2. Causes the adder to overflow in the reference period during which the VCO has advanced a full cycle of phase

The record of total phase advancement is used each reference period to drive the API section. The four most significant digits of the 12 digits in the phase register are used to preset four API counters. When these counters are clocked by the API clock, they generate an output pulse inversely proportional to the preset number and drive the API section, which develops a signal that counteracts the changing phase detector signal, resulting in an unchanging tune voltage. The overflow of the adder indicates the reference period in which the NF loop VCO has advanced a full cycle of VCO phase. The overflow decode triggers the units counter during the pulse remove enable interval of the loop sequence to divide by three for one output pulse of the first stage. Since this stage has been providing an output for every two input pulses (divide by 2), it effectively has removed a VCO cycle by dividing by three for one output pulse. The cycle of phase the NF loop VCO has advanced has been removed and the phase relationship of the NF loop VCO and N times the reference is reset.

The API section consists of two parts:

1. The API counters
2. The API current sources

All API current sources are turned on by the Bias command each reference period. The four most significant digits of the phase register preset the API counters, which control when each of the four API current sources turn off. The smaller the phase register digits, the longer the API current sources are on.

The phase detector compares the sequencer output "Bias" with a 100-kHz reference signal. The Bias signal is first reclocked to Tens Clock (VCO/10) and then to the NF loop VCO signal itself. If the NF loop VCO is operating with a fractional component, the reclocked Bias signal applied to the phase detector gains phase each reference period with respect to the reference signal. The output applied to the integrator is an increasing voltage. The purpose of the API section is to negate the effects of the increase in the phase detector output.

The method used to generate the NF loop VCO tune voltage is similar to that used in the divide-by-N loop. Currents are integrated and the integrated voltage is transferred to a holding capacitor.

A block diagram of the currents integrated by the NF loop in a phase-locked condition is shown in Figure 3-22. Figure 3-23 illustrates the integrator waveform, showing the contributions of the different currents. A constant-current source, I (Bias), supplies current at all times to the Bias/API summing node. The Bias command from the sequencer goes high each reference period to connect this node to the

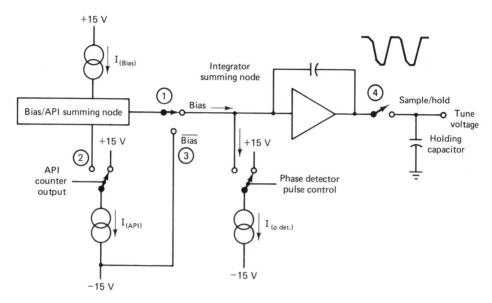

Figure 3-22 NF loop integrated currents. (Courtesy of Hewlett-Packard Company.)

integrator summing node. Following the Bias command, the phase register data causes the API current source to draw current from the Bias/API summing node and therefore keeps this current from being integrated. The amount of API current is determined by the magnitude of the phase register number. Once the Bias event has occurred and the Bias/API summing node is disconnected from the integrator summing node, the phase detector pulse occurs and draws current out of the integrator summing node. When the loop is phase locked, the current entering the integrator node from the Bias/API current sources is equal to the current drawn out by the phase detector current source and the integrated voltage remains constant. After integrating the two currents, the voltage is transferred to a holding capacitor and becomes the tune voltage.

Sequence of events:

1. Bias/API summing node is connected to the integrator and Bias current integrated.
2. API current source is connected to Bias/API summing node, decreasing the amount of Bias current integrated.
3. Bias/API summing node is disconnected and phase detector is connected to integrator. Phase detector current is integrated.
4. After the phase detector current has been integrated and the voltage settled, the voltage is transferred to a holding capacitor. This voltage is the NF loop VCO tune voltage.

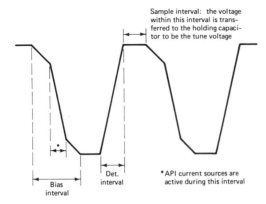

Sample interval: the voltage within this interval is transferred to the holding capacitor to be the tune voltage

Bias interval

Det. interval

*API current sources are active during this interval

Figure 3-23 NF loop integrated currents. (Courtesy of Hewlett-Packard Company.)

Note. When phase locked, the Bias/API current is equal to the phase detector current. The API current tracks the increasing phase detector current, canceling the fractional component of VCO phase.

Refer again to Figure 3-20. Assume that the loop operates without a fractional component (data in the phase register remain constant). The loop can be viewed as just a divide-by-N loop with an elaborate method of developing the tune voltage. The data in the phase register are constant; therefore, the API current sources are sinking the same amount of current from the Bias/API summing node each reference period. Since the current entering the integrator from the Bias/API summing node is always a constant value, the phase detector changes the tune voltage just as it does in the divide-by-N loop. A change in the phase relationship causes the phase detector pulse to change in duration, which changes the amount of current the phase detector source draws from the integrator. The result is a change in the integrated voltage after this reference period, and therefore the tune voltage has been changed. The direction of change is such that the NF loop VCO is pulled back into a phase-locked condition.

The Sample command from the sequencer transfers the integrated voltage to the holding capacitor at the appropriate period of the integrator output. This period occurs after the Bias/API summing interval and the phase detector interval have occurred and the integrator output has returned to an unchanging value. This value is the tune voltage.

The increase-frequency current source is shown on the simplified block diagram of Figure 3-20. This current source is also connected to the integrator summing node and is responsible for rapidly changing the tune voltage if a large increase in frequency is programmed; the phase detector connects this current source to the integrator in place of the phase detector current source. Instead of sinking current from the integrator, the current source drives current into the integrating node to add to the current already supplied by the Bias/API interval. This causes the tune voltage to change the NF loop VCO frequency rapidly. Once the newly programmed frequency has been reached, the phase detector again begins operation using the phase detector current source.

The NF loop VCO signal is divided by 20 to aid spur attenuation and reduce phase noise. The division by 20 results in an improvement of 26 dB in the noise sideband and phase noise.

   While this system allows extremely high resolution, the synthesizer, so to speak, consists of two loops, one being a 100-kHz loop with the lock-up time probably 8 to 20 cycles of reference or 800 μs to 2 ms, depending on the loop filter.

   The fractional portion of the loop theoretically would lock up within one cycle of reference or 10 μs. However, because of active low-pass filters and speed requirements for the D/A converter, the actual lock-up time is somewhat of a compromise between these values and should be in the vicinity of 1 to 2 ms and, therefore, about the same as the 100-kHz loop.

   Modern integrated circuits having frequency synthesizers on one chip can be used to build such systems.

   The British subsidiary of Philips, Mullard, has recently introduced the HEF4750 and HEF4751 integrated circuits. A one-digit extension based on the fractional N is used, and since this concerns mostly the dividers, more information on this circuit is given in Chapter 4.

   The noise sideband performance of this synthesizer depends highly on the accuracy of the D/A converter and its ability to remove the reference noise sideband. Egan [7] discusses a method used in the Racal receiver for which Racal has applied for a patent, and this phase detector output has a zero-running average area. This is effective in reducing the low frequencies produced when the output is near a multiple of the reference and when many corrections are made during each period of the phase detector output.

REFERENCES

1. G. C. Gillette, "Digiphase Principle," *Frequency Technology*, August 1969.
2. Jerzy Gorski-Popiel, *Frequency Synthesis: Techniques and Applications*, IEEE Press, New York, 1975.
3. Hewlett-Packard, "Synthesizer/Level Generator 3335A," Instruction Manual, pp. 816–836.
4. Racal, "RA6790 Receiver," Instruction/Repair Manual, 1978.
5. Vadim Manassewitsch, *Frequency Synthesis*, Wiley, New York, 1976; 2nd ed., 1980.
6. U. L. Rohde, "Modern Design of Frequency Synthesizers," *Ham Radio*, July 1976.
7. William F. Egan, *Frequency Synthesis by Phase Lock*, Wiley, New York, 1981.
8. F. Telewski, K. Craft, E. Drucker, and J. Martins, "Delay Lines Give RF Generator Spectral Purity, Programmability," *Electronics*, August 28, 1980, pp. 133–142.
9. U. L. Rohde, "Low-Noise Frequency Synthesizers Using Fractional N Phase Locked Loops," *Proceedings of Modern Solid-State Devices, Techniques, and Applications for High-Performance RF Communications Equipment*, 1981 Southcon Professional Program, Georgia World Congress Center, January 13–15, 1981, pp. 15/1/1–15/1/10.
10. J. Tierney, C. M. Rader, and B. Gold, "A Digital Frequency Synthesizer," *IEEE Transactions on Audio and Electroacoustics*, Vol. AU-19, No. 1 (March 1971), pp. 48–57.
11. AEG Telefunken Instruction and Repair Manual for E1500, E1700 Receiver.
12. U.S. Patent 3,959,737, Frequency Synthesizer Having Fractional Frequency Divider in Phase Locked Loop, William J. Tanis, Wayne, NJ, Engelmann Microwave, Montville, NJ, May 25, 1976.

4

Loop Components

4-1 OSCILLATOR DESIGN

The phase-locked loop generally has two oscillators, the oscillator at the output frequency and the reference oscillator. The reference oscillator at times can be another loop that is being mixed in, and the voltage-controlled oscillator is controlled by either the reference or the oscillator loop. The voltage-controlled oscillator is one of the most important parts of the phase-locked loop system because its performance is determined inside the loop bandwidth by the loop and outside the loop bandwidth by its design. To some designers, the design of the voltage-controlled oscillator (VCO) appears to be magic. Shortly, we will go through the mathematics of the oscillator and some of its design criteria, but the results have only limited meanings. This is due to component tolerances, stray effects, and most of all, nonlinear performance of the device, which is modeled with only a certain degree of accuracy. However, after building oscillators for awhile, a certain feeling will be acquired for how to do this, and certain performance behavior will be predicted on a rule-of-thumb basis rather than on precise mathematical effort. For reasons of understanding, we will deal with the necessary mathematical equations, but I consider it essential to explain that these are only approximations.

4-1-1 Basics of Oscillators

An electronic oscillator is a device that converts dc power to a periodic output signal (ac power). If the output waveform is approximately sinusoidal, the oscillator is referred to as *sinusoidal*. There are many other oscillator types normally referred to as *relaxation* oscillators. For applications in frequency synthesizers, we will only try to build sinusoidal oscillators for reasons of purity and noise sideband performance, and we will deal only with those.

All oscillators are inherently nonlinear. Although the nonlinearity results in some distortion of the signal, linear analysis techniques can normally be used for the analysis and design of oscillators. Figure 4-1 shows, in block diagram form, the

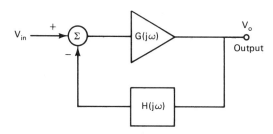

Figure 4-1 Block diagram of an oscillator showing forward and feedback loop components.

necessary components of an oscillator. It contains an amplifier with frequency-dependent forward loop gain $G(j\omega)$ and a frequency-dependent feedback network $H(j\omega)$. The output voltage is given by

$$V_o = \frac{V_{in}G(j\omega)}{1 + G(j\omega)H(j\omega)} \tag{4-1}$$

For an oscillator, the output V_o is nonzero even if the input signal $V_i = 0$. This can only be possible if the forward loop gain is infinite (which is not practical), or if the denominator

$$1 + G(j\omega)H(j\omega) = 0 \tag{4-2}$$

at some frequency ω_o. This leads to the well-known condition for oscillation (the *Nyquist criterion*), where at some frequency ω_o

$$G(j\omega_o)H(j\omega_o) = -1 \tag{4-3}$$

That is, the magnitude of the open-loop transfer function is equal to 1:

$$|G(j\omega_o)H(j\omega_o)| = 1 \tag{4-4}$$

and the phase shift is 180°:

$$\arg[G(j\omega_o)H(j\omega_o)] = 180° \tag{4-5}$$

This can be more simply expressed as follows: If in a negative feedback system, the open-loop gain has a total phase shift of 180° at some frequency ω_o, the system will oscillate at that frequency provided that the open-loop gain is unity. If the gain is less than unity at the frequency where the phase shift is 180°, the system will be stable, whereas if the gain is greater than unity, the system will be unstable.

This statement is not correct for some complicated systems, but it is correct for those transfer functions normally encountered in oscillator design. The conditions for stability are also known as the *Barkhausen criterion*, which states that if the closed-loop transfer function is

$$\frac{V_o}{V_i} = \frac{\mu}{1 - \mu\beta} \tag{4-6}$$

the system will oscillate provided that $\mu\beta = 1$. This is equivalent to the Nyquist criterion, the difference being that the transfer function is written for a loop with positive feedback. Both versions state that the total phase shift around the loop must be 360° at the frequency of oscillation and the magnitude of the open-loop gain must be unity at that frequency.

The following analysis of the relatively simple oscillator shown in Figure 4-2

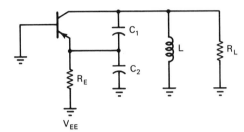

Figure 4-2   Oscillator with capacitive voltage divider.

illustrates the design method. The linearized (and simplified) equivalent circuit of Figure 4-2 is given in Figure 4-3. h_{rb} has been neglected, and $1/h_{ob}$ has been assumed

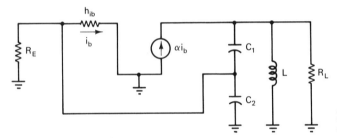

Figure 4-3   Linearized and simplified equivalent circuit of Figure 4-2.

to be much greater than the load resistance R_L and is also ignored. Note that the transistor is connected in the common base configuration which has no voltage phase inversion (the feedback is positive), so the conditions for oscillation are

$$|G(j\omega_o)H(j\omega_o)| = 1 \qquad (4\text{-}7)$$

and

$$\arg[G(j\omega_o)H(j\omega_o)] = 0° \qquad (4\text{-}8)$$

The circuit analysis can be greatly simplified by assuming that

$$\frac{1}{\omega(C_2 + C_1)} \ll \frac{h_{ib}R_E}{h_{ib} + R_E} \qquad (4\text{-}9)$$

and also that the Q of the load impedance is high. In this case the circuit reduces to that of Figure 4-4, where

$$V = \frac{V_oC_1}{C_1 + C_2} \qquad (4\text{-}10)$$

and

$$R_{eq} = \frac{h_{ib}R_E}{h_{ib} + R_E}\left(\frac{C_1 + C_2}{C_1}\right)^2 \qquad (4\text{-}11)$$

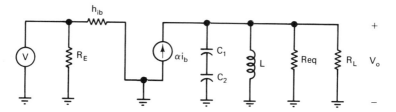

Figure 4-4   Further simplification of Figure 4-2, assuming high-impedance loads.

Then the forward loop gain

$$G(j\omega) = \frac{h_{fb}}{h_{ib}} Z_L = \frac{\alpha}{h_{ib}} Z_L \qquad (4\text{-}12)$$

and

$$H(j\omega) = \frac{C_1}{C_1 + C_2} \qquad (4\text{-}13)$$

where

$$Y_L = \frac{1}{Z_L} = \frac{1}{j\omega L} + \frac{1}{R_{eq}} + \frac{1}{R_L} + \frac{1}{j\omega C} \qquad (4\text{-}14)$$

A necessary condition for oscillation is that

$$\arg [G(j\omega)H(j\omega)] = 0° \qquad (4\text{-}15)$$

Since H does not depend on frequency in this example, if arg GH is to be zero, the phase shift of the load impedance Z_L must be zero. This occurs only at the resonant frequency of the circuit,

$$\omega_o = \frac{1}{\sqrt{L[C_1 C_2/(C_1 + C_2)]}} \qquad (4\text{-}16)$$

At this frequency

$$Z_L = \frac{R_{eq} R_L}{R_{eq} + R_L} \qquad (4\text{-}17)$$

and

$$GH = \frac{h_{fb}}{h_{ib}} \left(\frac{R_{eq} R_L}{R_{eq} + R_L}\right) \frac{C_1}{C_1 + C_2} \qquad (4\text{-}18)$$

The other condition for oscillation is the magnitude constraint that

$$G(j\omega)H(j\omega) = \frac{\alpha}{h_{ib}} \left(\frac{R_{eq} R_L}{R_{eq} + R_L}\right) \frac{C_1}{C_1 + C_2} = 1 \qquad (4\text{-}19)$$

Although the block diagram formulation of the stability criteria is the easiest to express mathematically, it is frequently not the easiest to apply since it is often difficult to identify the forward loop gain $G(j\omega)$ and feedback ratio $H(j\omega)$ in electronic systems. A direct analysis of the circuit equations is frequently simpler than the block diagram interpretation (particularly for single-stage amplifiers). Figure 4-5 shows a generalized circuit for an electronic amplifier. The small-signal equivalent circuit is

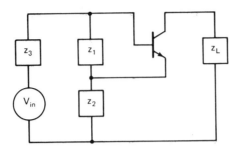

Figure 4-5 Generalized circuit for an oscillator using an amplifier model.

given in Figure 4-6 (where h_{re} has been neglected). Normally, h_{oe} can also be assumed sufficiently small and can be neglected. The loop equations are then

$$V_{in} = I_1(Z_3 + Z_1 + Z_2) - I_b Z_1 + \beta I_b Z_2 \qquad (4\text{-}20)$$

$$0 = -I_1 Z_1 + I_b(h_{ie} + Z_1) \qquad (4\text{-}21)$$

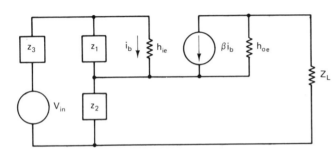

Figure 4-6 Small-signal equivalent circuit of Figure 4-5.

For the amplifier to oscillate, the currents I_b and I_1, must be nonzero even when $V_1 = 0$. This is only possible if the system determinant

$$\Delta = \begin{vmatrix} Z_3 + Z_1 + Z_2 & \beta Z_2 - Z_1 \\ -Z_1 & h_{ie} + Z_1 \end{vmatrix} \qquad (4\text{-}22)$$

is equal to 0. That is,

$$(Z_3 + Z_1 + Z_2)(h_{ie} + Z_1) - Z_1^2 + \beta Z_1 Z_2 = 0 \qquad (4\text{-}23)$$

which reduces to

$$(Z_1 + Z_2 + Z_3)h_{ie} + Z_1 Z_2 \beta + Z_1(Z_2 + Z_3) = 0 \qquad (4\text{-}24)$$

Only the case where the transistor input impedance h_{ie} is real will be considered here (a valid approximation for oscillators operating below 50 MHz). The more complicated case, in which h_{ie} is complex, can be analyzed in the same manner. Assume for the moment that Z_1, Z_2, and Z_3 are purely reactive impedances. [It is easily seen that Eq. (4-24) does not have a solution if all three impedances are real.] Since both the real and imaginary parts must be zero, Eq. (4-24) is equivalent to the following equations if

$$h_{ie}(Z_1 + Z_2 + Z_3) = 0 \qquad (4\text{-}25)$$

and

$$Z_1[(1 + \beta)Z_2 + Z_3] = 0 \qquad (4\text{-}26)$$

Since β is real and positive, Z_2 and Z_3 must be of opposite sign for Eq. (4-26) to hold. That is,

$$(1 + \beta)Z_2 = -Z_3 \qquad (4\text{-}27)$$

Therefore, since h_{ie} is nonzero, Eq. (4-25) reduces to

$$Z_1 + Z_2 - (1 + \beta)Z_2 = 0 \qquad (4\text{-}28)$$

or

$$Z_1 = \beta Z_2$$

Thus, since β is positive, Z_1 and Z_2 will be reactances of the same kind. If Z_1 and Z_2 are capacitors, Z_3 is an inductor and the circuit is as shown in Figure 4-7. It is referred

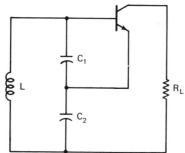

Figure 4-7 Colpitts oscillator.

to as a *Colpitts oscillator*, named after the person who first described it. If Z_1 and Z_2 are inductors and Z_3 is a capacitor as illustrated in Figure 4-8, the circuit is called a *Hartley oscillator*.

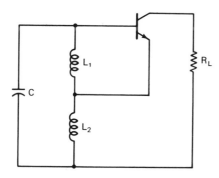

Figure 4-8 Hartley oscillator.

Example 1

Design a Colpitts circuit to oscillate at 2 MHz, using a transistor that has an input impedance

$$h_{ie} = 1 \, k\Omega \qquad \text{and} \qquad \beta = 49$$

Solution.   For the Colpitts circuit Z_1 and Z_2 are capacitive reactances and Z_3 is an inductive reactance. Let $Z_2 = -10 \, j\Omega$; then [Eq. (4-27)]

$$-Z_3 = (1 + \beta)Z_2 = j500 \, \Omega$$

and [Eq. (4-25)]

$$Z_1 = -Z_2 = -Z_3 = -j490 \, \Omega$$

At 2 MHz these impedances correspond to component values of

$$C_1 = 162 \text{ pF}$$

$$C_2 = 7.96 \text{ nF}$$

$$L = 39.8 \text{ } \mu H$$

The completed circuit, except for biasing, is shown in Figure 4-9.

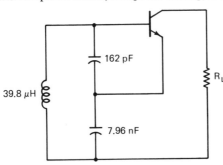

Figure 4-9 Design example of a Colpitts oscillator.

If Z_1, Z_2, Z_3, or h_{ie} is complex, the preceding analysis is more complicated, but the conditions for oscillation can still be obtained from Eq. (4-24). For example, if in the Colpitts circuit, there is a resistor R in series with L ($Z_3 = R + j\omega L$), Eq. (4-24) reduces to the two equations

$$h_{ie}\left(\omega L - \frac{1}{\omega C_1} - \frac{1}{\omega C_2}\right) - \frac{R}{\omega C_1} = 0 \tag{4-29}$$

and

$$h_{ie}R - \frac{1 + \beta}{\omega^2 C_1 C_2} + \frac{1}{\omega C_1}\omega L = 0 \tag{4-30}$$

Define

$$C_1' = \frac{C_1}{1 + R/h_{ie}} \tag{4-31}$$

The resonant frequency at which oscillations will occur is found from Eq. (4-29) to be

$$\omega_o = \frac{1}{\sqrt{L[C_1' C_2/(C_1' + C_2)]}} \tag{4-32}$$

and for oscillations to occur $R_e(h_{ie})$ must be less than or equal to

$$R_e(h_{ie}) \leq \frac{1 + \beta}{\omega_o^2 C_1 C_2} - \frac{L}{C_1} \tag{4-33}$$

If R becomes too large, Eq. (4-31) cannot be satisfied and oscillations will stop. In general, it is advantageous to have

$$X_{C_1}X_{C_2} = \frac{1}{\omega^2 C_1 C_2} \tag{4-34}$$

with $X \triangleq 1/\omega c$ as large as possible since then R can be large. However, if C_1 and C_2

are too small (large X_{C_1} and X_{C_2}), the input and output capacitors of the transistor, which shunt C_1 and C_2, respectively, become important. A good, stable design will always have C_1 and C_2 much larger than the transistor capacitances they shunt.

Example 2

In Example 1 will the circuit still oscillate if the inductor has a $Q_u = 100$? If the transistor input capacitance is 5 pF, what effect will this have on the system?

Solution.   In Example 1,

$$X_L = 500 \qquad C_1 = 162 \text{ pF}$$

and

$$C_2 = 0.0079 \ \mu F$$

Since $C_1 = 162$ pF, adding 5 pF in parallel will change the equivalent C_1 to 167 pF. As the inductor $Q_u = 100$, the equivalent resistance R in series with the lossless inductor is

$$R = \frac{500}{100} = 5.0 \ \Omega$$

The new resonant frequency can be determined from Eqs. (4-31) and (4-32):

$$C_1 = \frac{C_1}{1 + R/h_{ie}} = \frac{167}{1 + 5/1000} = 166.9 \text{ pF}$$

and

$$f_o = \frac{1}{2\pi L[C_1' C_2/(C_1' + C_2)]} \simeq 1.97 \text{ MHz}$$

The effect of the finite inductor Q causes a negligible change in the oscillating frequency compared to the effect of the transistor input capacitance, which reduces the resonant frequency 1.5%. To determine if the circuit oscillates, Eq. (4-33) must be verified.

$$\frac{1 + \beta}{\omega_o^2 C_1 C_2} - \frac{L}{C_1} \frac{50}{(2\pi \times 2 \times 10^6)^2 \times 167 \times 10^{-12} \times 79 \times 10^{-10}}$$

$$- \frac{39.78 \times 10^{-16}}{167 \times 10^{-12}} = 2.4 \times 10^5 - 2.38 \times 10^5 = 2 \times 10^3$$

which is not greater than $R(h_{ie}) = 5 \text{ k}\Omega$, so the circuit will not oscillate. Either an inductor with a higher Q_u is needed or smaller capacitors and a larger inductor are necessary.

Although Eqs. (4-25) and (4-26) can be used to determine the exact expressions for oscillation, they are often difficult to use and add little insight into the design process. An alternative interpretation, although not as accurate, will now be presented. It is based on the fact that an ideal tuned circuit (infinite Q), once excited, will oscillate infinitely because there is no resistance element present to dissipate the energy. In the actual case where the inductor Q is finite, the oscillations die out because energy is dissipated in the resistance. It is the function of the amplifier to maintain oscillations by supplying an amount of energy equal to that dissipated. This source of energy can be interpreted as a negative resistor in series with the tuned circuit. If the total resistance is positive, the oscillations will die out, while the oscillation amplitude will increase if the total resistance is negative. To maintain oscillations, the two resistors must be of equal magnitude. To see how a negative resistance is realized, the input impedance of the circuit in Figure 4-10 will be derived.

It h_{oe} is sufficiently small ($h_{oe} \ll 1/R_L$), the equivalent circuit is as shown in Figure 4-10. The steady-state loop equations are

$$V_{in} = I_{in}(X_{C_1} + X_{C_2}) - I_b(X_{C_1} - \beta X_{C_2}) \tag{4-35}$$

$$0 = -I_{in}(X_{C_1}) + I_b(X_{C_1} + h_{ie}) \tag{4-36}$$

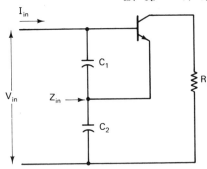

Figure 4-10   Calculation of input impedance of the negative resistance oscillator.

After I_b is eliminated from these two equations, Z_{in} is obtained as

$$Z_{in} = \frac{V_{in}}{I_{in}} = \frac{(1 + \beta)X_{C_1}X_{C_2} + h_{ie}(X_{C_1} + X_{C_2})}{X_{C_1} + h_{ie}} \tag{4-37}$$

If $X_{C_1} \ll h_{ie}$, the input impedance is approximately equal to

$$Z_{in} \approx \frac{1 + \beta}{h_{ie}} X_{C_1}X_{C_2} + (X_{C_1} + X_{C_2}) \tag{4-38}$$

$$Z_{in} \approx \frac{-g_m}{\omega^2 C_1 C_2} + \frac{1}{j\omega[C_1 C_2/(C_1 + C_2)]} \tag{4-39}$$

That is, the input impedance of the circuit shown in Figure 4-11 is a negative resistor,

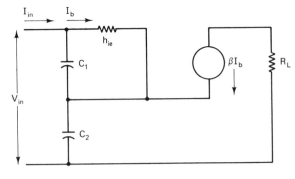

Figure 4-11   Equivalent small-signal circuit of Figure 4-10.

$$R = \frac{-g_m}{\omega^2 C_1 C_2} \tag{4-40}$$

in series with a capacitor,

$$C_{\text{in}} = \frac{C_1 C_2}{C_1 + C_2} \tag{4-41}$$

which is the series combination of the two capacitors. With an inductor L (with the series resistance R_s) connected across the input, it is clear that the condition for sustained oscillation is

$$R_s = \frac{g_m}{\omega^2 C_1 C_2} \tag{4-42}$$

and the frequency of oscillation

$$f_o = \frac{1}{2\pi\sqrt{L[C_1 C_2/(C_1 + C_2)]}} \tag{4-43}$$

This interpretation of the oscillator readily provides several guidelines which can be used in the design. First, C_1 should be as large as possible so that

$$X_{C_1} \ll h_{ie}$$

and C_2 is to be large so that

$$X_{C_2} \ll \frac{1}{h_{oe}}$$

When these two capacitors are large, the transistor base-to-emitter and collector-to-emitter capacitances will have a negligible effect on the circuit's performance. However, Eq. (4-42) limits the maximum value of the capacitances since

$$r \leq \frac{g_m}{\omega^2 C_1 C_2} \leq \frac{G}{\omega^2 C_1 C_2} \tag{4-44}$$

where G is the maximum value of g_m. For a given product of C_1 and C_2, the series capacitance is a maximum when $C_1 = C_2 = C_m$. Thus Eq. (4-44) can be written

$$\frac{1}{\omega C_m} > \sqrt{\frac{r}{G}} \tag{4-45}$$

This equation is important in that it shows that for oscillations to be maintained, the minimum permissible reactance $1/\omega C_m$ is a function of the resistance of the inductor and the transistor's mutual conductance g_m.

An oscillator circuit known as the *Clapp circuit* or *Clapp–Gouriet circuit* is shown in Figure 4-12. This oscillator is equivalent to the one just discussed, but it has

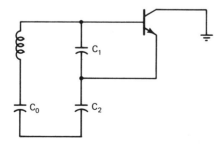

Figure 4-12   Circuit of a Clapp oscillator.

the practical advantage of being able to provide another degree of design freedom by making C_o much smaller than C_1 and C_2. It is possible to use C_1 and C_2 to satisfy the condition of Eq. (4-44) and then adjust C_o for the desired frequency of oscillation ω_o, which is determined from

$$\omega_o L - \frac{1}{\omega_o C_o} - \frac{1}{\omega_o C_1} - \frac{1}{\omega_o C_2} = 0 \qquad (4\text{-}46)$$

Example 3

Consider a Clapp–Gouriet oscillator as shown in Figure 4-12. The transistor used has $G_{max} = 9 \times 10^{-3}$ S, and it is operated at $g_m = 6$ mS. The coil used has an unloaded $Q_u = 200$ at 1 MHz and a reactive impedance of $800\,\Omega$ ($R_s = 4\,\Omega$). What are the required conditions for the circuit to oscillate?

Solution. To satisfy Eq. (4-45), we must have

$$\frac{1}{\omega C_m} \geq \sqrt{\frac{r}{g_m}} = 25.8\,\Omega$$

Therefore, at 1 MHz,

$$C_m \leq 6200 \text{ pF}$$

C_m corresponds to the case of maximum series capacitance of the parallel combination of C_1 and C_2 and occurs for $C_1 = C_2 = C_m$. If both C_1 and C_2 are 6200 pF, the reactance of the series combination of C_1 and C_2 is $51.6\,\Omega$. Other combinations of C_1 and C_2 can be selected which may provide more gain, provided that Eq. (4-44) is satisfied. C_o must be selected so that $X_L = X_C$ at 1 MHz.

Amplitude stability.   Linearized analysis of the oscillator is convenient for determining the frequency but not the amplitude of the oscillation. The Nyquist stability criterion defines the frequency of oscillation as the frequency at which the loop phase shift is 360°, but it says nothing about the oscillation amplitude. If no provisions are taken to control the amplitude, it is susceptible to appreciable drift. Two frequently used methods for controlling the amplitude are operating the transistor in the nonlinear region or to use a second stage for amplitude limiting. For the single-stage oscillator, amplitude limiting is accomplished by designing an unstable oscillator; that is, the loop gain is made greater than 1 at the frequency where the phase shift is 180°. As the amplitude increases, the β of the transistor decreases, causing the loop gain to decrease until the amplitude stabilizes. This is a self-limiting oscillator. There are nonlinear analysis techniques predicting the amplitude of oscillation, but their results are approximate except in idealized cases, forcing the designer to resort to an empirical approach.

An example of a two-stage emitter-coupled oscillator is shown in Figure 4-13. In this circuit, amplitude stabilization occurs as a result of current limiting in the second stage. This circuit has the additional advantage that it has output terminals which are isolated from the feedback path. The emitter signal of Q_2, having a rich harmonics content, is normally used as output. Harmonics of the fundamental frequency can be extracted at the emitter of Q_2 by using an appropriately tuned circuit. Note that the collector of Q_2 is isolated from the feedback path.

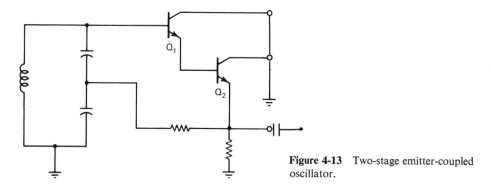

Figure 4-13   Two-stage emitter-coupled oscillator.

Phase stability.   An oscillator has a frequency or phase stability which can be considered in two separate parts. First, there is the long-term stability in which the frequency changes over a period of minutes, hours, days, weeks, or even years. This frequency stability is normally limited by the circuit component's temperature coefficients and aging rates. The other part, the short-term frequency stability, is measured in terms of seconds. One form of short-term instability is due to changes in phase of the system; here the term "phase stability" is used synonomously with frequency stability. It refers to how the frequency of oscillation reacts to small changes in phase shift of the open-loop system. It can be assumed that the system with the largest rate of change of phase versus frequency $d\phi/df$ will be the most stable in terms of frequency stability. Figure 4-14 shows the phase plots of two open-loop systems used in oscillators. At the system crossover frequency, the phase shift is $-180°$. If some external

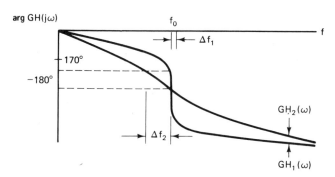

Figure 4-14   Phase plot of two open-loop systems with different Q of the resonator.

influence causes a change in phase, say it adds $10°$ of phase lag, the frequency will change until the total phase shift is again $0°$. In this case the frequency will decrease to the point where the open-loop phase shift is $170°$. Figure 4-14 shows that Δf_2, the change in frequency associated with the $10°$ change in phase of GH_2, is greater than the change in frequency Δf_1, associated with open-loop system GH_1, whose phase is changing more rapidly near the open-loop crossover frequency.

This qualitative discussion illustrates that $d\phi/df$ at $f = f_o$ is a measure of an oscillator's phase stability. It provides a good means of quantitatively comparing the

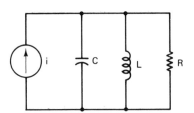

Figure 4-15 Parallel tuned circuit for phase shift analysis.

phase stability of two oscillators. Consider the simple parallel tuned circuit shown in Figure 4-15. For the circuit, the two-port is

$$\frac{V_o(j\omega)}{I(j\omega)} = \frac{R}{1 + jQ[(\omega/\omega_o) - (\omega_o/\omega)]} \tag{4-47}$$

where

$$\omega_o = \frac{1}{\sqrt{LC}} \quad \text{and} \quad Q = \frac{R}{\omega_o L} \tag{4-48}$$

The circuit phase shift is

$$\arg\frac{V_o}{I} = \theta = \tan^{-1} Q\left(\frac{\omega}{\omega_o} - \frac{\omega_o}{\omega}\right) \tag{4-49}$$

and

$$\frac{d\theta}{d\omega} = \frac{1/Q}{1/Q^2 + [(\omega^2 - \omega_o^2)/\omega_o\omega]^2} \frac{\omega^2 + \omega_o^2}{(\omega_o\omega)^2} \tag{4-50}$$

at the resonant frequency ω_o,

$$\left.\frac{dQ}{d\omega}\right|_{\omega=\omega_o} = \frac{2Q}{\omega_o} \tag{4-51}$$

The frequency stability factor is S_F defined as the change in phase $d\phi/d\omega$ divided by the normalized change in frequency $\Delta\omega/\omega_o$. That is,

$$S_F = 2Q. \tag{4-52}$$

S_F is a measure of the short-term stability of an oscillator. Equation (4-51) indicates that the higher the circuit Q, the higher the stability factor. This is one reason for using high-Q circuits in oscillator circuits. Another reason is the ability of the tuned circuit to filter out undesired harmonics and noise.

4-1-2 Low-Noise LC Oscillators

In Chapter 2 we derived a formula that allows an estimate of the noise performance of an oscillator. Under the assumption that the output energy is taken off the resonator rather than from an isolation amplifier, Eq. (2-29) can be rewritten in the form

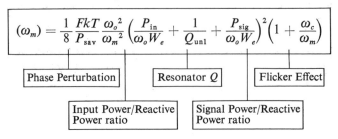

In frequency synthesizers, we have no use for *LC* oscillators without a tuning diode, but it may still be of interest to analyze the low-noise fixed-tuned *LC* oscillator first and later make both elements, inductor and capacitor, variable.

Later I will show the performance changes if we utilize the two possible ways of getting coarse and fine tuning in oscillators:

1. Use of tuning diodes
2. Use of switching diodes

We will spend some time looking at the effects that switching and tuning diodes have in a circuit because they will ultimately influence the noise performance stronger than the transistor itself.

The reason is that the noise generated in tuning diodes will be superimposed on the noise generated in the circuit while switching diodes have losses that cause a reduction of circuit *Q*. The selection of the proper tuning and switching diodes is important, as is the proper way of connecting them. As both types are modifications of the basic *LC* oscillator, we start with the *LC* oscillator itself.

Signal generators as they are offered by several companies (e.g., Rohde & Schwarz, Hewlett-Packard, Boonton Electronics, or Marconi), if they are not synthesized, use an air-variable capacitor or, as in the case of one particular Hewlett-Packard generator, the Model 8640, a tuned cavity.

Tuning here is accomplished by changing the value of an air-variable capacitor or changing the mechanical lengths of a quarter-wave resonator.

Using the equations shown previously, it is fairly easy to calculate oscillators and understand how they work, but this does not necessarily optimize their design. For crucial noise application, the oscillator shown in Figure 4-16 used in the Rohde & Schwarz SMDU is currently the state of the art. Its noise performance is equivalent to the noise found in the cavity tuned oscillator made by Hewlett-Packard, and because of the unique way a tuning diode is coupled to the circuit, its modulation capabilities are substantially superior to any of the signal generators offered currently. To develop such a circuit from design equations is not possible. This circuit is a result of many years of experience and research and looks fairly simple. The grounded gate field-effect transistor circuit provides the best performance because it fulfills the important requirements of the equation above.

The tuned circuit is not connected directly to the drain, but the drain is put on a tap of the oscillator section. Therefore, the actual voltage across the tuning capacitor is higher than the supply voltage, and therefore the energy stored in the capacitor is much higher than in a circuit connected between the gate electrode and ground, the normal Colpitts-type oscillator. In addition, the high output impedance of the field-effect transistor does not load the circuit, which also provides a reduced noise contribution. Since this oscillator is optimized for best frequency modulation performance in the FM frequency range, it becomes apparent that it fits the requirements of low-distortion stereo modulation.

For extremely critical locking measurements in the 2-m band ranging from 140

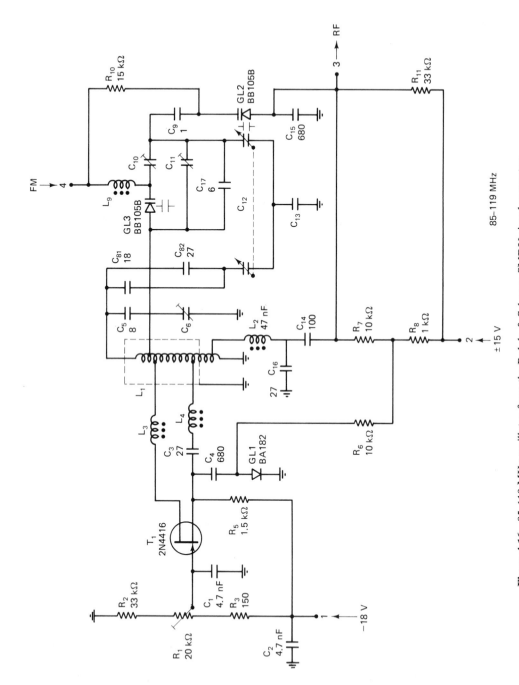

Figure 4-16 85–119 MHz oscillator from the Rohde & Schwarz SMDU signal generator. (Courtesy of Rohde & Schwarz.)

to 160 MHz, the noise specifications 20 kHz off the carrier are of highest importance, while the peak modulation typically does not exceed 5 kHz. Figure 4-17 shows the schematic of the oscillator section optimized for this frequency range.

It has been found experimentally that it is not recommended to use these *LC* oscillators above $\approx$ 500 MHz but rather to use a doubler stage. Analyzing the signal generators currently on the market, their highest base band ranges typically from 200 to 500 MHz using frequency doublers to 1000 MHz. For those interested in low-noise oscillators, Figure 4-18 shows a schematic. As can be seen in Figure 4-19, the mechanical layout of such an oscillator is extremely compact.

4-1-3 Switchable/Tunable LC Oscillators

The VCO for a frequency synthesizer, as the division ratio is larger than 100, is responsible for the noise performance outside the loop bandwidth of 1 to 10 kHz, while multiple-loop synthesizers using division ratios of less than 100 typically operate at extremely large bandwidths to increase the switching speed and frequency agility of the oscillator for critical applications such as frequency hopping and spread-spectrum techniques. Because of the wide loop bandwidth ($>$ 100 kHz) and the relatively small division ratio, the loop is able to clean up oscillator phase noise, making the oscillator noise performance be of second order. In a one-loop synthesizer using a wide-range diode tuned oscillator, the oscillator sensitivity K_0 at the lower end is much higher than at the higher end. This ratio can be as high as 1:10 and cause loop instabilities and pickup problems on the control line. It is, therefore, desirable to reduce the diode tuned range and coarse tune the oscillator by switching inductors or capacitors in parallel. It is somewhat questionable which approach is better. I have generally found that higher Q values are obtained if capacitors are switched in, and as the capacitor is increased toward the low-frequency end and the division ratio decreases also, this offsets to a degree the higher voltage gain of the VCO. One might call this "linearization of the tuning range."

Figure 4-20 shows a VCO using switchable capacitors of the Rohde & Schwarz EK070 shortwave receiver. This oscillator operates from 40 to 70 MHz and a noise power of $\approx$145 dB/Hz at 25 to 30 kHz off the carrier. The loop bandwidth of the PLL using this oscillator is set to $\approx$3 kHz, which takes care of microphonics. To improve noise performance, AGC is used.

A different route was chosen by Hewlett-Packard in their 8662A synthesized oscillator. Figure 4-21 shows the schematic of this oscillator. The inductors shown in this circuit are in reality transmission lines (see Section A-1-5). According to Hewlett-Packard, this loop is also operated at several kilohertz bandwidth, and therefore the noise performance outside the loop bandwidth is determined by the losses of the oscillator.

Another method of coarse steering is the use of tuning diodes. This oscillator, while avoiding diode switching current, is somewhat noisier because of tuning diode noise.

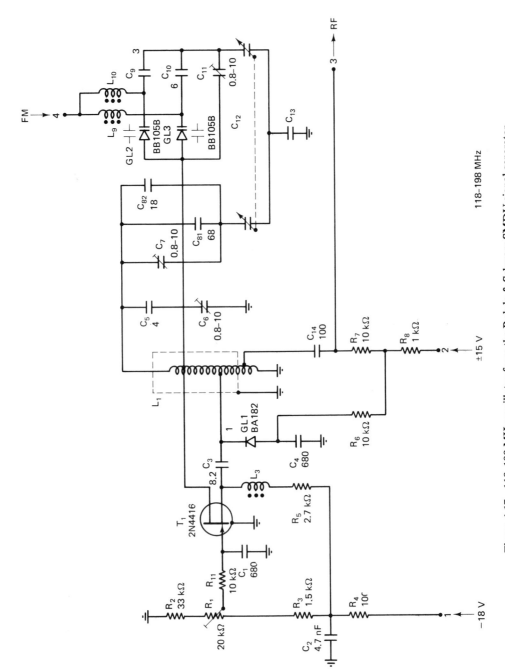

Figure 4-17 118–198 MHz oscillator from the Rohde & Schwarz SMDU signal generator. (Courtesy of Rohde & Schwarz.)

158

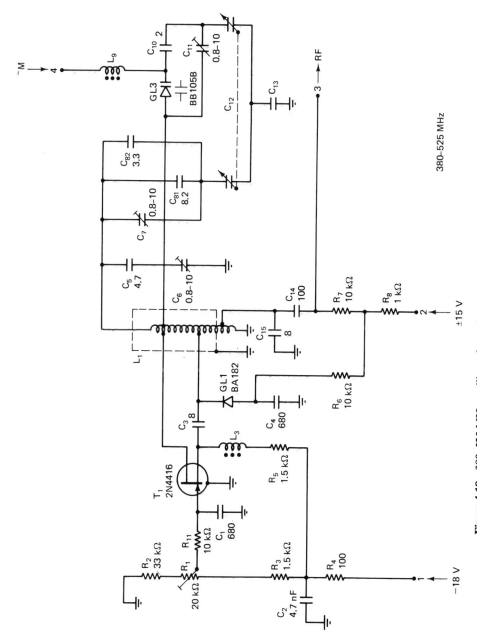

Figure 4-18 380–525 MHz oscillator from the Rohde & Schwarz SMDU signal generator. (Courtesy of Rohde & Schwarz.)

Figure 4-19 Photograph of the helical resonator system from the Rohde &
Schwarz SMDU signal generator. (Courtesy of Rohde & Schwarz.)

Figure 4-22 shows the oscillator used in the Rohde & Schwarz ESH2/ESH3
receiver. The three oscillators cover a frequency range from 75 to 105 MHz in 10-MHz
ranges. A digital-to-analog converter combined with the synthesizer decoding generates the voltage to coarse set the frequency, while fine tune input is used for actual
frequency locking.

A clever technique is used to select the different ranges, and an isolation power
amplifier stage decouples the oscillator from the loop circuitry. Figure 4-23 shows the
noise sideband performance of this oscillator section. It is interesting to compare
this with the SSB noise for the Rohde & Schwarz SMDU oscillator, where different
types of tuning diodes are applied. While the one line refers to a tuning diode of
10 kHz/V tuning sensitivity, the other curves refer to the noise performance for
tuning diodes of higher sensitivity. Apparently, the noise performance already is
degraded from 200 Hz off the carrier to as much as 10 MHz off the carrier. Above
10 MHz all curves meet.

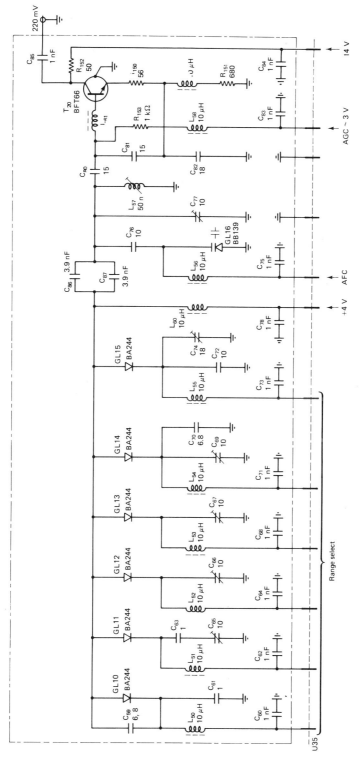

Figure 4-20 Schematic of the coarse-tuned VCO from the **Rohde & Schwarz EK070** receiver. (Courtesy of Rohde & Schwarz.)

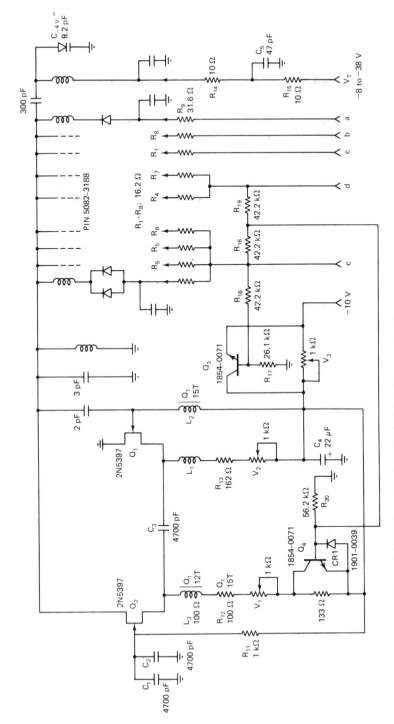

Figure 4-21 Schematic of the HP8662A VCO operating from 260 to 520 MHz. (Courtesy of Hewlett-Packard Company.)

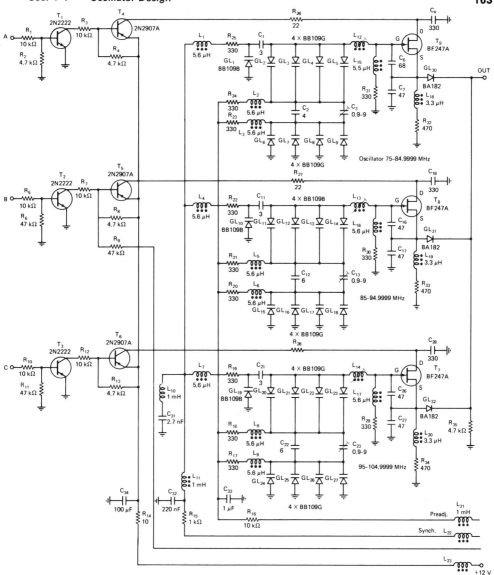

Figure 4-22 Oscillator and switching section of the Rohde & Schwarz ESH2/ESH3 test receiver. (Courtesy of Rohde & Schwarz.)

Let us look next at some oscillator circuits used for less demanding applications. Figure 4-24 shows three oscillators that cover the range 225 to 480 MHz using the low-noise Siemens transistor BFT66. The tuned circuit is loosely coupled to the oscillator transistor and output is taken from the collector in order to increase the isolation. In this particular case, no attempts were taken to reduce any harmonic contents, as these outputs have to drive digital dividers.

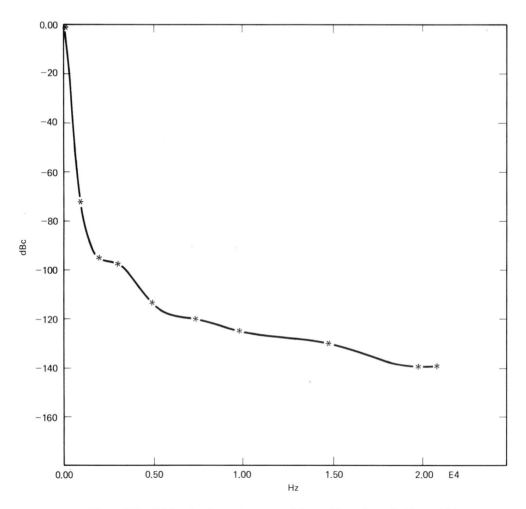

Figure 4-23   Sideband noise performance of the oscillator shown in Figure 4-22.

Finally, let us take a look at Figure 4-25, which shows a wideband oscillator operating in the 500-MHz range taken from the Rohde & Schwarz SMS signal generator and a wideband oscillator taken from the Rohde & Schwarz ESM500 receiver (Figure 4-26). The oscillator noise of the ESM500 is extremely small and is used with a loop bandwidth of about 10 Hz. Outside the 10-Hz bandwidth, this circuit by itself is responsible for the noise performance of the synthesizer, and data taken from blocking measurements indicate that the noise floor of 135 dB/Hz 25 kHz off the carrier is at least 20 dB better than previous circuit designs. The oscillator section shown in Figure 4-27 from the Rohde & Schwarz ESV receiver covering the same frequency range is based on the same principle and has a coarse and fine tuning input.

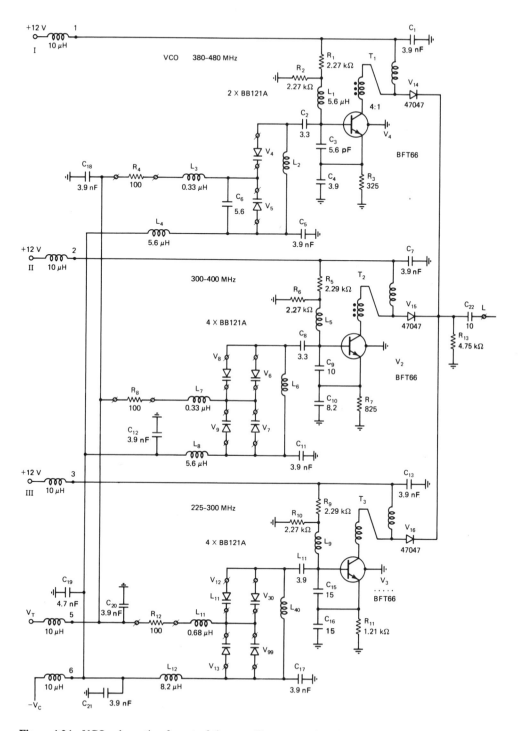

Figure 4-24 VCO schematic of a set of three oscillators covering the range from 225 to 480 MHz with bipolar transistors. (Courtesy of Rohde & Schwarz.)

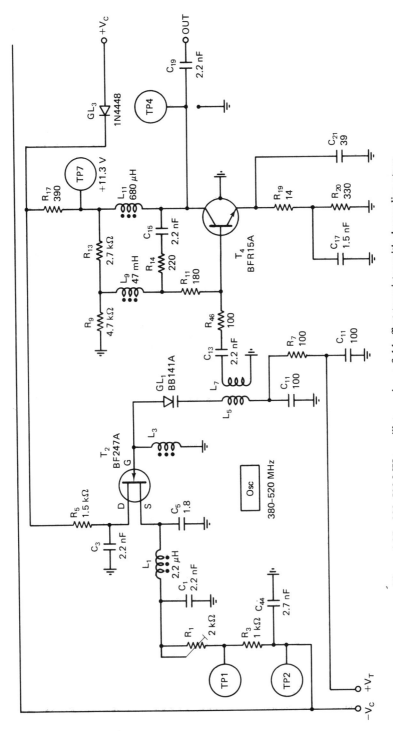

Figure 4-25 380–520 MHz oscillator using a field-effect transistor with decoupling stage. (Courtesy of Rohde & Schwarz.)

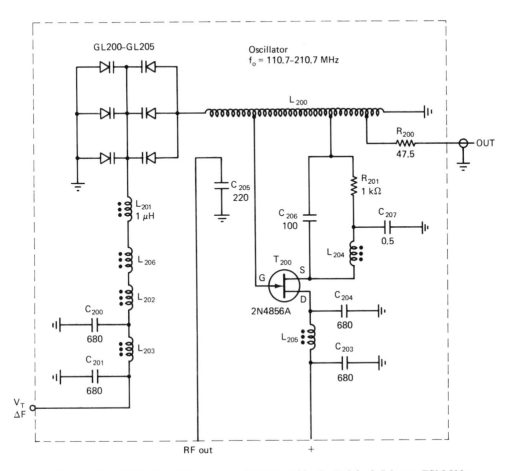

Figure 4-26 110.7–210.7 MHz wideband VCO used in the Rohde & Schwarz ESM 500 receiver. (Courtesy of Rohde & Schwarz.)

This oscillator operates together with the HEF4750 and 4751 LOCMOS frequency divider and synthesizer ICs.

The selection and use of the tuning diodes is extremely crucial, and in order to understand and distinguish between the various diodes offered on the market, the following section is devoted to understanding these principles.

4-1-4 Use of Tuning Diodes

In order to tune the oscillator within the required range, so-called tuning diodes are used. These diodes are often called varactors or voltage sensitive diodes. By way of approximation, we can use the equation

$$C = \frac{K}{(V_R + V_D)^n} \tag{4-54}$$

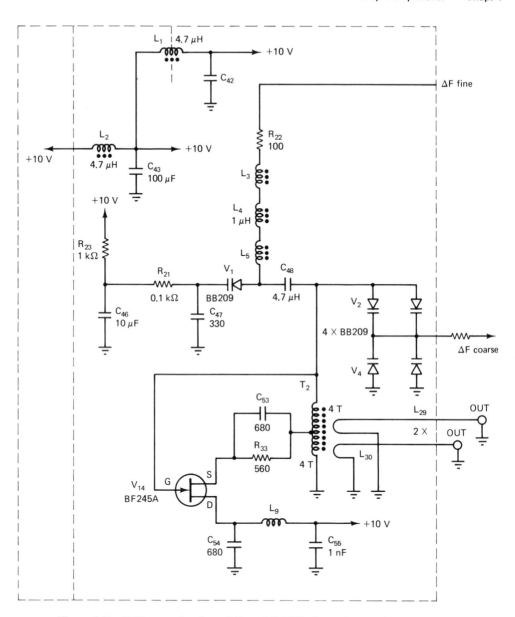

Figure 4-27 VCO operating from 160 to 260 MHz from the Rohde & Schwarz ESV receiver. (Courtesy of Rohde & Schwarz.)

wherein all constants and all parameters determined by the manufacturing process are contained in *K*. The exponent is a measure of the slope of the capacitance/voltage characteristic and is 0.5 for alloyed diodes, 0.33 for single diffused diodes and (on average) 0.75 for tuner diodes with an hyperabrupt PN-junction [7] [8]. Figure 4-28

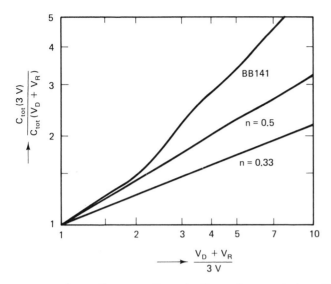

Figure 4-28 Capacitance/voltage characteristic for (a) an alloyed capacitance diode; (b) a diffused capacitance diode; (c) a wide-range tuner diode (BB141). (Courtesy of ITT Semiconductors, Freiburg, West Germany.)

shows the capacitance/voltage characteristics of an alloyed, a diffused, and a tuner diode.

Recently, an equation is indicated which, although purely formal, describes the practical characteristic better than Eq. (4-54):

$$C = C_o \left(\frac{A}{A + V_R} \right)^m \tag{4-55}$$

wherein C_o is the capacitance at $V_R = 0$, and A is a constant whose dimension is a volt. The exponent m is much less dependent on voltage than the exponent n in Eq. (4-54).

The operating range of a capacitance diode or its useful capacitance ratio.

$$\frac{C_{max}}{C_{min}} = \frac{C_{tot}(V_{Rmin})}{C_{tot}(V_{Rmax})} \tag{4-56}$$

is limited by the fact that the diode must not be driven by the alternating voltage superimposed on the tuning voltage either into the forward mode or the breakdown mode. Otherwise, rectification would take place which would shift the bias of the diode and considerably affect its figure of merit.

There are several manufacturers of tuning diodes. Motorola is a typical supplier in this country, and Siemens of West Germany or Philips provide good diodes. The following table contains information for three typical tuning diodes as they might be considered useful for our applications.

Capacitance		MV209	BB105	MVAM125
at $V_R = 1$ V	C_{tot}	40 pF	18 pF	500 pF
at $V_R = 25$ V	C_{tot}	6 pF	2 pF	33 pF
useful capacitance ratio	$\dfrac{C_{tot}(1\ V)}{C_{tot}(25\ V)}$	6	9	15

Diode tuned resonant circuits.

Tuner Diode in Parallel Resonant Circuit.   Figures 4-29, 4-30, and 4-31 illustrate three basic circuits for the tuning of parallel resonant circuits by means of capacitance diodes. In the circuit diagram of Figure 4-29, the tuning voltage is applied to the tuner

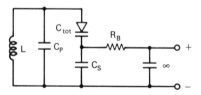

Figure 4-29 Parallel resonant circuit with tuner diode, and bias resistor parallel to the series capacitor.

diode via the tank coil and the bias resistor R_B. Series-connected to the tuner diode is the series capacitor C_S, which completes the circuit for the alternating current but isolates the cathode of the tuner diode from the coil and thus from the negative terminal of the tuning voltage. Moreover, a fixed parallel capacitance C_P is provided. The decoupling capacitor preceding the bias resistor is large enough to be disregarded in the following discussion. Since for high-frequency purposes the biasing resistor is connected in parallel with the series capacitor, it is transformed into the circuit as an additional equivalent shunt resistance R_c. We have the equation

$$R_c = R_B \left(1 + \frac{C_S}{C_{\text{tot}}}\right)^2 \tag{4-57}$$

If in this equation the diode capacitance is substituted by the resonant circuit frequency ω, we obtain

$$R_c = R_B \left(\frac{\omega^2 L C_S}{1 - \omega^2 L C_P}\right)^2 \tag{4-58}$$

The resistive loss R_c, caused by the bias resistor R_B, is seen to be highly frequency dependent, and this may result in the bandwidth of the tuned circuit being dependent on frequency if the capacitance of the series capacitor C_S is not chosen sufficiently high.

Figure 4-30 shows that the tuning voltage can also be applied directly and in

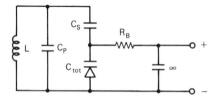

Figure 4-30 Parallel resonant circuit with tuner diode, and bias resistor parallel to the diode.

parallel to the tuner diode. For the parallel loss resistance transformed into the circuit, we have the expression

$$R_c = R_B \left(1 + \frac{C_{\text{tot}}}{C_S}\right)^2 \tag{4-59}$$

and

$$R_c = R_B \left[\frac{\omega^2 L C_S}{\omega^2 L (C_S + C_P) - 1} \right]^2 \tag{4-60}$$

The influence of the bias resistor R_B in this case is larger than in the circuit of Figure 4-29, provided that

$$C_S^2 > C_S(C_{tot} + C_P) + C_{tot}C_P$$

This is usually the case because the largest possible capacitance will be preferred for the series capacitor C_S, and the smallest for the shunt capacitance C_P. The circuit of Figure 4-29 is therefore normally preferred to that of Figure 4-30. An exception would be the case in which the resonant circuit is meant to be additionally damped by means of the bias resistor at higher frequencies.

In the circuit of Figure 4-31, the resonant circuit is tuned by two tuner diodes

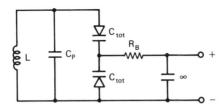

Figure 4-31   Parallel resonant circuit, with two tuner diodes.

which are connected in parallel via the coil for tuning purposes, but series-connected in opposition for high-frequency signals. This arrangement has the advantage that the capacitance shift caused by the ac modulation takes effect in opposite directions in these diodes and therefore cancels itself. The bias resistor R_B which applies the tuning voltage to the tuner diodes is transformed into the circuit at a constant ratio throughout the whole tuning range. Given two identical, loss-free tuner diodes, we obtain the expression

$$R_c = 4R_B \tag{4-61}$$

Capacitances Connected in Parallel or in Series with the Tuner Diode. Figures 4-29 and 4-30 show that a capacitor is usually in series with the tuner diode, in order to close the circuit for alternating current and, at the same time, to isolate one terminal of the tuner diode from the rest of the circuit with respect to direct current, so as to enable the tuning voltage to be applied to the diode. If possible, the value of the series capacitor C_S will be chosen such that the effective capacitance variation is not restricted. However, in some cases, for example in the oscillator circuit of receivers whose intermediate frequency is of the order of magnitude of the reception frequency, this is not possible and the influence of the series capacitance will then have to be taken into account. By connecting the capacitor C_S, assumed to be loss-free, in series with the diode capacitance C_{tot}, the tuning capacitance is reduced to the value

$$C^* = C_{tot} \frac{1}{1 + C_{tot}/C_S} \tag{4-62}$$

The Q-factor of the effective tuning capacitance, taking into account the Q-factor of the tuner diode, increases to

$$Q^* = Q\left(1 + \frac{C_{\text{tot}}}{C_S}\right) \tag{4-63}$$

The useful capacitance ratio is reduced to the value

$$\frac{C_{\max}^*}{C_{\min}^*} = \frac{C_{\max}}{C_{\min}} \frac{1 + C_{\min}/C_S}{1 + C_{\max}/C_S} \tag{4-64}$$

wherein $C_{\max}$ and $C_{\min}$ are the maximum and minimum capacitance of the tuner diode.

On the other hand, the advantage is gained that, due to capacitive potential division, the amplitude of the alternating voltage applied to the tuner diode is reduced to

$$\hat{v}^* = \hat{v}\,\frac{1}{1 + C_{\text{tot}}/C} \tag{4-65}$$

so that the lower value of the tuning voltage can be smaller, and this results in a higher maximum capacitance $C_{\max}$ of the tuner diode and a higher useful capacitance ratio. The influence exerted by the series capacitor, then, can actually be kept lower than Eq. (4-63) would suggest.

The parallel capacitance C_P which appears in Figures 4-29 to 4-31 is always present, since wiring capacitances are inevitable and every coil has its self-capacitance. By treating the capacitance C_P, assumed to be loss-free, as a shunt capacitance, the total tuning capacitance rises in value and, if C_S is assumed to be large enough to be disregarded, we obtain

$$C^* = C_{\text{tot}}\left(1 + \frac{C_P}{C_{\text{tot}}}\right) \tag{4-66}$$

The Q-factor of the effective tuning capacitance, derived from the Q-factor of the tuner diode, is

$$Q^* = Q\left(1 + \frac{C_P}{C_{\text{tot}}}\right) \tag{4-67}$$

or, in other words, it rises with the magnitude of the parallel capacitance. The useful capacitance ratio is reduced:

$$\frac{C_{\max}^*}{C_{\min}^*} = \frac{C_{\max}}{C_{\min}} \frac{1 + C_P/C_{\max}}{1 + C_P/C_{\min}} \tag{4-68}$$

In view of the fact that even a comparatively small shunt capacitance reduces the capacitance ratio considerably, it is necessary to ensure low wiring and coil capacitances in the layout stage.

Tuning Range. The frequency range over which a parallel resonant circuit according to Figure 4-29 can be tuned by means of the tuner diode depends on the useful capacitance ratio of the diode and on the parallel and series capacitances present in the circuit. The ratio is

$$\frac{f_{\max}}{f_{\min}} = \sqrt{\frac{1 + \dfrac{C_{\max}}{C_P(1 + C_{\max}/C_S)}}{1 + \dfrac{C_{\max}}{C_P(C_{\max}/C_{\min} + C_{\max}/C_S)}}} \tag{4-69}$$

In many cases the series capacitor can be chosen large enough for its effect to be negligible. In that case, Eq. (4-69) is simplified as follows:

$$\frac{f_{\max}}{f_{\min}} = \sqrt{\frac{1 + C_{\max}/C_P}{1 + C_{\min}/C_P}} \tag{4-70}$$

From this equation, the diagram shown in Figure 4-32 is computed. With the aid of

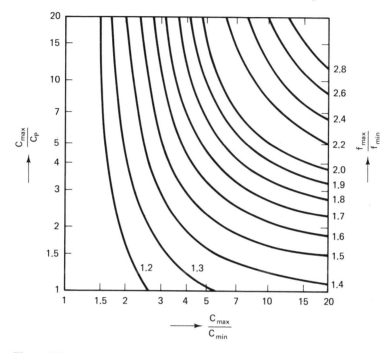

Figure 4-32 Diagram for determining the capacitance ratio and maximum capacitance. (Courtesy of ITT Semiconductors, Freiburg, West Germany.)

this diagram the tuning diode parameters required for tuning a resonant circuit over a stipulated frequency range (i.e., the maximum capacitance and the capacitance ratio) can be determined. Whenever the series capacitance C_s cannot be disregarded, the effective capacitance ratio is reduced according to Eq. (4-64).

Tracking.   When several tuned circuits are used on the same frequency, diodes have to be selected for perfect tracking.

Practical Circuits.   After so much theory, it may be nice to take a look at some practical circuits such as the one shown in Figure 4-22. This oscillator is being used in the Rohde & Schwarz ESH2/ESH3 field strength meter and in the HF1030 receiver to be produced by Cubic Communications, San Diego. This circuit combines all the various techniques shown previously. A single diode is being used for fine tuning a narrow range of less than 1 MHz; coarse tuning is achieved with the antiparallel diodes.

Several unusual properties of this circuit are apparent:

1. The fine tuning is achieved with a tuning diode that has a much larger capacitance than that of the coupling capacitor to the circuit. The advantage of this technique is that the fixed capacitor and the tuning diode form a voltage divider whereby the voltage across the tuning diode decreases as the capacitance increases. For larger values of the capacitance of the tuning diode, the Q changes and the gain K_0 increases. Because of the voltage division, the noise contribution and loading effect of the diode are reduced.

2. In the coarse-tuning circuit, several tuning diodes are used in parallel. The advantage of this circuit is a change in LC ratio by using a higher C and storing more energy in the tuned circuit. There are no high-Q diodes available with such large capacitance values, and therefore preference is given to using several diodes in parallel rather than one tuning diode with a large capacitance, normally used only for AM tuner circuits.

I have mentioned previously that, despite this, the coarse-tuning circuit will introduce noise outside the loop bandwidth where it cannot be corrected. It is, therefore, preferable to incorporate switching diodes for segmenting ranges at the expense of switching current drain.

Figure 4-33 shows a circuit using a combined technique of tuning diodes for fine- and medium-resolution tuning and coarse tuning with switching diodes. The physics and technique of using switching diodes is explained in the next Section.

4-1-5 Use of Diode Switches

The diode switches described here differ somewhat from the switching diodes used in computer and pulse technology. In normal diodes, the signal itself triggers the switching operation—current does or does not pass through the switching diode in dependence on the signal level. Diode switches allow an alternating current to be switched on or off by application of a direct voltage or a direct current. The diode switches BA243, BA244, and the later version BA238 by ITT or the Motorola MPN 3401 series were developed especially for such a purpose and constitute the present state of the art. However, diodes can also be employed to advantage for switching audio signals (i.e., in tape recorders or amplifiers).

Diode switches for electronic band selection. The advantages of the electronic tuning of VHF–UHF circuits become fully effective only when band selection also takes place electronically and no longer by means of mechanically operated switching contacts subject to wear and contamination. Figure 4-34 shows an example of the use of diode switches.

Diode switches are preferable to mechanical switches because of their higher reliability and virtually unlimited life. Since the diode switches BA243 and BA244 permit range switching without mechanical contacts, and since they can be controlled in a similar way as capacitance diodes by the application of a direct current, there

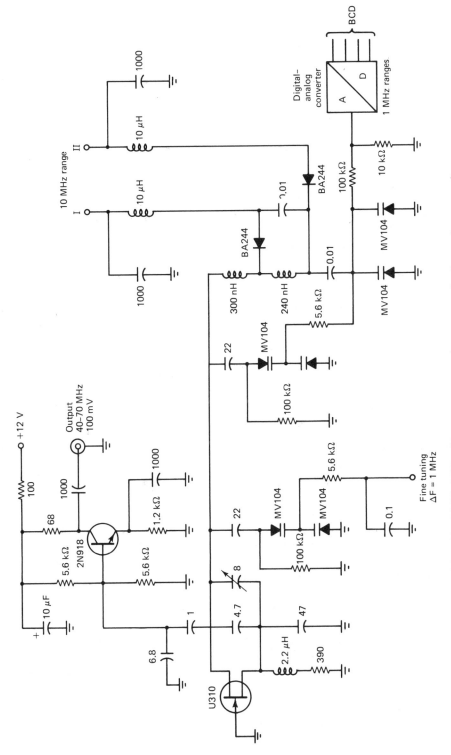

Figure 4-33 40–70 MHz VCO with two coarse-steering ranges and a fine-tuning range of 1 MHz.

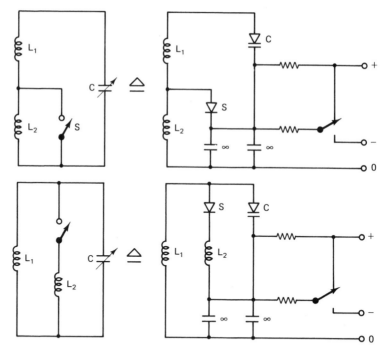

Figure 4-34 Comparison of mechanically and electronically tuned and switched resonant circuits. (Courtesy of ITT Semiconductors, Freiburg, West Germany.)

should be many new applications for these devices in remote control receivers. Their use obviates the need for mechanical links between the front-panel control and the tuned circuit to be switched, allowing a VHF–UHF circuit to be located in the most favorable place with regard to electrical or thermal influence, giving the designer more freedom in front-panel styling. Moreover, because the tuner is no longer subject to mechanical stress, its chassis may be injection-molded from a plastic material which can be plated for screening purposes. All this makes for smaller, more compact tuners and results in considerable savings in production.

Let us take a look at three oscillators that are designed around switching diodes. Figure 4-20 shows an oscillator that is used in the Rohde & Schwarz EK070 shortwave receiver and presets the value of the frequency within a few hundred kHz off the final frequency. The fine tuning then is accomplished by the use of varactor diodes or tuning diodes.

The advantage of using one oscillator for the entire frequency range lies in the fact that the switching speed is not slowed down by the settling time of an oscillator circuit being activated and showing the familiar initial drift phenomena.

The gain of the oscillator K_o now changes due to the parallel capacitance switched into the tuning diodes and the loop, therefore, requires some gain adjustments. This is further discussed in Section 4-7.

While the above circuit uses external AGC, which is frequently used with bipolar transistors, Figure 4-35 shows a similar circuit operating from 42 to 72 MHz using field effect transistors and switching diodes.

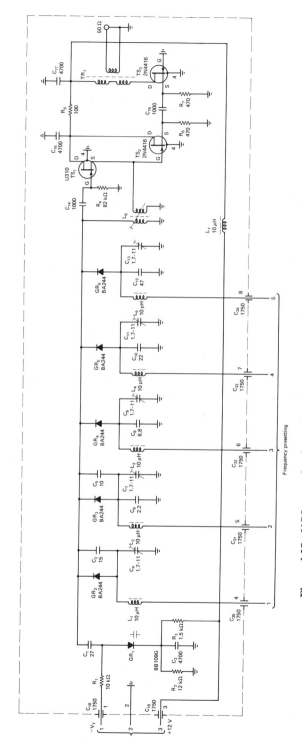

Figure 4-35 VCO operating from 42 to 72 MHz with coarse tuning by switching diodes and high-isolation output stage.

Those previously shown circuits switch capacitors rather than inductors. Figure 4-21 shows a circuit that is being used in the HP signal generator type 8962. High Q inductors are being switched in and out rather than capacitors, thereby avoiding the gain variation of the oscillator to a large degree.

This oscillator also uses a differential amplifier feedback circuit, and the advantage of this circuit is that the signal-to-noise ratio is further improved. Details on differential limiter low-noise design can be found in the literature [35].

4-1-6 Use of Diodes for Frequency Multiplication

In this section we have been dealing with free-running oscillators which are being locked to a reference with the PLL. I mentioned earlier that some synthesizer simplification is possible when using a heterodyne technique. The auxiliary frequency for this heterodyne action can be obtained from the frequency standard by multiplication. There are a number of ways in which to obtain harmonic outputs, and probably the best one is the highest frequency of operation and the use of special diodes, such as step recovery diodes or snap-off diodes, for this purpose. This application would lead us into microwave techniques, which are beyond the scope of this book. Figure 4-36 shows a schematic of a 100–1700 MHz frequency multiplier. More information about frequency multiplication is found in the references at the end of this section.

4-2 REFERENCE FREQUENCY STANDARDS

4-2-1 Requirements

Frequency standards are the heart of the synthesizer, as they control the accuracy of the frequency (if we are dealing with a phase coherent synthesizer) and within the loop bandwidth, the noise sideband performance of the synthesizer.

There are several frequency standards available, and basically they can be put in three categories:

1. Cesium frequency standards
2. Rubidium frequency standards
3. Crystal oscillators

Only crystal oscillators are currently being incorporated in frequency synthesizers. The short-term stability and noise of the crystal oscillator is typically equal to the rubidium frequency standard and better than a cesium standard. Depending on the price and the performance of the synthesizer, we find frequency standards from a simple crystal oscillator to a temperature-compensated crystal oscillator or a crystal oscillator in a proportionally controlled oven. Let us take a look at Table 4-1, which shows the performance of a temperature-compensated crystal oscillator.

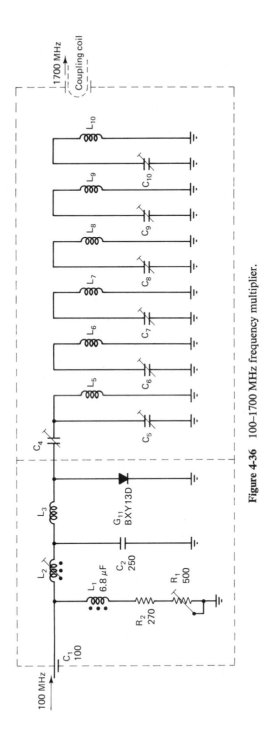

Figure 4-36 100–1700 MHz frequency multiplier.

TABLE 4-1 SPECIFICATIONS FOR A TYPICAL
TEMPERATURE-COMPENSATED CRYSTAL OSCILLATOR

Temperature stability	-20 to $+70°C$
Center frequency	10 MHz
Output level	1 V rms into 1000 Ω
Supply voltage	15 V $\pm$ 5%
Current	5 to 15 mA
Aging	5×10^{-7} per year,
	3×10^{-9} per day average
Short-term	1×10^{-9} per second under constant environment
Stability vs. supply	2×10^{-8} per 1% change in supply voltage
Frequency adjustment	Range sufficient to compensate for 5 to 10 years of crystal aging: setable to $<1 \times 10^{-7}$
Electronic tuning	Permits remote frequency adjustment or locking on to an external frequency source

These temperature-compensated crystal oscillators are typically used in frequency synthesizers of medium-phase noise requirements; also, the short-term stability is not very good compared to a high-performance oscillator such as a double proportional oven-controlled device.

4-2-2 Typical Examples for Frequency Standards

Let us assume that we have a frequency synthesizer that has a comb generator and locks a loop on the appropriate harmonic of the crystal oscillator. In this case, within the loop bandwidth, the phase noise is multiplied up, and therefore, the noise sideband performance of the TCXO is reflected in the loop performance.

Depending on the design of the frequency synthesizer, whether the loops are using dividers, or whether straight multiplication appears at the output, the noise sideband requirements on the crystal oscillator and the frequency standard may differ. In the medium price range, it has become customary to use either temperature-compensated crystal oscillators that can be locked onto an external standard or simple crystal oscillators with proportionally controlled ovens which are optimized for noise sideband performance rather than for aging.

It can be shown that the signal-to-noise ratio and the noise sideband performance of the oscillator depend on the drive level of the crystal. There is a direct relationship between drive level and aging. Typically, a dissipation of 50 μW is applied to a low-aging crystal, while the noise performance suffers as a result of this low drive level. In many cases, therefore, additional circuitry is required to reduce the sideband noise. There are currently two ways of doing this:

1. Insert an external additional crystal that filters out the close-in noise
2. Use the crystal oscillator in such a way that the crystal also acts as a noise filter. We will see this in Section 4-7.

In high-performance frequency synthesizers, we do not want to be dependent on the availability of external standards, and a high-performance crystal oscillator such as the Rohde & Schwarz XSF frequency standard is an appropriate choice. Table 4-2 shows the most important characteristics.

TABLE 4-2 SPECIFICATIONS FOR A HIGH-PERFORMANCE CRYSTAL OSCILLATOR FOR THE HIGH-PERFORMANCE ROHDE & SCHWARZ XSF

Frequency	5 MHz
Crystal	5 MHz fifth overtone
Frequency error	1×10^{-10} per day after 30 days of continuous operation; 5×10^{-10} per day after 5 days of operation

Short-term stability	Averaging time (s)	Stability
	10^{-3}	1.5×10^{-10}
	10^{-2}	1.5×10^{-11}
	10^{-1}	5×10^{-12}
	10^{0}	5×10^{-12}
	10^{1}	5×10^{-12}
	10^{2}	1×10^{-11}

Recent development in new crystal techniques such as the stress-compensated crystal, together with improved design of crystal oscillators, has improved the noise performance. Table 4-3 shows the noise sideband performance as a function of frequency for a cesium atomic frequency standard, a rubidium frequency standard, and a crystal oscillator.

TABLE 4-3 FREQUENCY STABILITY OF VARIOUS FREQUENCY SOURCES (ROHDE & SCHWARZ)

Offset from signal f (Hz)	Phase noise ratio, $\mathcal{L}(f)$ (dB/Hz)		
	XSC cesium standard	XSRM rubidium standard	XSD2 crystal oscillator
10^{-3}	-10	-35	
10^{-2}	-30	-62	
10^{-1}	-50	-80	
10^{0}	-85	-105	-90
10^{1}	-125	-132	-120
10^{2}	-140	-140	-140
10^{3}	-144	-145	-157
10^{4}	-150	-150	-160

By definition, the cesium atomic frequency standard is a primary standard and does not require any calibration during the lifetime of the tube. We will take a look at the mechanism of a rubidium frequency standard later, as it contains a phase-locked loop. The cesium frequency standard is based on the invariant resonance frequency of the cesium atoms as they are passing through a microwave cavity, maintaining the output frequency of the cesium standard constant to an extremely high accuracy. In the rubidium frequency standard, a buffer gas is required to reduce collisions between the rubidium atoms and the gas cell, and the resonant frequency varies slightly with the pressure of the buffer gas and is more susceptible to other influences. As a result, the rubidium standard has to be calibrated and the frequency drifts slowly with time because of small changes in gas pressure and other effects within the cell and lamp. As can be seen, the rubidium cell has a higher signal-to-noise ratio, which results in excellent short-term stability and lower cost of the device because of simple design.

For most applications and in-house tests, a cesium frequency standard is not required.

A rubidium standard is a recommended laboratory standard, especially when crystal oscillators are being designed and phase noise comparison has to be made. Although we will take a brief look at a rubidium frequency standard to understand how it works, our main interest now lies in the crystal oscillator.

4-2-3 Crystal Specifications

The crystal, together with the proportionally controlled oven and the electronic circuit, determine the quality and performance of the frequency standard. Tables 4-4, 4-5, and 4-6 show the required specifications for a 5-MHz third-overtone, 10-MHz third-overtone, and 5-MHz fifth-overtone crystal. The crystal becomes "stiffer" as the mode increases. This means that a 5-MHz fifth-overtone is stiffer and allows less pulling than a third-overtone crystal.

TABLE 4-4 SPECIFICATIONS FOR A HIGH-PRECISION 5-MHz THIRD-OVERTONE CRYSTAL[a] (5M3-A1851)

1. Crystal enclosure	Type A1851 or A1851/L (HC-27/U or with wires)
2. Nominal frequency	$f_0 = 5$ MHz (third-overtone mode)
3. Frequency adjustment tolerance	$\frac{\Delta f}{f_0} \pm 1 \times 10^{-6}$ at turnover point of frequency curve
4. Load capacitance	$C_L = 30$ pF parallel resonance
5. Turnover point	In the range $+60$ to $+80°C$; if the turnover point is specified, tolerance is $\pm 5°C$
6. Temperature coefficient	$< 1 \times 10^{-8}$ per °C $\pm 0.5°C$ at the turnover point
7. Long-time stability (aging)	$\frac{\Delta f}{f_0} \leq 5 \times 10^{-10}$ per day after 3 days
	$\leq 3 \times 10^{-10}$ per day after 30 days
	$\leq 10 \times 10^{-8}$ per year after 90 days
8. Short-time stability	$\frac{\Delta f}{f_0} \leq 3 \times 10^{-11}$ integrating time 0.1 s over 10 s
9. Shutoff and restart	$\leq 1 \times 10^{-9}$ 24 h after restart

TABLE 4-4   (CONT.)

10. Motional resistance	$R_1 \leq 50\ \Omega$
11. Quality factor	$Q \geq 1 \times 10^6$
12. Motional inductance	$L_1 = 2.1\ \text{H} \pm 20\%$
13. Shunt capacitance	$C_0 \leq 5\ \text{pF}$
14. Crystal current	$J \leq 100\ \mu\text{A}$

[a]Courtesy of Quarzkeramik, a member of the Rohde & Schwarz group.

TABLE 4-5   SPECIFICATIONS FOR A HIGH-PRECISION 10-MHz THIRD-OVERTONE CRYSTAL[a]   (10M3-A1851)

1. Crystal enclosure	Type A1851 or A1851/L (HC-27/U or with wires)
2. Nominal frequency	$f_0 = 10$ MHz (third-overtone mode)
3. Frequency adjustment tolerance	$\dfrac{\Delta f}{f_0} \pm 1 \times 10^{-6}$ at turnover point of frequency curve
4. Load capacitance	$C_L = 30$ pF parallel resonance
5. Turnover point	In the range $+60$ to $+80°$C; if the turnover point is specified, tolerance is $\pm 5°$C
6. Temperature coefficient	$< 1 \times 10^{-8}$ per °C $\pm 0.5°$C at the turnover point
7. Long-time stability (aging)	$\dfrac{\Delta f}{f_0} \leq 5 \times 10^{-10}$ per day after 3 days
	$\leq 3 \times 10^{-10}$ per day after 30 days
	$\leq 10 \times 10^{-8}$ per year after 90 days
8. Short-time stability	$\dfrac{\Delta f}{f_0} \leq 10 \times 10^{-11}$ integrating time 0.1 s over 10 s
9. Shutoff and restart	$\dfrac{\Delta f}{f_0} \leq 2 \times 10^{-9}$ 24 h after restart
	$\leq 5 \times 10^{-10}$ 72 h after restart
10. Motional resistance	$R_1 \leq 55\ \Omega$
11. Quality factor	$Q \geq 1 \times 10^6$
12. Motional inductance	$L_1 = 0.9\ \text{H} \pm 20\%$
13. Shunt capacitance	$C_0 \leq 6\ \text{pF}$
14. Crystal current	$J \leq 100\ \mu\text{A}$

[a]Courtesy of Quarzkeramik, a member of the Rohde & Schwarz group.

TABLE 4-6   SPECIFICATIONS FOR A HIGH-PRECISION 5-MHz FIFTH-OVERTONE CRYSTAL[a]   (5M5-A20)

1. Crystal enclosure	Type A20 vacuum-sealed hard glass
2. Nominal frequency	$f_0 = 5$ MHz (fifth-overtone mode)
3. Frequency adjustment tolerance	$\dfrac{\Delta f}{f_0} \pm 1 \times 10^{-6}$ at turnover point of frequency curve
4. Load capacitance	$C_L = 32$ pF parallel resonance
5. Turnover point	In the range $+70$ to $+85°$C; if the turnover point is specified, tolerance is $2°$C
6. Temperature coefficient	$< 3 \times 10^{-8}$ per °C $\pm 0.5°$C at the turnover point

TABLE 4-6 (CONT.)

7. Long-time stability (aging)	$\dfrac{\Delta f}{f_0} \le 5 \times 10^{-10}$ per day after 3 days
	$\le 1 \times 10^{-10}$ per day after 30 days
	$\le 2.5 \times 10^{-8}$ per year after 90 days
8. Short-time stability	$\dfrac{\Delta f}{f_0} \le 5 \times 10^{-11}$ integrating time 0.1 s over 10 s
9. Shutoff and restart	$\le 1 \times 10^{-9}$ 24 h after restart
	$\le 5 \times 10^{-10}$ 72 h after restart
10. Motional resistance	$R_1 \le 140\ \Omega$
11. Quality factor	$Q \ge 2 \times 10^6$
12. Motional inductance	$L_1 = 9.2\ \text{H} \pm 20\%$
13. Shunt capacitance	$C_0 \le 5\ \text{pF}$
14. Crystal current	$J \le 70\ \mu\text{A}$

[a]Courtesy of Quarzkeramik, a member of the Rohde & Schwarz group.

The majority of manufacturers of frequency synthesizers, however, build their own frequency standards, as very precise frequency standards are highly expensive. In addition, frequency synthesizers use auxiliary frequencies generated by a crystal oscillator phase locked to the master standard. A substantial amount about the crystal, the various cuts, and its performance, as well as knowledge about the optimum design of crystal oscillators, will be presented in the following sections.

4-2-4 Crystal Oscillators

Fundamental mode AT cut crystals. The most popular crystal cut is the AT cut. AT crystals are thickness–shear vibrators. They cover a fundamental frequency range from approximately 750 kHz to 20 MHz (and some exceptions from 500 kHz to 30 MHz).

Table 4-7 gives the frequency ranges of the various crystal shapes together with their typical equivalent data (1 fF = 10^{-3} pF) which are required for physical reasons. The temperature response is a third-order parabola whose form can be influenced by selection of the cutting angle. It is given in ppm.

$$\frac{\Delta f}{f} = a_1(T - T_{\text{inv}}) + a_3(T - T_{\text{inv}})^3 \qquad (4\text{-}71)$$

where the coefficients are

$$a_1 \approx -0.084 \times \Delta\phi$$
$$a_3 \approx 10^{-4}$$

The inversion temperature T_{inv} is in the order 22 to 33°C according to the range. $\Delta\phi = \phi_0 - \phi$ is the angular difference (in minutes of arc) to the zero TC angle ϕ_0 (at this cut angle the temperature coefficient will be zero at the inversion point).

As shown in Table 4-7, the typical resonance resistance R_1 will be between 10 and 500 Ω and decreases with increasing frequency.

TABLE 4-7 EQUIVALENT DATA OF AT FUNDAMENTAL CRYSTALS

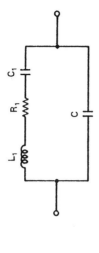

Shape of crystal	Frequency range (MHz) for cases			Typical equivalent data[a]			
	HC-6/U	HC-25/U	HC-35/HC-45	C_0	C_1	Q	R_1
Biconvex	0.75–1.5	—	—	3–7 pF	8 fF	> 100 000	100–500 Ω
Planoconvex	1.5–3	2.7–5.2	—	4–7 pF	10 fF	> 100 000	<200 Ω
Planoparallel with bevel	2–7	4.5–10.5	10–13	5–7 pF	20 fF [10 fF]	> 50 000	10–100 Ω
Plane	7–20 (30)	10.5–20 (30)	13–20 (30)				

[a]Values in brackets are for HC-35/HC-45.

185

The most common type of circuit for fundamental AT crystals are aperiodic oscillators, that is, oscillators without additional selectivity. The most important types of parallel-resonant oscillators are Pierce, Colpitts, and Clapp oscillators, which can be derived from a circuit by varying the ground point (Figure 4-37). The crystal operates at a point where it exhibits the same characteristic as a high Q inductance.

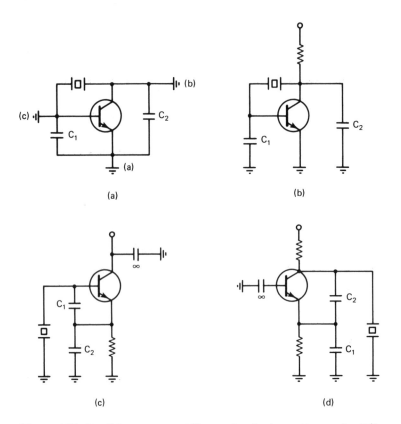

Figure 4-37 Parallel-resonance oscillators for fundamental crystals (RF equivalent diagram): (a) general circuit; (b) Pierce oscillator; (c) Colpitts oscillator; (d) Clapp oscillator. (Courtesy of Kristall-Verarbeitung Neckarbischofsheim GMBH.)

A circuit equipped with a Darlington stage is shown in Figure 4-38 as an example of the successful Colpitts oscillator. Because of the high input impedance, it is possible for the divider capacitors C_1 and C_2 to take on large values. This means that the reaction of the transistor stage on the oscillator frequency is very small. The effective load capacitance of the crystal is represented by the series connection of C_1 and C_2. In order to obtain suitable standard values of approximately 30 pF (typical range 10 to 50 pF), an additional capacitance of this order should be placed in series with the crystal in practice in order to align the crystal frequency.

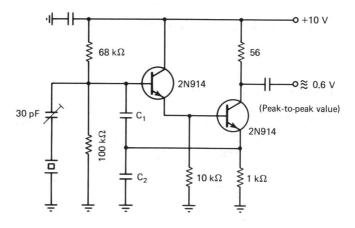

Frequency (MHz)	C_1 (pF)	C_2 (pF)
3–6	560	470
6–15	560	220
15–30	220	100

Figure 4-38 Colpitts oscillator with Darlington stage suitable for fundamental crystals. (Courtesy of Kristall-Verarbeitung Neckar-bischofsheim GMBH.)

A disadvantage of aperiodic oscillator circuits is the tendency to oscillate at the third or higher overtone of the crystal, or at a nonharmonic spurious resonance. In difficult cases, capacitance C_2 should be replaced by a resonant circuit, which is detuned so that it is capacitive at the nominal frequency (principle of the Tritet oscillator).

Generally speaking, the positive feedback should not be greater than required for starting and maintaining stable oscillation. In the case of the Colpitts circuit, the values of C_1 and C_2 can be derived from the following equations:

$$\frac{C_1}{C_2} = \sqrt{\frac{r_{be}}{r_a}} \tag{4-72}$$

$$C_1 C_2 = \frac{g'm}{\omega_o^2 R_1'} \tag{4-73}$$

where r_{be} = (RF) impedance between base and emitter (of the Darlington)

r_a = ac output impedance (measured at the common emitter)

$g'm$ = transconductance (= $1/R_{in}$ with an emitter follower)

R_1 = resonant resistance of the crystal transformed by the load capacitance

Figure 4-39 gives an example of a Pierce oscillator for 1 MHz equipped with a MOSFET [27]. A TTL output level is available if the output of the crystal oscillator drives a Schmitt trigger (7413). Such an oscillator is a suitable clock for frequency counters.

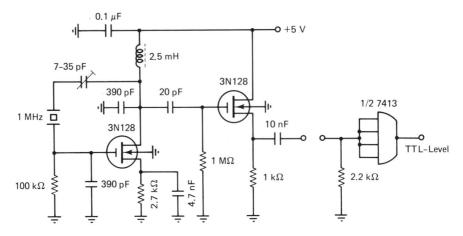

Figure 4-39 Crystal oscillator equipped with a MOSFET. (Courtesy of Kristall-Verarbeitung Neckarbischofsheim GMBH.)

Overtone AT-crystal oscillators.   If a thickness–shear vibrator is excited at an overtone, the crystal disk will oscillate in several subdisks in antiphase (see Table 4-8). Only odd overtones can be excited. The fundamental frequency of an AT crystal is inversely proportional to the thickness of the disk. For instance, a fundamental crystal for 30 MHz will have a thickness of approximately 55 μm. If this crystal is now excited at the third overtone (i.e., at 90 MHz), the electrical effective subdisk thickness will be one-third, which amounts to approximately 18 μm.

However, the overtone frequency is not exactly a multiple of the fundamental mode frequency, but this so-called "anharmony" will become smaller with increasing overtones order. For this reason, it is relatively simple to operate crystal oscillators up to $\approx$ 300 MHz, although the usual upper frequency limit is 200 MHz/ninth overtone; one can operate the crystal at the eleventh or thirteenth overtone, which is virtually exactly $\frac{11}{9}$ or $\frac{13}{9}$ times the ninth overtone. However, a crystal with the highest possible fundamental-frequency should be selected (20 to 30 MHz), so that the overtone modes are well spaced.

The typical equivalent data are given in Table 4-8. The motional capacitance C_1 reduces as the square of the overtone n:

$$C_{1\,typ} \sim \frac{1}{n^2} \tag{4-74}$$

The attainable Q-value will also fall on increasing frequency. For this reason, the R_1 values will increase, and will range typically from 20 to 200 Ω.

With increasing frequency, the static capacitance C_o will form an ever-increasing bypass for the crystal. The results of this can be seen in Figure 4-40. Given is the locus of the complex crystal impedance. In the vicinity of parallel and series resonance, it will represent a circle which cuts the real axis at f_s and f_p. The spacing of the center point of the circle from the real axis will become greater the lower the reactive resistance of C_o. At low values of X_{C_o}, the phase slope in the vicinity of series resonance will

TABLE 4-8 EQUIVALENT DATA OF AT OVERTONE CRYSTALS

Over-tone	Frequency range (MHz) for cases			Typical equivalent data[a]			
	HC-6/U	HC-25/U	HC-35/HC-45	C_0	C_1	Q	R_1
3	18–60 (80)	20–60 (90)	27–60 (90)	5–7 pF [2–4 pF]	2 fF [1 fF]	$> \dfrac{4 \times 10^6}{f\,(\mathrm{MHz})}$	20 Ω [40 Ω]
5	40–115 (130)	40–115 (150)	50–125		0.6–0.8 fF [0.4 fF]		40 Ω [80 Ω]
7	70–150	70–150	70–175		0.3–0.4 fF [0.2 fF]	$> \dfrac{5 \times 10^6}{f\,(\mathrm{MHz})}$	100 Ω [150 Ω]
9	150–200	150–200	150–200		0.2–0.3 fF [0.1 fF]		150 Ω [200 Ω]

[a]Values in brackets are for HC-35/HC-45.

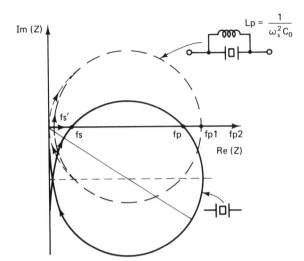

Figure 4-40 Locus of a crystal with and without C_0 compensation.

be lower; especially, the phase deviation will be less in the inductive direction. Finally, it can happen that the circumference no longer cuts the real axis, which means that no real resonant point exists at which the crystal is purely ohmic. For this reason the static capacitance should be compensated for by using a parallel inductance:

$$L_p = \frac{1}{\omega_s^2 C_o} \tag{4-75}$$

in excess of a certain limit.

A rule of thumb for this limit is: C_o compensation should be provided when $X_{C_o} < 5 \times R_1$, or generally in excess of 100 MHz.

The result of the compensation is given in Figure 4-40 as a dashed line. The locus is symmetrical to the real axis. However, two parallel resonances exist above and below f_s. The attainable total phase deviation is up to $\pm 90°$.

A compensating coil having a low Q ($R_p > 10\, R_1$) is suitable, and the compensation condition [29] need not be maintained exactly. It is sufficient to use a standard value inductance (or a corresponding number of turns wound on a 10-kΩ resistor).

Aperiodic oscillators will not operate reliably with overtone crystals, even when this is stated from time to time [28]. A resonant circuit should always be provided to avoid oscillation at the fundamental frequency.

When using a Pierce circuit as shown in Figure 4-37b, the collector capacitor can be replaced by a capacitively detuned circuit. Since overtone crystals are usually aligned in series resonance, this will result in a residual load capacitance for this circuit, which means that only customer-specified crystals will operate satisfactorily.

In order to pull the crystal frequency toward a lower value, an inductance is often connected in series with the crystal. However, it is possible for parasitic oscillations to be excited across this inductance I and the static capacitance of the crystal C_o, which could be difficult to neutralize.

It is therefore better to use a true series-resonant circuit, as shown in Figure 4-41.

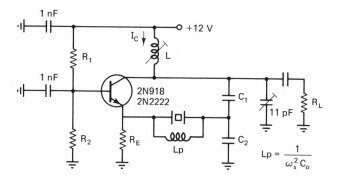

	75 MHz	120 MHz	150 MHz	200 MHz
C_1 [pF]	8	8	5	3
C_2 [pF]	100	50	25	20
I_c [mA]	25	25	5	5
R_E [Ω]	510	390	1.1 kΩ	1.1 kΩ
R_L [Ω]	470	300	600	600
Lp [μH]	0.25	0.10	0.08	0.05

Figure 4-41 Overtone crystal oscillator up to 200 MHz. (Courtesy of Kristall-Verarbeitung Neckarbischofsheim GMBH.)

The values of C_1 and C_2 are selected so that sufficient loop gain results. This is reduced both by the divider C_1/C_2 and by the voltage division across the crystal impedance and the input impedance at the emitter [8]

When selecting a suitable transistor, a rule of thumb is that the transit frequency should be at least 10 times that of the oscillator frequency. In addition to this, transistors are to be recommended that have high dc gain (h_{FE}) and low base resistance ($r_{bb'}$).

Load capacitance; oscillators with parallel and series resonance.

The designations "series" and "parallel" resonance are often combined in a confusing manner. In the case of series-resonance crystal oscillators, the crystal will oscillate together with its pulling elements at the low-impedance resonance. Such a case is the example of the Butler oscillator given in Figure 4-42. However, this does not mean that the oscillator operates at the series-resonance frequency of the crystal. The Butler remains a series-resonance oscillator, even when the crystal is pulled with the aid of a series capacitor, or even when (at higher frequencies) the phase angle of the transistor gain deviates from 0 or 180°.

On the other hand, another commonly used definition is not advisable: It states that a series-resonance oscillator is designated by the fact that the oscillator will also oscillate when the crystal is replaced by a resistor. If this were the case, the Butler oscillator given in Figure 4-42 would not be a series-resonance oscillator;

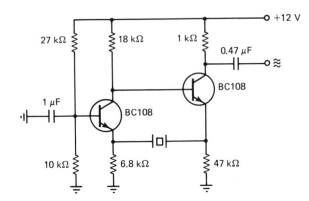

Figure 4-42 Buffer oscillator for 50 to 500 kHz. (Courtesy of Kristall-Verarbeitung Neckarbischofsheim GMBH.)

however, it would be if the collector resistor of transistor 1 was replaced by a resonant circuit.

A series load capacitance C_L will generate a new series resonance at

$$f_{C_L} = f_s\left[1 + \frac{C_1}{2(C_o + C_L)}\right] \tag{4-76}$$

In the case of a parallel-resonance oscillator, the oscillator will operate at a high-impedance resonance together with its adjacent (pulling) elements. In the case of the Colpitts oscillator shown in Figure 4-38, C_1 and C_2 are connected in series across the crystal. In the case of an ideal amplifier stage they will form the load capacitance C_L and reduce the parallel resonance frequency of the crystal to f_{C_L}. If this value of C_L is just as great as the series C_L in the upper case, the pulled series-resonance frequency will be the same as the pulled parallel-resonance in the last example. In both cases, the crystal will operate at a point at which it behaves as a high-Q inductance. This is summarized in Figure 4-43.

Crystals that are specified with a load capacitance are usually aligned by the manufacturer in conjunction with a series capacitor. However, since both measurements are equivalent, it is immaterial for the crystal specification whether a parallel or series resonance oscillator is to be used. It is sufficient for a load capacitance to be given. In this case it is advisable, if possible, to use standard values of C_L (i.e., 30 pF) by varying the other capacitances of the oscillator.

Frequency stability of crystal oscillators.

Long-term Stability. The long-term stability is dependent on the aging characteristics of the external components, especially on the Q of the resonant circuits and the damping effect of the transistors on the Q of the crystal. It is also dependent, of course, on the aging of the crystal, which differs according to the type of crystal and its drive level and will amount to a typical value of 1 to 3×10^{-6} per year during the first year. Since the aging is reduced logarithmically as a factor of time, it is possible to reduce this by aging the crystal, if possible by the manufacturer, at a temperature between 85 and 125°C.

The drive level of the crystal should be as low as possible for an oscillator that

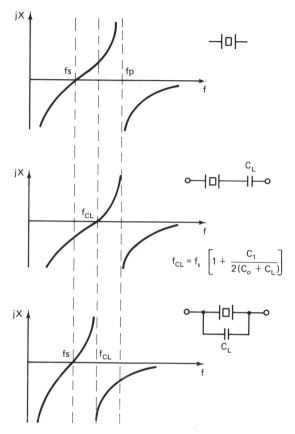

Figure 4-43 Crystals with load capacitances.

is to have a good long-term stability (1 to 20 μW). Because of their better temperature characteristics, AT crystals are preferable. When very stable crystal oscillators are required, relatively low-frequency overtone AT crystals should be used due to their higher Q and higher L_1/C_1 ratio. In this case, crystals operating at their third or fifth overtone of 5 or 10 MHz are used.

Short-term Stability.   The short-term stability of crystal oscillators was only of interest in the past for high-precision oscillators such as secondary frequency and time standards. Recently, however, this has become more and more important due to the widespread use of synthesizers in HF, and especially in VHF and UHF receivers, as well as for oscillator chains for the microwave frequencies.

The noise content at the output of a crystal oscillator

$$U(t) = [U_o + \epsilon(t)] \sin [\omega_o t + \phi(t)] \qquad (4\text{-}77)$$

will have a mean amplitude U_o, which will vary in the order of a noise component $\epsilon(t)$, and an overall phase with the center frequency ω_o, which has a noise component $\phi(t)$. Since a phase variation $d\phi/dt$ as a function of time is correlated with a frequency, this means that

$$f(t) = f_o + \frac{1}{2\pi} \frac{d\phi}{dt} \tag{4-78}$$

The oscillator signal will thus be modulated by the phase noise and will possess noise sidebands, which will be visible on a sensitive, selective spectrum analyzer.

In the receive mixer, the input signals are mixed with the oscillator signal and its noise sidebands. This means that a noise signal will be present in the passbands in addition to the selected input signal. This noise component can be so large that it is able to block the receiver [29, 30].

Simple methods of measuring phase noise were described in Refs. 31 and 32. Further details were given in Ref. 33. The measuring and evaluation method described by the IEC in Ref. 34 has found international recognition.

Details regarding the noise behavior of crystals are given in Refs. 35 and 36. The following aspects should be considered during the design of short-term, stable crystal oscillators:

In contrast to extremely long-term, stable crystal oscillators, the drive level to the crystal should be relatively high (100 to 500 μW) for this application.

The Q of the crystal will be dampened in any oscillator; in the case of single-stage, self-limiting oscillators, the effective Q will amount to only 15 to 20% of the Q of the crystal. Usually, series-resonance oscillators are more favorable than parallel-resonance oscillators.

In the case of bipolar transistors, the noise will be dependent primarily on the base–emitter path. In this case, the noise of PNP transistors will be lower than a complementary NPN transistor. MOSFETs have a very high noise level, where $1/f$ noise dominates at low frequencies, and thermal noise of the drain–source path at higher frequencies. Junction FETs possess lower noise levels than those of bipolar transistors and MOSFETs. For this reason, a high-current power FET such as type CP643 or P8000 [37] is recommended for low-noise crystal oscillators.

If bipolar transistors are to be used, one should select types with the highest possible dc gain (h_{FE}) but with very low base resistance ($r_{bb'}$) (i.e., typical VHF transistors), which should then be used at the lowest collector current.

However, the short-term stability can be improved by using the method described above (even including specially designed crystal). Single-stage crystal oscillators should be avoided. They possess a very high phase noise, since the transistor is driven into limiting. In this case, the collector base voltage will be virtually zero during part of the cycle, and the base–emitter threshold voltage (silicon: 0.6 V) will be exceeded. The transistor impedance that is "seen" by the crystal will fluctuate in time with the RF signal, which will generate strong noise sidebands on the oscillator signal.

This means that the limiting function of an amplifier stage connected to a crystal oscillator must be avoided. However, an amplitude control loop is unfavorable, since this could generate additional phase noise.

The best means of improving the short-term stability is to use a strong RF feedback. A well-proved circuit, introduced in 1972 by M. M. Driscoll [21], uses a third-overtone 5-MHz crystal. Since then, several circuits based on this have been published that possess very good short-term characteristics up to 100 MHz [38–41]. The basic circuit is given in Figure 4-44. It comprises a two-stage, three-pole oscillator

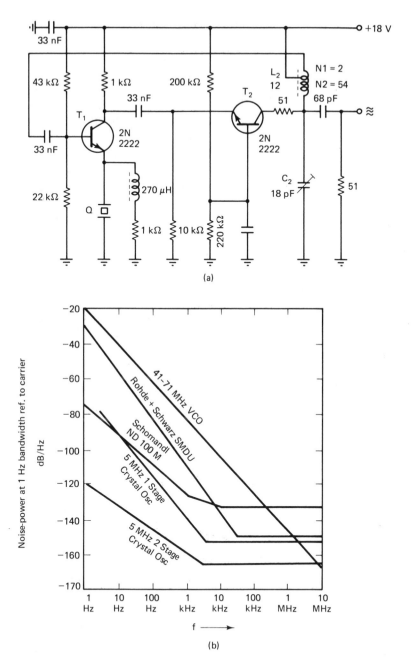

Figure 4-44 (a) Crystal oscillator (5 MHz/third overtone) with exceptional short-term stability; (b) Sideband noise of various signal generators compared to the 5-MHz oscillator shown in Figure 4-44a according to [42]. (Courtesy of Kristall-Verarbeitung Neckarbischofsheim GMBH.)

with the resonant circuit L_2/C_2. A cascode circuit is used as amplifier (low internal feedback), in which the first transistor is provided with feedback in the emitter circuit by the crystal (compensated with L_o). Transistor T_1 operates stably in class A ($I_C = 5$ mA). Transistor T_2 is isolated from the crystal and operates at a quiescent current of only 0.8 mA. This means that this stage is amplitude limited first and will determine the oscillation amplitude. The higher the series-resonance resistance R_1 (for a given Q) of the crystal, the better will be the short-term stability, since this will increase the negative feedback of T_1.

The crystal dissipation amounts to 85 μW in this oscillator, the RF output level will be in the order of 4 dBm, and the effective Q will amount to approximately 50% of the crystal Q. Figure 4-44b shows the results of measurements of phase noise that were given in Ref. 42.

The amplitude limiting can also be achieved with biased Schottky diodes connected in antiphase at the output of T_2 (due to the low $1/f$ noise of these diodes).

A low-noise oscillator that has been designed for use with a 96 MHz crystal according to this principle is shown in Figure 4-45. Power FETs of type P8000 are used

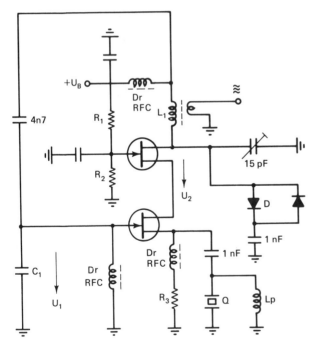

Figure 4-45 Recommended circuit for a short-term stable VHF crystal oscillator (96 MHz). (Courtesy of Kristall-Verarbeitung Neckarbischofsheim GMBH.)

and adjusted for stable class A (R1, R2, R3). The circuit is provided with a low feedback with the aid of C1 by selecting a relatively high capacitance value. The value of L_p is calculated according to

$$L_p = \frac{1}{\omega_s^2 C_o} \tag{4-79}$$

with $C_o = 5$ pF. Inductance L1 should have approximately 0.25 μH, and diodes D used for amplitude limiting are Schottky diodes such as HP2800.

For alignment, the limiting diodes should be disconnected and the crystal short-circuited. With the aid of the trimmer, the self-excited frequency is aligned to approximately 96 MHz. After connecting the crystal, compensation coil L_p is aligned to 96 MHz with the aid of a dipper with the oscillator switched off. The oscillator must commence crystal-controlled oscillation immediately on connecting the operating voltage. The RF amplitude will drop to approximately half the value of the self-limiting oscillator on connecting the diode (U_{limit}). More details on this circuit were published recently [49]. It is also possible to use the limiting characteristics of a subsequent differential amplifier instead of this [41].

Stable short-term crystal oscillators up to 100 MHz can be constructed according to this cascade principle with the crystal in the emitter circuit. A further reduction of the noise sidebands is obtained by placing a simple crystal filter after the crystal oscillator, as shown in Figure 4-46. L_2 is wound bifilar on a toroid core and aligned to

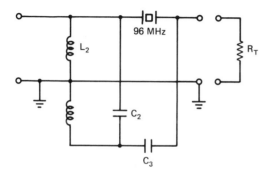

Figure 4-46 Simple crystal filter for reducing phase noise. (Courtesy of Kristall-Verarbeitung Neckarbischofsheim GMBH.)

the center frequency with the aid of C_2. The capacitance C_3 should be selected so that it is equal to the static capacitance C_o of the crystal. The terminating impedance [43] is

$$R_T = \frac{1}{2\pi f_o C_o} \tag{4-80}$$

where the bandwidth is dependent on the C_1/C_o ratio:

$$B = f_o \frac{C_1}{2C_o} \tag{4-81}$$

4-2-5 Schematic of a High-Performance Crystal Oscillator

Very few design engineers will attempt to build a low-noise frequency standard and most will probably buy an off-the-shelf item.

For those who like the challenge of getting involved and some hands-on experience, the following discussion will lead to the design of an ultra-low-noise crystal oscillator with exceptional stability. Its ultimate signal-to-noise ratio a few kilohertz off the carrier has been measured to be as low as 168 dB/Hz.

The design is based on a crystal oscillator that I had published previously in *Electronic Design* [50]. It uses the traditional Colpitts circuit, with a small resistor placed in series with the crystal. Under these circumstances, the crystal acts as a filter and because of the constant-current condition, harmonics are substantially reduced. Remember that the crystal in this operating mode is an inductor, and therefore the capacitive voltage divider attenuates the harmonics. (Figure 4-47).

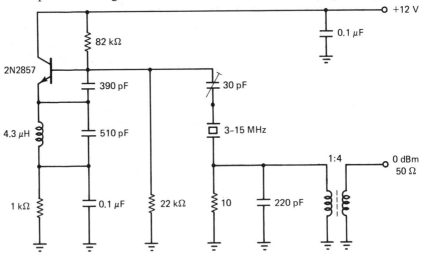

Figure 4-47   Low-noise crystal oscillator with high harmonic suppression.

Because of the fairly high series resistance, which is 20 to 30% of the loss resistor of the crystal, the Q is deteriorated. Figure 4-48 shows a modification of the principle of this circuit. Instead of using the resistor in series with the crystal, we now use a grounded base transistor which has an inherent low input impedance, for all practical purposes purely resistive, and 2 to 3 Ω in value. Relative to the 55 Ω that the crystal series resistor represents, this is now 5% or less, which means that the Q of the crystal has deteriorated by only a few percent. The same transistor can now be used as a low-noise amplifier to bring the output voltage to the required value, and an AGC circuit at the output will help to maintain the proper drive level at the crystal. We have learned that a drive level of less than 50 μW should be maintained. The inductor in the emitter prevents the crystal from oscillating at either its fundamental or at higher frequencies. It may not be commonly known that the noise figure of the grounded base transistor stage is extremely small when a fairly large drive impedance is used. Again the crystal operating in series mode provides such a condition, and therefore the noise figure can be kept extremely low. Probably the best transistor for this application but probably not readily available in the United States is the Siemens BFT66 or another member of this transistor family. The aging in this circuit is determined by the drive level and performance of the crystal, and a proportional thermostat should be used. Modern stress-compensated crystals can be used in this circuit, which will reduce oven requirements. However, my findings were that, as far as noise is

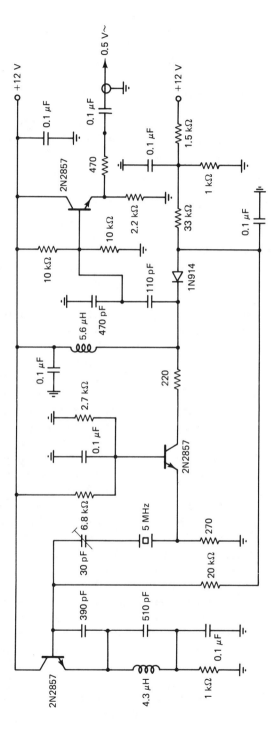

Figure 4-48 Recommended circuit for ultra-low-noise crystal oscillator with AGC.

concerned, no improvement was found. The Quarzkeramik crystals, which have an overproportionally high motional inductance relative to the other suppliers, are the best choice.

4-2-6 Atomic Frequency Standards

Where extremely high frequency stability is required, the crystal oscillator is not competitive. Atomic resonant effects can be used to synchronize a phase-locked loop.

There are three basic atomic standards:

1. The hydrogen maser
2. Cesium frequency standard
3. Rubidium standard

The hydrogen maser is a fairly large device and used as a primary standard. Its use under laboratory conditions is unlikely, and its main application is to measure age and drift of cesium atomic frequency standards. Therefore, it will not be covered here.

The cesium atomic frequency standard is considered a primary frequency standard. The cesium beam standard is an atomic resonant device which provides access to one of nature's invariant frequencies in accordance with the principles of quantum mechanics. The cesium standard is also a primary standard and requires no other reference or calibration. The rubidium frequency standard features a high order of both short-term and long-term frequency stability. Its aging or drift is typically 100 times smaller than the best quartz crystal standards, and its short-term stability or noise is better than that of a cesium frequency standard. This is the reason why the rubidium frequency standard should be used as an inexpensive, in-house frequency standard for many applications, such as synchronizing synthesizers and counters. Figure 4-49 shows the block diagram of a rubidium frequency standard. The rubidium-87 gas has an atomic resonant frequency of 6.834682641 GHz, which is extremely precise and scarcely influenced by the ambient conditions. A cylindrical resonant cell, which is surrounded by a cavity resonator of this frequency, is filled with a mixture of rubidium vapor and inert gas. A spectral lamp containing the same mixture is excited by an RF generator operating at 100 MHz. The entire cavity is stabilized by a thermostat, while a Peltier element produces a cool spot on the cavity resonator to condense the gas before it can deposit on the front face of the cavity. The cavity is excited via a coupling link by a storage varactor that receives its input from a multiplier. The constant magnetic field required for the atomic resonance is produced by a coil wound around the resonator, and the magnetic field can be adjusted externally. The output of the spectral lamp passes through the resonant cell and falls on a photodiode. If the cavity resonator is excited such that the high-frequency magnetic field with the rubidium resonance frequency builds up in the longitudinal direction of the resonant cell, the light attenuation of the resonant cell increases and the photodiode current decreases. The frequency at which light attenuation occurs can be

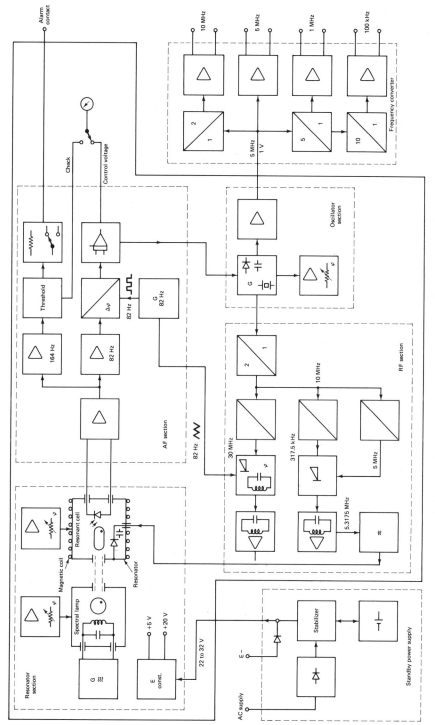

Figure 4-49 Block diagram of a rubidium frequency standard. (Courtesy of Rohde & Schwarz.)

slightly varied by means of the adjustable dc magnetic field generated in parallel to the resonant cell. The ovens mentioned previously virtually suppress effects of ambient temperature on the resonant cell and spectral lamp.

The 5-MHz crystal oscillator of extreme frequency stability generates several auxiliary frequencies. After doubling the 5 MHz up to 10 MHz, 20/63 MHz = 0.317 MHz is generated and 5 MHz is added. In addition, 30 MHz is generated from the 5-MHz oscillator. The varactor diode is driven from the 30 + 5.3175 MHz, resulting in the desired harmonic of 6.834 GHz.

The synthesizer input signal, and thus also the 6.834-GHz frequency in the cavity, is phase modulated with 82 Hz. When the average of the modulated 6.834-GHz frequency agrees exactly with the rubidium resonance frequency, the photodiode supplies a current with twice the modulation frequency (164 Hz). After selective amplification and detection, this signal is indicated on a meter. If the average of the modulated 6.834-GHz frequency does not agree with the rubidium resonance frequency, the photodiode delivers a current with the modulation frequency (82 Hz). After selective amplification, this signal is rectified with a phase-sensitive detector. The resulting voltage contains the magnitude and phase of the device from the center frequency as controlled criteria. It is used to pull the 5-MHz crystal oscillator.

4-3 MIXER APPLICATIONS

In multi-loop synthesizers, the heterodyne principle is used, and various frequencies are combined with mixers. For frequency synthesizer applications, only double-balanced mixers should be used. They fall into the following categories and are considered a component. Active mixers typically do not show enough suppression of unwanted frequencies as can be obtained in passive double-balanced mixers.

1. *Single-sideband mixer*. A single-sideband mixer is capable of delivering an IF output composed of one sideband only. Figure 4-50 shows a combination that provides the upper sideband at port A and the lower sideband at port B.

2. *Image-rejection mixers*. An LO frequency of 75 MHz and a desired RF frequency of 25 MHz would produce an IF difference frequency of 50 MHz. Similarly, an image frequency of 125 MHz at the mixer RF port would produce the same 50-MHz difference frequency. The image-rejection mixer shown in Figure 4-51 produces a desired IF difference frequency at port C while rejecting difference frequencies from RF signals which are greater than the LO frequency.

3. *Termination-insensitive mixers*. While the phrase "termination insensitive" is somewhat misleading, a combination as shown in Figure 4-52 results in a mixer design that allows a fairly high VSWR at the output without third-order intermodulation distortion being much affected by port mismatches.

Double-balanced mixers are manufactured by several companies; the best known are probably Anzac, Lorch, Mini-Circuit Laboratories, and Watkin-Johnson. Some of them specialize in high performance mixers at very high costs, others in large-volume inexpensive devices. It is advisable to contact the manufacturer before deciding

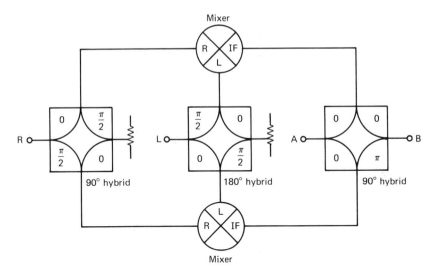

Figure 4-50   Single-sideband mixer. (Courtesy of Adams Russell, Anzac Division.)

on a particular mixer, as technology changes and new mixer combinations are being introduced. Most manufacturers supply detailed application reports and information about their mixers. Therefore, these details do not have to be covered here.

Table 4-9 is of interest as it shows the typical spurious response of a high-level double-balanced mixer and information about unwanted products to be gathered. In the Appendix, we find a program that calculates and determines all the frequency combinations.

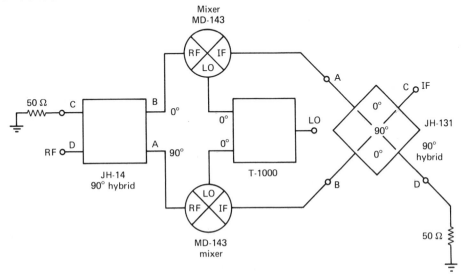

Figure 4-51   Image-rejection mixer. (Courtesy of Adams Russell, Anzac Division.)

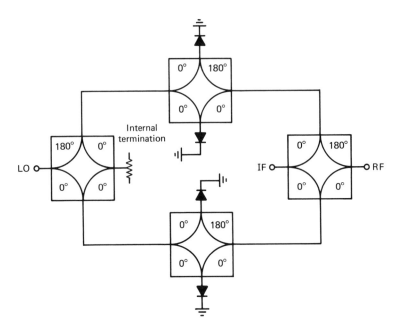

Figure 4-52   Termination-insensitive mixer. (Courtesy of Adams Russell, Anzac Division.)

Important: Make absolutely sure that the mixer sees a 50 Ω resistive load; this is achieved either by diplexer, resistive padding, or the use of feedback amplifiers that have 50Ω input impedance or grounded gate FET amplifiers using devices such as the CP643.

TABLE 4-9   TYPICAL SPURIOUS RESPONSE: HIGH-LEVEL DOUBLE-BALANCED MIXER[a]

Harmonics of f_{RF}		$1f_{LO}$	$2f_{LO}$	$3f_{LO}$	$4f_{LO}$	$5f_{LO}$	$6f_{LO}$	$7f_{LO}$	$8f_{LO}$
$8f_{RF}$	100	100	100	100	100	100	100	100	100
$7f_{RF}$	100	97	102	95	100	100	100	90	100
$6f_{RF}$	100	92	97	95	100	100	95	100	100
$5f_{RF}$	90	84	86	72	92	70	95	70	92
$4f_{RF}$	90	84	97	86	97	90	100	90	92
$3f_{RF}$	75	63	66	72	72	58	86	58	80
$2f_{RF}$	70	72	72	70	82	62	75	75	100
$1f_{RF}$	60	0	35	15	37	37	45	40	50
		60	60	70	72	72	62	70	70

[a]RF harmonic referenced to RF input signal; LO harmonic referenced to LO input signal. Spurious responses caused by internal harmonic generation and mixing of the input signals are shown. The mixing products are referenced in dB below the desired $f_{LO} \pm f_{RF}$ output or 0 level at f_{IF}. This performance can be typically attained with f_{LO} and f_{RF} at approximately 100 MHz, f_{LO} at $+17$ dBm, and f_{RF} at -0 dBm using broadband resistive terminations at all ports.

4-4 PHASE FREQUENCY COMPARATORS

In Chapter 1 we looked at the phase-locked loop as the fundamental building block of any synthesizer that uses its principle, and we decided to use two classifications, analog and digital loops. The main criterion was the phase/frequency comparator.

The phase/frequency comparator can be divided into two types:

1. Phase detectors
2. Phase/frequency comparators

This means that the phase comparator has limited means to compare two signals and only accepts phase, not frequency, information. In this case, particular measures have to be taken to pull the VCO into the locking range. The phase comparators require special locking help, and we dealt with this in Section 1-10. Here we are only analyzing the performance.

The phase detectors we will treat are the diode ring, the exclusive-OR gate, and the sample/hold comparator. The digital phase/frequency comparator (the exclusive-OR gate, because of the waveforms, is a digital device, and the sample/hold comparator because of its special signal processing, can also be considered in this category) comes in several versions. Here our main interest will be in the tri-state or sequential phase/frequency comparator.

4-4-1 Diode Rings

The diode ring is normally driven with two signals with sinusoidal waveform and also is some sort of a mixer. Here it will suffice to derive the gain characteristic K_θ of the device. If the input signal is $\theta_i = A_i \sin \omega_o t$, and the reference signal is $\theta_r = A_r \sin(\omega_o t + \phi)$, where ϕ is the phase difference between the two signals, the output signal θ_e is

$$\theta_e = \theta_i \theta_r = \frac{A_i A_r}{2} K \cos \phi - \frac{A_i A_r}{2} K \cos(2\omega_o t + \phi) \tag{4-82}$$

where K is the mixer gain. One of the primary functions of the low-pass filter is to eliminate the second harmonic term before it reaches the VCO. The second harmonic will be assumed to be filtered out and only the first term will be considered, so

$$\theta_e = \frac{A_i A_r}{2} K \cos \phi \tag{4-83}$$

When the error signal is zero, $\phi = \pi/2$. Thus the error signal is proportional to phase differences from 90°. For small changes in phase $\Delta\phi$,

$$\theta_e \simeq \frac{\pi}{2} + \Delta\phi = \frac{A_i A_r}{2} K \left[\cos\left(\frac{\pi}{2} + \Delta\phi\right) \right]$$
$$= \frac{A_i A_r}{2} K \sin \Delta\phi \tag{4-84}$$

For a small phase perturbation $\Delta\phi$,

$$\theta_e \simeq \frac{A_i A_r K}{2} \Delta\phi \qquad (4\text{-}85)$$

Since the phase detector output was assumed to be

$$\theta_e = K_\theta(\theta_i - \theta_o) \qquad (4\text{-}86)$$

the phase detector scale factor K_θ is given by

$$K_\theta = \frac{A_i A_r K}{2} \qquad (4\text{-}87)$$

The phase detector scale factor K_θ depends on the input signal amplitudes; the device can be considered linear only for constant-amplitude input signals and for small deviations in phase. For larger deviations in phase,

$$\theta_e = K_\theta \sin \Delta\phi \qquad (4\text{-}88)$$

which describes a nonlinear relation between θ_e and ϕ.

In frequency synthesizers, the reference is typically generated from a reference oscillator and is lower than the VCO frequency, which is divided by a programmable divider. Both signals, therefore, are square waves rather than sine waves, and theoretically, a diode ring can be driven from those two signals.

A drawback is that the output voltage of the diode ring is very small, about several hundred millivolts at most, and a post-amplifier is required, which is bound to generate noise. Some modification of this analog circuit is possible to increase the voltage.

Figure 4-53 shows a phase detector circuit used in the frequency synthesizer of the Rohde & Schwarz EK47 shortwave receiver. This balanced mixer arrangement has a limited capture range but supplies enough output voltage, and therefore does not require an additional amplifier. There are several possible combinations of this circuit, and because it is not a double-balanced mixer, some harmonics may be at the output, and care has to be taken to avoid having any unwanted spikes on the control line.

4-4-2 Exclusive ORs

The exclusive-OR gate is, to a certain degree, the equivalent of a balanced mixer. However, there are certain restrictions. Let us take a look at several waveform combinations. Figure 4-54 shows the case where two waveforms of equal frequency and different phase are applied, and the resulting output from the exclusive-OR gate. If the reference and the VCO waveform have the same duty cycle, the output of the phase/frequency discriminator is clearly defined. In the case of a phase shift of $\pi/2$, the output results in a square wave twice the frequency, with a duty cycle of 50%. If the waveforms do not have the same duty cycle, things become more complicated. If the VCO frequency is divided by a programmable counter, the pulses from the programmable divider are fairly narrow and thus the duty cycle becomes very small. It is possible, therefore, because of the unsymmetrical form of the waveform, that the output voltage is the same for two different phase errors, depending on the duty cycle.

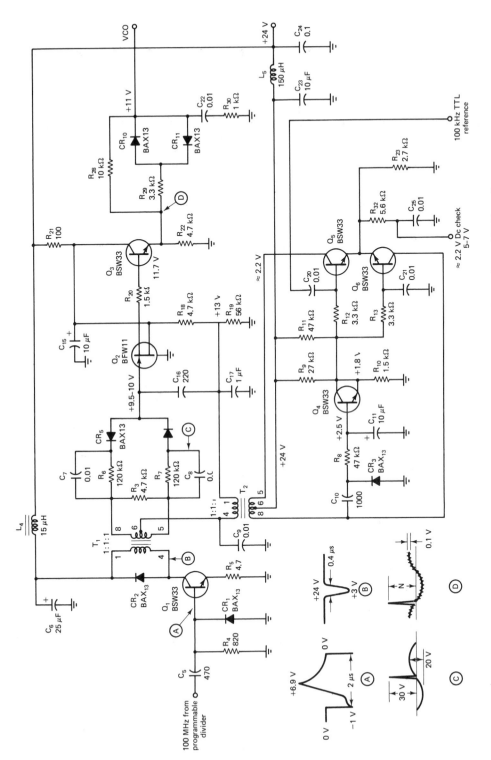

Figure 4-53 Phase detector circuit and loop filter for the Rohde & Schwarz EK47 receiver. (Courtesy of Rohde & Schwarz.)

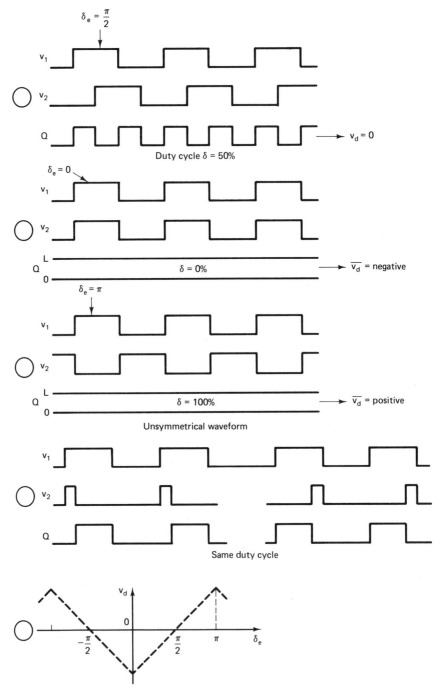

Figure 4-54 Performance of the exclusive-OR phase detector relative to different waveforms at the input.

To avoid difficulties, it is necessary to add an additional stage that acts as a pulse stretcher, and this pulse stretcher will make the waveform approximately symmetrical.

The exclusive-OR gate phase/frequency discriminator should really be used only in cases where the reference and VCO frequency are fairly high and very close together. Figure 4-55 shows a typical application where the exclusive OR gate is recommended.

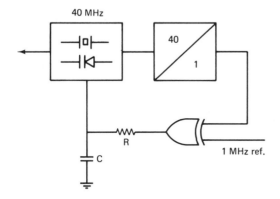

Figure 4-55 Block diagram of a 40-MHz single-loop synthesizer using an exclusive OR gate as phase detector.

A 40-MHz crystal oscillator is divided down by 10 and by 4 and provides 1 MHz of output. The reference oscillator is divided down to 1 MHz. Since the crystal oscillator at most will be 1 or 2 kHz off the reference frequency, it is well within the capture range of the exclusive-OR gate, and if both duty cycles are equal and 50%, the circuit can be made stable with a fairly simple RC low-pass filter. This is a type 1 second-order phase-locked loop and will follow the equations in Chapter 1. As the loop bandwidth can be made as narrow as 10 Hz, it will probably compensate only for temperature drift and aging of the crystal relative to the frequency standard.

Example 6

Let us assume that we have a crystal which can be pulled 2 kHz with 10 V, and that our phase detector operates from 0 to 5 V. The product $K = K_o K_\theta / N$ then equals 100 Hz. The 3-dB bandwidth of this simple synthesizer without any loop filter added would result in a loop bandwidth of 100 Hz. An additional filter would be required to reduce the loop bandwidth down to 10 Hz. In Section 1-10 we learned that there is a best frequency generated at the output of the phase detector, and the 10-Hz low-pass filter will attenuate the output voltage at the beat frequency.

Let us assume that our initial condition is that the 40-MHz crystal is aligned to be within 1 Hz of final frequency and that the loop is closed. For most receivers, a proportionally controlled crystal oscillator is used that has a warm-up time of 1 or 2 min for the internal standard to reach final frequency. As a result, the initial offset at the output can be 2000 Hz or 200 Hz at the phase/frequency comparator. In this case, our formula for the pull-in range applies,

$$T_p = \frac{\Delta\omega_o^2}{2\zeta\omega_n^3} \tag{4-89}$$

and we will insert the values

$$\Delta\omega = 2000 \times 2\pi$$
$$\zeta = 0.7$$
$$\omega_n = 10 \times 2\pi$$

or

$$T_p = \frac{2000}{1.4\pi} = 454 \text{ s}$$

However, as the final error after 1 min or 90 s approaches 1 Hz, the pull-in time T_p becomes 4.49 ms.

Most oven-controlled frequency standards have a type 2 second-order servo control system, and therefore the frequency of the frequency standard will go through the desired value and become higher, and then it will settle at the final frequency. Because of this, the frequency standard, so to speak, sweeps the 40-MHz crystal, and therefore the locking is made much faster than 454 s, even under the assumption that the initial frequency error was 2000 Hz because of aging or drift.

4-4-3 Sample/Hold Detectors

Phase detection can also be accomplished with a linear time-varying switch which is closed periodically. Mathematically, the switch can be described as a pulse modulator, as shown in Figure 4-56. If the operation of the sampling switch is periodic, that is,

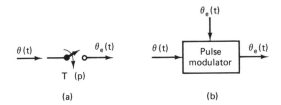

Figure 4-56   Switch shown as a pulse modulator.

(a)   (b)

if the sampler closes for a short interval P at instants $T = 0, T, 2T, \ldots, nT$, the sampling is uniform. The wave shapes of the input and output signals of a uniform rate sampling device are shown in Figure 4-57. The output can be considered to be

$$\theta_e(t) = \theta_i(t)\theta_r(t) \qquad (4\text{-}90)$$

where $\theta_r(t)$ can be assumed to be a periodic train of constant-amplitude pulses of

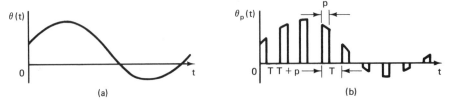

Figure 4-57   Input and output waveform of a uniform sampling device.

amplitude A_r, width p, and period T. Since $\theta_r(t)$ is periodic, it can be expanded in a Fourier series as [plot $\theta_r(t)$ here]

$$\theta_r(t) = \sum_{n=0}^{\infty} C_n \cos n\omega_o t \qquad (4\text{-}91)$$

where

$$C_n = \frac{2}{T} \int_{-P/2}^{P/2} \frac{A_r}{2} \cos n\omega_o t \, dt$$

$$= 2\frac{A_r}{T} \left[\left(\sin \frac{n\omega_o P}{2} \right) - \frac{1}{n\omega_o} \right] \quad (n \neq 0) \longrightarrow \frac{A_r}{T} P \quad (n \sim 0) \qquad (4\text{-}92)$$

Thus

$$\theta_r(t) = \frac{A_r}{T} P + \sum_{n=1}^{\infty} 2\frac{A_r}{T} \sin \frac{n\omega_o P/2}{n\omega_o} \cos n\omega_o t \qquad (4\text{-}93)$$

If the input signal is a sine wave,

$$\theta_i(t) = A_i[\sin (\omega_i t + \theta_i)] \qquad (4\text{-}94)$$

then

$$\theta_e(t) = \theta_r(t)\theta_i(t)$$

$$= \frac{A_i A_r}{T} \left\{ P \sin (\omega_i t + \theta) + \sum_{n=1}^{\infty} \sin \frac{n\omega_o P/2}{n\omega_o} \right. \qquad (4\text{-}95)$$

$$\times [\sin (n\omega_o + \omega_i)t + \theta_i] + \sin (\omega_i t + \theta_i - n\omega_o t) \}$$

when the loop is in lock ($\omega_i = \omega_o$). The dc term is

$$\theta_e(t)_{\text{dc}} = \frac{A_i A_r}{T} \sin \frac{\omega_o P/2}{\omega_o} (-\sin \theta_i) \qquad (4\text{-}96)$$

For small θ_i, the error signal is proportional to the phase difference θ_i. Therefore, the linear time-varying switch is able to serve as a phase detector. It differs from the mixer in that the dc output is zero when $\sin \theta_i = 0$, that is, when the oscillator and reference signal are in phase. The mixer type of phase detector is nulled when the two signals are in phase quadrature. Also, when the loop is in lock ($\omega_i = \omega_o$), the mixer output contains a dc term and the second harmonic, whereas the sampled output contains a dc term plus all harmonics of the input frequency. Therefore, the low-pass filter requirements for the sampling type of phase detector are more stringent than those for the sinusoidal mixer.

Fortunately, there are filters that can easily be implemented for the sampling PD. The most commonly used is the *zero-order data hold* (ZODH) or "boxcar generator." The zero-order data hold is a device that converts the pulse of width P to constant-amplitude pulses of width T, as shown in Figure 4-58. The output of the zero-order data hold $\theta_o(t)$ between the sampling instants t_i and t_{i+1} is

$$\theta_o(t) = \theta_e(t_i)[u(t) - u(t_i)] \qquad (4\text{-}97)$$

where $\theta_e(t_i)$ is the value of $\theta_e(t)$ at the sampling time t_i. Although the exact analysis of the finite pulse width sampler and ZODH combination is complex, the frequency response can be closely approximated if the sampling process is replaced by an "ideal

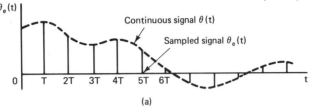

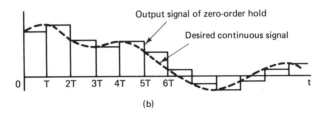

Figure 4-58 Zero-order data hold filter.

sampler" whose output is a train of impulses. That is, the sampled signal $\theta^*(t)$ is a train of amplitude-modulated impulses

$$\theta^*(t) = \theta_i(t)\delta_T(t) \tag{4-98}$$

where $\delta_T(t)$ is a unit impulse train of period T:

$$\delta_T(t) = \sum_{n=-\infty}^{\infty} \delta(t - nT) \tag{4-99}$$

where $\delta(t - nT)$ represents an impulse of unit area occurring at time $t = nT$. Since $\delta_T(t)$ is periodic, it can be expressed by the Fourier series

$$\delta_T(t) = \sum_{n=-\infty}^{\infty} C_n e^{-jn\omega_o t} \tag{4-100}$$

where

$$\omega_o = \frac{2\pi}{T} \tag{4-101}$$

The constants C_n are determined from

$$C_n = \frac{1}{T}\int_{-T/2}^{T/2} \delta_T(t)e^{-jn\omega_o t}\, dt = \frac{1}{T} \tag{4-102}$$

That is, the frequency spectrum of impulse train of period T contains a dc term plus the fundamental frequency and all harmonics, all with an amplitude of $1/T$.

$$\delta_T(t) = \frac{1}{T}\sum_{n=-\infty}^{\infty} e^{jn\omega_o t} \qquad \omega_o = \frac{2\pi}{T} \tag{4-103}$$

and since

$$e^{jn\omega_o t} + e^{-jn\omega_o t} = 2\cos n\omega_o t \tag{4-104}$$

$$\delta_T(t) = \frac{1}{T} + \frac{2}{T}\sum_{n=1}^{\infty} \cos n\omega_o t \tag{4-105}$$

Therefore, Eq. (4-98) can be written

$$\theta^*(t) = \theta_i(t)\frac{1}{T} + \frac{2}{T}\sum_{n=1}^{\infty}\cos n\omega_o t \tag{4-106}$$

If the input $\theta_i(t)$ is a sine wave $\theta_i(t) = A_i \sin(\omega_i t + \theta_i)$,

$$\theta^*(t) = \frac{A_i}{T}\left[\sin(\omega_i t + \theta_i) + 2\sum_{n=1}^{\infty}\cos n\omega_o t \sin(\omega_i t + \theta_i)\right] \tag{4-107}$$

This equation is similar to the result obtained in Eq. (4-95) for the more realistic finite-pulse-width model of the sampler. The difference is that for the finite-pulse-width model, the harmonics are attenuated by the factor

$$\frac{\sin(n\omega_o P/2)}{n\omega_o}$$

With the impulse sampler, all harmonics are of amplitude $2/T$.

The impulse response of the ZODH is

$$u(t) - u(t - T) = \frac{1 - e^{-sT}}{s} \tag{4-108}$$

and the ZODH frequency response is

$$\frac{1 - e^{-j\omega T/2}}{j\omega} = \frac{2}{T}e^{-j\omega T/2}\frac{e^{j\omega T/2} - e^{-j\omega T/2}}{j\omega T/2} \tag{4-109}$$

$$G_z(j\omega) = \frac{2}{T}e^{-j\omega T/2}\frac{\sin(\omega T/2)}{\omega T/2} \tag{4-110}$$

which is a digital low-pass filter with a linear phase response, as illustrated in Figure 4-59. An important feature of this filter is that it has zero gain at the sampling frequency and at all harmonics thereof. As Eq. (4-95) or (4-107) shows, when the input

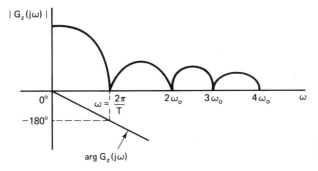

Figure 4-59 Transfer characteristic of the ZODH filter.

and sampling frequencies are equal, the output of the sampler contains a dc term and all harmonics of the sampling frequency. Since the ZODH has zero gain at these frequencies, the unwanted harmonics are completely removed by the filter. This is one of the primary reasons for the widespread application of samplers in phase-locked loops. The ZODH has a phase lag which increases linearly with frequency. This negative phase shift can seriously degrade loop stability.

Whenever the only frequency-sensitive components in the PLL are the VCO and the sampler plus zero-order data hold, the loop stability and frequency response are readily analyzed. When the loop is in frequency lock, the system can be represented as shown in the block diagram of Figure 4-60. The open-loop transfer function is

$$G(j\omega) = \frac{2}{T} \frac{K_v e^{-j\omega T/2}}{j\omega} \frac{\sin (\omega T/2)}{\omega T/2} \tag{4-111}$$

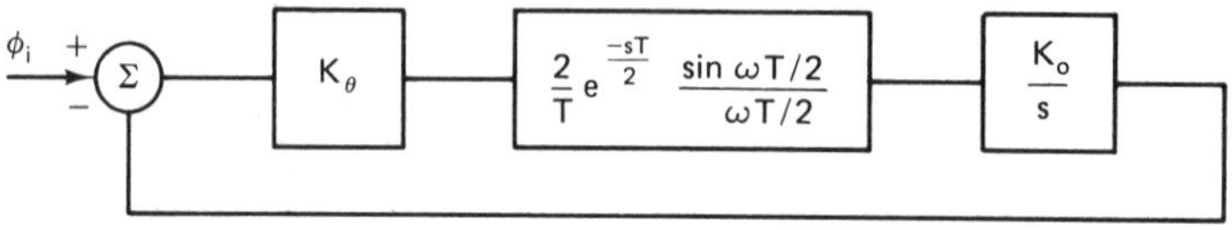

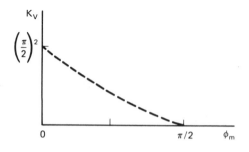

Figure 4-60   Block diagram of a PLL with a sample/hold comparator.

At the crossover frequency ω_c, the open-loop phase shift is

$$\phi = -\frac{\pi}{2} - \frac{\omega_c T}{2} \tag{4-112}$$

and the phase margin is

$$\phi_m = \pi + \phi = \frac{\pi}{2} - \frac{\omega_c T}{2} \tag{4-113}$$

Since the magnitude of the open-loop gain at ω_c is unity,

$$K_v \frac{\sin (\omega_c T/2)}{(\omega_c T/2)^2} = 1 \tag{4-114}$$

or

$$K_v = \frac{(\omega_c T/2)^2}{\sin (\omega_c T/2)}$$
$$= \frac{(\pi/2 - \phi_m)^2}{\sin (\pi/2 - \phi_m)} \tag{4-115}$$

Equation (4-115) describes the relation between phase margin ϕ_m and loop gain K_v. The plot of K_v as a function of ϕ_m given in Figure 4-61 shows that for each value of

Figure 4-61   Plot of K_V as a function of ϕ_m.

ϕ_m, there is a single value of K_v. For a $K_v = (\pi/2)^2$, the phase margin is 0°. As K_v is decreased, the phase margin increases and reaches 90° for $K_v = 0$.

The effect on loop performance on changes in the sampling rate T can be determined in the same manner. Since at the crossover frequency ω_c the magnitude of the open-loop gain is unity,

$$K_v \frac{\sin(\omega_c T/2)}{(\omega_c T/2)^2} = 1 \qquad (4\text{-}116)$$

If K_v remains constant and the sampling rate T is changed, ω_c must change such that

$$\omega_c T = \text{constant}$$

That is, if the sampling rate is decreased (T increases), the crossover frequency must decrease so that $\omega_c T$ remains constant. Therefore, changing the sampling rate of the system has no effect on the system phase margin or system stability; it affects only the loop bandwidth.

Example 7

Calculate the value of K_v required for a 45° phase margin in a PLL whose open-loop transfer function is given by Eq. (4-111).

Solution.   In order to have a 45° phase margin, the phase lag of the sample and hold must be 45° at the crossover frequency. Therefore,

$$\frac{\omega_c T}{2} = \frac{\pi}{4} \qquad (4\text{-}117)$$

and the crossover frequency must be

$$\omega_c = \frac{\pi}{2T} \qquad (4\text{-}118)$$

Since the magnitude of the open-loop gain is unity at the crossover frequency, K_v is determined frpm

$$K_v \frac{\sin(\pi/4)}{(\pi/4)^2} = 1 \qquad (4\text{-}119)$$

or

$$K_v = \left(\frac{\pi}{4}\right)^2 \sqrt{2} \qquad (4\text{-}120)$$

The sample/hold comparator, however, has a somewhat limited frequency range. In frequency synthesizer applications, it is not very likely that it will be used below a few hundred hertz, and the upper limit is determined by the speed of the following circuit and the crosstalk. Crosstalk depends on the isolation of the CMOS switch.

Let us take a look at a practical circuit using the sample/hold comparator. It is typically used in a cascaded form, which means that there are two samplers. The reason for this is the fact that one gets better reference suppression. Figure 4-62 shows a dual sample/hold comparator with the additional filtering circuits. The 10-kHz output from the divider, depending on the division ratio, is 200 to 500 ns wide, and a special circuit acts as a pulse stretcher to increase the width of these pulses to 2 μs.

The two CD4009's decouple the circuit. Two CD4016's are being used as CMOS switches. The first CD4009 generates the ramp, and the two 8007 operational amplifiers again provide the necessary decoupling and high input impedances.

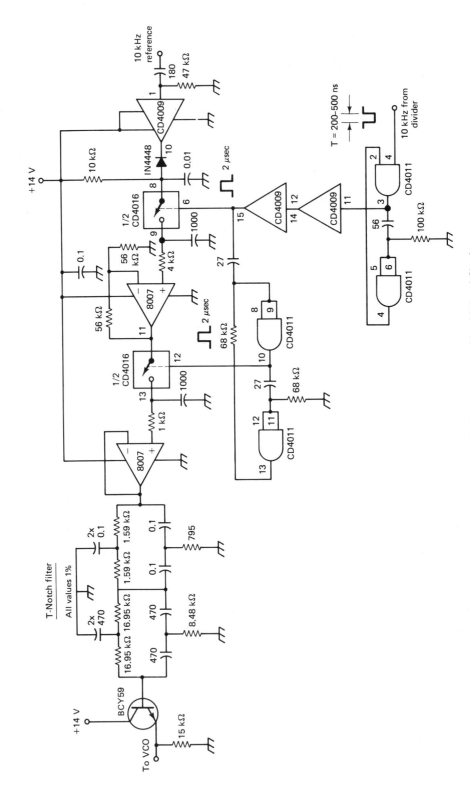

Figure 4-62 Dual sample/hold comparator with additional filtering.

In the output of the second 8007, we have a *T-notch filter*, which is a minimal phase shift filter with about 40 dB of suppression of the reference. In this particular circuit two T-notch filters are being used to suppress the fundamental and first harmonic frequency. In Section 4-7 it will be shown that at times the active second-order low-pass filter is a good replacement for the T-notch filter because it attenuates all harmonics rather than two discrete frequencies and requires fewer low-tolerance components.

Figure 4-63 shows the T-notch filter with the design formulas.

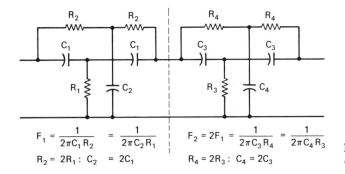

$$F_1 = \frac{1}{2\pi C_1 R_2} = \frac{1}{2\pi C_2 R_1}$$
$$R_2 = 2R_1 : C_2 = 2C_1$$

$$F_2 = 2F_1 = \frac{1}{2\pi C_3 R_4} = \frac{1}{2\pi C_4 R_3}$$
$$R_4 = 2R_3 : C_4 = 2C_3$$

Figure 4-63   T-notch filter with design equations.

The highest recommended frequency of operation for the phase/frequency comparator is approximately 5 kHz. At frequencies above this, the CMOS switches are not fast enough. The high impedance and parasitic capacitance produce crosstalk, and only 60 dB of attenuation is possible.

While sample/hold comparators will typically operate from 12 to 24 V, the minimum crosstalk voltage that determines the resolution and the reference suppression is about 10 μV. The attenuation possible with the sample/hold comparator is, therefore, about 110 dB. This is a highly theoretical value and in practice depends on the relationship of reference frequency and desired cutoff frequency. In many cases, the loop bandwidth is set to one-half of the reference frequency, and then delays and stray effects become very critical.

4-4-4 Edge-Triggered JK Master/Slave Flip-Flops

The fundamental idea of the sequential phase comparator we will be dealing with is that there are two outputs available, one to charge and one to discharge a capacitor. Output 1 then is high if the signal 1 frequency is greater than the signal 2 frequency; or if the two frequencies are equal, if signal 1 leads signal 2 in phase.

Output 2 is high if the frequency of signal 2 is greater than that of signal 1, or if the signal frequencies are the same and signal 2 leads signal 1 in phase.

Figure 4-64 shows the minimum configuration to build such a phase comparator. It can be operated from -2π to $+2\pi$, and an active amplifier is recommended as a charge pump. The Q output of the JK master/slave flip-flop is set to one by the negative edge of the signal 1, while the negative edge of the signal 2 resets it to zero.

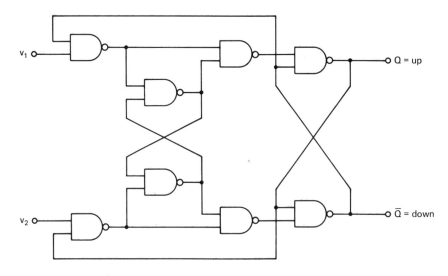

Figure 4-64 Edge-triggered JK master/slave flip-flop.

Therefore, the output $\bar{Q}$ is the complement of Q. The output voltage $\bar{V}$ is defined as the weighted duty cycle of Q and $\bar{Q}$. This means that a positive contribution is made when $Q = 1$ and a negative contribution (discharge) is made when $Q = 0$. The averaging and the filtering of the unwanted ac component is done by the following integrator. The integrator circuit then is called a *charge pump*, as the loop capacitor is being charged and discharged depending on whether Q is high or low.

If the system using the JK flip-flop is not in lock and there is a large difference between frequencies F1 and F2 at the input, the output is not going to be zero but will be positive or negative relative to one-half supply voltage. This is an advantage and indicates that this system is frequency sensitive. We therefore call it a *phase/ frequency comparator* because of its capability to detect both phase and frequency offsets. In its locking performance and pull-in performance, it is similar to the exclusive-OR gate.

For better understanding, let us look at a few cases where the system is in lock. It should be noted that whereas the exclusive-OR gate was sensitive to the duty cycle of the input signals, the JK flip-flop responds only to the edges, and therefore the phase/frequency comparator can be used for unsymmetrical waveforms. Let us assume first that the input signals 1 and 2 have the same frequency. Figure 4-65 shows what happens if the phase error is about 0, π, and 2π. In those cases, the duty cycle at the output is about 0, 50%, or 100%, respectively. The narrow output pulses may cause spikes on the power supply line and lines in the vicinity, and certain precautions have to be taken to filter them.

The output voltage $\bar{V}$ is the average of the signal Q, and is a linear function of the phase error.

Now let us take a look at several cases where the system is not in lock. Figure 4-66 shows the case where frequency 1 is substantially higher than frequency 2. As a result, the output duty cycle is close to 100% and the VCO frequency is being pulled up to higher frequencies. If the frequency at input 2 is much higher than that at input 1, the opposite is true. This proves that this device is sensitive to frequency changes.

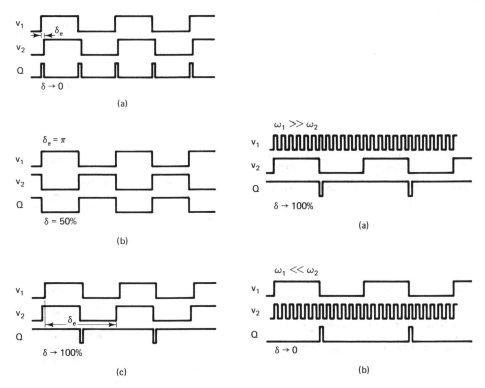

Figure 4-65 Performance of the JK phase/frequency comparator for different input signals.

Figure 4-66 Phase detector output for two input frequencies which are substantially different.

In cases where both frequencies are about the same, as shown in Figure 4-67, the crossover area is not clearly defined. The first picture shows the case where frequency 2 is 10% higher than frequency 1 and the duty cycle is changing periodically between 0 and 100%. Therefore, the ac voltages look like a sawtooth, with a rate equal to the difference of both frequencies. The same holds true if the two inputs are reversed. In the case where both frequencies are identical, the JK flip-flop behaves the same way as an exclusive-OR gate. From this discussion it can be concluded that, while this phase/frequency comparator was included to explain how it works, it is not a very desirable device because of the uncertainty of its behavior close to lock.

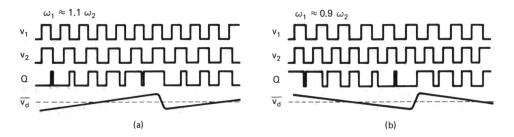

Figure 4-67 Performance of the phase detector for small frequency errors.

4-4-5 Digital Tri-State Comparators

The digital tri-state phase/frequency comparator is probably the most universally used and most important next to the sample/hold comparator. Although the ring and exclusive-OR gate have some applications, the tri-state phase/frequency comparator can be used widely. Even in cases where a sample/hold comparator theoretically could be used, it may be inferior as far as reference attenuation or noise is concerned, but it is generally well behaved. Unfortunately, the tri-state system is very complex and shows a number of unusual phenomena. Such a digital tri-state comparator is shown in Figure 4-68 using two D flip-flops and a NAND gate. The Q_2 output signal

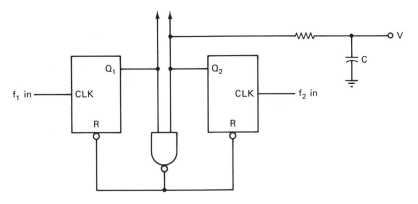

Figure 4-68 Phase detector with two D flip-flops and a NAND gate. This type of phase detector will be called a tri-state comparator.

is filtered with the low-pass filter. The operation of this logic circuit is readily analyzed using the state transition diagram shown in Figure 4-69. The D flip-flop outputs go high on the leading edge of their respective clock inputs and remain high until they are reset. The reset signal occurs when both inputs are high. When both signals are in phase and of the same frequency, both outputs will remain low, and no signal will be applied to the operational amplifier. When the two signal frequencies are the same, the dc output voltage transfer characteristic will be as shown in Figure 4-70. If the two signal frequencies are not the same, the output voltage will depend on both the relative frequency difference and the phase difference. The timing diagram of Figure 4-71 illustrates the case in which $f_2 = 3f_1$. In part (a) of the figure, the leading edge of f_1 occurs just after that of f_2, so that Q_2 is high 50% of the time, and the average value of the PD output is 50%. In part (b) of the figure, the leading edge of f_1 occurs just before that of f_2, so Q_2 is high almost all the time and the average output voltage is approximately V. The output voltage averaged over all of the phase differences is then 67% for $f_2 = 3f_1$. In general, it can be said that the average output (averaged over all phase differences) is given by

$$V_{ave} = 1 - \frac{f_1}{f_2}V \qquad (4\text{-}121)$$

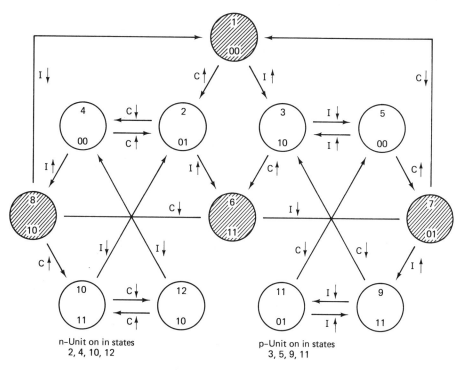

n–Unit on in states
2, 4, 10, 12

p–Unit on in states
3, 5, 9, 11

Phase–pulses output (pin 1) high in states 1, 6, 7, 8 and low in states
2, 3, 4, 5, 9, 10, 11, 12

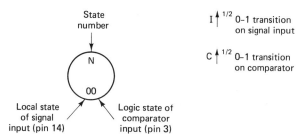

State
number

$I \uparrow^{1/2}$ 0–1 transition
on signal input

$C \uparrow^{1/2}$ 0–1 transition
on comparator

Local state
of signal
input (pin 14)

Logic state of
comparator
input (pin 3)

Figure 4-69 Logic diagram of the tri-state detector.

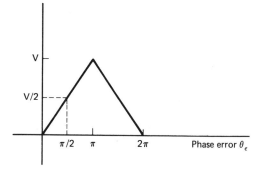

Figure 4-70 Transfer characteristic of
the tri-state phase/frequency
comparator.

221

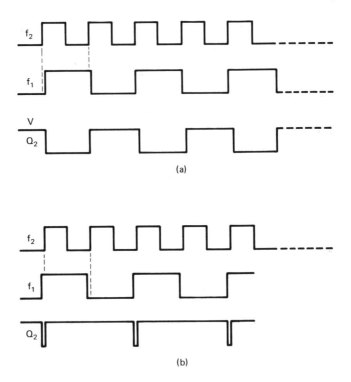

(a)

(b)

Figure 4-71 Output waveforms of the tri-state frequency comparators for different input frequencies.

provided that f_2 is greater than f_1. This expression is plotted in Figure 4-72 together with the cases in which f_1 is greater than f_2.

The digital network used in this realization is only one of a large number of logic circuits that could be used. Many IC manufacturers now produce a *quad-D circuit* which functions much like the dual D flip-flop; the main difference is that when the frequency of one signal is more than twice that of the other signal, the corresponding output will be high all of the time. Therefore, a larger voltage is applied to the VCO and the loop response is faster. An example of a quad-D circuit is shown in Figure 4-73.

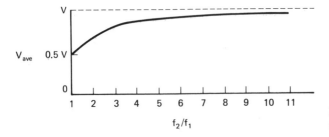

Figure 4-72 Average output voltage as a function of frequency ratio.

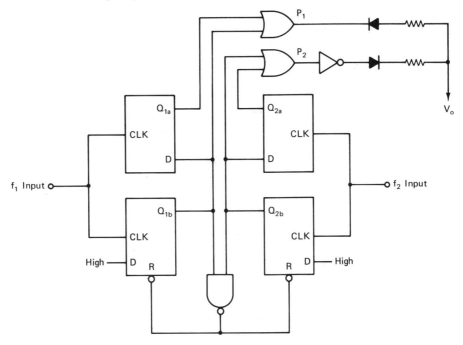

Figure 4-73   Example of a quad-D circuit.

The most popular digital tri-state phase/frequency comparator on the market is the one used in the CD4046 PLL IC, shown in Figure 4-74. It contains an additional phase comparator, an exclusive-OR gate that can be used as a lock indicator. In addition, two field-effect transistors are used to sum the two outputs. A slightly faster version in TTL technique is the Motorola MC4044.

The fastest version in ECL is the MC12040, also made by Motorola, shown in Figure 4-75. Sometimes it is convenient to build the phase/frequency comparator in discrete technique to add additional features. Figure 4-76 shows an example.

This particular tri-state phase/frequency comparator has a peculiarity that was first mentioned by Egan [1]. When actually building a phase-locked loop with this phase/frequency comparator or the CD4046 type by going through the normal mathematical design routine, it will become apparent that the expected performance and the actual results are not the same.

1. The reference suppression will be better than expected.
2. The phase error or tracking will be worse than expected.
3. The phase margin will differ and the system may not lock despite the fact that the calculation is correct.

The reason for this is due to two effects:

1. The flip-flops are not absolutely alike, and as a result of this, the output in the crossover region is not zero.

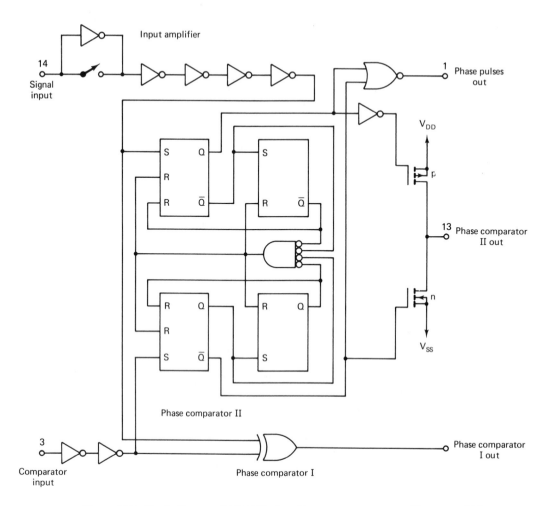

Figure 4-74 Block diagram of CD4046 phase/frequency comparator. (Courtesy of Motorola Semiconductor Products, Inc.)

2. If there is very little or no correction voltage required, the gain of the phase detector will drop substantially.

Let us assume the ideal situation where the output of the phase/frequency comparator feeding the charge pump does not have to correct any error, the system is drift free, and there are no leakage currents. The holding capacitor of the charge pump would maintain constant voltage, and as there is no drift, no correction voltage is necessary.

The flip-flops, however, introduce a certain amount of jitter, and a certain amount of jitter is also introduced by the frequency dividers, both the reference divider and the programmable divider. This jitter results in an uncertainty regarding

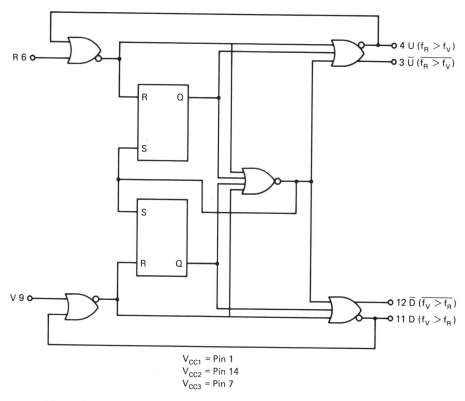

Figure 4-75 Block diagram of Motorola MC12040 phase/frequency comparator. (Courtesy of Motorola Semiconductor Products, Inc.)

the zero crossings, and extremely narrow pulses will appear at the output of this summation amplifier used in the CD4046.

Under the ideal assumption that there are no corrections required and those pulses would not exist, the reference suppression would be infinite, as there is no output and, therefore, the reference suppression, disregarding the effect of the loop filter, depends only on how well this condition is met.

The change of gain seems somewhat surprising, but as we think of it, if there is no correction and no update, there is also no gain. It is impossible to meet this condition, which is fortunate, but with regard to the temperature stability and aging effect of some devices, we may have some difficulties as far as predicting the actual performance.

There are several remedies to this problem. A simple version is to introduce a controlled amount of leakage. While the electrolytic capacitor required in the charge pump will have a leakage current, it is better to use a leakage current that is independent of temperature and aging. This can be accomplished by putting a 1-MΩ resistor from the output of the CD4046 to ground. The phase/frequency comparator then has to deliver an output current, and this output current is determined by a resistor that

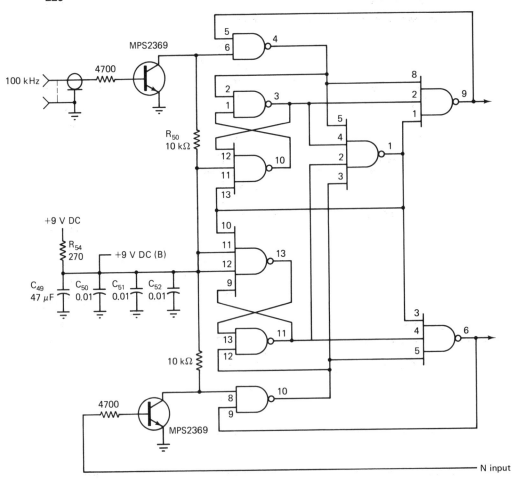

Figure 4-76   Possible version of tri-state phase/frequency comparators.

can be independent of temperature and other effects. As a result of this, the duty cycle of the output pulses of the phase/frequency comparator will change and the pulses will become wider. As these pulses contain more energy, the reference suppression will suffer.

It is theoretically possible to put one side of the 1-MΩ resistor, instead of to ground, to the wiper of a potentiometer and set the voltage in such a manner that this offset is compensated, but again, as the phase will shift theoretically, one has to adjust the potentiometer according to the actual phase error. This is not a very convenient arrangement.

A somewhat better method was proposed by Fairchild several years ago, but the hardware was never realized. It was proposed to insert a gate in one of the output arms of the phase/frequency comparator before the signal is fed to the summation amplifier and a periodic current disturbance is introduced. This disturbance has the same rate as the reference frequency, and is of extremely small duration, so that the output contains only fairly high harmonics of reference, which is easily filtered as it contains very little energy. This periodic disturbance offsets the output of the phase/ frequency comparator and therefore has an effect similar to that of a leakage resistor. The advantage of this method, however, is that this is done at a fairly high frequency and does not introduce low-frequency noise generated by the 1-MΩ resistor.

Figure 4-77 shows the circuit that accomplishes this, and Figure 4-78 shows the effect on the output pulses. The charge pump output exhibits a short negative-going pulse followed immediately by a short positive-going pulse. This can also be called an *antibacklash* feature, and it prevents operating in the dead zone. This zone is not really a dead zone because of the leakage currents in the tuning diode. The duration and proximity of these pulses are such that they cause no net change to the charge of the integrator. Figure 4-79 shows the response of a phase/frequency detector near loop lock, including the dead zone; this may not be true for ECL.

Another method, developed by Mr. Fritze of Rohde & Schwarz, Munich, is used in the Rohde & Schwarz ESM 500 receiver and described below.

Tri-state phase/frequency comparator with pulse compensation.

Because of the leakage in capacitors and the tuning diodes, the phase/frequency comparator has to supply current pulses until the phase difference becomes zero, and as mentioned, under ideal conditions (i.e., without drift), the output would be zero. As the ideal configuration cannot be realized and because of the finite switching times of the current sources, there are some pulses required all the time.

Using the 1-MΩ resistor, the effect that is occurring is that the charge, even under extremely narrow conditions contained in those pulses, may be more than is required to compensate for the drift caused by the leakage. While the resistor now has effectively prevented the dead zone, the 1 MΩ may have overcompensated this effect. As a result, we have avoided the instabilities of the loop caused by the dead zone and traded them for another type of oscillation that appears like residual FM very close to the carrier as a result of the overcompensation.

The sources that can be practically built have residual currents which do not fully cancel, and the two residual currents are not identical. This, together with any charging phenomena, generates a disruptive effect and causes a permanent charge and discharge of the holding capacitor, and a frequency modulation occurs. The invention by Mr. Fritze avoids the disadvantages in the steady-state condition described, and most important, fluctuations due to residual currents from the current sources or reverse currents from the tuning diodes are avoided without negatively influencing the noise characteristic of the oscillator. Let us take a look at the schematic, Figure 4-80. It contains the familiar phase/frequency comparator and the two charging pumps. An auxiliary circuit has been added to overcome the difficulties described. Capacitor 6 is charged, and capacitor 7, capacitor 6, and the parallel resistor form the familiar time constant for the lag network. An additional auxiliary circuit consisting of an operational amplifier and several capacitors and diodes, generates a correction current which is proportional to the integral of the difference of the charge pulses

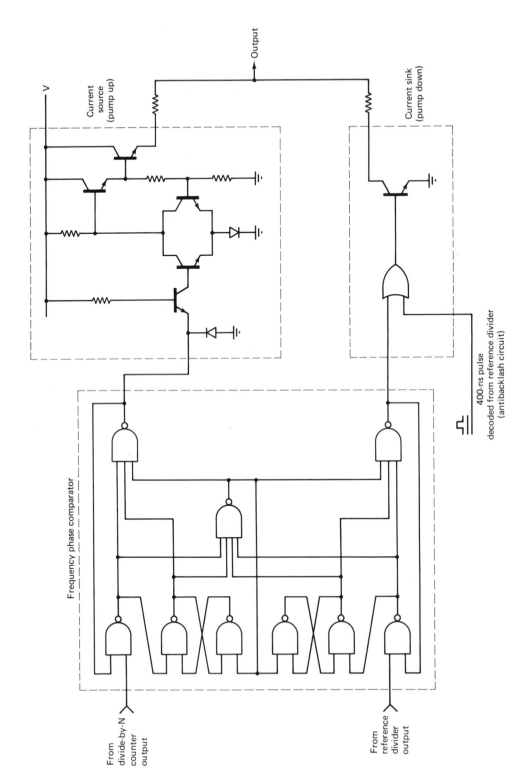

Figure 4-77 Tri-state detector with antibacklash circuit included.

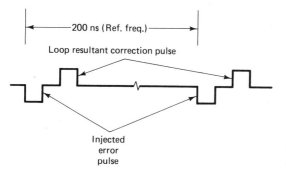

Figure 4-78 Output of frequency/phase detector with antibacklash circuit.

supplied by the current sources; that is, the current is directly proportional to the steady-state condition to proportional errors of the two mutually canceling charge amounts in the ideal state. By the use of such an auxiliary circuit, the constant recharging current pulses across the phase comparison circuit which are required in conventional circuits for the compensation of such errors are avoided, and the charging errors that may occur as a result of residual currents in the current sources or as a result of reverse currents of the varactor diodes are compensated by the correction current. No additional circuit arrangements are necessary, which may unfavorably influence the noise characteristic of the oscillator, and therefore the noise performance is not changed.

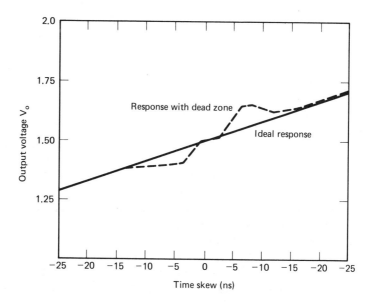

Figure 4-79 Response of frequency/phase detector near loop lock resulting in a dead zone.

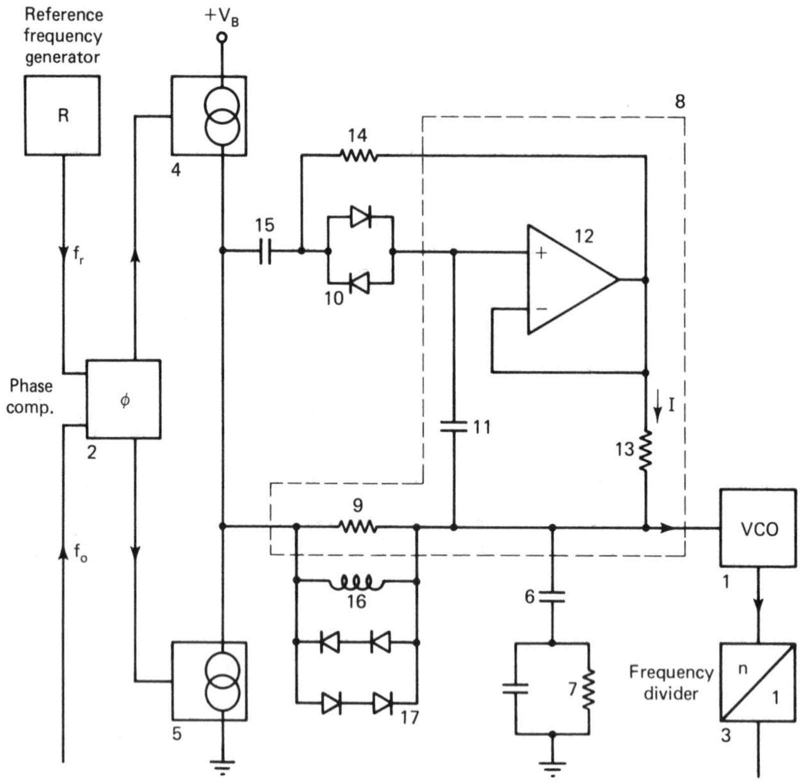

Figure 4-80 Phase/frequency comparator with spike compensation. (Courtesy of Rohde & Schwarz.)

A phase-controlled high-frequency oscillator is shown in Figure 4-81, having oscillator 1, which is frequency controlled by the application of a dc voltage. Oscillator 1 has an output frequency f_o which is compared in phase comparator 2 with a reference frequency f_r which is generated by reference frequency generator R. The output frequency of oscillator 1 may, for example, be changed in a known manner by means of interconnected frequency divider 3 which may have an adjustable division ratio. Depending on the phase relation of the oscillator frequency f_o with respect to the reference frequency f_r, phase comparison circuit 2 supplies appropriate control pulses to adjustable positive direct current source 4 and to a correspondingly adjustable negative direct current source, 5. Current source 4 is connected to a positive voltage U_B, while the negative current source is connected to ground. Control pulses from phase comparison circuit 2 are converted in switchable current sources 4 and 5 into current pulses of corresponding pulse duration, which are then supplied to charging capacitor 6, where the pulses are integrated to form the control voltage for oscillator 1. Oscillator 1 may be tuned, for example by varactor diodes. To avoid drift, charging capacitor 6 is connected in series to RC circuit 7.

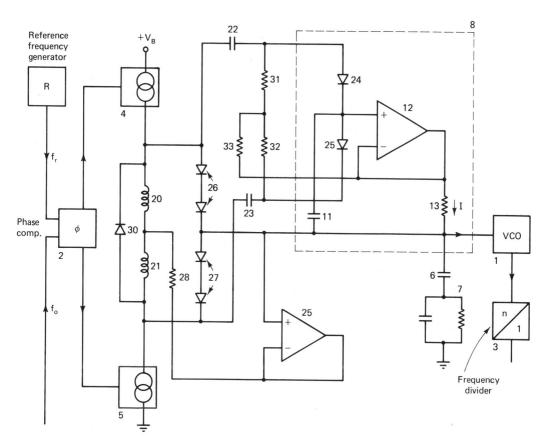

Figure 4-81   Schematic of the phase/frequency comparator with the spike suppression and linearized performance. (Courtesy of Rohde & Schwarz.)

In accord with the invention, a correction dc I is generated by auxiliary circuit 8 enclosed in the dashed lines of Figure 4-81.

It is approximately proportional to the integral of the difference between the charge pulses supplied from the respective current sources 4 and 5. Additional circuit elements, described in greater detail later, ensure that only relatively short charge pulses, which in the ideal case would mutually cancel, generate a corresponding correction current in auxiliary circuit 8. The term "relatively short charge pulses" designates pulses attributed only to potential disruptions or to the overlap in the steady-state and which are short in comparison to the charge pulses occurring as a result of deviation or fluctuation between f_o and f_r.

Such pulses which result from center frequency deviation have a duration, depending on the particular design of phase comparison circuit 2, which fluctuates between the period of the reference frequency f_r (given a very large center frequency deviation) and substantially zero (for the steady-state condition in the ideal state).

In contrast thereto, the "relatively short charge pulses" have a width of approximately 0.1 % of the period of the reference frequency f_r and depend on the dimensioning of the remainder of the components in the oscillator circuit.

In the circuit shown in Figure 4-81, in the simplest case auxiliary circuit 8 may consist of resistor 9 connected between the mutually connected current sources 4 and 5 and charging capacitor 6, at which a voltage drop occurs which is proportional to the difference between the current pulses supplied by the respective current sources 4 and 5. After rectification by rectifiers 10, the voltage is integrated by a second capacitor, 11, into a plurality of successive periods so that finally a voltage occurs at auxiliary capacitor 11, which under ideal conditions is proportional to the difference between the current pulses. By "ideal conditions" is meant the conditions wherein the two current sources, 4 and 5, respectively, supply current pulses of identical size and length in the quiescent state. As stated above, the current pulses would only be identical in the steady-state condition when the current sources have no residual currents and when no reverse currents resulting from the varactor diodes in oscillator 1 are present to contribute to the voltage formed by charging capacitor 6. When such residual currents or reverse currents exist, the charge pulses are no longer identical even in the steady-state condition, and auxiliary circuit 8 generates a correction current I from such differences. The correction current I, which is proportional to the voltage at the second capacitor, 11, is generated across a "times 1" amplifier 12 with a very low input current by means of impedance transformation and is supplied directly to charging capacitor 6 across resistor 13. The charging current circuit for rectifier diodes 10 is terminated by resistor 14, which is directly connected to the output of amplifier 12. This ensures that rectifier diodes 10 are biased with a voltage that corresponds to the rectified output voltage of amplifier 12. Thus no quiescent voltage appears at rectifiers 10; therefore, no undesired residual current is generated and, moreover, it is not necessary to supply constant pulses to the circuit for compensation of self-generated residual currents.

Auxiliary circuit 8 is separated by capacitor 15 from current sources 4 and 5. Capacitor 15 has a relatively small capacitance value, so that only relatively short charge pulses, such as occur as mutually overlapping pulses in the steady-state condition, are evaluated in auxiliary circuit 8 for generating the residual current. This is expedient so that longer current pulses such as occur, for example, as a result of a frequency change and which it is desired should render as fast as possible a recharging of charging capacitor 6 to the new frequency value, are not significantly considered in auxiliary circuit 8. That is, given a frequency change by means of relatively long current pulses, auxiliary circuit 8 retains the correction current previously generated in the steady-state condition, which is then directly utilized after termination of the frequency change. This is because one can make the valid assumption that errors due to residual currents or reverse currents are independent of the frequency; that is, such errors present at an initial frequency will also be present at the new frequency setting for oscillator 1. Auxiliary circuit 8 thus does not supply correction currents which would disrupt the tuning operation for a frequency change.

The blocking of auxiliary circuit 8 for relatively long switching pulses can be further improved as shown in Figure 4-81. An additional inductor 16 ensures that only relatively short current pulses generate a corresponding voltage drop evaluated in auxiliary circuit 8, and allows relatively long pulses to be transmitted unimpeded to capacitor 6. In the same manner, this separation effect between short and long pulses can be further improved by means of the interconnection of additional rectifiers 17, which, in comparison to rectifiers 10 of auxiliary circuit 8, have a higher forward-bias voltage. Relatively short current pulses, therefore, first arrive at rectifiers 10, and only when the higher transmission voltage of rectifier 17 is exceeded do longer current pulses, which occur as a result of a frequency change, arrive at charging capacitor 6 via rectifier 17.

It was assumed in the circuit of Figure 4-81 that the two current sources, 4 and 5, supply ideal current pulses of identical size as well as of identical length. Usually, this cannot be achieved in practice. A further development of the circuit of Figure 4-80, shown in Figure 4-81, ensures that such potential asymmetries of the current pulses are also compensated.

As shown in Figure 4-81, rectifiers 24 and 25 of auxiliary circuit 8 are driven separately by the current pulses from the two current sources, 4 and 5, respectively. Two inductors, 20 and 21, are connected at the outputs of the two current sources, 4 and 5. Inductors 20 and 21 do not affect the short current pulses which are supplied via blocking capacitors 22 and 23 to rectifiers 24 and 25. Inductors 20 and 21 serve in the quiescent condition, that is, between the individual current pulses, to avoid voltages at additional rectifiers 26 and 27 connected in parallel, thereto having a higher transmission voltage than rectifiers 24 and 25. Symmetry is produced via a resistor 28 and an additional "times 1" amplifier, 29. An additional rectifier, 30, limits voltage pulses at the turn-off of the current pulses. A voltage that is proportional to the integral of the difference of the current pulses from the two current sources, 4 and 5, is again integrated by the second capacitor, 11. Bias voltage resistors 31, 32, and 33 are allocated to rectifiers 24 and 25. Resistor 33 is connected to the output of amplifier 12 so that for every voltage present at capacitor 11 it is ensured that the voltage at diodes 24 and 25 beyond the pulse time is equal to zero, and therefore no residual currents flow through these circuit elements.

Blocking capacitors 22 and 23 are dimensioned so that capacitor 11 is not too strongly recharged upon the occurrence of a frequency change, and thus longer current pulses from current sources 4 and 5 flow only across additional rectifiers 26 and 27. Inductor 21 may be eliminated if resistor 28 has an appropriate resistance value.

The circuit shown in Figure 4-81 allows conduction of the entire charge of short pulses supplied by the current sources to charging capacitor 6 via the second capacitor, 11. Therefore, for short current pulses, the voltage change at capacitor 11 coincides with the voltage change at charging capacitor 6 not only with respect to polarity, but also as to proportionality. In the aligned condition, that is, for short current pulses, for example, the charge flows from voltage source 4 via separating capacitor 22 and rectifier 24 to capacitor 11, and from the current source 5 analogously via separating capacitor 23 and rectifier 25 to capacitor 11. From capacitor 11 the combined voltage is supplied to charging capacitor 6. A positive or negative voltage for the duration of the short pulses arises at diodes 26 and 27 during the charge pulses and capacitors 22 and 23, which are first discharged, can thus conduct the charge pulses to diodes 24 and 25. As long as capacitor 11 is discharged, the output voltage of amplifier 12 is identical to the oscillator control voltage at charging capacitor 6, so that no current flows across resistor 13. This is the case as long as the positive and the negative charge pulses produce equal charge amounts. Blocking capacitors 22 and 23 are quickly discharged across the resistor combination comprised of resistors 31, 32, and 33 after each pulse in such a manner that no voltage remains at diodes 24 and 25. Therefore, no undesired residual current can reach capacitor 11 via those diodes.

When the aligned or balanced condition is disrupted, for example due to residual currents from one of the two current sources or from the varactor diodes in oscillator 1, the current pulses have different lengths. During a frequency change, one pulse may temporarily disappear. Because short current pulses are not conducted via diodes 26 and 27, which have a higher transmission voltage, but rather are conducted primarily across diodes 24 and 25, capacitor 11 is charged and a current flows across resistor 13. The current across resistor 13 increases until the positive and negative current pulses are again of identical size. A false voltage at capacitor 11 after a frequency change, is compensated in the same manner, as is a potential oscillator drift or recharging effect of capacitor 6.

Amplifier 12 has a very low input current and may be, for example, a MOSFET amplifier having an input current which is less than the current of the blocked semiconductors by several magnitudes. It is important for capacitor 11 to have good insulating properties. The noise from amplifier 12 is decoupled from the control voltage at capacitor 6 by resistor 13. The time constant represented by capacitor 6 and resistor 13 is chosen to suppress noise interference. Moreover, the value of resistor 13 is made large in comparison to the resistor of *RC* circuit 7.

The circuit described above has the additional advantage that a potential stepwise detuning of the oscillator is made continuous. In phase-controlled high-frequency oscillators of this type, for example, the reference frequency is often supplied from a synthesizer which is adjustable in decades with crystal frequency precision. Frequency divider 3 may also be adjustable in decades. The frequency of such oscillators is thus variable in very fine steps, and when tuning of the synthesizer or of the frequency divider occurs over a number of decades via a suitable pulse control circuit, a quasi-continuous, that is, stepwise, tuning of oscillator 1 is achieved in a predetermined frequency range. The presence of such relatively small frequency steps results in correspondingly short charge pulses from the current sources, which, as described above, lead to the generation of a correction current via auxiliary circuit 8. Oscillator 1 is, therefore, no longer adjusted in terms of its frequency by jumps or steps, but is instead continuously adjusted via the auxiliary current.

4-5 WIDEBAND HIGH-GAIN AMPLIFIERS

4-5-1 Summation Amplifiers

Depending on the application, we have two types of high-gain amplifiers that require a fairly high bandwidth.

1. Operational amplifiers for the loop filter.
2. Wideband amplifiers that act either as isolation amplifiers or which transform sine-wave voltages into square-wave voltages (differential limiters), or power amplifiers that raise the output level of a synthesizer. Although they belong in the category of isolation amplifiers, they also require some different considerations.

Let us start with the operational amplifiers required for the loop filters. Although we will be dealing with loop filters, specifically active loop filters, in great detail, we should touch on the requirement for operational amplifiers. As in some cases the reference frequency will be as high as several megahertz, in order to maintain a wide loop bandwidth, the operational amplifier has to be able to track the frequencies involved. The *slew rate* of the operational amplifier, which determines how many volts per microsecond the operational amplifier can follow, is one figure of merit that has to be taken into consideration, and it is interesting that most operational amplifiers that do not have fixed internal frequency compensation are fairly poor in slew rate. In addition, the more familiar cutoff frequency of the operational amplifier indicates the 3-dB drop in gain in open-loop configuration. The open-loop configuration, however, is not used, as the loop filter will reduce the passband, and there are only a few cases in which the input frequency would come close to the cutoff frequency of the operational amplifier. As operational amplifiers are introduced very frequently, it is somewhat dangerous to indicate a particular type. However, it was found that the RCA operational amplifier CA3160 for low frequencies is a good choice (CA3130, CA3100).

The tri-state phase/frequency comparator has two outputs that are being fed together in a circuit which I call a *summation amplifier*. The high and low pulses generated by the digital portion are being fed simultaneously to two ports, and the amplifier then has to combine the two pulses into a single output. The simplest way of accomplishing this is to take an operational amplifier where the two inputs are put to the inverting and noninverting input, and the biasing is provided with identical resistors to avoid any offset problems. Many of the application reports, such as the one on the recent Motorola MC145156, recommend this circuit.

The drawback is that, as the pulses become faster in frequency, the operational amplifier will be unable to follow, and a discrete amplifier has to be built. There are several choices for discrete loop amplifiers, whose main purposes are:

1. To be able to follow the input pulses up to several hundred kilohertz or even several megahertz (good choice: CA3100, 9906, 9909)

2. To have very little or no dc drift

3. Not to introduce any significant noise

4. To be as symmetrical as possible, and therefore, avoid any leakage of reference at the output

5. To avoid a dead zone (the dead zone was mentioned previously in Section 2-6-3).

Figure 4-82 shows a dc amplifier that takes the two outputs from the phase/frequency comparator type 4044 made by Motorola, and then operates into the loop

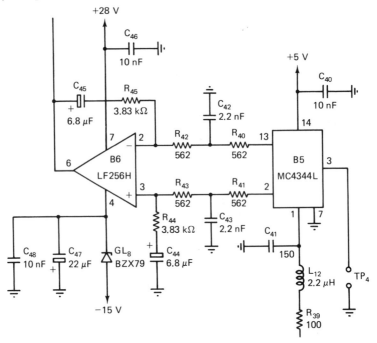

Figure 4-82 Schematic of the phase/frequency comparator MC4344 and an active loop filter using both inverting and noninverting input for stabilization. The first *RC* network is for transient suppression. (Courtesy of Rohde & Schwarz.)

filter. This is a fairly complex arrangement, and Figure 4-83 shows a circuit with basically the same performance that operates from an ECL phase/frequency comparator, which by definition has less dc output voltage. Figure 4-84 shows a phase/frequency comparator with the discrete operational amplifier containing several diodes for temperature compensation, as well as voltage shifts.

When analyzing operational amplifiers, it becomes apparent that those which have very little output saturation voltage (i.e., CMOS outputs) cannot tolerate a high supply voltage. The discrete amplifier can be operated up to 30 or 40 V.

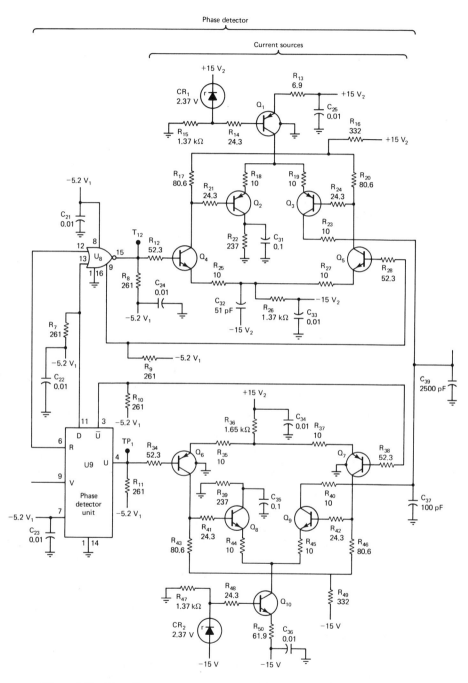

Figure 4-83 Phase/frequency comparator and discrete summation amplifier for low-noise operation. The loop filter is not shown. (Courtesy of Hewlett-Packard Company.)

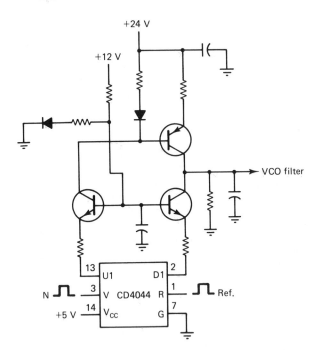

Figure 4-84 Discrete summation amplifier recommended for use with the CD4044 up to 1 MHz.

It was indicated, however, that most tuning diodes become noisy, and the operating voltage should be restricted to less than 30 V. In addition, using such a high voltage, one will find that the voltage gain of the diode becomes so small that the loop gain has to be adjusted to avoid sluggish performance at the top of the band.

Several combinations of these circuits are possible, and depending on the transistors or new integrated circuits, these loop amplifiers may change from time to time. The additional dc gain has to be taken into consideration as the simple amplifier that is used in monolithic devices, such as the CD4046, has unity gain, and the more complex circuits, such as those above, have gain that can be adjusted by selecting component values. In the case of the temperature-compensated amplifier, the two resistors in series with the emitters determine the open-loop gain. In order to provide sufficient frequency response, very fast switching transistors should be used and matched where possible. So far, none of these amplifiers are available in integrated form, but this may be only a question of time.

We will now take a look at RF applications, the first one being the requirement to drive frequency dividers from a sine-wave source.

4-5-2 Differential Limiters

The easiest way to convert a sine wave into a square wave is to use an integrated circuit called a *line receiver*. A line receiver is an amplifier, practically always a differential limiter, that converts a sine wave into an ECL- or TTL-compatible waveform. Integrated TTL line receivers are relatively slow (about 5 MHz maximum), and it is

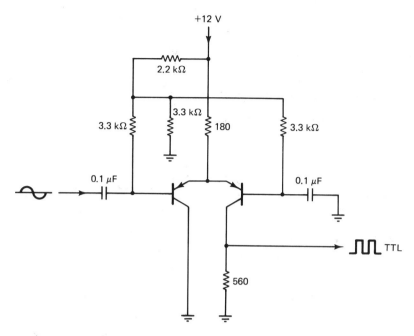

Figure 4-85   Schematic of a differential amplifier operating up to 10 MHz.

common practice to build a discrete line receiver using two PNP transistors, as shown in Figure 4-85. The gain of such a device depends on the ratio of collector resistor to emitter differential resistance ($RD = 26$ mV/I_e). For a current of 5 mA, this RD is about 5 Ω, and if a 500-Ω collector resistor is used, the gain is 100 or 40 dB. Depending on the collector resistor and the collector voltage, these devices can be made to work for ECL, TTL, or 12-V CMOS logic. The differential limiter should be made as fast as possible, which means that the rise and fall time should be extremely short. It is important to minimize hysteresis or zero-crossing errors. It has been shown several times that if a poorly designed differential limiter follows a low-noise frequency standard, the introduction of noise by the slow limiter determines the system's noise rather than the crystal oscillator. Modern integrated circuits, such as the Plessey swallow counters, can be driven with sine-wave inputs and have open collector outputs. The open collector outputs allow the use of the necessary resistor and voltage from the power supply to adapt to the following circuits, and therefore no line receivers are required. The line receivers are absolutely necessary for TTL and CMOS logic.

In most cases, however, we do not want to limit the output, but rather isolate output from input without distorting the transferred waveform output of a required output power, so that reverse feedback and isolation have to be considered. These isolation amplifiers are described next.

4-5-3 Isolation Amplifiers

The output from the voltage-controlled oscillator (VCO) is fed into an amplifier that has to drive the frequency divider chain, and an additional output provides the desired frequency $N \times f_{\text{ref}}$.

There are several ways to accomplish this task. Obviously, it is important to use a low-noise amplifier, which suggests the use of a dual-gate MOSFET amplifier which, driven by the VCO, is excellent for low noise and high reverse isolation. Because of the high-impedance nature of these devices, they will work well only in conjunction with an impedance transformation circuit as shown in Figure 4-86. In the frequency

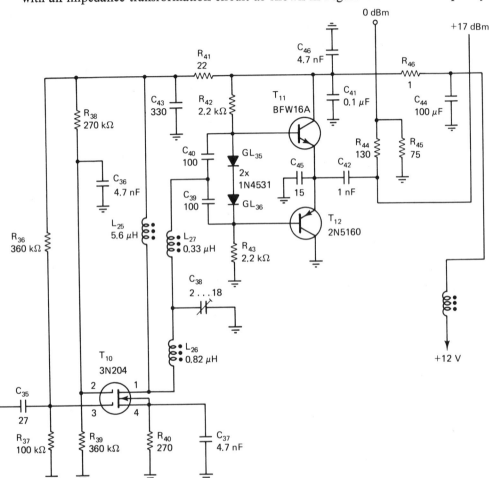

Figure 4-86 High-power output stage with isolation amplifier delivering about +17 dBm. This circuit works well up to 100 MHz. (Courtesy of Rohde & Schwarz.)

range 30 to 120 MHz, this circuit has enough reverse isolation (at least 60 dB) and is capable of driving stages such as high-level mixers requiring +23 dBm of drive. For wider frequency ranges, Figure 4-87 shows a multistage amplifier that will meet this requirement.

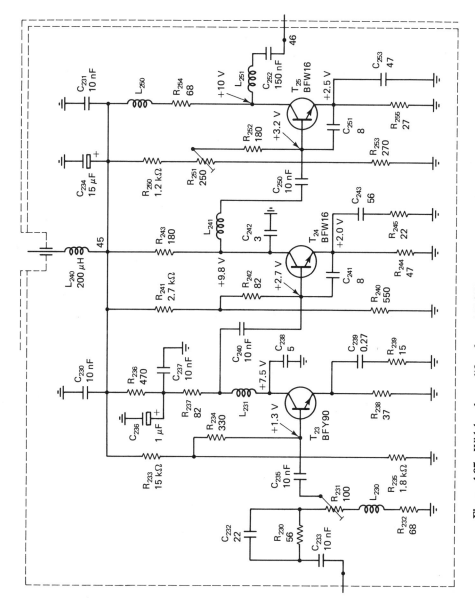

Figure 4-87 Wideband amplifier from 100 kHz to 600 MHz. (Courtesy of Rohde & Schwarz.)

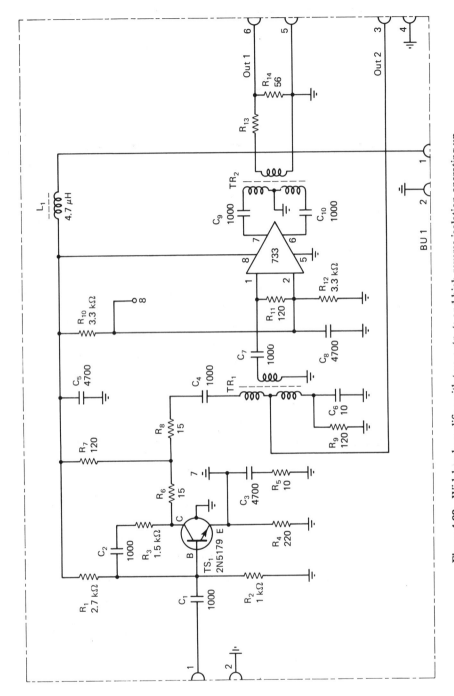

Figure 4-88 Wideband amplifier with two outputs and high reverse isolation operating up to 100 MHz. TR1 is a 3-dB coupler.

Another solution is offered in Figure 4-88. It shows the combination of a discrete transistor type 2N5179 driving a power splitter, sometimes called a *hybrid coupler*, and a wideband monolithic amplifier type 733, which is manufactured by several companies, including Motorola and Fairchild.

The 2N5179 transistor has a very low reverse feedback, and the hybrid coupler is capable of up to 40-dB isolation. Although in many cases designers use two different amplifiers, the use of a hybrid coupler should be preferred, as it is a passive device and has no power consumption and a long life expectancy.

The 733 amplifier is a unique device that allows programming internal gain. By setting the appropriate bypass capacitor, different gain can be chosen, and this amplifier can even be used in a linear mode exhibiting good intermodulation distortion.

As it is an internal push-pull configuration, it is recommended to use balanced output terminals. Several monolithic amplifiers are available as isolation stages, and amplifiers such as the RCA CA3028 can be used in a differential mode and AGC can be applied.

In Section 4-3 we learned that the proper termination of the mixer is absolutely essential. The following feedback amplifier will provide extremely low noise and perfect matching. This is an example of several feedback amplifiers that can be constructed, and this combination seems to be the best. It is based on Patent No. 3891934 issued to David Norton. This type of lossless feedback amplifier, shown in Figure 4-89, consists of a three-winding transformer connected to a common-base transistor in such a manner as to provide gain and impedance matching.

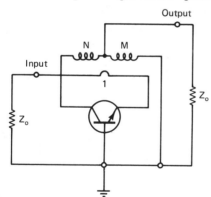

Figure 4-89 Feedback amplifier using the noiseless feedback technique.

This circuit can be analyzed under the simplifying assumptions that the common-base transistor has a zero input impedance, an infinite output impedance, and unity current gain, while the transformer is considered to be ideal. With these assumptions it can easily be shown that a two-way impedance match to Z_o will be obtained if the transformer turns ratio is chosen such that $n = m^2 - m - 1$.

With this choice, the power gain is m^2, the load impedance presented to the collector is $(n + m)Z_o$ and the source impedance presented to the emitter is $2Z_o$. Turns ratios for m equal to 2, 3, and 4 yield gains of 6, 9.5, and 12 dB and load impedances of 3, 8, and $15Z_o$, respectively.

It is seen that, similar to a conventional common-base amplifier, the gain of the stage is determined by the ratio of the load impedance, Z_1, to the input impedance, Z_{in}. In this case the gain is given by $Z_1/Z_{in} + 1$, whereas it is just Z_1/Z_{in} in the conventional configuration. The significant difference is that the transformer-coupled device provides a two-way impedance match, which is obtained by coupling the load impedance to the input, and the source impedance to the output by transformer action.

The dynamic range considerations for this device are similar to those of the directional coupler circuit, but with some important differences. First the operation of the circuit depends on the completely mismatched conditions presented by the transistor to the circuit (i.e., the emitter presents a short circuit and the collector an open circuit). Hence there is no requirement to introduce resistive elements for impedance matching as in the directional coupler circuit. Therefore, a noise-figure advantage is obtained with this circuit. Second, the source impedance of $2Z_o$ presented to the emitter tends to give optimum noise figure performance with low collector currents, which also favors lower noise figures. Finally, in spite of the small currents involved, relatively large output powers can be provided because of the high load impedance, which goes along with the higher-gain versions.

The main disadvantage of the circuit is that the high load impedance tends to limit the bandwidth. Nevertheless, sufficient bandwidth can be achieved to provide broadband IF gain with noise figures competitive with those that could be obtained previously only in very narrowband units.

As this is a very convenient circuit, let us look at the actual working design shown in Figure 4-90. Both transistors are made by Siemens.

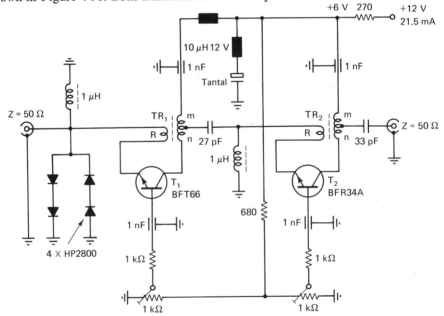

Figure 4-90   Two-stage ultra-low-noise high dynamic amplifier.

The antiparallel diodes at the input can be omitted. The core material used in the transformers depends on the frequency range. Siemens ferrite material type B62152-A8-X17, U17 for frequencies from 100 MHz up and K30 material for frequencies below, should be used.

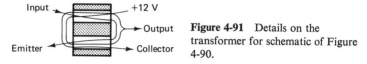

Figure 4-91 Details on the transformer for schematic of Figure 4-90.

Figure 4-91 shows the winding arrangement for the transformer. This amplifier has the following characteristics.

1. Power gain 19 dB.
2. Noise figure 1.35, equivalent to 1.3 dB.
3. Third-order intercept point 14 dBm at the input or 33 dBm at the output.
4. 1-dB compression $+18$ dBm.
5. Input impedance $50 \pm 2\ \Omega$.
6. Bandwidth 70 to 570 MHz (can be made to work at lower frequencies with the higher-permeability core).
7. Dynamic range 102 dB determined from the fact that two signals separated in frequency of 3.17 mV at the input of the amplifier result in two intermodulation-distortion products of 25.4 nV. The noise figure of 1.3 dB at 2.4-kHz bandwidth results in the same noise voltage of 25.4 nV. If the noise floor of -138.8 dBm equivalent to the 25.4 nV is subtracted from the -36.96 dBm or the 3.17 mV which generates the two intermodulation distortion products, the difference is approximately 102 dB.
8. Power supply 12 V/21 mA.

4-6 PROGRAMMABLE DIVIDERS

4-6-1 Asynchronous Counters

In frequency synthesizers, the VCO is operating at a much higher frequency than the reference. There are two ways to provide information for the phase/frequency comparator.

1. The use of harmonic sampling. Here the reference generates extremely narrow high harmonic contents, pulses that are being fed together with the VCO frequency to the phase detector. In addition, a coarse steering circuit pretunes the oscillator so that the oscillator frequency is very close to the required harmonic of the comb generator.
2. The input frequency is divided to the reference frequency. The same is correct

for the reference frequency, as the reference oscillator may be much higher than the desired reference frequency or step size. In most cases, the reference frequency is at 5 or 10 MHz, sometimes even as high as 100 MHz, while the comparison frequency applied to the phase/frequency comparator may lie between 1 MHz and 1 kHz.

The reference divider for most cases requires only a simple asynchronous counter, whereas the programmable divider chain requires synchronous and resettable counters.

While the simplest counter or divider is a flip-flop dividing by 2, modern design uses dividers of high integration.

Originally, the dividers were built in RTL logic, then TTL logic, then Schottky clamped, and then CMOS integrated circuits were developed.

In parallel, the ECL technology was expanded up in frequency, and we now have dividers that operate well above 1000 MHz. Power consumption of these devices naturally is very high, while the CMOS technology was developed to reduce power consumption. TTL devices are probably the least expensive but very noisy, and we will find that most synthesizers now go from ECL to CMOS directly, avoiding TTL as much as possible. The more advanced frequency dividers, such as the one made by Plessey, have the ECL to TTL or CMOS translators built in. TTL circuitry is probably used only to support the dual modulus counters, as you will see later.

The following types of counters are currently offered in CMOS:

1. Seven-stage ripple counter
2. Decade counter/divider
3. Presettable divide-by-N counter
4. Decade counter (asynchronous clear)
5. Decade counter (synchronous clear)
6. 4-bit presettable up/down counter
7. BCD up/down counter
8. Programmable divide-by-N 4-bit counter (BCD)
9. 12-bit binary counter
10. 14-bit binary counter
11. Octal counter/divider
12. 4-bit binary counter (asynchronous clear)
13. 4-bit binary counter (synchronous clear)
14. Binary up/down counter
15. Programmable divide-by-N 4-bit counter (binary)
16. Dual BCD up-counter
17. Dual binary up-counter
18. Dual programmable BCD/binary counter

19. Three-digit BCD counter
20. Real-time five-decade counter
21. Industrial time-base generator

Similar dividers are available in ECL and TTL. Special devices in ECL are bi/quinary counters and swallow counters.

Figure 4-92 shows a speed/power characteristic of major logic lines. It is apparent that CMOS is indicated only in quiescent dissipation. The reason for this is the fact that the power consumption is a function of actual input frequency. Depending on the particular device and the manufacturing process, it is very possible that TTL dividers at 10 MHz require less power than a similar CMOS device. However, the additional interface circuit may justify the use of CMOS rather than involving three different logic families.

The simplest divider is a flip-flop. The flip-flop divides by 2, and input frequency ranges up to 2300 MHz are handled.

Several of these flip-flops can be cascaded, and the drawback of this circuit is the resulting division

$$N = 2^n$$

where n is the number of stages. The figures referred to below show configurations where flip-flops are being cascaded to provide dividers with random division rates. This is accomplished by feedback loops.

A typical application of this technique is used in the familiar 7490 divide-by-10 counter which is an asynchronous decade counter. Figure 4-93 shows the internal arrangement. It consists of four master/slave flip-flops. The asynchronous dividers are slow, as the input signal triggers the first flip-flop, which then triggers the second flip-flop, and so on. In the synchronous divider, the clock is fed to all the clock input simultaneously, and, therefore, the delay is avoided.

4-6-2 Programmable Synchronous Up/Down Counters

In frequency synthesizers, asynchronous dividers have very little application, while synchronous dividers are of greater importance. In this section we deal with synchronous dividers and a special version of them, presettable dividers, as the synthesizer requires that the division ratio be selective rather than hard-wired. Figure 4-94 shows synchronous counters consisting of several flip-flops with the according waveforms.

Several applications require up/down counters. The reason for this is that for a programmed division ratio, the decoding of the circuit becomes easy. The series 74192/74193 counters provide this facility.

Both the 74192 and 74193 are synchronous reversible (up/down) counters with four master/slave flip-flop stages. Inputs include the separate up/down count, load preset, overriding clear, and individual preset data input to each stage. The 74192 BCD counter is capable of counting either up from zero to BCD nine or down from BCD nine to zero. The 74193 is a four-stage binary counter operating in exactly the

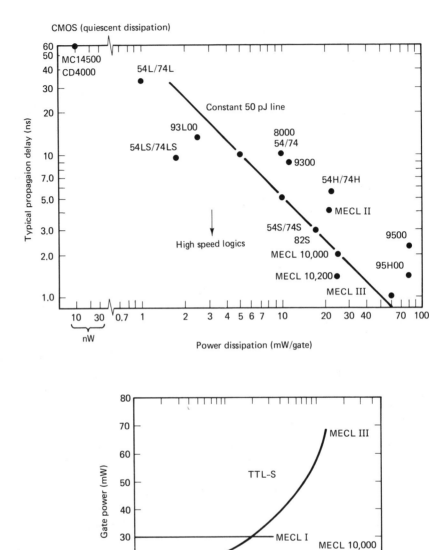

Figure 4-92 Power consumption of different divider technologies as a function of frequency. (Courtesy of Motorola Semiconductor Products, Inc.)

Decade counter

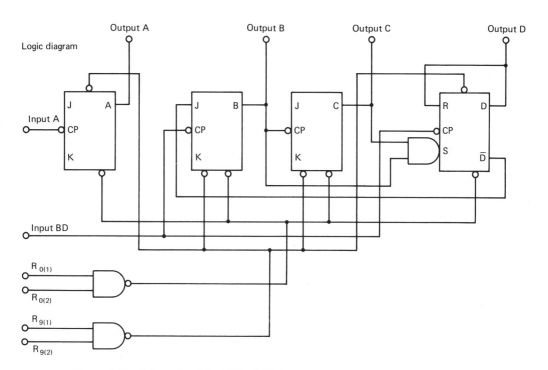

Figure 4-93 Schematic of the 7490 divide-by-10 counter. (Courtesy of Motorola Semi-conductor Products, Inc.)

same manner, except that it can count up to binary fifteen from zero and down from binary fifteen to zero.

The state of the counter outputs depends on the number of count (clock) input pulses received on either the count-up or count-down input. The counter is advanced to its next appropriate state on the positive transitions of the count pulses, while the unused count input is held high. To count in the up direction, the count-up input is pulsed, and to count down, the count-down input is pulsed. The count direction is changed by taking both count inputs high before entering the count signal on the other count input.

In addition to changing the counter state in the normal counting mode, when the counter outputs respond to the incoming pulses, the counter state can be easily taken to any desired state within its range. This is achieved using the fully presettable facilities of the counter. The desired new count state is entered in parallel on the preset data inputs, and the load preset input is taken low, enabling the preset data to be presented to the outputs. The signals on the outputs then agree with those on the preset data inputs independent of any further clock information received while the

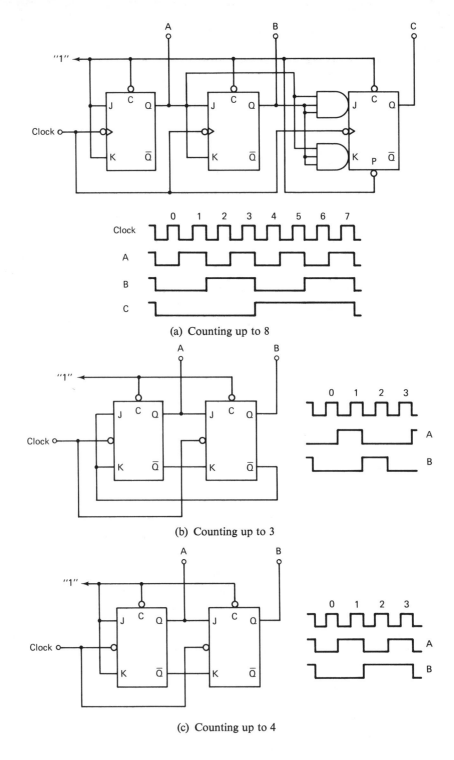

(a) Counting up to 8

(b) Counting up to 3

(c) Counting up to 4

Figure 4-94 Synchronous counters. (Courtesy of Motorola Semiconductor Products, Inc.)

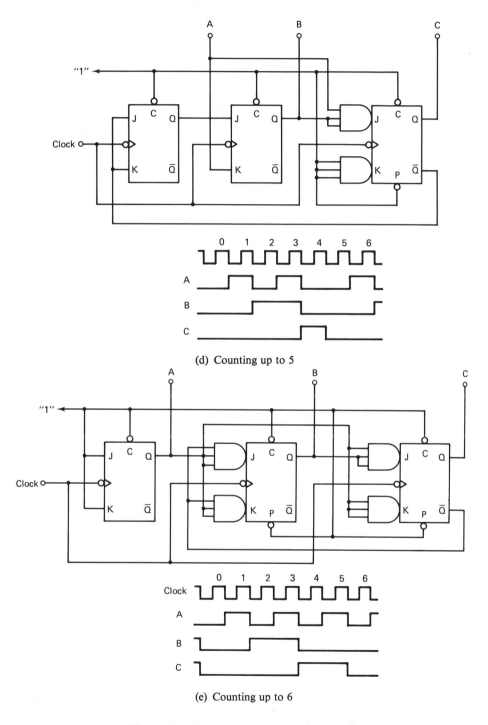

(d) Counting up to 5

(e) Counting up to 6

Figure 4-94 Synchronous Counters. (*continued.*)

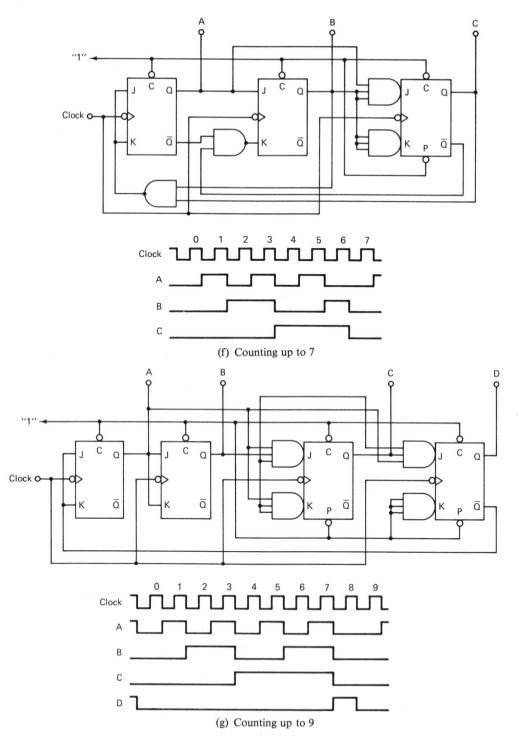

(f) Counting up to 7

(g) Counting up to 9

Figure 4-94 Synchronous Counters. (*continued.*)

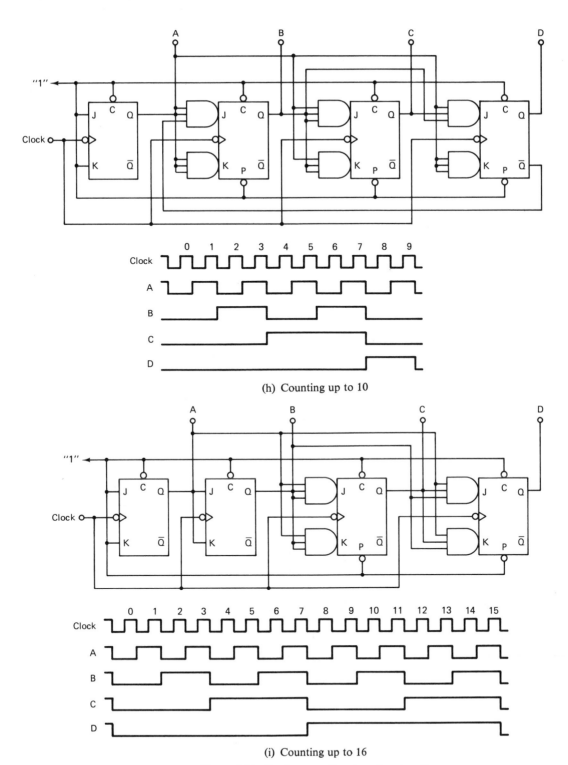

(h) Counting up to 10

(i) Counting up to 16

Figure 4-94 Synchronous Counters. (*continued.*)

8	4	2	1	Decimal value
O	O	O	O	0
O	O	O	L	1
O	O	L	O	2
O	O	L	L	3
O	L	O	O	4
O	L	O	L	5
O	L	L	O	6
O	L	L	L	7
L	O	O	O	8
L	O	O	L	9

(j) Truth table to convert 1248 BCD to decimal

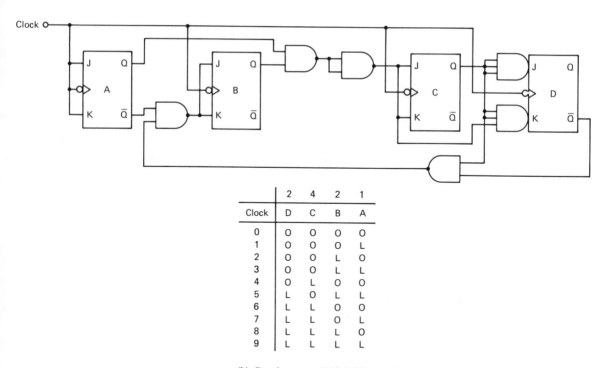

	2	4	2	1
Clock	D	C	B	A
0	O	O	O	O
1	O	O	O	L
2	O	O	L	O
3	O	O	L	L
4	O	L	O	O
5	L	O	L	L
6	L	L	O	O
7	L	L	O	L
8	L	L	L	O
9	L	L	L	L

(k) Synchronous 1248 BCD counter

Figure 4-94 Synchronous Counters. (*continued.*)

load preset input is low. This preset state is stored in the counter when the load preset input goes high. Further count input pulses then clock the counter to its next appropriate state.

To reset all outputs to zero, the clear input is taken high. The overriding clear is independent of load and count inputs.

These counters can be cascaded without additional logic. When the counter overflows, the carry output produces a pulse of equal width to that of the count-up input pulse. Similarly, the borrow output pulse width equals that of the count-down input pulse when the counter underflows.

All inputs have input clamping diodes to reduce line termination effects and outputs are of standard 74 series configuration.

Figure 4-95 shows the various signals in the clear, load, and count sequences for the 74192. Figure 4-96 shows the same for the 74193. Figure 4-97 is a logic diagram for the 74192 and Figure 4-98 is a logic diagram for the 74193.

The 7496 is a similar powerful divider that provides:

1. Preset parallel input
2. Parallel or serial input
3. Parallel and serial output
4. Buffered clear, clock, and serial input
5. Serial to parallel/parallel to serial converter capability

Figure 4-99 shows the block diagram. The 7496 consists of five RS master/slave flip-flops connected to form a 5-bit shift register. The clock, clear, and serial inputs are buffered by four inverters. The preset inputs A to E are connected to the flip-flop preset inputs via five two-input NAND gates. The second input of each gate is connected to the common preset input, which when at logical 1 enables all preset inputs. A logical 1 on these inputs sets the flip-flops to the logical 1 state. A logical 1 on the clear input sets all flip-flops to the logical 0 state simultaneously. Right shift in the register occurs on the positive edge of the clock pulse. The serial input data must be present prior to the clock edge. All inputs have clamping diodes and outputs are standard 74 series configuration. The registers may be cascaded to provide any length of register.

There are basically two forms of parallel input shift registers: the preset parallel input type such as the 7494 and 7496 and the clocked parallel input type such as the 7495.

The inputs of the preset type are connected to the flip-flop preset inputs via appropriate gating. The application of a logical 1 voltage to the input sets the flip-flop to logical 1 state, but the application of a logical 0 voltage then has no effect. To set flip-flops to logical 0 state, the clear input must be used.

The inputs of the clocked type are connected to the RS flip-flop inputs via appropriate gating. The application of a logical 1 voltage at the input prior to clocking sets the flip-flops to a logical 1 state. Similarly, the application of a logical 0 voltage

Typical clear, load, and count sequences for the 74192 Decade Counter

Illustrated below is the following sequence:

1. Clear all outputs to zero.
2. Preset to BCD seven.
3. Count up to eight, nine, carry, zero, one, and two.
4. Count down to one, zero, borrow, nine, eight, and seven.

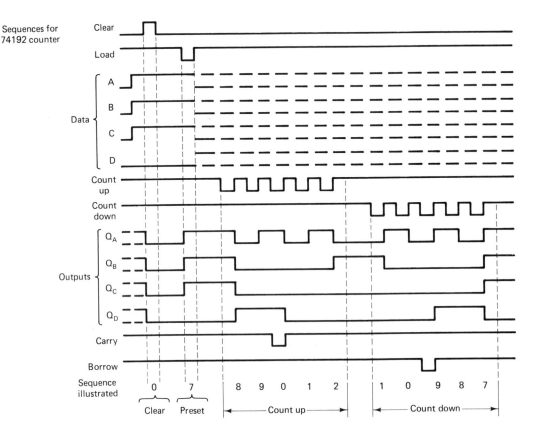

Notes:
1. Clear overrides all other inputs.
2. When counting up, count-down input must be high;
   when counting down, count-up input must be high.

Figure 4-95 Timing table to the 74192 decade counter. (Courtesy of Motorola Semiconductor Products, Inc.)

at the input sets the flip-flops to a logical 0 state. Hence the clocked parallel register is most suitable for applications where the parallel data are applied for a predetermined time, as is the case for the accumulator of a multiplier. The preset parallel input register is more suitable for applications where the input data arrive randomly or are present for a very short time, as can be the case in some types of analog-to-digital conversion systems.

The various counters mentioned earlier, available in CMOS and TTL, are spin-offs that may be advantageous for certain applications. It is important to consult the

Typical clear, load and count sequences for the 74193 Binary Counter
Illustrated below is the following sequence:

1. Clear outputs to zero
2. Preset to binary thirteen
3. Count up to fourteen, fifteen, carry, zero, one and two
4. Count down to one, zero, borrow, fifteen, fourteen and thirteen

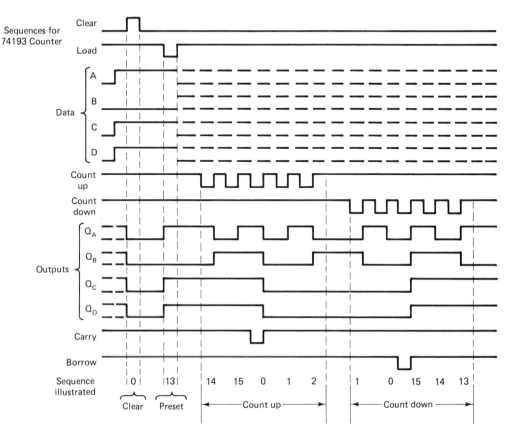

Notes:

1. Clear overrides all other inputs
2. When counting up, count-down input must be high, when counting down, count-up input must be high

Figure 4-96 Timing table for the 74193 binary counter. (Courtesy of Morotola Semiconductor Products, Inc.)

data books of the various manufacturers to see and determine which divider is the best for a particular application. What this means is that the divider that has the highest flexibility may also be the most expensive, and in some cases, not all capabilities are required simultaneously. In order to select the right device, a price/performance analysis has to be done. As a result of price/performance analysis, as I have mentioned earlier, choosing CMOS devices and avoiding TTL may be such an example.

Although these divider changes have to remain programmable, the simultaneous

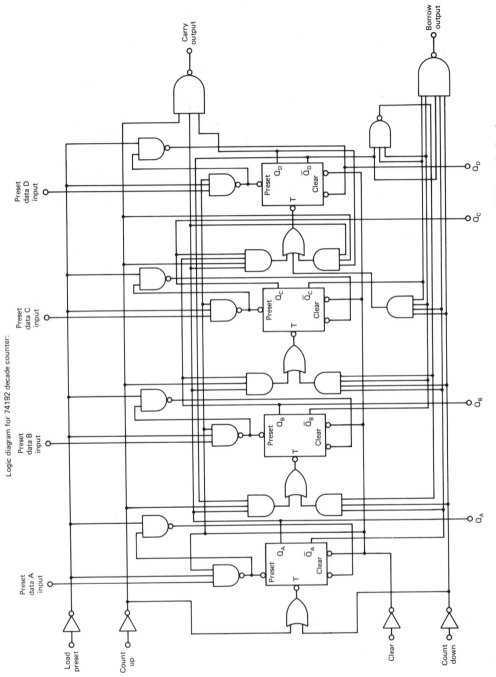

Logic diagram for 74192 decade counter:

Preset data D input

Preset data C input

Preset data B input

Preset data A input

Load preset

Count up

Clear

Count down

Carry output

Borrow output

Q_D

Q_C

Q_B

Q_A

Figure 4-97 Logic diagram for the 74192 decade counter. (Courtesy of Motorola Semiconductor Products, Inc.)

Logic diagram for 74193 binary counter:

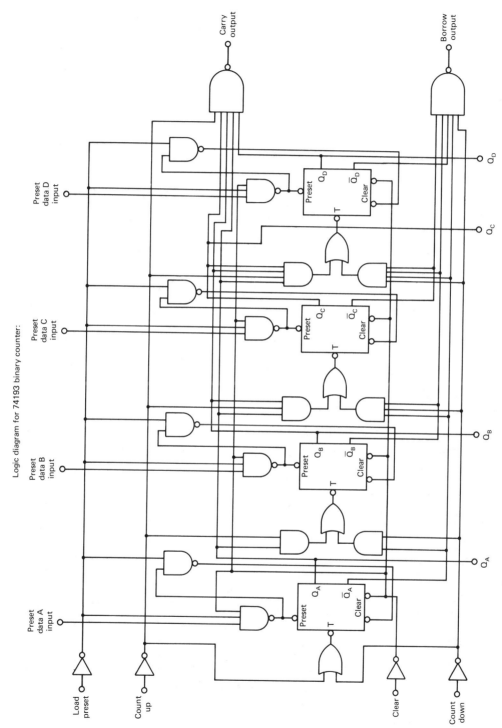

Figure 4-98 Logic diagram for the 74193 binary counter. (Courtesy of Motorola Semi-conductor Products, Inc.)

259

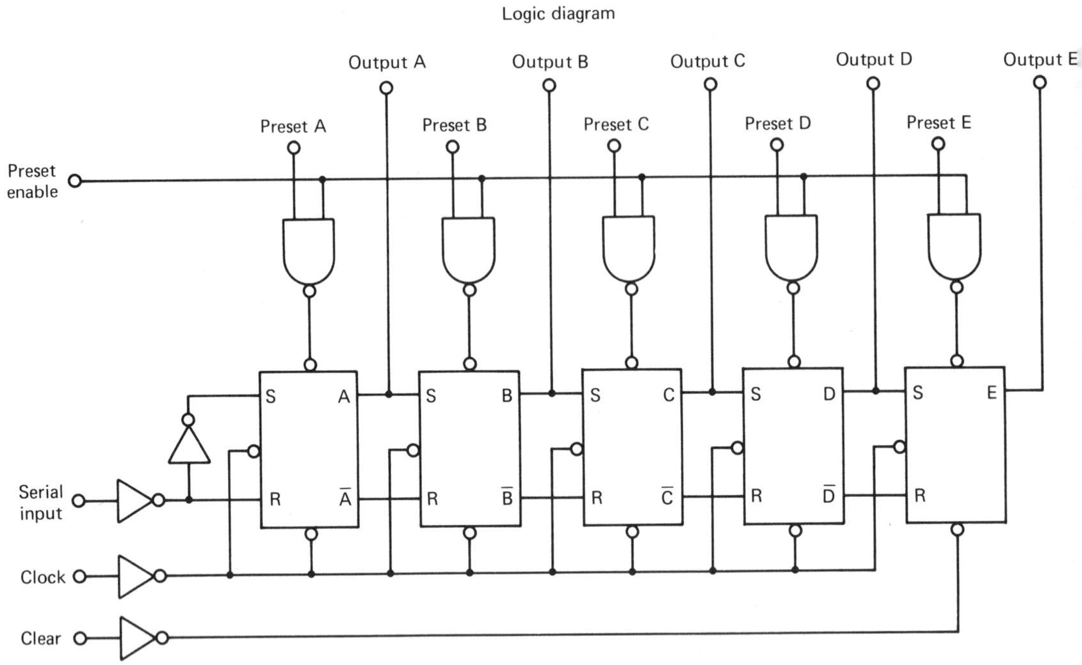

Logic diagram

Figure 4-99 Block diagram of the 7496 counter. (Courtesy of Motorola Semiconductor Products, Inc.)

availability of parallel and serial loading may not be a requirement. In some designs, however, the serial loading may ease the concept; microprocessor applications, for instance, will make the design much easier and require fewer wires if serial loading is used.

Several modern integrated circuits are offered that have all the required dividers on one chip. This may be a convenience for a particular design, but only in cases where the integrated circuit is specifically designed for the application will the integrated circuit have sufficient flexibility. Generally, there is a trade-off between high integration and flexibility. As the number of available pins on the integrated circuit and decoding format limits the number of different tasks, some particular design efforts may require the use of discrete integrated circuits rather than LSI circuits.

A frequency synthesizer for CB application is the typical example where the market requires certain capabilities, and several manufacturers offer basically the entire synthesizer on one chip. AM/FM radios are another typical example. However, for high-performance synthesizers, these devices are probably not suitable. Motorola has recently introduced the MC145156 one-chip frequency synthesizer, and Philips has introduced the HEF4750 and HEF4751 frequency synthesizer integrated circuits. We will now take a look at those two devices to see what advantages can be obtained from these very latest designs.

Motorola is manufacturing a family of low-power frequency synthesizer chips,

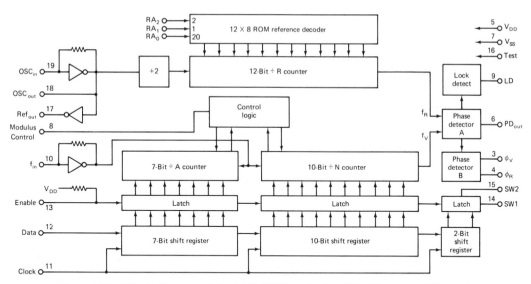

Figure 4-100   Block diagram of the MC145156 synthesizer IC. (Courtesy of Motorola Semiconductor Products, Inc.)

and for microprocessor application, the MC145156 is probably the most interesting one. Figure 4-100 shows a block diagram of this device.

The MC145156 is programmed by a clocked, serial input, 19-bit data stream. The device features consist of a reference oscillator, selectable reference divider, digital phase detector, 10-bit programmable divide-by-N counter, 7-bit programmable divide-by-A counter and the necessary shift register and latch circuitry for accepting the serial input data. When combined with a loop filter and VCO, the MC145156 can provide all the remaining functions for a PLL frequency synthesizer operating up to the device's frequency limit. For higher VCO frequency operation, a down mixer or a dual modulus prescaler can be used between the VCO and MC145156.

It can be used for the following applications.

1. General-purpose applications: CATV, AM/FM radios, two-way radios, TV tuning, scanning receivers, amateur radio
2. Low power drain
3. 3.0 to 9.0 V dc supply range
4. >30 MHz typical input capability at 5 V dc
5. Eight user-selectable reference divider values: 8, 64, 128, 256, 640, 1000, 1024, 2048
6. On- or off-chip reference oscillator operation with buffered output
7. Lock detect signal
8. Two open-drain switch outputs
9. Dual modulus/serial programming

10. Divide-by-N range $= 3$ to 1023

11. "Linearized" digital phase detector, which enhances transfer function linearity

12. Two error signal options: single ended (three state) and double ended

Figure 4-101 shows the phase comparator output waveforms. It was mentioned earlier that this type of integrated circuit fits well together with a microprocessor, and Figure 4-102 shows a block diagram of an Avionics NAV and COM synthesizer, while Figure 4-103 shows an FM/AM broadcast radio synthesizer. Such devices will be made available by various companies, and their usage extends over several years; improvements will yield to a different design.

The MC145156 is not really a general-purpose frequency synthesizer chip but the reason why the frequency synthesizer chips are included under programmable dividers is because most of the integrated circuit contains logic circuit either for reference, division, or VCO frequency division.

The general-purpose frequency synthesizer chip HEF4750 and HEF4751 has been mentioned several times already. The two integrated circuits together form a versatile LSI frequency synthesizer system. The HEF4750 integrated circuit contains a reference oscillator, the reference divider, a phase modulator, and two phase detec-

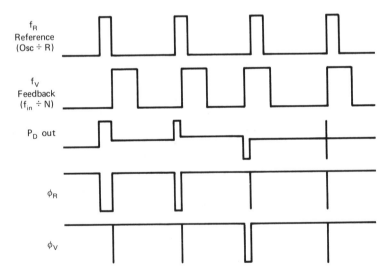

Note:
The P_D output state is equal to either V_{DD} or V_{SS} when active. When not active, the output is high impedance and the voltage at that pin is determined by the low-pass filter capacitor.

Figure 4-101 Phase detector output waveforms of the MC145156 PLL IC. (Courtesy of Motorola Semiconductor Products, Inc.)

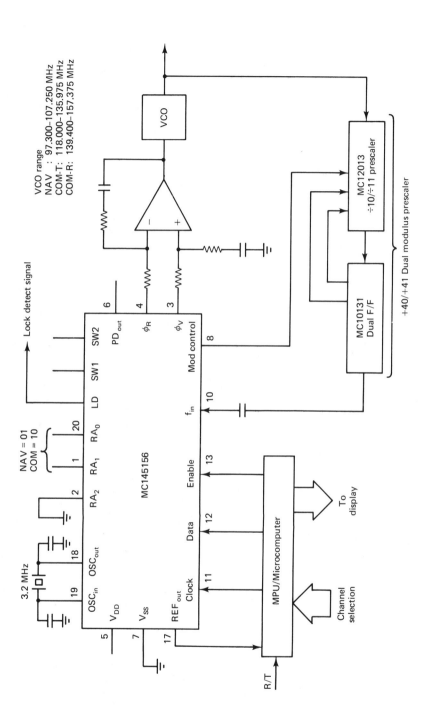

Figure 4-102 Recommended use of the MC145156 PLL synthesizer IC for NAV/COM applications. (Courtesy of Motorola Semiconductor Products, Inc.)

Notes:
1) for NAV: $F_R = 50$ kHz, $\div R = 64$ using 10.7 MHz lowside injection, $N_{total} = 1946–2145$
for COM-T $F_R = 25$ kHz, $\div R = 128$ using 21.4 MHz highside injection, $N_{total} = 4720–5439$
for COM-R $F_R = 25$ kHz, $\div R = 128$ using 21.4 MHz highside injection, $N_{total} = 5576–6295$
2) A $\div 32/\div 33$ dual modulus approach is provided by substituting an MC12011 ($\div 8/\div 9$) for the MC12013. The devices are pin equivalent.
3) A 6.4 MHz oscillator crystal can be used by selecting $\div R = 128$ (code 010) for NAV and $\div R = 256$ (code 011) for COM

263

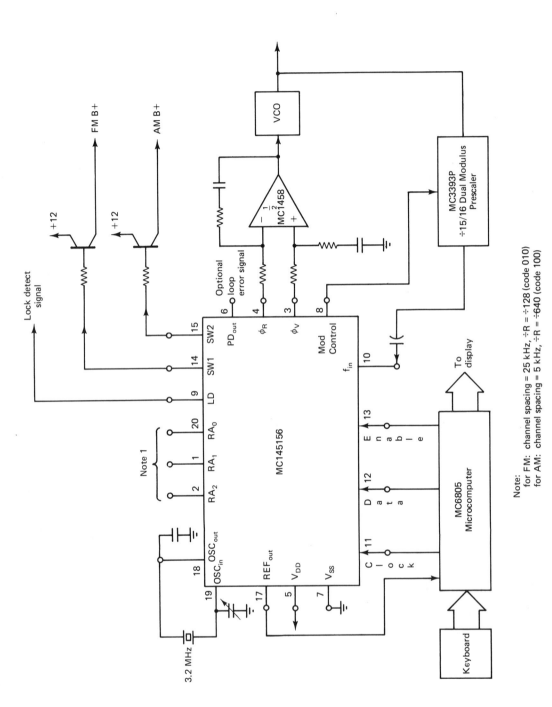

Figure 4-103 Recommended use of the MC145156 in a car radio (AM–FM range). (Courtesy of Motorola Semiconductor Products, Inc.)

Note:
for FM: channel spacing = 25 kHz, ÷R = ÷128 (code 010)
for AM: channel spacing = 5 kHz, ÷R = ÷640 (code 100)

tors on board. Its internal structure is shown on Figure 4-104. The programmable divider section is contained in the HEF4751. This universal divider contains several dual modulus dividers and other programmable dividers, which results in substantial flexibility. Programmability of $4\frac{1}{2}$ decades, with a guaranteed input frequency of 9 MHz at a 10-V supply voltage, make this a very universal chip. The additional internal circuitry allows the use of up to three external 10/11 prescalers.

Figure 4-105 shows the internal structure. With the external prescalers, a maximum configuration of $6\frac{1}{2}$ decades and a maximum input of 4.5 GHz can theoretically be obtained. Programming is performed in BCD code in a bit-parallel decade serial format. Details about the programming can be found in the data sheet. One other programmable feature is the fractional channel selection and half-channel offset.

The fractional channel selection allows a decrease of the step size up to a factor of 16, which means that the step size can be 1/16 of the reference. This may cause some difficulties in programming, and it is recommended to use this feature only up to one-tenth of the reference. A typical application would be a one-loop synthesizer with a 10-kHz reference and 1-kHz resolution.

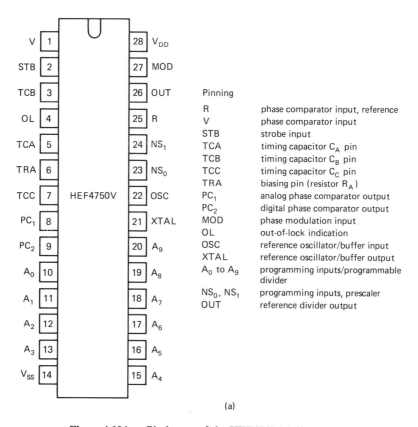

(a)

Figure 4-104a   Pin layout of the HEF4750 LOCMOS IC.

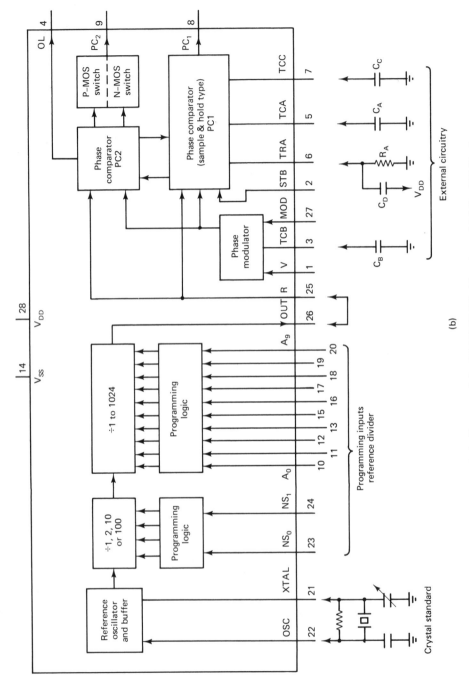

Figure 4-104b Block diagram of the HEF4750 IC. (Courtesy of Mullard/Philips.)

(b)

Universal divider

The HEF4751V is a universal divider (U.D.) intended for use in high performance phase lock loop frequency synthesizer systems. It consists of a chain of counters operating in a programmable feedback mode. Programmable feedback signals are generated for up to three external (fast) ÷10/11 prescaler.

The system comprising one HEF4751V U.D. together with prescalers is a fully programmable divider with a maximum configuration of: 5 decimal stages, a programmable mode M stage ($1 \leqslant M \leqslant 16$, non-decimal fraction channel selection), and a mode H stage (H = 1 or 2, stage for half channel offset). Programming is performed in BCD code in a bit-parallel, digit-serial format.

To accommodate fixed or variable frequency offset, two numbers are applied in parallel, one being subtracted from the other to produce the internal program.

The decade selection address is generated by an internal program counter which may run continuously or on demand. Two or more universal dividers can be casacaded, each extra U.D. (in slave mode) adds two decades to the system. The combination retains the full programmabliity and features of a single U.D.

The U.D. provides a fast output signal FF at output OFF, which can have a phase jitter of ± 1 system input period, to allow fast frequency locking. The slow output signal FS at output OFS, which is jitter-free, is used for fine phase control at a lower speed.

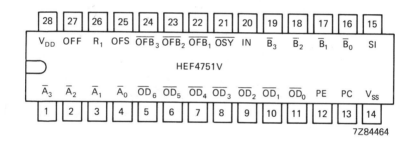

Supply voltage

Rating	Recommended operating
−0.5 to +18	4.5 to 12.5 V

HEF4751VP: 28-lead DIL; plastic (SOT-117)
HEF4751VD: 28-lead DIL; ceramic (SOT-135).

(a)

Figure 4-105a   Pin layout of the HEF4751 universal divider.

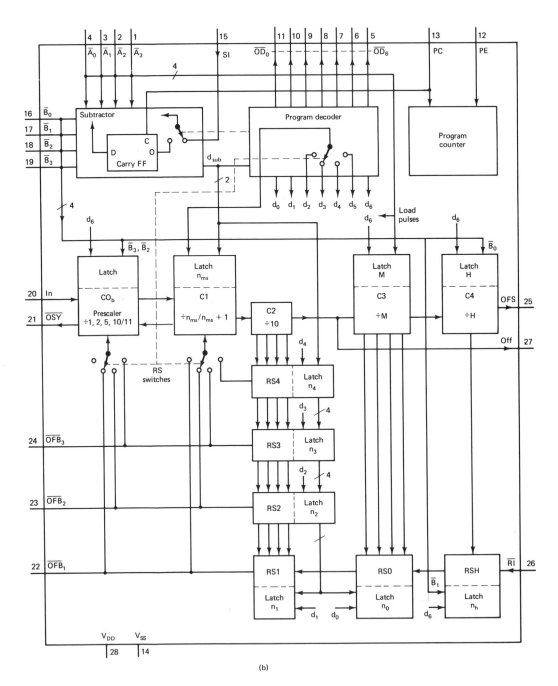

Figure 4-105b Block diagram of the HEF4751 universal divider.

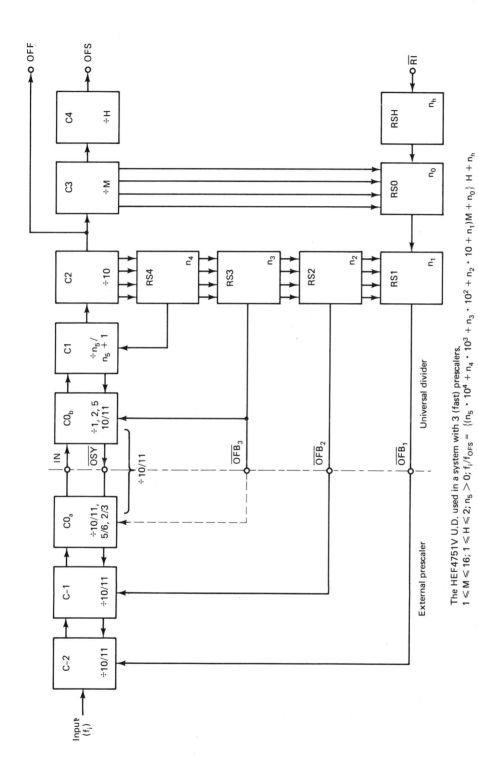

The HEF4751V U.D. used in a system with 3 (fast) prescalers.

$1 \leqslant M \leqslant 16; 1 \leqslant H \leqslant 2; n_5 > 0; f_i/f_{OFS} = \{(n_5 \cdot 10^4 + n_4 \cdot 10^3 + n_3 \cdot 10^2 + n_2 \cdot 10 + n_1)M + n_0\} H + n_h$

(c)

Figure 4-105c Block diagram of the universal divider type HEF4751 including external prescalers.

269

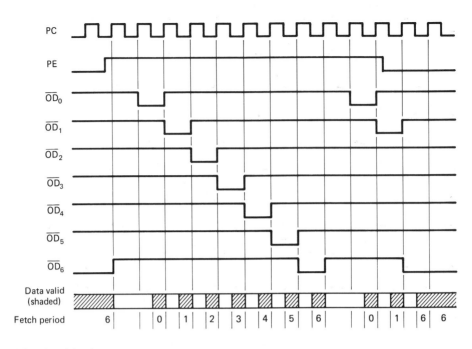

Allocation of data input

Fetch period	Inputs								SI
	$\overline{A}_3$	$\overline{A}_2$	$\overline{A}_1$	$\overline{A}_0$	$\overline{B}_3$	$\overline{B}_2$	$\overline{B}_1$	$\overline{B}_0$	
0		n_{0A}				n_{0B}			b_{in}
1		n_{1A}				n_{1B}			X
2		n_{2A}				n_{2B}			X
3		n_{3A}				n_{3B}			X
4		n_{4A}				n_{4B}			X
5		n_{5A}				n_{5B}			X
6		M			CO_b control		$\frac{1}{2}$ channel control		X

Allocation of data input $\overline{B}_3$ to $\overline{B}_0$ during fetch period 6

$\overline{B}_3$	$\overline{B}_2$	CO_b division ratio
L	L	1
L	H	2
H	L	5
H	H	10/11

$\overline{B}_1$	$\overline{B}_0$	$\frac{1}{2}$ channel configuration
L	L	H = 1
L	H	H = 2; n_h = 0
H	H	H = 2; n_h = 1
H	L	Test state

H = HIGH state (the more positive voltage)
L = LOW state (the less positive voltage)
X = state is immaterial

(d)

Figure 4-105d Timing diagram of the HEF4751 universal divider.

Program data input

The programming process is timed and controlled by input PC and PE. When the program enable (PE) input is HIGH, the positive edges of the program clock (PC) signal step through the internal program counter in a sequence of 8 states. Seven states define fetch periods, each indicated by a LOW signal at one of the corresponding data address outputs ($\overline{OD}_0$ to $\overline{OD}_6$). These data address signals may be used to address the external program source. The data fetched from the program source is applied to inputs $\overline{A}_0$ to $\overline{A}_3$ and $\overline{B}_0$ to $\overline{B}_3$. When PC is LOW in a fetch period an internal load pulse is generated, the data is valid during this time and has to be stable. When PE is LOW, the programming cyclus is interrupted. On the first positive edge of PC. On the next negative edge at input PC fetch period 6 is entered. Data may enter asynchronously in fetch period 6.

Ten blocks in the U.D. need program input signals. Four of these (CO_b, C3, C4 and RSH) are concerned with the configuration of the U.D. and are programmed in fetch period 6. The remaining blocks (RSo to RS4 and C1) are programmed with number P, consisting of six internal digits n_0 to n_5.

$$P = (n_5 \cdot 10^4 + n_4 \cdot 10^3 + n_3 \cdot 10^2 + n_2 \cdot 10 + n_1) \cdot M + n_0$$

These digits are formed by a subtractor from two external numbers A and B and a borrow-in (b_{in}).

$$P = A - B - b_{in} \text{ or if this result is negative; } P = A - B - b_{in} + M \cdot 10^5$$

The numbers A and B each consisting of six four bit digits n_{0A} to n_{5A} and n_{0B} to n_{5B}, are applied in fetch period 0 to 5 to the inputs $\overline{A}_0$ to $\overline{A}_3$ (data A) and $\overline{B}_0$ to $\overline{B}_3$ (data B) in binary coded negative logic.

$$A = (n_{5A} \cdot 10^4 + n_{4A} \cdot 10^3 + n_{3A} \cdot 10^2 + n_{2A} \cdot 10 + n_{1A}) \cdot M + n_{0A}$$

$$B = (n_{5B} \cdot 10^4 + n_{4B} \cdot 10^3 + n_{3B} \cdot 10^2 + n_{2B} \cdot 10 + n_{1B}) \cdot M + n_{0B}$$

Borrow-in (b_{in}) is applied via input SI in fetch period 0 (SI = HIGH: borrow, SI = LOW: no borrow).

Counter C1 is automatically programmed with the most significant non-zero digit (n_{ms}) from the internal digits n_5 to n_2 of number P. The counter chain C − 2 to C1 is fully programmable by the use of pulse rate feedback.

Rate feedback is generated by the rate selectors RS4 to RS0 and RSH, which are programmed with digits n_4 to n_0 and n_h respectively. In fetch period 6 the fractional counter C3, half channel counter C4 and CO_b are programmed and configured via data B inputs. Counter C3 is programmed in fetch period 6 via data A inputs in negative logic (except all HIGH is understood as: M = 16). The counter C0 is a side steppable 10/11 counter composed of an internal part CO_b and an external part CO_a. CO_b is configured via $\overline{B}_3$ and $\overline{B}_2$ to a division ratio of 1 or 2 or 5 or 10/11; CO_a must have the complementary ratio 10/11 or 5/6 or 2/3 or 1 respectively. In the latter case CO_b comprises the whole C0 counter with internal feedback, CO_a is then not required.

The half channel counter C4 is enabled with $\overline{B}_0$ = HIGH and disabled with $\overline{B}_0$ = LOW. With C4 enabled, a half channel offset can be programmed with input $\overline{B}_1$ = HIGH, and no offset with $\overline{B}_1$ = LOW.

(e)

Figure 4-105e Program data input instructions for the HEF4751 universal divider.

Feedback to prescalers

The counters C1, C0, C − 1 and C − 2 are side-steppable counters, i.e. its division ratio may be increased by one, by applying a pulse to a control terminal for the duration of one division cycle. Counter C2 has 10 states, which are accessible as timing signals for the rate selectors RS1 to RS4. A rate selector, programmed with $n(n_1$ to n_4 in the U.D.) generates n of 10 basic timing periods an active signal. Since $n \leqslant 9$, 1 of 10 periods is always non-active. In this period RS1 transfers the output of rate selector RS0, which is timed by counter C3 and programmed with n_0. Similarly, RS0 transfers RSH output during one period of C3. Rate selector RSH is timed by C4 and programmed with n_h. In one of the two states of C4, if enabled, or always, if C4 is disabled, RSH transfers the LOW active signal at input $\overline{R1}$ to RS0. If $\overline{RI}$ is not used it must be connected to HIGH. The feedback output signals of RS1, RS2 and RS3 are externally available as active LOW signals at outputs $\overline{OFB_1}$, $\overline{OFB_2}$ and $\overline{OFB_3}$.

Output $\overline{OFB_1}$ is intended for the prescaler at the highest frequency (if present), $\overline{OFB_2}$ for the next (if present) and $\overline{OFB_3}$ for the lowest frequency prescaler (if present). A prescaler needs a feedback signal, which is timed on one of its own division cycles in a basic timing period. The timing signal at $\overline{OSY}$ is LOW during the last U.D. input period of a basic timing period and is suitable for timing of the feedback for the last external prescaler. The synchronization signal for a preceding prescaler is the OR-function of the sync. input and sync. output of the following prescaler (all sync. signals active LOW).

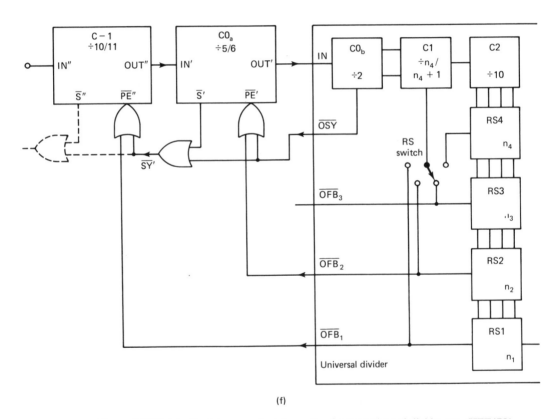

(f)

Figure 4-105f Feedback to prescaler information for the universal divider type HEF4751.

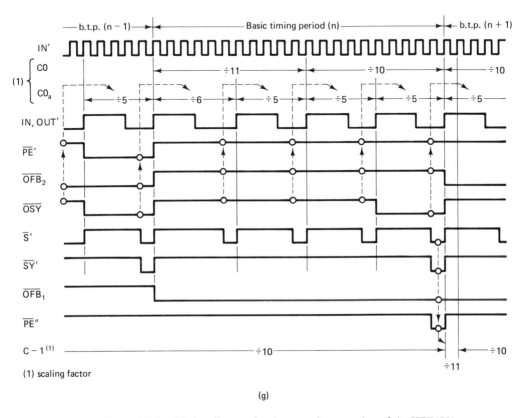

(g)

Figure 4-105g Timing diagram for the prescaler operation of the HEF4751.

Cascading of U.D.s

A U.D. is programmed into the 'slave' mode by the program input data: $n_{2A} = 11$, $n_{2B} = 10$, $n_{3A} = n_{4A} = n_{3B} = n_{4B} = n_{5B} = 0$. A U.D. operating in the slave mode performs the function of two extra programmable stages C2' and C3' to a 'master' (not slave) mode operating U.D. More slave U.D.s may be used, every slave adding two lower significant digits to the system.

Output $\overline{OFB}_3$ is converted to the borrow output of the program data subtractor, which is valid after fetch period 5. Input SI is the borrow input (both in master and in slave mode), which has to be valid in fetch period 0. Input SI has to be connected to output $\overline{OFB}_3$ of a following slave, if not present, to LOW. For proper transfer of the borrow from a lower to a higher significant U.D. subtractor, the U.D.s have to be programmed sequentially in order of significance or synchronously if the program is repeated at least the number of U.D.s in the system.

Rate input $\overline{RI}$ and output OFS must be connected to rate output $\overline{OFB}_1$ and the input IN of the next slave U.D. The combination thus formed retains the full programmability and features of one U.D.

Output

The normal output of the U.D. is the slow output OFS, which consists of evenly spaced LOW pulses. This output is intended for accurate phase comparison. If a better frequency acquisition time is required, the fast output OFF can be used. The output frequency on OFF is a factor $M \cdot H$ higher than the frequency on OFS. However, phase jitter of maximum ± 1 system input period occurs at OFF, since the division ratio of the counters preceding OFF are varied by slow feedback pulse trains from rate selectors following OFF.

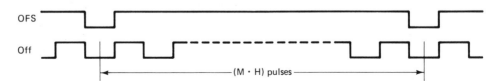

Figure 4-105h Connection information for cascading of several universal dividers.

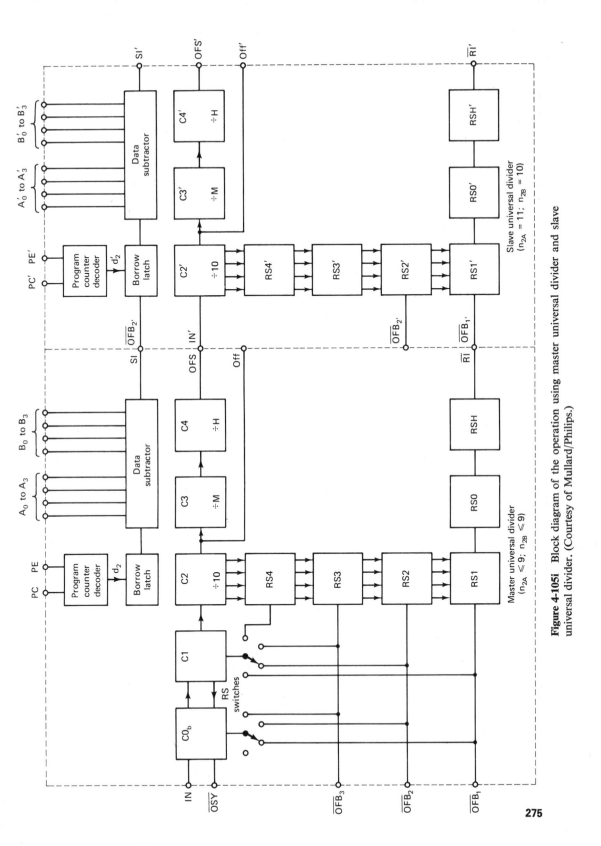

Figure 4-105i Block diagram of the operation using master universal divider and slave universal divider. (Courtesy of Mullard/Philips.)

275

One of the two-phase comparators is a dual cascaded sample/hold detector which provides a jitter-free output used for fine phase control of the synthesizer. Although not all details of how this is achieved are known, this integrated circuit appears extremely promising for future designs. It is currently being used in the new Rohde & Schwarz ESV 20 to 1000 MHz EMI/RFI and field strength receiver.

I have mentioned several times that the TTL and CMOS devices operate only up to 30 MHz at most, and higher input frequencies require faster dividers. A way around the speed requirements is to use ECL swallow counters. Swallow counters are treated in the following section.

4-6-3 Swallow Counters/Dual Modulus Counters

To extend the frequency range beyond 30 MHz, swallow counters are being used; they also are often referred to as two- or dual-modulus prescalers. Figure 4-106 shows the block diagram of such a device. The three flip-flops are wired in such a manner that by changing the decoding, the division ratio can be changed between a division ratio of 2, 5, 6, 10, 11, or 12. The Motorola MC12012 shown in the figure can be used for this. There are several ways to interface these dual-modulus prescalers, which I prefer to refer to as swallow counters. What actually happens is that out of a chain of pulses, one or two pulses are being swallowed, but let us first take a look at how the system works.

The most popular swallow counters are the 95H90 (350 MHz) and 11C90 (520 MHz) made by Fairchild, and the Plessey SP8692 (200 MHz, 14 mA, 5/6), SP8691 (200 MHz, 14 mA, 8/9), SP 8690 (200 MHz, 14 mA, 10/11), and SP8786 (1300 MHz, 85 mA, 20/22). The division ratio of a swallow counter is controlled by two inputs. The counter will divide by 10 when either input is in the high state and by 11 when both inputs are in the low state.

This 10/11 division ratio enables one to build fully programmable dividers to 500 MHz. The switch counting principle means that high-frequency prescaling occurs without any reduction in comparison frequency. The disadvantage of this technique is that a fully programmable divider is required to control the 10/11 division ratio and that a minimum limit is set on the possible division ratio, although this is not a serious problem in practice. Figure 4-107 uses a division ratio of $P/(P + 1)$, which is set to 10/11. The A counter counts the units, and the B counter counts the tens.

Consider the system shown in Figure 4-107. If the $P/(P + 1)$ is a 10/11 divider, the A counter counts the units and the M counter counts the tens. The mode of operation depends on the type of programmable counter used, but the system might operate as follows. If the number loaded into A is greater than zero, then the $P/(P + 1)$ divider is set to divide by $P + 1$ at the start of the cycle. The output from the $P/(P + 1)$ divider clocks both A and M. When A is full, it ceases counting and sets the $P/(P + 1)$ divider into the P mode. Only M is then clocked, and when it is full, it resets both A and M and the cycle repeats.

The divider chain therefore divides by

$$(M - A)P + A(P + 1) = MP + A \qquad (4\text{-}122)$$

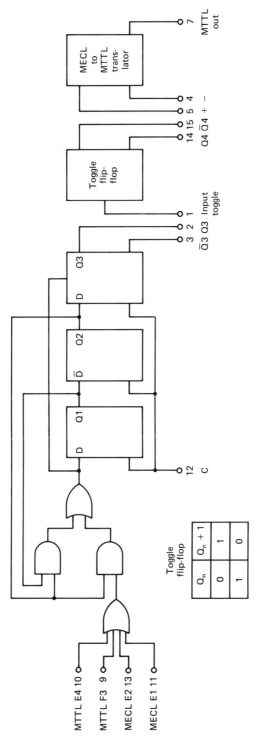

Figure 4-106 Block diagram of the Motorola MC12012 universal dual-modulus counter. (Courtesy of Motorola Semiconductor Products, Inc.)

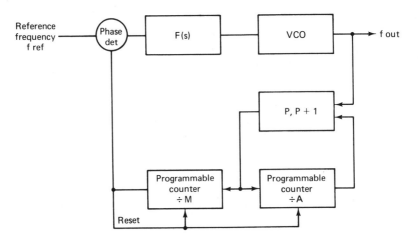

Figure 4-107 System using dual-modulus counter arrangement.

Therefore,

$$f_{\text{out}} = (MP + A)f_{\text{ref}} \tag{4-123}$$

If A is incremented by one, the output frequency changes by f_{ref}. In other words, the channel spacing is equal to f_{ref}. This is the channel spacing that would be obtained with a fully programmable divider operating at the same frequency as the $P/P+1$ divider.

For this system to work, the A counter must underflow before the M counter does; otherwise, $P/(P+1)$ will remain permanently in the $P+1$ mode. There is, therefore, a minimum system division ratio, M_{min}, below which the $P/(P+1)$ system will not function. To find that minimum ratio, consider the following.

The A counter must be capable of counting all numbers up to and including $P-1$ if every division ratio is to be possible, or

$$A_{\text{max}} = P - 1 \tag{4-124}$$

$$M_{\text{min}} = P \qquad \text{since } M > A \tag{4-125}$$

The divider chain divides by $MP + A$; therefore, the minimum system division ratio is

$$\begin{aligned} M_{\text{min}} &= M_{\text{min}}(P + A_{\text{min}}) \\ &= P(P + 0) = p^2 \end{aligned} \tag{4-126}$$

Using a 10/11 ratio, the minimum practical division ratio of the system is 100.

In the system shown in Figure 4-107, the fully programmable counter, A, must be quite fast. With a 350-MHz clock to the 10/11 divider, only about 23 ns is available for counter A to control the 10/11 divider. For cost reasons it would be desirable to use a TTL fully programmable counter, but when the delays through the ECL-to-TTL translators have been taken into account, very little time remains for the fully programmable counter. The 10/11 function can be extended easily, however, to give

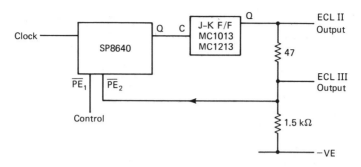

Figure 4-108 Level shifting information for connecting the various ECL2 and ECL3 stages.

a $+N/(N + 1)$ counter with a longer control time for a given input frequency, as shown in Figures 4-108 and 4-109. Using the 20/21 system shown in Figure 4-108, the time available to control 20/21 is typically 87 ns at 200 MHz and 44 ns at 350 MHz. The time available to control the 40/41 (Figure 4-109) is approximately 180 ns at 200 MHz and 95 ns at 350 MHz.

This frequency-division technique can, of course, be extended to give 80/81, which would allow the control to be implemented with CMOS, but which would increase the minimum division ratio to 6400 (80^2). This ratio is too large for many synthesizer applications, but it can be reduced to 3200 by making the counter an 80/81/82. Similarly, a 40/41 can be extended to 40/41/42, as shown in Figure 4-110, to reduce the minimum division ratio from 1600 to 800. The available time to control

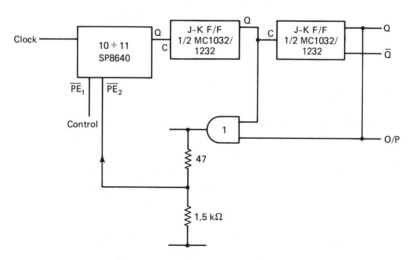

Figure 4-109 Level-shifter diagram to drive from ECL2 to ECL3 levels.

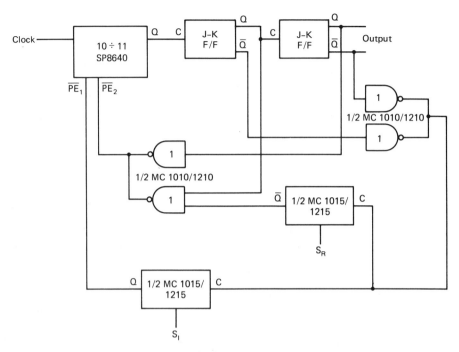

Figure 4-110　40/41/42 three-modulus counter.

the 40/41/42 is a full 40 clock pulses (i.e., 200 ns with a 200-MHz input clock or 110 ns at 350 MHz). The principle of operation is:

$$\text{Minimum division ratio}$$
$$800 = (20 \times 40) + (0 \times 41) + (0 \times 42)$$
$$801 = (19 \times 40) + (1 \times 41)$$
$$802 = (19 \times 40) + (2 \times 42)$$

More information can be found in Ref. 1.

4-6-4 Look-ahead and Delay Compensation

The swallow counter can be used, as we have seen, as a synchronous counter, often referred to as a prescaler. The term "prescaler" for a dual-modulus or swallow counter is really not recommended because a prescaler refers to a divider inserted between the VCO and the programmable divider, which is not necessarily resettable at the same clock rate, and therefore, one loses resolution. A typical example: Assume that we have a VCO operating from 100 to 200 MHz, and we use a divide-by-10 prescaler followed by a programmable divider that drives a phase comparator with a reference input of 1 kHz. If this phase-locked loop is closed, we will find that, for each 1-kHz step, the programmable divider is changed; in reality, we get a 10-kHz step at the output frequency of the VCO. This indicates that the prescaler is not in synchronous condition with the other counters. The dual-modulus technique, when applied properly, allows the frequency extension of standard dividers without losing resolution.

All the various integrated circuits have a propagation delay, especially the CMOS integrated circuits, as they are much slower than the ECL.

We are now concerned with analyzing a programmable divider using a 95H90 divide-by-10/11 counter.

Let us take a look at Figure 4-111. The frequency range of 21.500 to 49.990 from

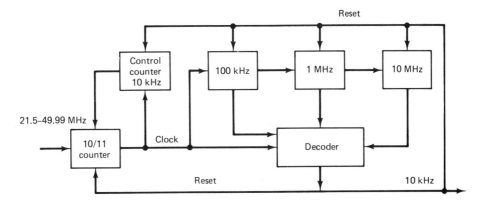

Figure 4-111 Simplified block diagram of the four-stage counter using swallow counter principle and programmable counters.

a VCO will be divided down to a 10-kHz reference. Four counters and several flip-flops are required to provide the necessary timing. It seems convenient to divide this module into two portions and analyze them first.

1. 10/11 divider with control counter
2. Programmable dividers with decoding

The programmable dividers, as well as decoders, can be built in CMOS technology. A programmable divider is the CD4018. They can be used as divide-by-N counters and will operate at a maximum clock frequency of 5 MHz. Therefore, we will use the 95H90 Fairchild divide-by-10/11 counter. [Note that the device is called a $P/(P + 1)$ counter rather than a prescaler.] It was mentioned earlier that there are several different dividers available in ECL technology, and this particular circuit was later used in the design of the Plessey 8940 to reduce power consumption. However, this change does not affect the operating principle. The three programmable dividers permit a division ratio from 002 to 999. The dividers are being programmed via five lines using the Johnson code, where a 00001 equals 0 in decade count, 00011 is equivalent to 1, and so on. As the counter always returns to the zero position, the input must be arranged so that the 9 is equivalent to a 0 count in the counter, position 8 is equivalent to a 1 count, position 7 to a 2 count, and so on. In this case, the counter gets the

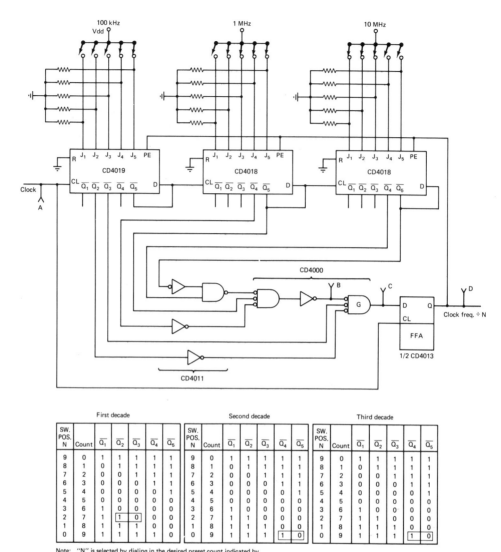

Figure 4-112 Schematic of the CMOS divider section and its truth table.

First decade

SW. POS. N	Count	$\overline{Q}_1$	$\overline{Q}_2$	$\overline{Q}_3$	$\overline{Q}_4$	$\overline{Q}_5$
9	0	1	1	1	1	1
8	1	0	1	1	1	1
7	2	0	0	1	1	1
6	3	0	0	0	1	1
5	4	0	0	0	0	1
4	5	0	0	0	0	0
3	6	1	0	0	0	0
2	7	1	[1]	[0]	0	0
1	8	1	1	1	0	0
0	9	1	1	1	1	0

Second decade

SW. POS. N	Count	$\overline{Q}_1$	$\overline{Q}_2$	$\overline{Q}_3$	$\overline{Q}_4$	$\overline{Q}_5$
9	0	1	1	1	1	1
8	1	0	1	1	1	1
7	2	0	0	1	1	1
6	3	0	0	0	1	1
5	4	0	0	0	0	1
4	5	0	0	0	0	0
3	6	1	0	0	0	0
2	7	1	1	0	0	0
1	8	1	1	1	0	0
0	9	1	1	1	[1]	[0]

Third decade

SW. POS. N	Count	$\overline{Q}_1$	$\overline{Q}_2$	$\overline{Q}_3$	$\overline{Q}_4$	$\overline{Q}_5$
9	0	1	1	1	1	1
8	1	0	1	1	1	1
7	2	0	0	1	1	1
6	3	0	0	0	1	1
5	4	0	0	0	0	1
4	5	0	0	0	0	0
3	6	1	0	0	0	0
2	7	1	1	0	0	0
1	8	1	1	1	0	0
0	9	1	1	1	[1]	[0]

Note: "N" is selected by dialing in the desired preset count indicated by the switch settings: The "9" counts from the second and third decade (shown as [1][0]) are gated with the "7" count (shown as [1][0]) from the first decade to activate the "preset enable" once per counter cycle.

command to divide by 10, which means that the following counter gets one-tenth of the input. At the same time, the outputs $\overline{Q1}$ to $\overline{Q5}$ of the divider can be decoded, and it can be checked whether the end pulse has reached the divider and one cycle is finished. This information will be used to reset the counter to its original condition. In the case of the three-digit counter, one cycle is finished after all three stages deliver the pulses simultaneously, which are decoded and form the output and reset pulse. Figure 4-112 shows the CMOS divider chain including the truth table. The programmable inputs J1 through J5 are tied to Vdd via 100-kΩ resistors. If the switch is closed, a logic 1 applies. The complete divider is being reset via PE after one cycle is complete and the output flip-flop goes to logic 1. Since each of the dividers contains five flip-flops, $\overline{Q5}$ outputs are available which, connected with D, allow the determination of the division.

$\overline{Q5}$-D results in divide by 10, $\overline{Q4}$, $\overline{Q5}$-D results in 9, $\overline{Q4}$-D results in divide by 8, and so on. It is important to understand that the five outputs $\overline{Q1}$ to $\overline{Q5}$ provide a pulse sequence that allows a function of the clock pulses to obtain the output pulse. This is shown in the previously indicated truth table. Let us assume that the third input pulse should be detected at the $\overline{Q}$ outputs; the 3-equivalent, 6, has to be programmed. Therefore, the divider requires three steps until $\overline{Q4}$ is at 1 and $\overline{Q5}$ is at 0. Now it becomes apparent that, regardless of what combination is chosen, the final result at the $\overline{Q}$ outputs is always the same. That is the reason why $\overline{Q4}$ and $\overline{Q5}$ of the 100-kHz and 10-kHz dividers are being used. The 1-MHz divider decodes at $\overline{Q2}$ and $\overline{Q3}$, which means that two pulses prior to the cycle count, the information is extended. The reason for this, as we will see in more detail, is to compensate for the delays in the decoders, gates, and flip-flops.

Division by 584.   Let us assume that $\overline{Q4}$ and $\overline{Q5}$ of the 1-MHz divider decodes t. Also, the 100-kHz and 10-kHz dividers have reached their final count. Point B of the decoder is at zero, and the 1-MHz divider now supplies the pulses as shown in Figure 4-113. It becomes apparent that two pulses of the cycle are lost

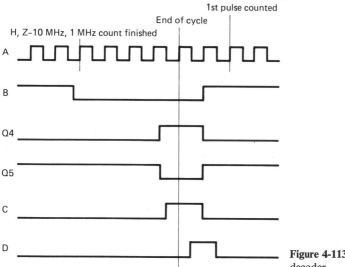

Figure 4-113 Timing diagram of the decoder.

because of the delay in gate 3 and flip-flop A. If the 1-MHz divider is decoded in such a way that it provides an output two pulse counts earlier, the delay is compensated.

10/11 counter (ECL).   We have learned that the CMOS divider can operate up to a maximum of 5 MHz. Higher frequencies can be handled by using the 10/11 counter. The combination of the 10/11 counter and the control circuit together with the additional counter is referred to as a "swallow" counter. This term is used because of the fact that one pulse count is "swallowed" from time to time using the divide-by-10 or divide-by-11 principle. Figure 4-114 shows the truth table determining divide by

e1	e2	÷
0	0	11
0	1	10
1	0	10
1	1	10

Figure 4-114 Truth table of the 10/11 divider.

10 or divide by 11 as a function of the input at E1 and E2 of the 10/11 counter shown in Figure 4-115. To control this facility, a control counter that determines how often one divides by 10 or 11 is required. This circuit works on the principle that, as required, either 10 or 11 input pulses produce one output pulse. At times, one pulse gets removed or swallowed.

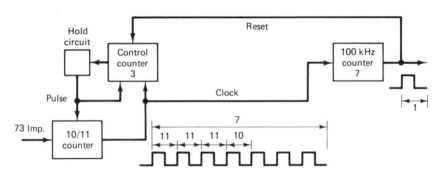

Figure 4-115 Timing of the 10/11 divider.

Example 8

Let us assume that a two-digit counter is constructed using the 95H90 with a control counter following a CMOS divider. If a division ratio of 73 is required, the 10/11 counter will divide three times by 11; then the control counter is full and the 10/11 counter is set to divide by 10. The programmable divider must take four more sequences, during which it divides by 10. As a result, the output pulse occurs after 73 input pulses. Figure 4-115 shows a block diagram with the timing. The control counter is responsible for the 1-MHz digit, and the programmable counter is responsible for the 10-MHz digit.

Delays. A limitation of this system is that there is a clearly defined minimum division ratio at which the system will no longer function. More critical is the fact that there is a time delay in the 10/11 division path. The delay must not be more than $1/(10/f_{in})$, typically 6 ns, determined by the ECL/CMOS level shifters, the CMOS logic, and back through the CMOS/ECL level shifters. This means that 6 ns prior to the critical pulse it has to be known whether division by 10 or 11 is required. Only $5/f_{in}$—6 ns time is available between two pulses. This can be seen from the pulse

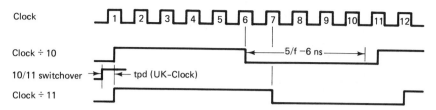

Figure 4-116   Switching and delay times of the 95H90 counter.

diagram, Figure 4-116, showing the switching time of the 95H90. Therefore, there are limits for the delay.

Figure 4-117 shows the complete schematic of the divider chain. Before we analyze this circuit in further detail, let us note that the 10/11 counter is shown in the last portion of the figure; the 2N2907 is used as a level shifter from ECL to CMOS and drives the counter chain.

The first CD4018 is the control counter. The swallow counter, therefore, consists of the 10/11 counter, the control counter, the flip-flop (CD4013), the ECL-to-CMOS level shifter transistor, and the CMOS-to-ECL level shifter being clamped by the two diodes. The gates shown in the circuit are used for decoding purposes, and this function will be discussed when we go into the details of the programmable counter that uses the three CD4018's on the right of the figure. Let us go back to our delays.

1. There is a limit for the delay. The control counter has to determine the division ratio divide 10 or 11. It has to be remembered that the prescaler has to be clamped to 10 and the logic that is doing this attains additional delay.
2. There is a delay from the flip-flop CD4013 via PE and $\overline{Q4}$ of the control counter and the logic to reset to divide by 11 at the end of the cycle.

According to the data sheet, the CD4018 has a propagation delay for PE—$\overline{Q4}$ and clock—$\overline{Q4}$ of 125 ns at 10 V.

To compensate for the delay from clock to $\overline{Q4}$, it is sufficient to decode the output pulse one count before it actually occurs.

To compensate for the delay in the output flip-flop and PE—$\overline{Q4}$, a different circuit is required. It is not possible to take the reset pulse for the divide by 10 from the $\overline{Q}$ output of FFN to the 95H90; instead, it has to go through the control counter. In the case where a straight division by 10 is possible, the 10/11 counter must be prevented from dividing by 11. This decision can be made only by the control counter, with the disadvantage that the additional circuit adds additional delay. In a test circuit, it was found that despite the attempted presetting of the control counter, the timing was still not correct. The width of the PE pulse is a function of the clock frequency, and the delays are constant. As a result of this, there are crossovers between the two areas which prevent proper function of the circuit.

Since this is a technological problem, it has to be taken into consideration in the

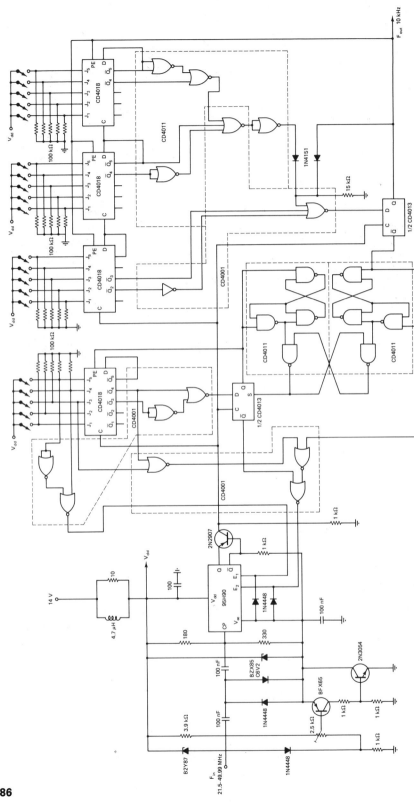

Figure 4-117 Schematic of the 21.5-49.99 MHz divider used for determining the design of delay compensation and look-ahead schematics.

decoding circuit. To understand this better, let us analyze the divider cycle. Let us assume that the divider of the whole system is set at 3754, which means that the output pulse has to occur after 3751 pulse at the input. Regarding the 10/11 counter, the following happens:

$$
\begin{array}{rrl}
4x \div 11 & 44 & \text{Control counter full} \\
296x \div 10 & 2960 & \text{10-MHz counter full} \\
70x \div 10 & 700 & \text{1-MHz counter full} \\
5x \div 10 & \underline{50} & \text{100-kHz counter full} \\
& 3754 &
\end{array}
$$

Figure 4-118 shows the complete cycle. The critical time intervals and positions a, b, c, d, e, f, g, h, and i are indicated.

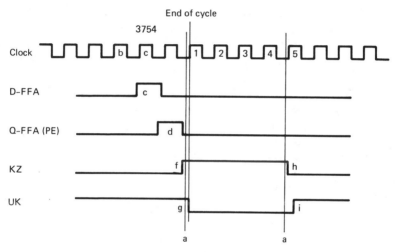

Figure 4-118   Timing diagram for an entire cycle, showing the effects of the various delays.

- a. In this moment, the control counter has to have told the 10/11 counter to switch the division ratio.
- b. Two pulses before final count, decoding is activated.
- c. The D input of the flip-flop A receives information "Logic High."
- d. The next clock pulse (e) triggers flip-flop A.
- f. This information appears much later at the control counter.
- g. It now is too late to be fed into the 10/11; the same applies for the changing for h and i.

Analysis.   During the entire cycle, we divide N times by 11 and it does not matter when in time this happens. It is only important how often the division by 11 occurs. Let us assume that the 10/11 divider receives the "change to" information only after the second pulse, and the control counter follows. This only means that the entire pulse chain is shifted by one count. The final result remains the same. We then get

$$
\begin{array}{rr}
1x \div 10 & 10 \\
4x \div 11 & 44 \\
295x \div 10 & 2950 \\
70x \div 10 & 700 \\
5x \div 10 & \underline{\hphantom{00}50} \\
& 3754
\end{array}
$$

As the 10/11 counter is still set to divide by 10, it will divide by 10 first and then switch over. To do this, a second flip-flop B is required, as well as a NAND latch and two edge detectors FD1 and FD2, which provide only negative pulses at positive edges.

Function.   The rising signal at $\bar{Q}$ is fed to FD1; at the output of FD1 a very narrow pulse is generated that switches the NAND latch and FFB is set to zero via the S input. The $\bar{Q}$ output of FFB changes the divide ratio of the 10/11 counter using some gates in line. These gates are necessary to support the control counter. As the control counter is being decoded to 1 before its final count, it is not possible to determine the division ratio $1x \div 11$. In this case, the output is taken directly from the control counter, connected with $\bar{Q}$ of FFA and applied to the input E1.

Figure 4-119 shows the minimum configuration, consisting of the swallow counter (10/11 counter, 95H90 control counter, FFB, latch, FD1, FD2) and the programmable divider chain with its decoder and FFA.

In case there is no requirement to divide by 11, we can take the output from the control counter and apply it directly to the second input of the 10/11 counter. This blocks any switching into the other mode. This can be seen from the truth table of the

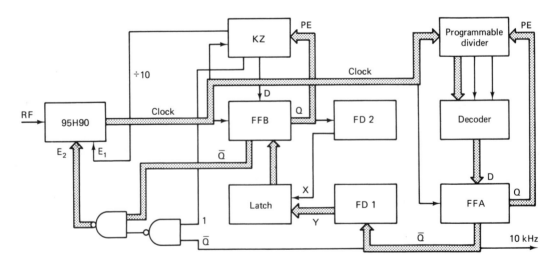

Figure 4-119   Presetting for division by 11 beginning of the cycle.

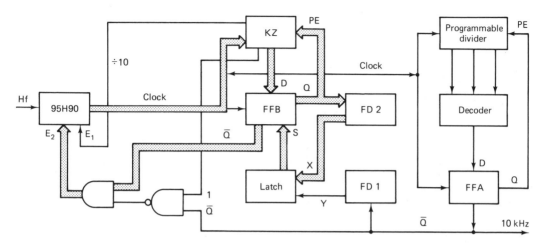

Figure 4-120 Programming of the divider chain to divide by 10 after the control counter is finished.

10/11 counter that was listed earlier. For all other division ratios after the initial division by 11, the 10/11 counter has to be switched to divide by 10. One pulse before the control counter is full, it will supply a logic high to the D input of FFB. With the next clock pulse, this information appears at $\bar{Q}$ via the gates to the input E2. At the same time, FD2 resets the latch and is holding FFB, and therefore the control counter, via the input S. Now this cycle is repeated. To further help understanding, the following figures will give more insight. Figure 4-120 shows how the divider chain is set to divide by 10 after the control counter is full; Figure 4-121 shows division $1x \div 11$; Figure 4-122 shows constant division by 10. This circuit was built as indicated by the previously shown complete schematic, and the result confirmed the theoretical discussions.

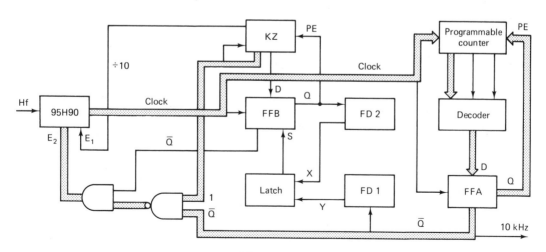

Figure 4-121 $1x \div 11$.

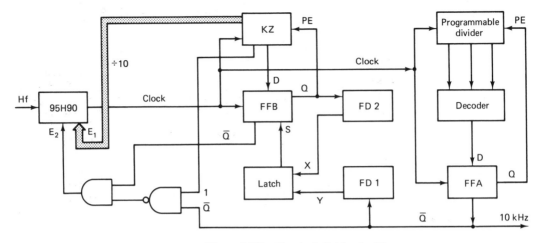

Figure 4-122 Constant division by 10.

The following pulse diagram explains this. The 10-kHz digit (swallow counter) is set $3x \div 11$. The clock pulses are numbered, and the delays are indicated (ns). The critical positions are marked a, b, c, d, and e (see Figure 4-123).

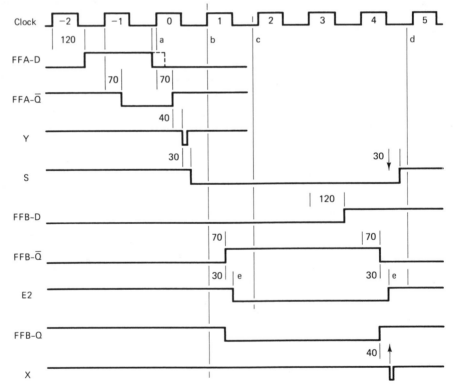

Figure 4-123 Pulse diagram for reset and switchover area for the $3x \div 11$ of the entire system.

a. Because of crosstalk on the printed circuit board, a pulse stretching of the output of FFA became apparent. Two diodes were used to force input D of FFA immediately after the output pulse $\bar{Q}$ appears at logic 0. This guarantees that FFA is reset to the next cycle.

b. Start of the cycle; this can also be seen, as pulse counts start with 1. The clock pulse is shown from -2 to $+5$.

c. Maximum time delay is reset.

d. Maximum time limit for switching divide by 11 to divide by 10.

e. Maximum time safety margin.

We can deduce from this that the second cycle pulse is being considered as the first pulse to the control counter, while the programmable divider chain reacts to the first clock count of the cycle. Depending on the timing, FFB—$\bar{Q}$ the swallow counter will divide 2 to $9x \div 11$. To divide by 11 only once, a different arrangement is used that sees to it that the changeover command for the divide by 10/11 does not occur at the same time as the other reset pulses occur. This is because the pulse is being fed from FFA $-\bar{Q}$ to E2 independent of FFB. A several-nanosecond time delay is available, and the actual circuit operated up to 55 MHz without difficulties.

Final Comments.   The circuit has some peculiarities:

1. Since the entire circuit operates from 14 V and the ECL divider can only be operated from 5.2 V, additional circuitry to provide a voltage drop of 8.8 V, using transistors BFX65 and 2N3054, was used. In a practical battery-operated device, this two-transistor circuit would be replaced by something like the IF and/or RF stages of the receiver to conserve energy, instead of using a voltage regulator, which dissipates the energy.

2. The input of the 95H90 has to be biased with the two resistors. The voltage is set in such a way that 50 mV rms are sufficient to drive the divider at 50 MHz.

3. There is a voltage difference between the ECL and CMOS dividers, as the ECL operates at 5.2 V and the CMOS at 14 V. The transistor 2N2907 performs the necessary level shift. In order to interface the CMOS to the ECL voltage, a configuration was chosen to avoid a transistor circuit for each input E1 and E2. Two diodes clamp the high-level signals to the V_{ee} level of the 95H90.

4. Because of the peculiarities of the divider, the 9-equivalent had to be programmed, and nonstandard encoder switches had to be used. This can be avoided by connecting the main contact of the switch to $+\text{Vdd}$.

Finally, the complete circuit was temperature cycled. At 80°C, the current was 145 mA, and the maximum frequency was 50 MHz. At -20°C, the current was 128 mA, and the cutoff frequency was 54.5 MHz.

Although this system could be constructed simply by a few integrated circuits, the circuit discussed has the advantage that one is forced to go through this detailed analysis, and a better understanding is possible. Some of the other circuits we use later are much easier to deal with. In Chapter 6 a somewhat simpler circuit is analyzed using the same principles.

4-7 LOOP FILTERS

Earlier, we became acquainted with some loop filters, and therefore this may be a repeat of some of the things already treated. As a convenient reference, the four most important filter types are described below.

4-7-1 Passive RC Filters

Figure 4-124 shows the simple RC filter with the transfer equation

$$F(s) = \frac{1/sC}{R + 1/sC} \tag{4-127}$$

or the frequency response

$$F(j\omega) = \frac{1}{j\omega CR + 1} \tag{4-128}$$

The magnitude of frequency response is

$$|F(j\omega)| = \frac{1}{\sqrt{1 + \omega^2 R^2 C^2}} \tag{4-129}$$

and the phase is

$$\phi(\omega) = -\arctan \omega CR \tag{4-130}$$

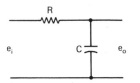

Figure 4-124 RC network.

The lag filter, Figure 4-125, has the transfer function

$$F(s) = \frac{sCR_2 + 1}{sC(R_1 + R_2) + 1} \tag{4-131}$$

The frequency response

$$|F(j\omega)| = \sqrt{\frac{1 + \omega^2 R_2^2 C^2}{1 + \omega^2 C^2 (R_1 + R_2)^2}} \tag{4-132}$$

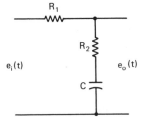

Figure 4-125 Lag filter.

4-7-2 Active RC Filters

Any high-performance loop will use an active filter because of the second integrator. Figure 4-82 shows such a circuit. In this particular case, the phase/frequency comparator, B5, having two outputs, drives the inverting and noninverting inputs of an operational amplifier B6. While the same equations hold true as those used with the passive device, note that the same bias as found in the inverting input is provided in the noninverting input to provide precisely symmetrical load. The additional *RC* network ahead of the loop filter is used for spike suppression. The 560 Ω/2200 pF *RC* combination can be calculated, and its effect can be determined by using the last of the computer programs. However, in the practical world, this filter is optimized experimentally.

Type 2 third-order loop as well as higher-order loop versions are created by adding additional *RC* time constants.

The real-life situation always requires some additional filtering, or the parasitic elements in a circuit act as such. Figure 4-126 shows the filter of the type 2 third-order loop that was discussed earlier.

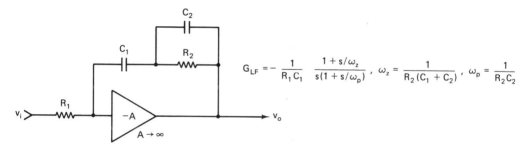

$$G_{LF} = -\frac{1}{R_1 C_1} \frac{1 + s/\omega_z}{s(1 + s/\omega_p)} , \quad \omega_z = \frac{1}{R_2(C_1 + C_2)} , \quad \omega_p = \frac{1}{R_2 C_2}$$

Figure 4-126   Type 2 third-order loop active filter.

Taking the three time constants

$$T_1 = C_1 R_1 \tag{4-133}$$

$$T_2 = R_2(C_1 + C_2) \tag{4-134}$$

$$T_3 = C_2 R_2 \tag{4-135}$$

the transfer characteristic

$$F(s) = \frac{1}{sT_1} \frac{1 + sT_2}{1 + sT_3} \tag{4-136}$$

Sometimes higher orders occur because of some additional low-pass filter requirement. Figure 4-126 can be redrawn in the form of Figure 4-127, which is electrically equivalent provided that V_0 is unloaded. The correlations are

$$G_{LF1} = -\frac{1}{R_1 C_1} \frac{1 + s/\omega_z}{s(1 + s/\omega_p)} \tag{4-137}$$

$$\omega_z = \frac{1}{R_2(C_1 + C_2)} \tag{4-138}$$

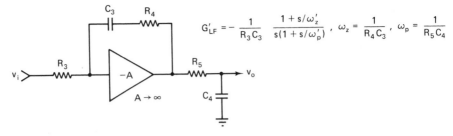

$$G'_{LF} = -\frac{1}{R_3C_3}\frac{1+s/\omega'_z}{s(1+s/\omega'_p)}, \quad \omega_z = \frac{1}{R_4C_3}, \quad \omega_p = \frac{1}{R_5C_4}$$

Figure 4-127 The additional *RC* output filtering converts this into a type 2 third-order loop filter.

$$\omega_p = \frac{1}{R_2C_2} \tag{4-139}$$

$$G_{LF2} = -\frac{1}{R_3C_3}\frac{1+s/\omega_z}{s(1+s/\omega_p)} \tag{4-140}$$

$$\omega_z = \frac{1}{R_4C_3} \tag{4-141}$$

$$\omega_p = \frac{1}{R_5C_4} \tag{4-142}$$

Using these equations, one schematic can be transformed into the other.

In a type 2 fifth-order loop, an active low-pass filter was added. The following sections give some insight into the mathematics of the active low-pass filter, which then becomes part of the loop filter.

4-7-3 Active Second-Order Low-Pass Filters

Active filters, compared to their passive counterpart, have a more rectangular frequency response, allowing for better noise suppression without sacrifice of reference suppression.

In Section 1-8 we have seen the transient response of the type 2 fifth-order loop, which was generated from a type 2 third-order loop with the addition of a second-order low-pass filter. Although there are various configurations available with which to build a second-order low-pass filter, the one shown in Figure 4-128 is probably the

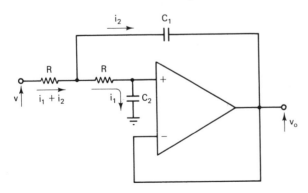

Figure 4-128 Active second-order low-pass filter.

294

most useful if noninverting operation is desired. The following is a short derivation of this type of filter and some applications of its use. I would like to state here that with this filter, depending on whether a Butterworth or Chebyshev response or something in between is chosen, different phase shift and amplitude response are obtained. By trading off skirt slope versus phase shift, it can be adapted for the purpose. The advantage of an active low-pass filter over a passive attenuator such as the T-notch filter is its low-pass filter action; the T-notch filter filters out only the particular frequency to which it is tailored. It seems that generally the second-order low-pass filter is a better choice provided that the operational amplifier used for this circuit does not introduce intolerable noise.

Let us use the abbreviation $j\omega = p$ and assume that the inverting and non-inverting input have the same potential. We obtain the following equations:

$$V_o = V - i_1 R - i_2 R - i_1 R \tag{4-143}$$

$$V_o = V - i_1 R - i_2 R - i_2 \frac{1}{pC_1} \tag{4-144}$$

$$V_o = i_1 \frac{1}{pC_2} \tag{4-145}$$

or

$$i_1 = V_o p C_2 \tag{4-146}$$

Substituting (4-146) in (4-143), we obtain

$$V_o = V - 2RV_o p C_2 - i_2 R \tag{4-147}$$

and from (4-147),

$$i_2 = \frac{V - V_o - 2RV_o p C_2}{R} \tag{4-148}$$

With (4-146), and (4-148) in (4-144), we obtain

$$V_o = V - RV_o p C_2 - V + V_o + 2RV_o p C_2 - \frac{V - V_o - 2RV_o p C_2}{RpC_1} \tag{4-149}$$

$$R^2 V_o p^2 C_1 C_2 - V + V_o + 2RV_o p C_2 = 0 \tag{4-150}$$

$$V_o(R^2 p^2 C_1 C_2 + 2RpC_2 + 1) = V \tag{4-151}$$

The transfer function

$$\frac{V_o}{V} = \frac{1}{R^2 p^2 C_1 C_2 + 2RpC_2 + 1} \tag{4-152}$$

from

$$R^2 C_1 C_2 = \frac{1}{\omega_n^2} \tag{4-153}$$

We define the frequency

$$\omega_n = \frac{1}{R\sqrt{C_1 C_2}} \tag{4-154}$$

Normalizing the values p, C_1, and C_2 yields

$$p_o = \frac{p}{\omega_c} \tag{4-155}$$

where ω_c is the cutoff frequency, and

$$C_{1N} = RC_1\omega_c \tag{4-156}$$

$$C_{2N} = RC_2\omega_c \tag{4-157}$$

We finally obtain

$$\frac{V_o}{V} = \frac{1}{p_o^2 C_{1N}C_{2N} + 2p_o C_{2N} + 1} \tag{4-158}$$

To solve this equation, we find the binomial expression for the denominator,

$$\frac{1}{p_o^2 C_{1N}C_{2N} + 2p_o C_{2N} + 1} = \frac{1}{(p - P_1)(p - P_2)} \tag{4-159}$$

where P_1 and P_2 are conjugate roots of form $(a \pm jb)$ and

$$\frac{1}{(p - P_1)(p - P_2)} = \frac{1}{(p + a \pm jb)^2} = \frac{1}{p^2 + 2ap + a^2 + b^2} \tag{4-160}$$

or

$$p_o^2 C_{1N}C_{2N} + 2p_o C_{2N} + 1 = p_o^2 + 2ap_o + a^2 + b^2 \tag{4-161}$$

with

$$p_o^2 C_{1N}C_{2N} = p_o^2 \tag{4-162}$$

$$2p_o C_{2N} = 2ap_o \tag{4-163}$$

$$1 = a^2 + b^2 \tag{4-164}$$

We finally obtain the coefficients C:

$$(a^2 + b^2)C_{2N}2p_o = 2ap_o \tag{4-165}$$

$$C_{2N} = \frac{a}{a^2 + b^2} \tag{4-166}$$

$$C_{1N} = \frac{1}{a} \tag{4-167}$$

The conjugate roots of the Chebyshev approximation are

$$P_v = -\sin\frac{2v - 1}{2n}\pi \sinh\phi + j\cos\frac{2v - 1}{2n}\pi \cosh\phi \tag{4-168}$$

where

$$\sinh\phi = \frac{1}{2}\left\{\left[\left(1 + \frac{1}{\epsilon^2}\right)^{1/2} + \frac{1}{\epsilon}\right]^{1/n} - \left[\left(1 + \frac{1}{\epsilon^2}\right)^{1/2} + \frac{1}{\epsilon}\right]^{-1/n}\right\} \tag{4-169}$$

$$\cosh\phi = \frac{1}{2}\left\{\left[\left(1 + \frac{1}{\epsilon^2}\right)^{1/2} + \frac{1}{\epsilon}\right]^{1/n} + \left[\left(1 + \frac{1}{\epsilon^2}\right)^{1/2} + \frac{1}{\epsilon}\right]^{-1/n}\right\} \tag{4-170}$$

with ϵ^2 the ripple tolerance.

Rather than looking up normalized values from published tables (Chebyshev filters have good stopband attenuation with small passband phase distortion), a ripple factor can be chosen and then the loop should be analyzed for phase margin. If the ripple is too high, it can be changed to obtain the desired response. This is done very easily by defining a damping factor

$$d^2 = \frac{1}{a^2 + b^2} = \frac{C_2}{C_1} \qquad (4\text{-}171)$$

The ripple is related inversely proportional to the damping factor. With $d = 1/\sqrt{2}$, the ripple is zero (i.e., Butterworth response). Smaller d values render increased ripple and increased stopband attenuation. What remains to be determined is ω_n, of which a good starting value is five times the required loop cutoff frequency. Modifying

$$d = \sqrt{\frac{C_2}{C_1}} \qquad (4\text{-}172)$$

and ω_n in the overall open-loop transfer function while Bode plotting will render the required phase and gain margins for stable loop performance. A phase margin of $>30° < 70°$ for $|A(p)| = 1$ and a gain margin of -10 dB for a phase value of $180°$ should be aimed at.

The overall open-loop transfer function is followed by including the damping factor d and the natural pole frequency ω_n:

$$A^* = \frac{\omega_n^2}{-\omega^2 + 2dp\omega_n + \omega_n^2} \qquad (4\text{-}173)$$

and therefore the open-loop gain of a type 2 fifth-order loop as an example would become

$$A(p) = \frac{\omega_n^2 K_o K_\theta}{NT_1\omega^2} \frac{-pT_2 - 1}{p[2d\omega_n + T_3(\omega_n^2 - \omega)] + (\omega_n^2 - \omega^2 - 2dT_3\omega_n\omega^2)} \qquad (4\text{-}174)$$

4-7-4 Passive LC Filters

While the active loop *RC* filter is a convenient way of improving reference suppression, as the realization of *LC* filters at times may be difficult, the use of normalized tables and the analysis program in Section A-2 permit optimizing loops with *LC* filters. The *LC* filter in the loop has the distinct advantage that the passive devices do not introduce noise, and filter design is well established. Figure 4-129 shows a lowpass filter with its proper termination at the input and output.

The 741 operational amplifier driving the filter theoretically would have zero impedance, and as this is not permissible, the proper filter source resistor R30 has to be added. Similarly, R31 serves as output termination since pin 6 of B22 is essentially at ac ground potential.

The particular filter chosen here is of the order of 7. Table 4-10 shows the values that can be taken from Anatol Zverev's *Handbook of Filter Synthesis*, page 287 [1]. Similar elliptical filters are found in Rudolf Saal's *Handbook of Filter Design* (AEG Telefunken, West Germany). A description of how to design filters is given in the book and is not repeated here.

The influence of this filter must be verified with the program shown in Section A-2 to make sure that it does not introduce any instabilities.

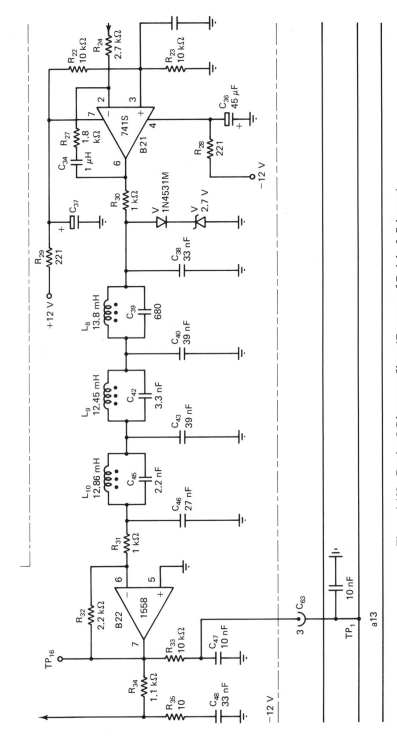

Figure 4-129 Passive *LC* low-pass filter. (Courtesy of Rohde & Schwarz.)

TABLE 4-10 ELLIPTICAL
LOW-PASS FILTER CC300750

θ	30.0
C_1	0.7085
C_2	0.0389
L_2	1.3566
C_3	1.6029
C_4	0.1604
L_4	1.4917
C_5	1.6792
C_6	0.1016
L_6	1.5876
C_7	1.4569
Ω_S	2.0000
A_{MIN}	105.37
σ_0	0.2036327
σ_1	0.0364992
σ_3	0.1103824
σ_5	0.1756643
Ω_1	0.9936072
Ω_2	4.3544
Ω_3	0.8183516
Ω_4	2.0445
Ω_5	0.4701232
Ω_6	2.4903

REFERENCES

Section 4-1

1. *Capacitance Diodes, Tuner Diodes, Diode Switches, PIN Diodes, Basics and Applications,* ITT Semiconductors, System-Druck GmbH & Co., Freiburg, West Germany, 1976/10.

2. H. Keller, "Properties and Applications of the Silicon Capacitance Diode," *Ionen + Elektronen*, April 1961, pp. 15–17.

3. H. Keller, M. Lehmann, and L. Micic, "Diffused Silicon Capacitance Diodes," *radio mentor*, Vol. 28, No. 8 (1962), pp. 661–667.

4. H. Keller, "An FM Receiver with Electronic Tuning and Automatic Station Tracking," *Funk-Technik*, Vol. 18, No. 22 (1963), pp. 827–828.

5. A. Gilly and L. Micic, "DC Amplifier with Capacitance Diodes for Low Power Input Signals," *Elektronik*, Vol. 12, No. 9 (1963), p. 263.

6. DIN 41791, sheet 8; DIN 41785, sheet 20 (German standards).

7. H. Keller, "Electronic UHF Tuning in TV Receivers," *Radio-Fernseh-Phono-Praxis*, No. 3, 1967.

8. L. Micic, "The Tuner Diode," *radio mentor electronic*, Vol. 32, No. 5 (1966), pp. 404–405.

9. B. Dietrich and M. Lehmann, "Epitaxial Planar Silicon Transistors—Technology and Properties," *radio mentor*, Vol. 29, No. 10 (1963), pp. 851–855.

10. W. Pruin and, A. Swamy, "Diode Switches BA243 and BA244," *Funk-Technik*, Vol. 24, No. 1 (1969), pp. 11–14.

11. U. Dolega, "Semiconductor Diodes," *Funkschau*, 1974: No, 20, pp. 789–791; No. 21, pp. 819–820; No. 22, pp. 857–858.

12. K. Reinarz, "AF Signal Switching by Means of Diodes," *Funkschau*, Vol. 43, No. 23 (1971), pp. 769–772.

13. "Diodes," ITT Intermetall data manual.

14. H. Sarkowski, *Dimensioning Semiconductor Circuits*, Lexika Verlag, 7031 Grafenau Doffingen, L, 1973.

15. H. Keller, "Radio and TV Receiver Tuning by Diodes," *Elektronik Anzeiger*, Vol. 1, No. 1/2 (1969), pp. 45–48.

16. H. Keller, "The Capacitance Diode in Parallel Resonant Circuits," *Funkschau*, Vol. 39, No. 7 (1967), pp. 185–188.

17. O. Dietrich and H. Keller, "Non-linear Distortion in Capacitance Diodes," *radio mentor electronic*, Vol. 33, No. 4 (1967), pp. 266–269.

18. U. Dolega, "Temperature-Compensated Zener Diodes," ITT Technical Information Semiconductors, Freiburg, W. Germany (Order No. 6200–73–1E).

19. H. Keller, "Station Selector Circuits for Receivers with Capacitance Diode Tuning," *Radio-Fernseh-Phono-Praxis*, No. 5, 1966, pp. 151–154.

20. P. Flamm, "Ultrasonic Remote Control Circuits with New IC's," *Funkschau*, 1975: No. 8, pp. 81–84; No. 9, pp. 67–69.

21. "Funktechnische Arbeitsblatter Re 91," *Funkschau*, 1973, No. 1.

22. *Reference Data for Radio Engineers*, Howard W. Sams, Indianapolis, IN, 1972.

23. K. Schroter, "VHF Tuner for Low Tuning Voltage," *Radio-Fernseh-Phono-Praxis*, No. 10, 1974, p. 5.

24. O. Dietrich and F. Lowel, "Electronically Tuned and Switched TV Tuners with Diodes BA141, BA142, and BA143," *Funk-Technik*, Vol. 22, No. 7 (1967), pp. 209–211.

25. E. Kinne, "A Survey on Tuners for TV Receivers," *Funk-Technik*, Vol. 25 (1970): No. 23, pp. 927–928; No. 24, pp. 961–964; Vol. 26 (1971) No. 1, pp. 16–18; No. 2, pp. 51–52.

26. K. Schurig, "VHF Tuner Containing Field Effect Transistors," *Funk-Technik*, Vol. 29, No. 21 (1974), pp. 743–745.

27. G. Bernstein, "Capacitance Diodes Employed as Diode Switches; A Combined CCIR and OIRT TV Tuner," *Funkschau*, Vol. 43, No. 7 (1971), pp. 189–190.

28. H. Keller, "VHF Tuner with Diode Tuning," *Funk-Technik*, Vol. 21, No. 8 (1966), pp. 266–267.

29. J. Backwinkel, "From the Combi Tuner to the Strip Line Tuner," *Funk-Technik*, Vol. 26, No. 13 (1971), pp. 489–492.

30. H. Bender and K. Schurig, "An All-Channel Tuner with Only Two Transistors," *Funkschau*, Vol. 38, No. 10 (1966), pp. 313–316.

31. W. Klein, "Interference-Proof Universal Tuner with Tuned VHF Input," *Funk-Technik*, Vol. 24, No. 5 (1969), pp. 163–164.

32. J. Novotny, "Measurements on Capacitance Diodes," *Messen und Prufen*, No. 1, 1969, pp. 28–32.

33. H. Dahlmann, "Automatic High Speed 'Jumbo' Tester for the Computer Controlled Sorting of Tuner Diodes in 1200 Groups," *Funkschau*, No. 24, 1974, pp. 939–940.

34. L. Micic, "Diode Tuned Resonant Circuit," *Internationale Elektronische Rundschau*, Vol. 22, No. 6 (1968), pp. 138–140.

35. Ulrich L. Rohde, "Mathematical Analysis and Design of an Ultra Stable Low Noise 100 MHz Crystal Oscillator with Differential Limiter and Its Possibilities in Frequency Standards," Ph.D. dissertation, Clayton University, May 1978. Also presented at the 32nd Annual Frequency Symposium, Fort Monmouth, NJ, June 1978.

36. Hiroyuki Abe et al., "A Highly Stabilized Low-Noise GaAs FET Integrated Oscillator with a Dielectric Resonator in the C Band," *IEEE Transactions on Microwave Theory and Techniques*, Vol. MTT-26, No. 3 (March 1978), pp. 156–162.

37. Robert Adler, "A Study of Locking Phenomena in Oscillators," *Proceedings of the IEEE*, Vol. 61, No. 10 (October 1973), pp. 1380–1385.

38. Richard M. Beach, "Hyperabrupt Varactor Tuned Oscillators," *Tech-Notes*, Vol. 5, No. 4 (July–August 1976), Watkins-Johnson Co., Palo Alto, CA.

39. R. Buswell, "Linear VCO's," *Tech-Notes*, Vol. 3, No. 2 (March–April 1976), Watkins-Johnson Co., Palo Alto, CA.

40. R. Buswell, "Voltage Controlled Oscillators in Modern ECM Systems," *Tech-Notes*, Vol. 1, No. 6 (December 1974), Watkins-Johnson Co., Palo Alto, CA.

41. R. J. Clark and D. B. Swartz, "Take a Fresh Look at YIG-Tuned Sources," *Microwaves*, February 1972.

42. A. Goodman, "Increasing the Band Range of a Voltage-Controlled Oscillator," *Electronic Design*, September 28, 1964, pp. 28–35.

43. C. Herbert and J. Chernega, "Broadband Varactor Tuning of Transistor Oscillators," *Microwaves*, March 1967, pp. 28–32.

44. T. E. Parker, "SAW Controlled Oscillators," *Microwave Journal*, October 1978, pp. 66 and 67.

45. P. Penfield and R. P. Rafuse, *Varactor Applications*, MIT Press, Cambridge, MA, 1962, Chap. 9.

46. *Solid-State Microwave Voltage Controlled Oscillators*, Frequency Sources, Inc., Chelmsford, MA 01824, 1974.

47. S. Hamilton and R. Hall, "Shunt-Mode Harmonic Generation Using Step Recovery Diodes," *Microwave Journal*, April 1967, pp. 69–78.

48. "How to Select Varactors for Harmonic Generation," *Micronotes*, Vol. 10, No. 1 (May 1973), Microwave Associates, Inc., Burlington, MA.

49. Kaneyuki Kurokawa, "Injection Locking of Microwave Solid-State Oscillators," *Proceedings of the IEEE*, Vol. 61, No. 10 (October 1973), pp. 1386–1410.

50. F. S. Barnes and G. F. Eiber, "An Ideal Harmonic Generator," *Proceedings of the IEEE*, Vol. 53, pp. 693–695.

51. B. E. Keiser, "The Cycle Splitter—A Wide-band Precision Frequency Multiplier," *IRE National Conference Record*, 1959, Vol. 7, pp. 4, 275–281.

52. V. E. Van Duzer, "500 kc/s–500 Mc/s Frequency Doubler," *Hewlett-Packard Journal*, Vol. 17 (October 1965).

53. D. Koehler, "The Charge-Control Concept in the Form of Equivalent Circuits, Representing a Link between the Classic Large Signal Diode and Transistor Models," *Bell System Technical Journal*, Vol. 46 (March 1967), pp. 523–576.

54. D. O. Scanlan and M. A. Laybourn, "Analysis of Varactor Harmonic Generators, with Arbitrary Drive Levels," *Proceedings of the IEE*, Vol. 114 (1967), pp. 1598–1604.

55. H. A. Watson, ed., *Microwave Semiconductor Devices and Their Circuit Applications*, McGraw-Hill, New York, 1969.

56. R. H. Johnston and A. R. Boothroyd, "Charge Storage Frequency Multipliers," *Proceedings of the IEEE*, Vol. 56 (1968), pp. 167–176.

57. J. J. Ebers and T. L. Moll, "Large Signal Behavior of Junction Transistors," *Proceedings of the IRE*, Vol. 42, (1954), pp. 1761–1772.

58. R. G. Harrison, "A Nonlinear Theory of Class C Transistor Amplifiers and Frequency Multipliers," *IEEE Journal of Solid-State Circuits*, Vol. SC-2 (1967), pp. 93–102.

59. M. Caulton et al., "Generation of Microwave Power by Parametric Frequency Multiplication in a Single Transistor," *RCA Review*, Vol. 26 (June 1965), pp. 286–311.

60. D. Halford, A. E. Wainright, and J. A. Barnes, "Flicker Noise of Phase in RF Amplifiers and Frequency Multipliers: Characterization, Cause, and Cure," *Proceedings of the 22nd Annual Frequency Control Symposium*, Fort Monmouth, NJ, 1968.

61. T. Watanabe and F. Yoshiharu, "Characteristics of Semiconductor Noise Generated in Varactor Frequency Multipliers," *Review of the Electrical Communication Laboratories (Tokyo)*, Vol. 15 (November–December 1967), pp. 752–768.

62. Y. Saburi, Y. Yasuda, and K. Harada, "Phase Variations in the Frequency Multiplier," *Journal of the Radio Research Laboratories (Tokyo)*, Vol. 10, pp. 137–175.

63. Hewlett Packard Associates, "Step Recovery Diode Frequency Multiplier Design," *Application Note 913*, Palo Alto, CA, May 15, 1967.

64. Hewlett Packard Associates, "Harmonic Generation Using Step Recovery Diodes and SRD Modules," *Application Note 920*, Palo Alto, CA, June 1968.

65. D. G. Tucker, "The Synchronization of Oscillators," *Electronic Engineering*, Part I, Vol. 15 (March 1943), pp. 412–418; Part II, Vol. 15 (April 1943), pps. 457–461; Part III, Vol. 16 (June 1943), pp. 26–30.

66. R. Adler, "A Study of Locking Phenomena in Oscillators," *Proceedings of the IRE*, June 1946, pp. 351–357.

67. L. J. Paciorek, "Injection Locking of Oscillators," *Proceedings of the IEEE*, November 1965, pp. 1723–1727.

Section 4-2

1. J. A. Barnes et al., "Characterization of Frequency Stability," *NBS Technical Note 394*, U.S. Dept. of Commerce, National Bureau of Standards, 1970.

2. W. S. Mortley, "Circuit Giving Linear Frequency Modulation of a Quartz Crystal Oscillator," *Wireless World*, Vol. 57 (October 1951), pp. 399–403.

3. O. P. Layden, W. L. Smith, A. E. Anderson, M. B. Bloch, D. E. Newell, and P. C. Sulzer, "Crystal Controlled Oscillator," *IEEE Transactions on Instrumentation and Measurement*, Vol. *IM-21*, 1972, pp. 277–286.

4. T. C. Anderson and F. G. Merrill, "Crystal Controlled Primary Frequency Standards: Latest Advances for Long Term Stability," *IRE Transactions on Instrumentation*, 1960, pp. 136–140.

5. Thomas F. Marker, "Crystal Oscillator Design Notes," *Frequency*, Vol. 6 (1968), pp. 12–16.

6. W. A. Edson, *Vacuum Tube Oscillators*, Wiley, New York, 1953.

7. "Field Effect Transistor Oscillators," *A Texas Instruments Application Report Bulletin CA-99*, pp. 219–225.

8. D. Firth, *Quartz Crystal Oscillator Circuits, Design Handbook*, The Magnavox Company, 1965. (Available from National Technical Information Service as AD 460377.)

9. G. G. Gouriet, "High Stability Oscillator," *Wireless Engineer*, April 1950, pp. 105–112.

10. J. K. Clapp, "An Inductance Capacitance Oscillator of Unusual Frequency Stability." *Proceedings of the IRE*, Vol. 36 (1949), pp. 356–358.

11. R. R. Zielger, "Know Your Oscillators," *Microwave Journal*, June 1976, pp. 44–47.

12. W. L. Smith, "Miniature Transistorized Crystal Controlled Precision Oscillators," *IRE Transactions on Instrumentation*, 1960, pp. 141–148.

13. A. J. Cote, Jr., "Matrix Analysis of Oscillators and Transistor Applications," *IRE Transactions on Circuit Theory*, 1958, pp. 181–189.

14. J. Helle, "VCX Theory and Practice," *Proceedings of the 29th Annual Symposium on Frequency Control*, 1975, pp. 300–307.

15. M. R. Frerking, *Crystal Oscillator Design and Temperature Compensation*, Van Nostrand Reinhold, New York, 1978.

16. E. O. Felch and J. O. Israel, "A Simple Circuit for Frequency Standards Employing Overtone Crystals," *Proceedings of the IRE*, 1955, pp. 596–603.

17. E. A. Gerber and R. A. Sykes, "State of the Art Quartz Crystal Units and Oscillators," *Proceedings of the IEEE*, Vol. 54 (1966), pp. 103–116.

18. Roger Harrison, "Survey of Crystal Oscillators," *Ham Radio*, March 1976, pp. 10–35.

19. P. J. Baxandall, "Transistor Crystal Oscillators and the Design of a 1Mc/s Oscillator Circuit Capable of Good Frequency Stability," *The Radio and Electronic Engineer*, April 1965.

20. M. Lane, "Transistor Crystal Oscillators to Cover Frequency Range 1 kHz–100 MHz," Australian Post Office Research Laboratories, *Report No. 6513*, 1970.

21. M. M. Driscoll, "Two-Stage Self-Limiting Series Mode Type Quartz Crystal Oscillator Exhibiting Improved Short-Term Frequency Stability," *Proceedings of the 26th Annual Frequency Control Symposium*, 1972, pp. 43–49.

22. R. L. Kent, "The Voltage Controlled Crystal Oscillator (VCXO), Its Capabilities and Limitations," *Proceedings of the 19th Annual Frequency Control Symposium*, Vol. 19.

23. R. A. Heising, *Quartz Crystals for Electrical Circuits*, Van Nostrand Reinhold, New York, 1946.

24. *Telefunken Laborbuch*, Vol. 3, Ulm, West Germany, 1968, p. 272.

25. Kristallverarbeitung Neckarbischofsheim, catalogue 1976. p. 14.

26. L. Omlin, "Analyse und Dimensionierung von Quarzoszillatoren," *Elektroniker-Hefte*. Vol. 6, No. 9 (1977), p. 12.

27. R. Harrison, "Survey of Crystal Oscillators," *Ham Radio*, Vol. 3 (1976), p. 10.

28. C. Hall, "Overtone Crystal Oscillators without Inductors," *Ham Radio*, Vol. 4 (1978). p. 50.

29. B. Priestley, "Oscillator Noise and Its Effect on Receiver Performance," *Radio Communications*, Vol. 7 (1970), p. 456.

30. M. Martin, "Empfangereingangsteil mit grossem Dynamikbereich und sehr geringen Intermodulationsverzerrungen," *CQ-DL*, Vol. 6 (1975), p. 326.

31. M. Martin, "Rauscharmer Oszillator fur ein Empfangereingangsteil mit grossem Dynamikbereich," *CQ-DL*, Vol. 12 (1976), p. 418.

32. U. L. Rohde, "Evaluating Noise Sideband Performance in Oscillators," *Ham Radio*. Vol. 10 (1978), p. 51.

33. *Proceedings on the IEEE–NASA Symposium on Short-Term Frequency Stability*, Goddard Space Flight Center, Greenbelt, MD, 1964 (Document NASA SP-80).

34. Paper IEC Working Group 49 (Secr.), p. 83.

35. A. E. Wainwright, F. L. Walls, and W. D. McCaa, "Direct Measurements of the Inherent Frequency Stability of Quartz Crystal Resonators," *Proceedings of the 28th Annual Symposium on Frequency Control*, Atlantic City, NJ, 1974, p. 177.

36. T. Musha, "$1/f$-resonant Frequency Fluctuation of a Quartz Crystal," *Proceedings of the 29th Annual Symposium on Frequency Control*, Atlantic City, NJ, 1975, p. 308.

37. M. Martin, "A Modern Receive Converter for 2m Receivers Having a Large Dynamic Range and Low Intermodulation Distortion," *VHF Communications*, Vol. 10, No. 4 (1978), pp. 218–229.

38. M. M. Driscoll, "Q-Multiplied Quartz Crystal Resonator for Improved HF and VHF Source Stabilization," *Proceedings of the 27th Annual Symposium on Frequency Control*, 1973, p. 157.

39. D. J. Healey III, "Low-Noise UHF Frequency Source," *Proceedings of the 27th Annual Symposium on Frequency Control*, 1973, p. 170.

40. D. J. Healey III, "$\mathcal{L}(t)$ Measurements on UHF Sources Comprising VHF Crystal Controlled Oscillator Followed by a Frequency Multiplier," *Proceedings of the 28th Annual Symposium on Frequency Control*, 1974, p. 190.

41. U. L. Rohde, "Mathematical Analysis and Design of an Ultra Stable Low Noise 100 MHz Crystal Oscillator with Differential Limiter and Its Possibilities in Frequency Standards," *Proceedings of the 32nd Annual Symposium on Frequency Control*, 1978, p. 409.

42. U. L. Rohde, "Effects of Noise in Receiving Systems," *Ham Radio*, Vol. 11 (1977), p. 34.

43. W. Herzog, *Siebschaltungen mit Schwingkristallen*, Hirtz, Wiesbaden, W. Germany, 1949.

44. TTL-Kochbuch, Texas Instruments, Freising, West Germany.

45. S. S. Eaton, "Timekeeping Advances through COS/MOS Technology," *RCA Application Note ICAN-6086*.

46. S. S. Eaton, "Micropower Crystal-Controlled Oscillator Design Using RCA COS/MOS Inverters," *RCA Application Note ICAN-6539*.

47. T. Luxmore and D. E. Newell, "The MXO-monolithic Crystal Oscillator," *Proceedings of the 31st Annual Symposium on Frequency Control*, 1977, p. 396.

48. J. D. Holmbeck, "Frequency Tolerance Limitations with Logic Gate Clock Oscillators," *Proceedings of the 31st Annual Symposium on Frequency Control*, 1977, p. 390.

49. B. Neubig, "Extrem rauscharmer 96-MHz-Quarzoszillator fur UHF/SHF," presented at the 25th Weinheimer URW-Tagung, September 1980, *VHF Communications*, 1981.

50. U. L. Rohde, "Crystal Oscillator Provides Low Noise," *Electronic Design*, October 11, 1975.

51. Rohde & Schwarz Operating and Repair Manual for the XSRM Rubidium Frequency Standard, 1979.

52. D. W. Allan, "Statistics of Atomic Frequency Standards," *Proceedings of the IEEE*, Vol. 54, No. 2 (February 1966), pp. 221–230.

53. A. W. Warner, "High-Frequency Crystal Units for Primary Frequency Standards," *Proceedings of the IRE*, 1952, pp. 1030–1033.

Section 4-3

1. R. S. Caruthers, "Copper Oxide Modulators in Carrier Telephone Repeaters," *Bell System Technical Journal*, Vol. 18, No. 2 (April 1939), pp. 315–337.

2. J. C. Holgarrd, "Spurious Frequency Generation in Frequency Converters, Part 1," *Microwave Journal*, Vol. 10, No. 7 (July 1967), pp. 61–64.

3. J. C. Holgarrd, "Spurious Frequency Generation in Frequency Converters, Part 2," *Microwave Journal*, Vol. 10, No. 8 (August 1967), pp. 78–82.

4. R. B. Mouw and S. M. Fukuchi, "Broadband Double Balanced Mixer Modulators, Part 1," *Microwave Journal*, Vol. 12, No. 3 (March 1969), pp. 131–134.

5. R. B. Mouw and S. M. Fukuchi, "Broadband Double Balanced Mixer Modulators, Part 2," *Microwave Journal*, Vol. 12, No. 5 (May 1969), pp. 71–76.

6. U. L. Rohde, "Optimum Design for High-Frequency Communications Receivers," *Ham Radio*, October 1976.

7. U. L. Rohde, "Performance Capability of Active Mixers," presented at Wescon/81, September 16, 1981.

8. Doug DeMaw and George Collings, "Modern Receiver Mixers for High Dynamic Range," *QST*, January 1981, p. 19.

9. U. L. Rohde, "Zur optimalen Dimensionierung von UKW-Eingangsteilen," *Internationale Elektronische Rundschau*, Vol. 27, No. 5 (1973) pp. 103–108.

10. U. L. Rohde, "High Dynamic Range Receiver Input Stages," *Ham Radio*, October 1975.

11. "Reactive Loads—The Big Mixer Menace," *Anzac Electronics Technical Note*.

Section 4-4

1. W. Egan and E. Clark, "Test Your Charge-Pump Phase Detectors," *Electronic Design*, Vol. 26, No. 12 (June 7, 1978), pp. 134–137.

2. U. L. Rohde, "Modern Design of Frequency Synthesizers," *Ham Radio*, July 1976.

3. G. Alonzo, "Considerations in the Design of Sampling-Based Phase-Lock-Loops,"

WESCON/66 Technical Papers, Session 23, Western Electronic Show and Convention, 1966, Part 23/2.

4. C. J. Byrne, "Properties and Design of the Phase Controlled Oscillator with a Sawtooth Comparator," *The Bell System Technical Journal*, March 1962, pp. 559–602.

5. Fairchild Data Sheet: "Phase/Frequency Detector, 11C44," Fairchild Semiconductor, Mountain View, CA.

6. Fairchild Preliminary Data Sheet: "SH8096 Programmable Divider—Fairchild Integrated Microsystems," April 1970.

7. J. D. Fogarty, "Digital Synthesizers . . . ," *Computer Design*, July 1975, pp. 100–102.

8. R. Funk, "Low-Power Digital Frequency Synthesizers Utilizing COS/MOS IC's," *Application Note ICAN-6716*. (RCA Solid State Division, Somerville, NJ 08876, March 1973.)

9. A. Jay Goldstein, "Analysis of the Phase-Controlled Loop with a Sawtooth Comparator," *The Bell System Technical Journal*, March 1962, pp. 603–633.

10. Wayne M. Grove, "A D.C. to 12 GHz Feedthrough Sampler for Oscilloscopes and Other R.F. Systems," *Hewlett-Packard Journal*, October 1966, pp. 12–15.

11. S. Krishnan, "Diode Phase Detectors," *The Electronic and Radio Engineer*, February 1959, pp. 45–50.

12. Venceslav Kroupa, *Frequency Synthesis Theory Design and Applications*, Wiley, New York, 1973.

13. Stephan R. Kurtz, "Mixers as Phase Detectors," *Tech-Notes*, Vol. 5, No. 1 (January–February 1978), Watkins-Johnson Co., Palo Alto, CA.

14. Stephan R. Kurtz, "Specifying Mixers as Phase Detectors," *Microwaves*, January 1978, pp. 80–87.

15. Motorola Data Sheet, MC12012, 1973. Motorola Semiconductor Products, Inc., Phoenix, AZ 85036.

16. Motorola Data Sheet: "Phase-Frequency Detector, MC4344, MC4044."

17. D. Richman, "Color-Carrier Reference Phase Synchronization Accuracy in NTSC Color Television," *Proceedings of the IRE*, January 1954, p. 125.

18. J. M. Cohen, "Sample-and-Hold Circuits Using FET Analog Gates," *EEE*, January 1971, pp. 34–37.

19. Roland Best, *Theorie und Anwendungen des Phase-locked Loops*, Fachschriftenverlag Aargauer Tagblatt AG, Aarau, Switzerland, 1976 (Order No. ISBN-3-85502-011-6).

20. Pending U.S. patent, Fritze, Rohde & Schwarz, Munich.

21. Floyd M. Gardner, "Charge Pump Phase-Lock Loops," *IEEE Transactions on Communications*, Vol. COM-28, No. 11 (November 1980).

Section 4-5

1. Rohde & Schwarz Operating and Repair Manual for the SMS Synthesizer.

2. Rohde & Schwarz Operating and Repair Manual for the ESH2 Test Receiver.

3. U.S. Patent 3,891,934 to David Norton.

Section 4-6

1. U. L. Rohde, "Modern Design of Frequency Synthesizers," *Ham Radio*, July 1976.

2. E. Horrman, "The Inductance–Capacitance Oscillator as a Frequency Divider," *Proceedings of the IRE*, Vol. 34 (1946), pp. 799–803.

3. B. Chance et al., eds., *Waveforms*, McGraw-Hill, New York, 1949.

4. A. L. Plevy and E. N. Monacchio, "Fail-Safe Frequency Divider," *Electronics*, Vol. 39 (September 1966), p. 127.

5. S. Plotkin and O. Lumpkin, "Regenerative Fractional Frequency Generators," *Proceedings of the IRE*, Vol. 48 (1960), pp. 1988–1997.

6. Y. Kamp, "Amorçage des diviseurs de fréquence à capacité non linéaire," *L'Onde électrique*, Vol. 48 (September 1968), pp. 787–793.

7. B. Preston, "A Microelectronic Frequency Divider with a Variable Division Ratio," *Electronic Engineering*, Vol. 37 (April 1965), pp. 240–244.

8. H. G. Jungmeister, "Eine bistabile Kippschaltung fur den Gigahertz-Bereich," *Archiv der elektrischen Ubertragung*, Vol. 21 (September 1967), pp. 447–458.

9. E. J. Kench, ed., *Electronic Counting: Circuits, Techniques, Devices*, Mullard, London, 1967.

10. W. E. Wickes, *Logic Design with Integrated Circuits*, Wiley, New York, 1968.

11. E. J. Kench, ed., *Integrated Logic Circuit Applications: Mullard FC Range*, Mullard, London, 1967.

12. L. F. Blachovicz, "Dial Any Channel to 500 MHz," *Electronics*, Vol. 39 (May 2, 1966), pp. 60–69.

13. J. Stinehelfer and J. Nichols, "A Digital Frequency Synthesizer for an AM and FM Receiver," *Transactions of the IEEE*, Vol. BTR-15, No. 3 (1969), pp. 235–243.

14. S. Jannazzo and G. Rustichelli, "A Variable-Ratio Frequency Divider Using Micrologic Elements," *Electronic Engineering*, Vol. 39 (July 1967), p. 419.

15. R. W. Frank, "The Digital Divider," *General Radio Experimenter*, Vol. 43 (January–February 1969), pp. 3–7.

16. J. L. Hughes, *Computer Lab Workbook*, Digital Equipment Corp., Maynard, MA, 1969.

17. "A 1 GHz Prescaler Using GPD Series Thin-Film Amplifier Modules," *Microwave Component Applications*, ATP-1036, Avantek, Inc., 3175 Bowers Avenue, Santa Clara, CA 95051, 1977.

18. S. Bearse, "TED Triode Performs Frequency Division," *Microwaves*, November 1975, p. 9.

19. W. R. Blood, Jr., *MECL System Designer's Handbook*, 2nd ed., Motorola Semiconductor Products, Inc., Mesa, AZ, 1972.

20. W. J. Goldwasser, "Design Shortcuts for Microwave Frequency Dividers," *The Electronic Engineer*, May 1970, pp. 61–65.

21. W. D. Kasperkovitz, "Frequency-Dividers for Ultra-High Frequencies," *Philips Technical Review* (Netherlands), Vol. 38, No. 2 (1978–1979), pp. 54–68.

22. S. Lee, *Digital Circuits and Logic Design*, Prentice-Hall, Englewood Cliffs, NJ, 1976.

23. R. L. Miller, "Fractional-Frequency Generators Utilizing Regenerative Modulation," *Proceedings of the IRE*, July 1939, pp. 446–457.

24. J. Nicholds and C. Shinn, "Pulse Swallowing," *EDN*, October 1, 1970, pp. 39–42.

25. SP8750–8752 Data Sheets, Plessey Semiconductors, 1641 Kaiser Avenue, Irvine, CA 92714.

26. M. J. Underhill et al., "A General Purpose LSI Frequency Synthesizer System," *Proceedings of the 32nd Annual Symposium on Frequency Control*, 1978, pp. 366–367.

27. Data sheet for the HEF 4750/51, Philips, Mullard, London.

28. M. J. Underhill, "Wide Range Frequency Synthesizers with Improved Dynamic Performance," private communication.

29. M. J. Underhill and R. I. H. Scott, "FM Models of Frequency Synthesizers," private communication.

Section 4-7

1. Anatol I. Zverev, *Handbook of Filter Synthesis*, Wiley, New York, 1967.

2. Floyd M. Gardner, *Phaselock Techniques*, 2nd ed., Wiley, New York, 1980.

3. Roland Best, *Theorie und Anwendungen des phase-locked Loops*, Fachschriftenverlag Aargauer Tagblatt AG, Aarau, Switzerland, 1976 (Order No. ISBN 3-85502-011-6).

4. Rohde & Schwarz internal communication.

5

Digital Loop Synthesizers

5-1 MULTILOOP SYNTHESIZERS USING DIFFERENT TECHNIQUES

By now, we have accumulated a large amount of knowledge about single-loop synthesizers. In Chapter 1 a loop with a mixer was described, which probably represents the most simple dual-loop synthesizer.

Adding an auxiliary frequency is the first step toward building a two-loop synthesizer, with this auxiliary frequency generated by another loop rather than by multiplying the reference frequency to mix down the VCO frequency to a lower frequency range for convenience of being able to use lower dividers. The frequency resolution is then equal to the reference frequency unless special techniques are used.

We have heard already about the fractional division N synthesizer, and we have seen the sequential phase shifter that enabled us to get additional resolution. In addition, the pure digital frequency synthesizer was explained where the waveform is generated with the aid of a lookup table. Multiloop synthesizers use a combination of these techniques.

Modern frequency synthesizers no longer use designs where each decade uses phase-locked loops that operate at the same frequency with the output divided by 10. These *mix-and-divide systems*, or *triple mix systems* with cancellation of drift, are seldom used, as they require an enormous amount of filtering, shielding, and power consumption. However, to be able to decide which building blocks to use, some of them have to be discussed here, and we will start with direct frequency synthesis showing various degrees of resolution.

5-1-1 Direct Frequency Synthesis

Direct frequency synthesis refers to the generation of new frequencies from one or more reference frequencies using a combination of multipliers, dividers, bandpass filters, and mixers. A simple example of direct synthesis is shown in Figure 5-1. The

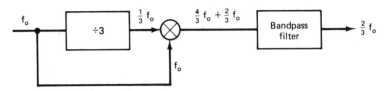

Figure 5-1 Direct frequency generation using the mix-and-divide principle. It requires excessive filtering.

new frequency $\frac{2}{3}f_0$ is realized from f_0 by using a divide-by-3 circuit, a mixer, and a bandpass filter. In this example $\frac{2}{3}f_0$ has been synthesized by operating directly on f_0.

Figure 5-2 illustrates the form of direct synthesis module most frequently used in commercial frequency synthesizers of the direct form. The method is referred to as

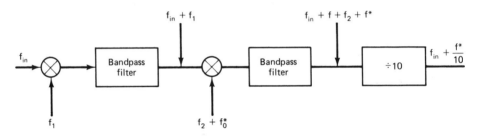

Figure 5-2 Direct frequency synthesizer using a mix-and-divide technique to obtain identical modules for high resolution.

the "double-mix-divide" approach. An input frequency f_{in} is combined with a frequency f_1, and the upper frequency $f_1 + f_{in}$ is selected by the bandpass filter. This frequency is then mixed with a switch-selectable frequency $f_2 + f^*$. (In the following, f^* refers to any one of 10 switch-selectable frequencies.) The output of the second mixer consists of the two frequencies $f_{in} + f_1 + f_2 + f^*$ and $f_{in} + f_1 - f_2 - f^*$; only the higher-frequency term appears at the output of the bandpass filter. If the frequencies f_{in}, f_1, and f_2 are selected so that

$$f_{in} + f_1 + f_2 = 10f_{in} \tag{5-1}$$

then the frequency at the output of the divide by 10 will be

$$f_{out} = f_{in} + \frac{f^*}{10} \tag{5-2}$$

The double-mix-divide module has increased the input frequency by the switch-selectable frequency increment $f*/10$. These double-mix-divide modules can be cascaded to form a frequency synthesizer with any degree of resolution. The double-mix-divide modular approach has the additional advantage that the frequencies f_1, f_2, and f_{in} can be the same in each module, so that all modules can contain identical components.

A direct frequency synthesizer with three digits of resolution is shown in Figure 5-3. Each decade switch selects one of 10 frequencies $f_2 + f*$. In this example the

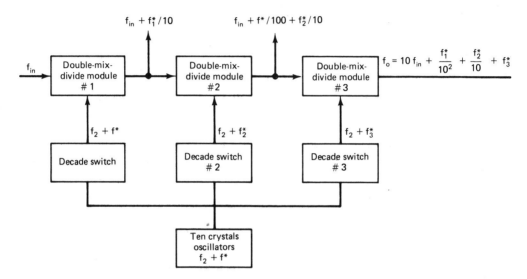

Figure 5-3   Phase incoherent frequency synthesizer with three-digit resolution.

output of the third module is taken before the decade divider. For example, it is possible to generate the frequencies between 10 and 19.99 MHz (in 10-kHz increments), using the three module synthesizer, by selecting

$$f_{in} = 1 \text{ MHz}$$
$$f_1 = 4 \text{ MHz}$$
$$f_2 = 5 \text{ MHz}$$

Since

$$f_{in} + f_1 + f_2 = 10 f_{in}$$

the output frequency will be

$$f_0 = 10 f_{in} = f_3^* + \frac{f_2^*}{10} + \frac{f_1^*}{100} \tag{5-3}$$

Since $f*$ occurs in 1-MHz increments, $f_1^*/100$ will provide the desired 10-kHz frequency increments.

Theoretically, either f_1 or f_2 could be eliminated provided that

$$f_{in} + f_1 \text{ (or } f_2) = 10 f_{in} \tag{5-4}$$

but the additional frequency is used in practice to provide additional frequency separation at the mixer output. This frequency separation eases the bandpass filter requirements. For example, if f_2 is eliminated, $f_1 + f_{in}$ must equal $10f_{in}$ or 10 MHz. If an f_1^* or 1 MHz is selected, the output of the first mixer will consist of the two frequencies 9 and 11 MHz. The lower of these closely spaced frequencies must be removed by the filter. The filter required would be extremely complex. If, instead, a 5-MHz signal f_2 is also used so that $f_{in} + f_1 + f_2 = 10$ MHz, the two frequencies at the first mixer output will (for an f_1^* of 1 MHz) be 1 and 11 MHz. In this case the two frequencies will be much easier to separate with a bandpass filter. The auxiliary frequencies f_1 and f_2 can only be selected in each design after considering all possible frequency products at the mixer output.

Direct synthesis can produce fast frequency switching, almost arbitrarily fine frequency resolution, low phase noise, and the highest-frequency operation of any of the methods. Direct frequency synthesis requires considerably more hardware (oscillators, mixers, and bandpass filters) than the two other synthesis techniques to be described. The hardware requirements result in direct synthesizers being larger and more expensive. Another disadvantage of the direct synthesis technique is that unwanted frequencies (spurious) can appear at the output. The wider the frequency range, the more likely that spurious components will appear in the output. These disadvantages are offset by the versatility, speed, and flexibility of direct synthesis.

5-1-2 Multiple Loops

Multiple-loop synthesizers, as found in signal generators and in communication equipment, are probably best understood when examining their block diagrams. Let us take a look at Figure 5-4, which provides us with the information about the frequency generation of a shortwave receiver, and several multiloop synthesizers are being used here. This block diagram shows the various methods that are currently being used.

The shortwave receiver operating from 10 kHz to 29.99999 MHz has a first IF of 81.4 MHz. The oscillator injection, therefore, requires operating from 80.465 to 110.45499 MHz, as seen in the block diagram.

The oscillator marked "G" in the block diagram uses an auxiliary frequency of 69.255 to 69.35499 MHz to down-convert the output loop to an IF from 11.2 to 41.4 MHz. Note that a bandpass filter is used to avoid any feedthrough of the higher frequencies in the mixer. A programmable divider divides this frequency band down to the reference frequency of 100 kHz, switching the output loop in 100-kHz increments.

The master standard is multiplied up to 80 MHz by using a PLL at 80 MHz to generate the auxiliary frequency, which, together with the fine-resolution synthesizer portion on the left, is used to generate the 69.255 to 69.35499 MHz window.

The fine resolution is achieved by operating a single-loop synthesizer from 64.501 to 74.5 MHz in 1-kHz steps and then dividing it by 100. The division by 100 gives a step size of 10 Hz, while good switching speed is offered by operating at 1 kHz

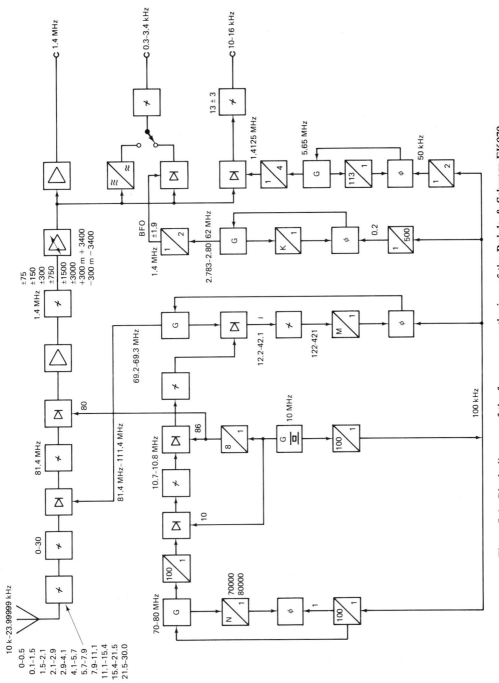

Figure 5-4 Block diagram of the frequency synthesizer of the Rohde & Schwarz EK070 shortwave receiver. (Courtesy of Rohde & Schwarz.)

reference. The output of about 700 kHz is mixed with the 10-MHz frequency standard to a 10.645- to 10.745-MHz IF. A crystal filter can be used to take out all unwanted frequencies, and this 10.7-MHz signal, together with the 80 MHz generated from the 10-MHz standard, then results in the auxiliary frequency to be mixed into the output loop.

This system has several advantages. The output loop is extremely fast, and the division ratio inside the loop is fairly small. The mixer inside the loop reduces the division ratio from approximately 1104 to about 411 at the most, and therefore the noise generated because of the multiplication is kept small relative to a single-loop approach. However, the divider ratio is now $4:1$; without the mixing, the ratio would have been $11:8$. Therefore, the loop has to cope with higher gain variations, and the loop filter has to incorporate a mechanism that changed the loop gain corresponding somewhat with the gain variation.

We have learned that the VCO, when switching diodes are used to add capacitance, has a lower loop gain at the lower frequency, where more capacitance is added than at the higher frequency. This provides a simple method to adjust the gain variation inside the loop. With a 100-kHz reference, a loop bandwidth of 2 or 3 kHz will provide enough suppression of reference, and a settling time in the vicinity of several milliseconds is achievable.

The fine-resolution loop that provides the 10-Hz increments now limits the switching time. Most likely, the loop filter will be in the vicinity of 10 Hz or 1% of reference, which will provide 40 dB of reference suppression. The division by 100 at the output increases the reference suppression by another 100, so that the reference at the output is suppressed by at least 80 dB. The use of special LC filters can easily increase this to 100 dB.

The noise sideband of the 64-MHz oscillator depends mainly on the VCO. Even a very simple LC oscillator should provide 120 dB/Hz 20 kHz off the carrier, and the additional 40-dB improvement based on the division by 100 will theoretically increase the noise to 160 dB. This is not very likely, and the noise floor is now determined by the noise floor of the dividers, the mixers, and postamplifiers and will be in the vicinity of 150 dB.

The output loop operating with about 2 kHz of bandwidth will, outside the loop bandwidth, reproduce the noise performance of the oscillator. We have learned a great deal about low-noise oscillators in this book, and it would be considered standard practice to divide the output loop into at least three oscillators of 10-MHz range so that relative bandwidth $\Delta f/f$ is about 10% or less.

The RF has to pass an 80.455-MHz crystal filter ± 6 kHz wide and then is mixed down to the second IF of 455 kHz. The second LO is derived from the same 80 MHz that is used inside the synthesizer loop. This avoids another PLL because of the clever combination of frequencies.

The IF of 455 kHz offers the choice of different band filters, as can be seen from the block diagram, and in CW and single-sideband modes, a BFO is required. In addition, this receiver offers, as a novel approach, a recorder output where the IF frequency is mixed to a frequency band from 10 to 16 kHz. As a result of this, additional synthesizers are required. For reasons of short-term stability and noise, the BFO synthesizer is operated at twice the frequency and the output divided by 2 to obtain the final frequency. A similar approach is used to generate the 468 kHz required to obtain the 10 to 16 kHz of output.

Let us assume that the frequency resolution of this synthesizer has to be increased by the factor of 10. What would be the easiest approach? The easiest approach would be to take advantage of the recently developed HEF4750 and HEF4751 synthesizer ICs made by Philips.

The fractional offset portion of this single-loop synthesizer would allow a 100-Hz step size with the 1-kHz reference, and therefore the same switching speed would be maintained. The division by 100 is sufficient to suppress any possible reference problems if the loop filter is changed. This simple change would allow the required resolution.

A much higher resolution would be gained by substituting the 64.5–74.5 single-loop synthesizer with a high-resolution fractional division synthesizer, which then could give almost any arbitrary resolution. In doing so, it would be possible to increase the reference frequency to the 100 kHz used in the output loop, and as a result, the entire switching speed of the synthesizer would be a few milliseconds while at 1 kHz reference, and the 10-Hz loop filter would currently dictate a switching time of about 100 ms. This approach, because of the high division ratio at the output, guarantees the necessary cleanliness, and the mixing products that are generated in this frequency synthesizer can be calculated with the mixer program presented in Section A-2. The multiloop synthesizers require a certain amount of hand-holding as far as the construction is concerned. It is highly desirable to provide adequate shielding. Figure 5-5 shows the mechanical construction of an output loop similar to the one described.

Figure 5-5 Photograph of the output loop of a multiloop frequency synthesizer. The shielded box contains the VCO; the double-balanced mixer and the monolithic crystal filter can also be seen.

The metal can on the left contains the VCO. All voltages are fed to the VCO via feed through capacitors. On the top right side of the PC board, one can see the crystal filter marked 20.095 MHz. In this case, the 40–70 MHz oscillator is being mixed down to a 50–20 MHz IF, and the crystal filter shown on the PC board assembly is used to clean up the output from the fine-resolution synthesizer. Although this picture was taken from a lab model rather than a production unit, it indicates that it has to be built extremely carefully to give any meaningful results. Note the solid copper surface of the PC board, with all the wire connections underneath the PC board in printed form. Shielding is the next important thing to good reference suppression, and very frequently the design goal will not be met if the shielding is not optimized.

It is advisable to separate RF and logic circuits as much as possible. Figure 5-6 shows the digital frequency divider that is required for the dual-loop synthesizer shown in Fig. 5-5. The PC board has its own regulator to minimize transient crosstalk

Figure 5-6 Photograph of the frequency-divider chain of a multi-loop synthesizer. Note the ground-plane construction and the filtering to the input connector.

on the power supply terminals, and this PC board uses both ECL and CMOS dividers. On the left, the input connector provides the switching information to the dividers. Because of this arrangement, a minimum of shielding between the dividers and this connector is required. RF circuitry requires similar careful layout. Figure 5-7 shows a PC board containing the RF input stage of an experimental receiver. The top side of the board is again a solid surface, and therefore ground loops are minimized. The various input and output connections are achieved through the four connectors shown, and the switching is done under dc control with switching diodes. The dc information is fed through the connector on the lower left-hand side of the PC board.

Figure 5-7 Photograph of the input stage of a receiver. RF connections are accomplished via coaxial connectors. A solid ground plane avoids ground loops even on the first experimental layout.

5-2 SYSTEM ANALYSIS

During our various discussions, it has become apparent that the single-loop synthesizer really is somewhat limited in its application.

Unless the fractional division N principle or other methods are used, it is really not possible to build a clean frequency synthesizer at a high frequency output, say 100 to 150 MHz, in small increments such as 100 Hz or even 1 kHz with good switching time, reference suppression, and other important parameters.

This is probably most easily understood when we analyze various systems. Let us start with a single-loop synthesizer operating from 260.7 to 460.7 MHz, as may be used for a receiver (see Figure 5-8). These are the requirements:

Frequency range	260.7 to 460.7 MHz
Frequency increments	1 kHz
Frequency stability	1×10^{-8} per day
Spurious outputs	-70 dB
Switching time	20 ms
Phase noise	120 dB/Hz, 20 kHz off the carrier

These are the six most important requirements that have to be analyzed and kept track of in a system. The single-loop synthesizer is not really a system but a single phase-locked loop with a number of inherent limitations.

The frequency range is determined by the VCO. The phase noise of the loop

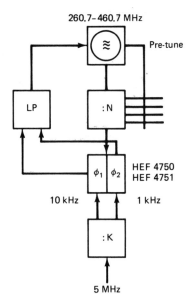

Figure 5-8 Single-loop synthesizer operating from 260.7 to 460.7 MHz in 1-kHz steps.

outside the loop bandwidth is determined by the influence of the tuning diodes and the question of whether or not the oscillator is coarse-tuned and whether or not several oscillators are used to cover the range. The following table shows the noise typically found in a free-running oscillator in this area of operation.

Phase noise, $\mathcal{L}(f)$ (dB/Hz)	Offset from the carrier
−55	10 Hz
−75	100 Hz
−95	1000 Hz
−120	10 kHz
−140	100 kHz
−160	1 MHz

Figure 5-9 shows a graph that compares the noise sideband of several different oscillators. It becomes apparent from this that similar designs have quite different noise performance if the design is not carefully analyzed and the purpose of the synthesizer is not fully understood from the beginning. Both the 41–71 MHz VCO and the Rohde & Schwarz SMDU signal generator use free-running oscillators. The 41–71 MHz VCO is divided into three subranges, and the SMDU uses mechanical tuning, while the maximum electronic tuning is about 1 MHz. This explains the difference in the noise performance, and in addition, the higher slope of the SMDU indicates also the higher Q of the circuit. The Schomandl ND100M is a frequency

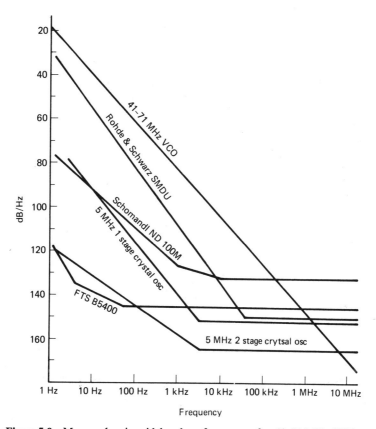

Figure 5-9   Measured noise sideband performance of a 41–71 MHz VCO, Rohde & Schwarz SMDU signal generator, Schomandl ND100M frequency synthesizer. Frequency and Time Services (FTS) B5400 modular 5-MHz crystal oscillator, and single- and double-stage 5-MHz crystal oscillators.

synthesizer constructed from many loops, and the improvement in noise there is due to division inside the loops, as we will see later in the chapter.

Two crystal oscillators are shown; the 5-MHz one-stage crystal oscillator shows fairly high noise below 10 Hz compared to the 5-MHz two-stage crystal oscillator. The phase noise discussions in Chapters 1 and 4 have explained the reason for the different performance.

Let us assume for a moment that our one-loop synthesizer, as shown in Figure 5-8, uses a 5-MHz two-stage crystal oscillator and a tuned-cavity oscillator ranging from 260.7 to 460.7 MHz.

Because of the high Q of the cavity, the VCO noise of this oscillator will be substantially better than that of the 41–71 MHz VCO shown in Figure 5-9.

In order to multiply the 1-kHz reference up to an average frequency of 300 MHz, a division ratio of 300,000 or a multiplication of 300,000 is required. Assuming that a

-160 dB/Hz reference signal is present at the output of the reference divider chain at 1 kHz, we can calculate the noise at 300 MHz from this multiplication. The multiplication of 300,000 is equivalent to 109.54 dB, and if we subtract this from 160 dB, the noise floor, the resulting signal-to-noise ratio is 50.46 dB/Hz, 1 kHz off the carrier.

However, if a 1-kHz reference is used, the loop filter has to be narrower than 1 kHz in order to get, say, 70-dB reference suppression.

It can be assumed that a carefully built tri-state phase/frequency comparator will have 40-dB reference suppression by itself, while at least an additional 30 dB of reference suppression has to be provided by the loop filter.

This roughly leads to a natural loop frequency of the PLL in the vicinity of 50 Hz. The reference noise removed more than 50 Hz from the carrier is then reproduced in the output, and we have to reduce our calculation and take 50 Hz rather than 1 kHz off the 5-MHz reference. For 50 Hz our frequency standard shows a noise sideband of -140 dB/Hz, and we have to do the same calculation and deduct 109.54 dB. from 140 dB, resulting in a signal-to-noise ratio of 30.46 dB. This signal-to-noise ratio is now less than the VCO would have had by itself, which means that we are actually making the VCO noisier than it would be by itself.

In order to have less influence from the loop, it would theoretically be better to use a wider-loop bandwidth to take advantage of the lower noise of the VCO, since the multiplication inside the loop is so tremendous. However, the reference suppression will then suffer.

Taking a 50-Hz loop bandwidth into consideration, lockup time will be in the vicinity of 60 to 100 ms, and we are not going to meet our target as far as switching time is concerned. In Section A-2 we present several computer programs that show the lockup time for both frequency and phase lock as a function of loop bandwidth, and we learned in Chapter 1 that the type 2 third-order loop provides faster lock and higher reference suppression than the type 2 second-order loop. Much-higher-order loops, such as fifth order or higher, have an advantage only if the reference frequency is much higher than the loop bandwidth, as the additional phase shift that is being introduced if both frequencies get too close will make the loop unstable; then the simple type 3 second-order loop is better.

Another way to overcome this problem is to use a sample/hold comparator, where the phase shift seems to be smaller.

The fractional division N principle with the zero averaging detector allows an extension of resolution. This method was explained previously and will not be treated again here.

The noise sideband performance outside the loop bandwidth is determined by the VCO, and the switching time by the loop filter. In order to increase the switching speed and improve the noise performance of the oscillator, let us use a design as shown in Figure 5-10. Here we split the range 260.7 to 460.7 MHz into a number of 50-MHz subbands by selecting the appropriate harmonic of a 50-MHz comb spectrum generated by the 5-MHz frequency standard with the help of a times-10 multiplier and a comb generator (using snap-off or MESFET varactors).

Let us take the same 300-MHz center frequency and use a 350-MHz comb line

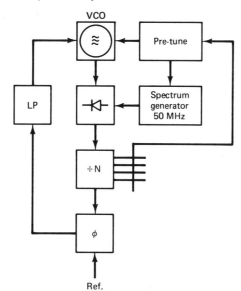

Figure 5-10 260.7–460.7 MHz dual-loop approach with a comb generated to obtain a low IF for the dividers.

to beat the 300 MHz down to an IF of 50 MHz. By doing this, we have decreased the division ratio inside the loop by 10 or 20 dB, and by using 10 discrete oscillators covering the range 260.7 to 460.7 MHz, we have decreased the noise sideband performance of the VCO by 20 dB. In doing so we have achieved both goals, increasing the close-in noise performance as well as the noise outside the loop bandwidth at the expense of additional circuits.

The additional circuits incorporate:

1. A large number of VCOs (can be simulated by the coarse switching range in increments of 50 MHz)
2. Designing a 5–50 MHz multiplier and a comb generator to mix frequency ranges down to a lower IF
3. Developing circuitry selecting the appropriate harmonic of the comb and steering the VCO to prevent lockup against the wrong comb harmonic

This is a somewhat drastic but effective method.

Figure 5-11 shows another way of achieving this. This dual-loop synthesizer now takes advantage of a high-gain loop using a reference frequency of 1 MHz; omitting the influence of the mixing for a moment, the multiplication in the coarse loop is now only 300 or the reduction in noise relative to the 5-MHz reference is about 50 dB.

As the noise floor-out is about 160 dB/Hz for the particular crystal oscillator, the noise floor is increased to −110 dB/Hz and we now can choose our loop filter to cross over with the VCO noise at this point. From the table we used to determine the noise performance of our UHF VCO, the 110-dB noise of the VCO can be measured at 5 kHz off the carrier.

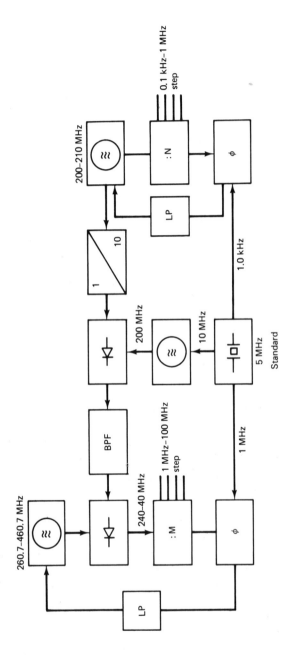

Figure 5-11 Dual-loop frequency synthesizer operating from 260.7 to 460.7 MHz with 100-Hz resolution.

It will, therefore, be reasonable to use a filter of 5-kHz bandwidth, as the VCO above this cutoff has less noise than the noise generated by the multiplication inside the loop.

Our reference frequency of 1 MHz would be suppressed by more than 60 dB from a filter having 1-kHz loop bandwidth, not taking the reference suppression of a tri-state and/or sample/hold comparator into consideration.

It is barely possible to build a 1-MHz sample/hold discriminator with low leakage, and the best possible choice will be a combination of some discrete flip-flops optimized in layout forming a flip-flop phase/frequency comparator. A reference suppression of 30 to 40 dB can be expected here, which adds to a total of 100 dB. The lockup time in this case will be in the vicinity of 1 ms, depending on the type of loop filter.

In Section 1-10 we learned that it is possible to use a dual-time-constant filter, where the frequency acquisition is speeded up by a factor of 20, and therefore the settling time is determined by phase lock rather than by frequency lock. The auxiliary synthesizer mixed into the loop is now responsible for the final resolution.

In our example, we have used an auxiliary synthesizer that has a 10-kHz reference rather than 1 kHz, and its output is also divided by 100. As a result of this, the switching speed of the auxiliary loop is now 10 times higher than the switching speed of our initial one-loop design, taking the same reference suppression into consideration, and the output noise from the VCO, even using the initial crude design where one VCO had to cover the entire frequency range, now permits 20-dB-better phase noise. Figure 5-12 shows the resulting phase noise (A + B) for the two frequency synthesizers as shown in Figures 5-8 and 5-11.

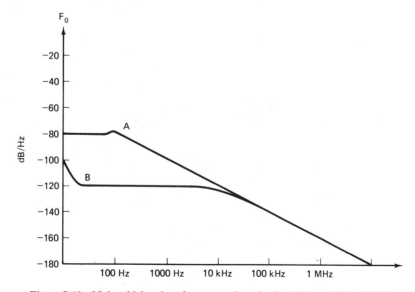

Figure 5-12   Noise sideband performance of synthesizer, Figures 5-8 and 5-11.

If finer frequency resolution is required and the digiphase system, for which Hewlett-Packard and Racal seem to have patents, has to be avoided or if a microwave frequency synthesizer has to be designed, the number of loops has to be increased.

The introduction of the mixer, however, causes two problems:

1. The filter that is required is designed with a variable divider. The mixer does not have constant delay and the change in delay can introduce loop stability problems. This filter must be optimized for flat delay inside the passband characteristic.

2. The mixer has a large number of spurious products, as we learned in Section 4-3.

Besides the question of proper drive and termination, proper bandpass filters at the output of the mixer are important, and a proper choice of frequencies is similarly important. The phase/frequency detector by itself is a highly nonlinear device capable of mixing actions, which may cause problems when such output is fed into the programmable divider. The programmable divider has only a limited suppression of its input frequency, and therefore the phase comparator will receive not only the output frequency but also, with some limited suppression, unwanted mixer products. It is, therefore, vital to incorporate a low-pass filter at the output of the divider chain, unless a slow divider chain such as a CMOS is used. I have found that combinations of swallow counters in ECL with CMOS dividers do not suffer from this difficulty, whereas ECL/TTL divider chains definitely require the additional low-pass filter. Similar difficulties have occurred in the past where the input signal from the fine-resolution loop, after being divided down by 10, was mixed into the main loop. It is absolutely necessary to incorporate a filter between the divide-by-10 stage and the mixer and to drive the mixer with a sine wave rather than a square wave.

The next important question is which of the two inputs of the mixer, the LO and RF portion, is being driven by the VCO output. This will determine the spurious response. In our particular case, where we suspect some spurious output to be generated because of the mixer action, it is advisable to use the fine-resolution loop as the LO and have the UHF VCO be at the RF input level.

Because of the losses inside the mixer, a postamplifier will be required that can be included in the bandpass filter driving the programmable counter for the output loop.

Another way to reduce output noise, avoid spurious response at the output, and use a triple loop synthesizer to achieve high resolution is shown in Figure 5-13. The output loop uses three VCOs covering the range from 75 to 105 MHz in 10-MHz increments. Each range has about 10% variations, where $\Delta f/f$ equals 10 MHz/85 MHz as the first range.

A second set of VCOs of identical design is locked in a single-loop synthesizer in increments of 100 kHz, and therefore, the programmable divider requires a division ratio between 750 and 1050. The fine resolution is achieved.

Let us take a look at the noise. The highest frequency, 105.1 MHz, dictates a multiplication of 1051 or reduces the noise relative to the reference at 100 kHz by 60.43 dB.

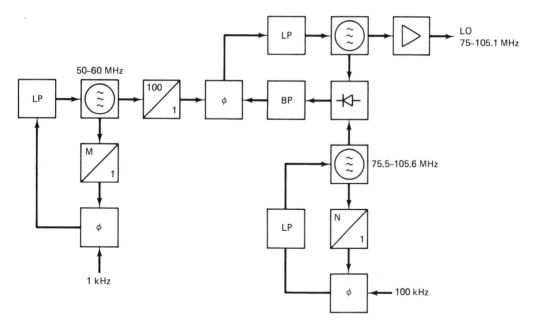

Figure 5-13   Three-loop synthesizer covering 75 to 105 MHz.

Let us assume that the VCO noise at 1 kHz is about -100 dB/Hz and about -130 dB/Hz at 10 kHz. If the 100-kHz reference noise is -160 dB/Hz (determined by the reference divider noise rather than the standard), the reference noise multiplied up would reduce the signal-to-noise ratio to about -100 dB/Hz, equivalent to the 1-kHz noise of the VCO. It is therefore advisable to set the loop bandwidth of the synthesizer at 1 kHz. Inside the loop bandwidth, the noise will now stay approximately -100 dB/Hz at 1 kHz, deteriorating to -60 dB/Hz at about 1 Hz off the carrier. Outside the loop bandwidth, the VCO determines the noise, and Figure 5-14 shows the resulting noise of this section of the synthesizer. We will call this the *coarse-tuning loop* or *step loop*, as we step through the entire frequency range in increments of 100 kHz. If those oscillator sections would be totally identical and mixed against each other, the resulting difference frequency would be zero.

We can, however, use a third loop, a single-loop synthesizer as the fine-resolution loop, and therefore compare the output of the mixing of the two loops with the fine-resolution loop.

The fine-resolution loop uses a 50–60 MHz VCO inside a 1-kHz reference loop.

If this loop is divided by 100 at the output, the resulting output frequency is 500 to 600 kHz in increments of 10-Hz steps.

This three-loop synthesizer has several unique features:

1. There is no divider at the output loop, and therefore the noise present at the phase comparator is not multiplied at the output.

2. The output noise is equal to the geometric average of the noises between the fine-resolution loop and the step loop.

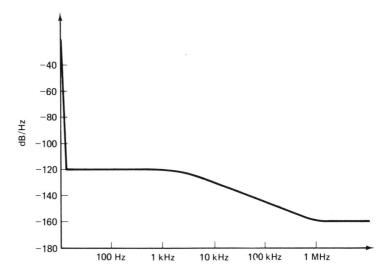

Figure 5-14 Noise sideband performance of the step loop of synthesizer, Figure 5-13.

3. The noise of the output loop is determined outside the loop bandwidth by the performance of the VCO and inside the loop bandwidth by the 500- to 600-kHz reference, which is improved by 40 dB because of the division and the step loop, which has a low-noise performance because of the low division ratio, where N remains less than 1100.

   The 100-kHz loop can be designed in such a way that the loop filter, together with the phase/frequency discriminator, achieves more than 90 dB suppression with enough safety margin for stability, and the switching time is in the vicinity of 1 ms.

4. The settling time of the fine-resolution loop can be made much faster due to the fact that the output frequency is divided by 100, and therefore the reference suppression is increased by an additional 40 dB.

   Let us assume that the required reference suppression of the 1-kHz reference is 100 dB. We know that the division by 100 at the output reduces the reference by 40 dB, so we have to achieve an additional 60 dB between the loop filter and the phase/frequency comparator.

   A tri-state phase/frequency comparator enables us to obtain at least 40 dB of reference suppression, so that the output filter only has to supply an additional 20 dB. As a result of this, the loop filter can be set to a loop bandwidth of approximately 100 Hz. In practice, however, one would drop the requirement of the reference suppression of 100 dB, setting it at 90 dB, and then a loop bandwidth of 300 Hz is sufficient. In doing this, a settling time in the vicinity of 6 ms is achievable, providing a total system's settling time in this vicinity, as the output loop and the step loop are much faster.

5. There is, however, a potential hazard. As both VCOs operate very close at such

a high frequency, care has to be taken that one VCO always remains higher than the other to avoid an image problem. Such an image problem would definitely allow false lock and therefore make the loop unstable, and would give the wrong output frequency. To avoid this, the output loop is receiving coarse-steering information from the step loop, and the step loop by itself is coarse set by a 100-kHz, 1-MHz, and 10-MHz activated D/A converter.

An additional auxiliary circuit is provided which assures that the one frequency always remains higher than the other, and a set of operational amplifiers, together with a frequency detector, takes care of this problem.

At first, this type of circuit may appear difficult, but this principle allows the design of an extremely low noise synthesizer together with a substantial reduction in spurious signal inside the loop, as two large frequencies are mixed against each other down to a low IF, which in our case is 500 to 600 kHz. Other combinations may have some advantages from certain design points but definitely have more spurious outputs and have worse noise performance. Table 5-1 shows the performance of this multiloop synthesizer.

TABLE 5-1 PERFORMANCE OF 75–105 MHz
MULTILOOP SYNTHESIZER, 10-Hz STEP SIZE

Stability	Depends on standard
Phase noise	−90 dB/Hz
	1 kHz off the carrier
	−135 dB/Hz
	20 kHz off the carrier
	−140 dB/Hz
	100 kHz off the carrier
	−85 dB/Hz
	60 Hz off the carrier
Switching speed	6 ms
Spurious output	−90 dB

5-2-1 Microwave Synthesizer

The conventional technique using tuned-cavity oscillators and UHF/SHF voltage-controlled oscillators ends around 2000 MHz. As the frequency-dependent Q of the tuning diode, in proportion, deteriorates overly rapid, and as a wide tuning range increases the noise substantially, this technique becomes questionable, and the performance will suffer.

At these frequencies, we have basically two choices:

1. The use of YIG oscillators tuned with an electromagnetic field, showing the fairly linear transfer characteristic of tuning current versus frequency. Deviations of 2% from linearity are typical and acceptable.

2. The use of tuned-cavity oscillators without multiplication. It is possible to build frequency multipliers with good efficiency, and although they are not treated in this book, it is useful to know that they behave, as far as noise sideband is concerned, the same way as a phase-locked loop where the reference is multiplied inside the loop bandwidth to the output frequency.

This immediately indicates a problem. Assume that we have to build a frequency synthesizer around 10 GHz in 1-kHz increments. The division ratio inside the loop would be 1 billion, or the noise multiplication factor 180 dB. If we would use a non-existing crystal oscillator as a standard with a signal-to-noise ratio of -180 dB/Hz at 1-kHz reference, the phase noise would be 0 dB/Hz at 1 kHz off the carrier. As a result of this, we would have an incidental FM of 1 kHz, if not more, and this system would be considered highly noisy, if not unstable, and, therefore, totally unacceptable. To build such a frequency synthesizer in the microwave area, several techniques have to be combined.

The output loop has to be mixed with a step loop to obtain an IF for which ECL dividers are available. Assume that the difference in frequency would be 1000 MHz; then we know from the available integrated circuits that we can only buy fixed dividers, called prescalers, that divide the input frequency down by a fixed ratio of 256 or by a similar value. In doing this we will lose resolution, and therefore this is not a highly desirable technique.

A way out of this is to build a system as shown in Figure 5-15. The output frequency is obtained by using a times-5 frequency multiplier and a mixer at the output loop, where the output-loop frequency is mixed down to an IF preferably below 500 MHz, in this case 20 to 40 MHz.

Around 500 MHz we have 5/6 and 10/11 dual-modulus counters available for fast frequency dividers without loss of resolution.

In operating a VCO around 100 MHz, we face the same problem that we have been plagued with even at lower frequencies: that we have to split the VCO into several ranges. A way out, to a degree, is to build a high-gain loop. In a high-gain loop the division ratio is very small and the loop bandwidth is very wide. As a result of this, the switching time is very fast, and in addition, we can use fairly high input frequencies. It is not uncommon to use reference frequencies between 50 and 100 MHz for this purpose, or even harmonic sampling.

The harmonic sampling technique, as mentioned earlier, avoids the necessity for high-frequency dividers but requires pretuning of the oscillator to avoid locking to the wrong output frequency.

In our example we require an output of about $+10$ dBm at 6550 to 7005 MHz. This is accomplished by multiplying by 5 the output of a cavity oscillator operating from 1310 to 1410 MHz. To avoid high-frequency dividers, this frequency is mixed down with the help of a step loop operating from 1.28 to 1.38 GHz.

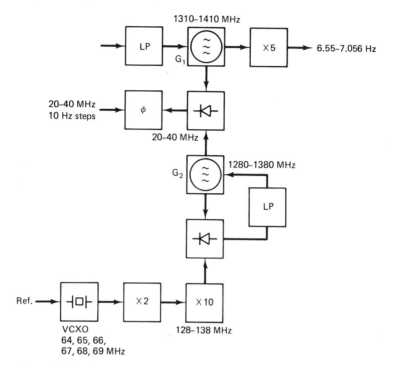

Figure 5-15   Microwave frequency synthesizer using an internal IF of 20 to 40 MHz. G_1 and G_2 are cavity oscillators. If a wider frequency range is required, YIG oscillators may be used to replace those oscillators and the times-5 multiplier in the output may not be necessary. (Courtesy of California Microwave.)

Its output frequency is generated by driving a times-10 multiplier from a bank of phase-locked VCXOs to supply the signal for the phase detector.

Mixing those two L-band oscillators results in an IF of 20 to 40 MHz, and this is used in the phase comparator of the output loop.

This phase comparator receives the 20–40 MHz input from a fine-resolution synthesizer system.

In doing so, extremely high performance is obtained. Figure 5-16 shows the resulting noise performance of this system, the Model CV3594 down-converter, at about 7000 MHz. To appreciate this phase noise curve, we must remember that our best cavity oscillator and synthesizers at 150 MHz showed a noise performance of −140 to −145 dB/Hz 25 kHz off the carrier, whereas here the resulting noise at roughly 50 times the frequency is 115 dB/Hz or only 30 dB worse. The straight multiplication would have decreased the noise performance by 50 or 34 dB.

Figure 5-17 shows a complete block diagram of this frequency down-converter where the various synthesizer sections are identified.

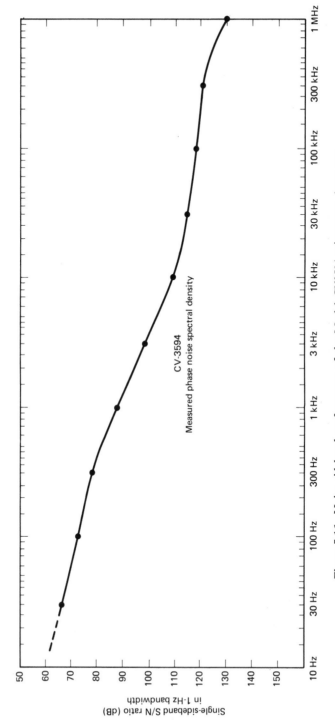

Figure 5-16 Noise sideband performance of the Model CV3594 microwave down-converter measured at 7000 MHz. (Courtesy of California Microwave.)

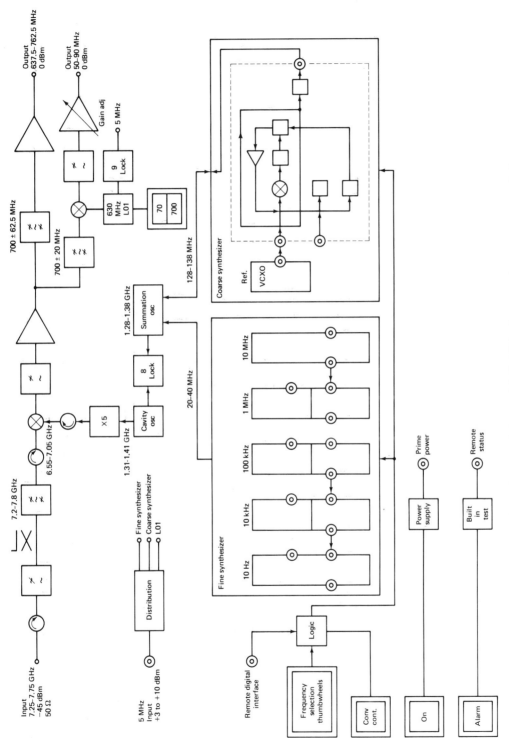

Figure 5-17 Block diagram of the Model CV3594 microwave down-converter made by California Microwave.

331

5-3 MICROPROCESSOR APPLICATIONS IN SYNTHESIZERS

Today's technology is changing at a fast pace, and it may be dangerous to go into great detail about microprocessor applications using specific devices, as constant improvements require the manufacturers to come out with new types of microprocessors. However, there are certain fundamentals which are independent of the particular manufacturer or device.

1. Modern frequency synthesizers have a certain intelligence. This is accomplished by incorporating a number of routines in the system. The most frequently used is a scanning routine where a start frequency, a stop frequency, and a frequency increment or step size can be defined. In addition, modern signal generators can be programmed in output power (dBm), output voltage (μV, mV, V), or dB above 1 μV. Different users of signal generators will use different specifications in their system, and to avoid conversion tables and possible errors in translating one figure into the other, the built-in intelligence of the signal generator via the microprocessor is capable of converting one value into another or receiving commands in different format.

2. Frequency synthesizers found in signal generators are typically multiloop synthesizers. In Section 1-10 we have seen that, depending on a change of loop gain and change of frequency range, certain compensations have to be done within the loop, causing the loop to go out of lock for a certain time. If the out-of-lock sensor used in all better circuits gives an error command to the microprocessor responsible for the housekeeping, the microprocessor will then either wait until lock is achieved, or if this is not done within a reasonable time determined by the program, it will alert the user that the frequency synthesizer is out of lock. This so-called built-in self-check, sometimes referred to as BITE (for Built-In Test Equipment), refers to the housekeeping capability of a microprocessor whereby under software control, certain routines are made available to verify the system operation. This can occur immediately after switching on the instrument or by pressing a check button which activates the relevant circuitry.

3. A number of loops may be used with what is called *offset*, which means that the actual command value given to the loop does not correspond to the value shown on the display. Therefore, the microprocessor has to perform certain arithmetic, offsetting certain frequencies. Again, this can be called housekeeping and is an essential part of the system. In addition to this, some loops are being mixed, and by determining which sideband is to be chosen from this mixing process, different output frequencies can be made available using the same oscillators. The microprocessor can keep track of the system's requirements, such as which oscillator range has to be operated, which actual programming has to be done with the various loops, what output filters have to be activated, what modulation capabilities have to be considered, and so on.

4. Advanced technology allows construction of synthesizers with large-scale integrated circuits. Because of the high complexity, several commands are required by the frequency divider. Supplied in parallel, the number of lines would be excessive. It is, therefore, a simplification to address the frequency dividers in serial format rather than parallel, and the microprocessor again has to keep track of the proper format.

The HEF4750/4751 is a typical example where both approaches are used, which means that there is a 4-bit parallel six-, seven-, or eight-digit serial input required. The number of digits depends on the number of external frequency dividers used and therefore may vary. If this had to be done in discrete logic, a large number of additional integrated circuits would be necessary.

What does this lead to? The various details I have just listed are most likely to be found in a modern frequency synthesizer and are all necessary at the same time. A microprocessor is essentially a serial device. This means that it performs one task after the other following a certain set of instructions. The programmed microprocessor sends certain commands to the ROMs and IO ports, which have latch circuits in them. Therefore, certain information can be initiated and held in latches. Updating is done by changing the contents of the latches and counters. It is apparent that once housekeeping, arithmetic, verifications, and switching exceed a certain amount, the microprocessor will be extremely busy.

Four-bit microprocessors are not suitable for this application because they are simply not fast enough to follow the changing demands. The 8-bit microprocessors are used in signal generators of medium requirements. A typical example where an 8-bit microprocessor is sufficient is the Rohde & Schwarz SMS, which we will analyze later to see what advantages the microprocessor technique will bring to a synthesizer and a synthesized signal generator, but the principal improvement really lies in the frequency synthesizer.

There are a large number of 8-bit microprocessors in use. Depending on the application, the most popular ones are the Z80 from Zilog, and the 8085 and its descendants from Intel. Motorola offers the 6800 and Rockwell the 6502 and its different versions. For reasons of flexibility and acting as a controller rather than an arithmetic device, the Intel 8085 and its variations are the choice for designing signal generators requiring 8-bit microprocessors.

As housekeeping becomes more difficult, the resolution, number of digits, and flexibility of the instrument increase, and 8-bit microprocessors may no longer be sufficient. There are some 12-bit microprocessors and a large number of 16-bit microprocessors available. Currently, Hewlett-Packard and Bell are introducing first samples of 32-bit microprocessors. What does this mean for us? The 16-bit microprocessor unquestionably is faster. The 16-by-16-bit multiplication can be accomplished in about 7 to 8 μs, and all 16-bit microprocessors have on-board mathematical routines which for 8-bit microprocessors have to be developed by the user.

Although the 16-bit microprocessor undoubtedly is faster, the question of saturation and how much one can expand the programs remains. It is, therefore, advisable to break a system up into a 16-bit housekeeping microprocessor and for other applications use slave microprocessors. The slave microprocessors can come from the same family which uses the interface and, in addition, can be separately addressed to perform certain tasks in parallel with the main microprocessor. A modern computer already works on this basis. A typical desktop calculator, usually called a computer, with built-in floppy disks, in reality already has three microprocessors. One microprocessor, the CPU, is responsible for the arithmetic, addressing the memory, and the input and output ports. The second microprocessor controls the

CRT, and although the device is called a CRT controller, it really should be called the slave microprocessor.

The same is true for the floppy disk, where the floppy disk controller does certain things and is verifying the system. There are several ways of addressing the frequency synthesizer or signal generator. The three most important are:

1. Manually from the front panel.
2. Parallel by the IEEE 488 bus, which is a parallel bus and an industry standard. Practically all modern generators and test equipment can be tied together, up to 20 in parallel, and addressed from a controller. Probably the most popular controllers are the Tektronix series 4041/36/45, 4051/52/54, and the Hewlett-Packard HP9826 controller/computer. Some other companies, including Fluke or Kontron, offer controllers; and even so-called "personal computers" such as the HP85, Pet, Commodore, and Apple Computer, now offer IEEE bus capabilities.
3. Serial RS232 in a speed range from 110 to over 9600 baud is being used to address certain peripherals. In designing a frequency synthesizer, these options have to be considered and specifically, the remote control capabilities require a certain self-check. By "self-check" I mean the fact that the controller tells the frequency synthesizer to go to a certain frequency and the frequency synthesizer has to acknowledge this command; this exchange is called a *handshake*. It is apparent that handshaking causes a loss of time, but it is essential to build in the capability of monitoring whether the request for a change in frequency, output level, or modulation capability—or whatever was requested—has been done. The IO ports require the generation of certain baud rates, and again several manufacturers offer baud-rate generators with built-in crystal oscillators, and there are specific devices for the IEEE bus. As these numbers may change, we do not want to look at particular devices but just be aware that designing a microprocessor-controlled signal generator requires these various activities or that at least requires that they be taken into consideration.

Sometimes, if a microprocessor is incorporated as part of a system such as a signal generator or communication equipment, the microprocessor section will be handled by a different design engineer, who takes care of the software. It is, however, important in the early stage that those two people coordinate their tasks, because even for fairly simple systems, where certain arithmetic processing digital-to-analog converting, supplying some mathematical offsets, or other simple tasks are required, it may be wise initially to make the microprocessor portion flexible enough to address the synthesizer in a highly flexible way for testing. As frequency synthesizers are being built, and a large number of frequencies are available, it becomes fairly difficult to test the performance of the synthesizer at all frequencies. If the microprocessor accepts a serial input for testing purposes, an automatic test system can be developed whereby the extremely large number of possible channels are being actually scanned and measured, and therefore the synthesizer can be evaluated. In multiloop synthesizers, there are some critical ranges where if the wrong tolerances in the various loops come together, loop stability may not be guaranteed, and therefore it may be a good idea to develop a test program and verification very early. This is the reason why these ideas have to be incorporated into the microprocessor and synthesizer design.

Let us now, however, after these more-or-less philosophical approaches, go back to some hard-core requirements, and we will use the Rohde & Schwarz SMS synthesized signal generator as a typical example of how to build an extremely flexible frequency synthesizer with the help of a microprocessor, which without it would not be possible. Because of the large amount of arithmetic and housekeeping involved, there is a distinct trade-off between software and microprocessor application versus discrete gates, decoding circuits, and switching of such a synthesizer system. Somewhere in the middle between the microprocessor and discrete decoding are the so-called programmable logic arrays which are large-scale integrated circuits and, similar to ROMs, customized for one particular application.

A typical example of a microprocessor-controlled synthesizer/signal generator is the Rohde & Schwarz SMS signal generator. As shown in Figure 5-18, it covers the

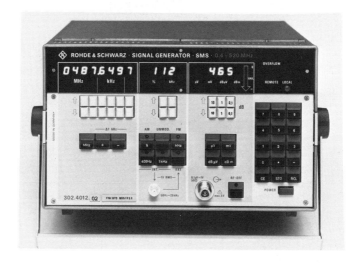

Figure 5-18 Photograph of the Rohde & Schwarz Model SMS synthesized generator. (Courtesy of Rohde & Schwarz.)

frequency range from 400 kHz to 520 MHz, and with the help of a frequency doubler, can be extended to 1040 MHz. In the base frequency range, the frequency resolution is 100 Hz. Frequency stability and drift depend on the reference standard used. Figure 5-19 gives short, condensed specifications.

Figure 5-20 shows the simplified block diagram. FM modulation is accomplished by modulating the 80/40 MHz PLL, which is locked to a 10-kHz reference. Because of the narrow loop, the average frequency will be correct, but the actual frequency then depends on the modulation.

Specifications
Frequency

Frequency range, Model 22	0.4 to 520/1040 MHz	Option SMS–B2
		see Specfications
Model 24	0.1 to 520/1040 MHz	"Options"

Frequency readout . . . . .8-digit LED display ; in MHz
   Resolution . . . . 100 Hz

Frequency error with reference oscillator

	Standard	Option
Aging	$< \pm 1 \times 10^{-6}$/month	$< \pm 5 \times 10^{-8}$/month
Temperature effect	$< \pm 1 \times 10^{-6}$/°C	$< \pm 1 \times 10^{-7}$
		(5 to 45° C)
Warm-up period		15 min

Output/input for internal/external reference frequency, 10 MHz
(single connector)
Output . . . . .TTL level
Input . . . . > 0.5 V (sinewave) or TTL level

Spectral purity

Harmonics	down $\geq$ 30 dBc[1])
Non-harmonic spurious	
responses	down $\geq$ 60 dBc[1]) ($\geq$ 5 kHz from carrier)
Spurious deviation, rms	
0.3 to 3 kHz . . .	$\leq$ 4 Hz
	(weighted in accordance with CCITT)
0.3 to 20 kHz	$\leq$ 16 Hz
Spurious AM, rms	
0.3 to 20 kHz . .	down $\geq$ 70 dBc[1])
Single-sideband phase noise	
(see also diagram below)	typ. down 120 dBc[1])
	(test bandwidth 1 Hz; 20 kHz from carrier)
Single-sideband broadband	
noise	typ. down 145 dBc[1])
	(test bandwidth 1 Hz; 1 MHz from carrier)

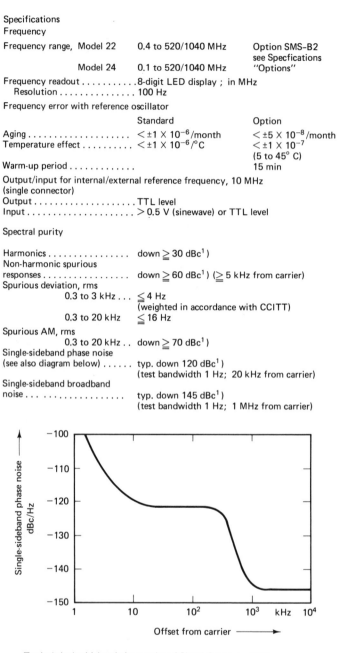

Typical single-sideband phase noise of Signal Generator SMS
($f_{carrier}$ = 360 MHz).

Figure 5-19 Specifications and plot of noise performance of the Rohde & Schwarz Model SMS synthesized signal generator. (Courtesy of Rohde & Schwarz.)

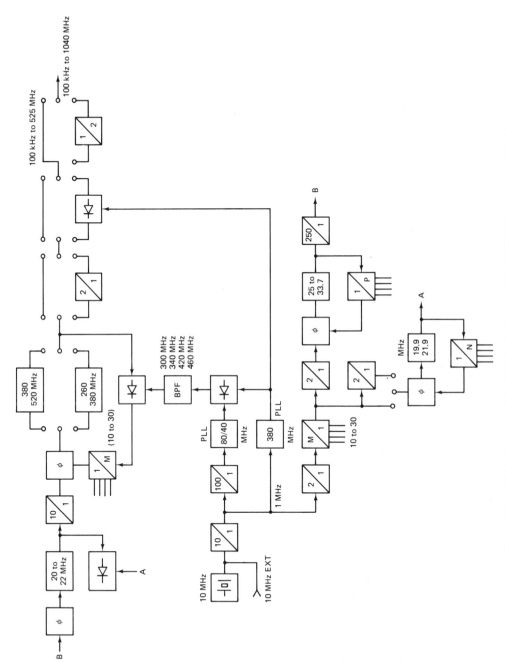

Figure 5-20 Block diagram of the Rohde & Schwarz Model SMS frequency synthesizer (distributed in the United States by Polarad, a subsidiary of Rohde & Schwarz).

337

AM modulation is not shown but is accomplished with the help of a pin diode-modulator at the output. A 10-MHz frequency standard is used and can be stabilized against a more accurate external 10-MHz source.

Several auxiliary frequencies are required. Because of the modulation capability, the 80-MHz loop, which under certain conditions is divided down to 40 MHz, is mixed with a fixed frequency of 380 MHz.

Depending on the ranges, as can be seen in Table 5-2, certain mixing combinations of the 380 MHz and the 80 and 40 MHz are used. For instance, 380 MHz plus 80 MHz results in 460 MHz, 380 MHz plus 40 MHz equals 420 MHz, 380 MHz minus 80 MHz equals 300 MHz, and finally, 380 MHz minus 40 MHz equals 340 MHz. Range selection and filter switching are controlled by the microprocessor.

Several programmable dividers are used; the M/1 divider is found twice, and a somewhat complex formula can be developed to describe the output frequency as a function of divider ratio settings. Let us first take a look at the output. The basic frequency range is 100 kHz (special version) to 525 MHz, and a switchable frequency doubler that has compensation for the change in amplitude expands the frequency range up to 1040 MHz. The main range of 260 to 520 MHz is obtained by taking the output of either of the two switchable oscillators of the output loop and feeding this to the output of the signal generator. The range 130 to 260 MHz is achieved by using the divide-by-2 stage, as shown in the block diagram. The noise performance of this frequency range will therefore be 6 dB better than that of the main range. The third range, 400 kHz (100 kHz) to 130 MHz, is obtained by mixing the signal with the auxiliary 250–380 MHz output.

The output loop receives a variable input frequency of about 2 to 2.2 MHz at the input, and by selecting the proper frequency between 300 and 460 MHz, the output of the two oscillators is converted down to an internal IF of 20 to 60 MHz. The variable divider, therefore, has a division ratio between 10 and 30. Without this mixing, the division ratio would have been substantially larger, and therefore the noise multiplication inside the loop would have been much higher.

The 20–22 MHz loop acts as a translation loop and receives the two inputs A and B. Input B covers the frequency range 100 to 135 kHz, which is generated from the fine-resolution or interpolation oscillator, and input A is generated from the 50-kHz interpolation oscillator with an output frequency of 19.88 to 21.88 MHz. The programmable divider of the loop generating the A signal covers the range 796 to 1592, and as this signal is mixed into the translation loop, the noise contribution of this loop appears with only 10% at the output since the output of the translation loop is divided by 10 to drive the output loop.

The fine resolution or interpolation loop, with the divider P ranging from 1000 to 3498, is divided by 250 and through the translation loop by 10, and therefore a total division ratio of 2500 is used. Therefore, the noise contribution of this loop is extremely small. Only the 380-MHz and 80/40-MHz signals do appear unchanged at the output and therefore determine the noise sideband performance. If the modulation requirement for the signal generator were to be omitted, the 80/40-MHz stage could be

TABLE 5-2 MICROPROCESSOR-SELECTED FREQUENCY RANGES IN THE ROHDE & SCHWARZ SMS, USED TO OBTAIN THE PROPER OUTPUT FREQUENCIES

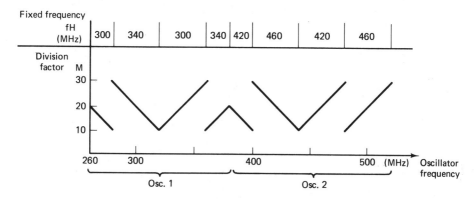

Microprocessor Selected Look-up Table
for Frequency Combinations

Generator output frequencies	0.4 to 5 MHz	5 to 130 MHz	130 to 190 MHz	190 to 260 MHz	260 to 520 MHz	520 to 1040 MHz
E	L	L	L	H	L	L
F	H	H	L	L	L	L
G	L	L	L	L	L	H
H	H	L	L	L	L	L

A	B	C	Frequency range (MHz)	Oscillator Y3
L	L	L	260 to 280	260 to 380 MHz
H	L	L	280 to 320	260 to 380 MHz
L	H	L	320 to 360	260 to 380 MHz
H	H	L	360 to 380	260 to 380 MHz
L	L	H	380 to 400	380 to 520 MHz
H	L	H	400 to 440	380 to 520 MHz
L	H	H	440 to 480	380 to 520 MHz
H	H	H	480 to 520	380 to 520 MHz

	0.4 to 130 MHz	130 to 260 MHz	260 to 1040 MHz
D	L	H	L

replaced by a crystal oscillator, and therefore the noise could be improved there; the same is correct for the 380-MHz loop, where the noise contribution of the oscillator appears without any improvement of the loop.

As the output loop is being operated at a fairly narrow bandwidth, the ultimate signal-to-noise ratio is then determined by those two VCOs outside the loop bandwidth, as can be seen from Figure 5-19, showing the noise sideband performance of the oscillator.

Table 5-2 shows the relationship among the four fixed frequencies, the division factor M, and the frequency of the main oscillator. The output frequency of the synthesizer can be expressed as

$$F_0 = \left| \pm F_A + R\left(\frac{P}{10^4} + \frac{N}{20}\right) \right| \tag{5-5}$$

$$F_A = \left.\begin{matrix} 300,\ 340 \\ 420,\ 460 \end{matrix}\right\} \quad \begin{matrix} P = 1000 \text{ to } 3498 \\ N = \ \ 796 \text{ to } 1592 \end{matrix}$$

$$R = 10 \text{ MHz}$$

Because so many frequencies change during the course of stepping this synthesizer through its range, it would be next to impossible to do this with discrete logic; and to obtain the same frequency range and the same performance with a mix-and-divide approach, such a large number of filters and auxiliary circuits would be required that it would not be feasible to build a device of the same performance. As the SMS, in addition, offers a memory capacity where the signal generator remembers 10 channels and the settings for modulation and output level, the microprocessor also updates the memory chips and makes sure that, as certain frequencies are recalled from memory, the other settings are adjusted. Thanks to the microprocessor, these things are possible today.

Similar approaches can be used for microwave synthesizers, where as in the case of our four frequencies (300, 340, 420, and 460 MHz) either selected discrete frequencies or a special comb will be generated derived from the master standard. With the help of these down-conversion systems, it is possible to build frequency synthesizers up to 10 GHz and more which provide excellent output phase noise. Figure 5-16 showed the phase noise of a microwave up/down converter made by California Microwave. Here oscillators are locked against such combs using fairly wide bandwidth, and high-Q cavity oscillators ensure very low noise performance outside the loop bandwidth.

Recent developments in new material other than quartz produce resonators to be operated at frequencies up to several thousand megahertz with extremely high Q, and therefore low noise. Again, combinations of these techniques require the use of microprocessors.

One final word on 16-bit microprocessors. The 68000 series microprocessor is probably the most popular, being used by such companies as Hewlett-Packard, Tektronix, and Fluke as main processors. The other 16-bit microprocessors seem to have applications in areas other than controllers, for test equipment or synthesizers.

5-4 TRANSCEIVER APPLICATIONS

In communication equipment offering the flexibility of quasi-unlimited choice of channels, the frequency synthesizer represents 30 to 50% of the design effort. In communication equipment using multiloop synthesizers, a number of auxiliary frequencies are required. Again, this is best understood if you look at Figure 5-21,

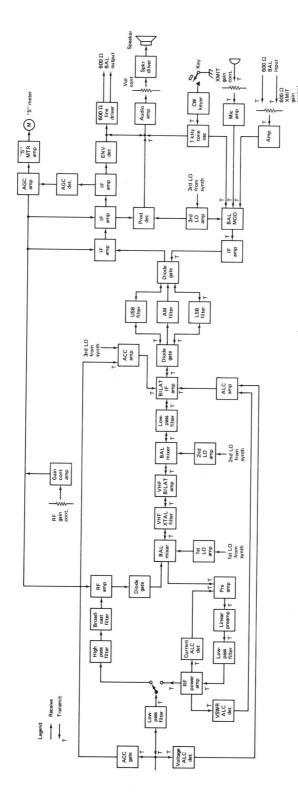

Figure 5-21 Block diagram of a transceiver covering 1.5 to 30 MHz.

which is the block diagram of a transceiver. The particular transceiver operates from 1.5 to 30 MHz. The first IF is 91.25 MHz, where the transceiver uses a crystal filter for high selectivity. The second IF is 10.5 MHz.

Therefore, the following frequencies are required: 91.2500 to 121.2499 MHz are required for the first LO. To mix the 91.25 MHz down to 10.5, a second LO frequency of 80.75 MHz must be provided. Finally, to operate the product detector, a BFO signal of 10.5 MHz must be provided for the upper and lower sideband. In transmit, as can be seen from the block diagram, some of the stages in the signal pass are used backward. Figure 5-22 shows the frequency synthesizer capable of delivering the required frequencies.

As a number of auxiliary frequencies are required, a spectrum generator using conventional mix-and-divide and filter schemes generates 21 MHz for the translator, 17 MHz for the fine-resolution loop as well as the 1-kHz reference, and the 25 kHz derived from the 100 kHz for the output loop.

The low-digit generator, or fine-resolution loop, operates from 15 to 15.999 MHz in 1-kHz steps and is then divided by 10 to provide the 1.5–1.5999 MHz output signal required to give 100-Hz resolution.

This will be translated up into a higher-frequency range by being mixed with 21 MHz. The 21 MHz is either generated from the spectrum generator or taken from a voltage-controlled crystal oscillator (VCXO). The VCXO allows interpolation between the 100-Hz steps the lower-digit generator provides.

The 1.5 to approximately 1.6 MHz is up-converted to 19.5 to 19.4001 MHz and then mixed with 100.75 MHz; this frequency is generated from 20 MHz from the spectrum generator and 80.75 MHz from a crystal oscillator.

This finally results in an output frequency of 81.25 to 81.3499 MHz. The output loop operating from 91.2500 to 121.2499 MHz is mixed with this signal, and the resulting IF covers the range from 10 to 39.9 MHz in 100-kHz steps. Because of the dividing-by-4 prescaler, the actual increment of the output loop is 100 kHz, whereas the reference is 25 kHz. If the higher resolution had to be maintained, a synchronous divider had to be used, or a swallow counter 10/11 system could have been used. For reasons of power conservation, this particular scheme was chosen.

This is a fairly complex synthesizer and is typical for communications equipment. Several design rules were followed:

1. Output oscillator is divided into several bands to obtain low phase noise.
2. A dc control voltage is generated from the frequency-controlled switches, and the coarse-steering voltage is generated and used to keep the VCO sensitivity low.
3. Extensive use of bandpass filters inside the loops is made to prevent unwanted spurious signals from appearing at the output.
4. To maintain a low division ratio, both the low-digit generator and the output loop use the approach where an auxiliary frequency is mixed in the loop to obtain a low IF. In the case of the low-digit generator, this reduces the division ratio by about a factor of 10, and therefore the noise generated inside the loop and multiplied up to the output is improved by the factor of 10.

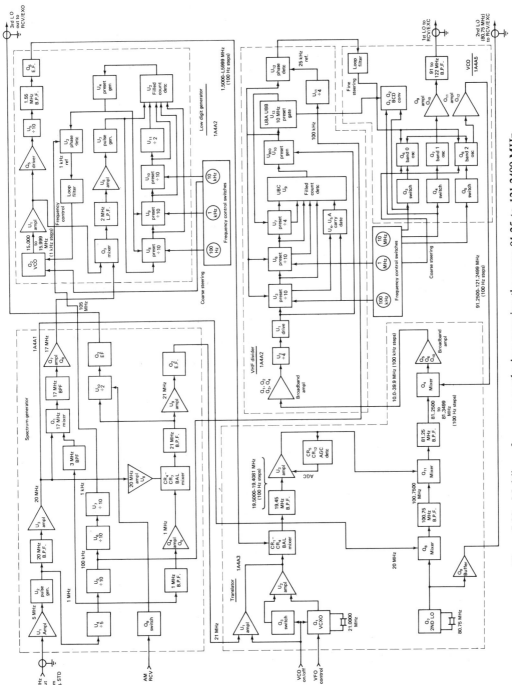

Figure 5-22 Multiloop frequency synthesizer covering the range 91.25 to 121.2499 MHz and providing first and second LO.

5. The drift-canceling technique is used between the first and second LOs. Since the second LO crystal oscillator's 80.75 MHz is mixed inside the loop and is responsible for the second LO, and drift will be canceled. It can be checked fairly easily that for any given frequency amount Δf that the second LO would increase, the frequency of the first LO is being decreased. This technique is called drift canceling and is generally used in translation systems.

Portable operations require low power consumption. Figure 5-23 shows the block diagram of a frequency synthesizer arrangement intended for a battery-operated manpack. Several techniques are used to improve the performance.

Again, we find a fine-resolution loop called a lower loop, where a 13–14 MHz oscillator is synchronized to the 1-kHz reference, and the output is divided by 10 and fed through a bandpass filter to remove the input frequency of the divider leaking to the output. This is a conventional loop and can be built using large-scale integrated circuits, probably a one-chip synthesizer.

The output frequency 69.5 to 98 MHz is generated in the output loop operating with a 50-kHz reference frequency. For reasons of power consumption and small division ratios, a translator system is built that supplies a 66.6–66.7 MHz signal cleaned by several bandpass filters before being mixed with the output signal of the output loop. Power dividers were used to achieve isolation and keep the energy requirements low. This requires some postamplification. Note that the mixer is being driven with $+10$ dBm while the auxiliary frequency is fed in at -50 dBm, resulting in -22 dBm output. Following a pulse-shaping stage and an asynchronous divider by 2, the programmable divider has a division ratio from 29 to 314. This results in a gain variation inside the loop of about 10:1, and proper steps have to be taken in the loop filter to compensate for this. The phase/frequency detector receives a reference frequency of 50 kHz. However, because of the division by 2, the actual step size will again be 100 kHz. The programmable divider input will be in the vicinity of 32 MHz at the highest point, too high for CMOS dividers, and therefore a combination of ECL CMOS with a 10/11 synchronous counter or some other combination is required.

The internal frequency standard is a 10.7-MHz TCXO and is also used to drive the product detector and to serve as BFO.

The 10.7 MHz is divided down to 50 kHz and to 1 kHz for reference frequencies, and is used to translate the 1.4/1.3 MHz up to 9.3/9.4 MHz.

A crystal oscillator of 57.3 MHz is used inside the translation loop and as the second LO, and the drift canceling technique is used again. Note that this synthesizer achieves basically the same as the previous version, with much fewer auxiliary frequencies. It is the result of a careful analysis of the system and choice of frequencies and minimizing auxiliary frequencies. The band information at the output loop is used to change the loop gain, a technique explained in Section 1-10. Finally, let us take a look at another frequency synthesizer, again for a manpack which combines two requirements:

1. Low power consumption
2. Can be highly integrated

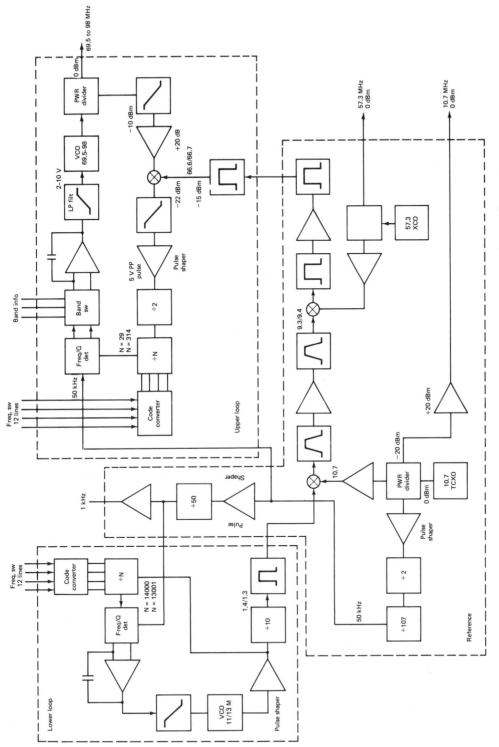

Figure 5-23 Block diagram of a frequency synthesizer for a manpack providing 69.5 to 98 MHz in 100-Hz steps. The drift-canceling technique is used.

345

Figure 5-24 shows the block diagram of this system. Again, the receiver and transmitter cover 1.5 to 30 MHz with a first IF of 67.5 MHz. The second IF is 7.5 MHz.

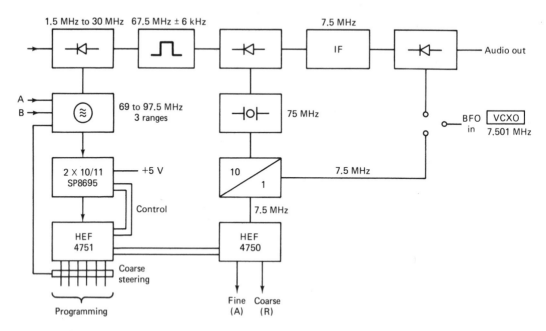

Figure 5-24 Block diagram of a 1.5–30 MHz transceiver using Philips HEF4750/51 integrated circuits, showing only the receive pass.

The frequency standard of 75 MHz is used for several purposes. It serves as the second LO and, being divided by 10, drives the product detector as a BFO signal. If CW reception is required, a separate 7.501-MHz crystal oscillator can be switched on to serve as the BFO.

This system uses HEF4750 and HEF4751 integrated circuits. The reference divider contained in the HEF4750 can operate up to 9 MHz, and therefore the 7.5-MHz input is not too high for the device. This frequency is internally divided down to 1 kHz, as the Philips ICs allow one-tenth of this, or 100-Hz resolution. Three VCOs are used in this one-loop synthesizer to cover the range 69 to 97.5 MHz. The total power consumption of this synthesizer is 12 V/60 mA or 720 mW and 5 V/60 mA or 300 mW. Total power consumption, therefore, is approximately 1 W. Typically, a frequency synthesizer in this frequency range and resolution takes several watts.

REFERENCES

1. Eric G. Breeze, "High Frequency Digital PLL Synthesizer," *Fairchild Journal of Semiconductor Progress*, November–December 1977, Fairchild Semiconductor, Mountain View, CA, pp. 11–14.

2. W. Byers et al., "A 500 MHz Low-Noise General Purpose Frequency Synthesizer," *Proceedings of the Twentieth Annual Frequency Control Symposium*, U.S. Army Electronic Command, Fort Monmouth, NJ, 1973.

3. H. W. Cooper, "Why Complicate Frequency Synthesis?" *Electronic Design*, July 19, 1974, pp. 80–84.

4. W. F. Egan, "LOs Share Circuitry to Synthesize 4 Frequencies," *Microwaves*, May 1979, pp. 52–65.

5. R. Papaiech and R. Coe, "New Technique Yields Superior Frequency Synthesis at Lower Cost," *EDN*, October 20, 1975, pp. 73–79.

6. Racal Technical Manual RA6790, HF Receiver RCI 84244, Racal Communications, Inc., 5 Research Place, Rockville, MD 20850, June 1979, pp. 4–11 to 4–22.

7. P. G. Tipon, "New Microwave-Frequency Synthesizers That Exhibit Broad Bandwidths and Increased Spectral Purity," *IEEE Transactions on Microwave Theory and Techniques*, Vol. MTT-22 (December 1974), p. 1251.

8. V. E. Van Duzer, "A 0–50 Mc Frequency Synthesizer with Excellent Stability . . . ," *Hewlett-Packard Journal*, Vol. 15, No. 9 (May 1964), pp. 1–6.

9. H. J. Finden, "The Frequency Synthesizer," *Journal of the IEE*, Part III, Vol. 90 (1943), pp. 165–180.

10. V. Kroupa, "Theory of Frequency Synthesis," *IEEE Transactions on Instrumentation and Measurement*, Vol. IM-17 (1968), pp. 56–68.

11. O. Perron, *Irrationalzahlen*, 3rd ed., Walter de Gruyter, Berlin, 1947.

12. L. Essen, E. G. Hope, and J. V. L. Parry, "Circuits Employed in the N. P. L. Caesium Standard," *Proceedings of the IEE*, Vol. 106, Part B (1959), pp. 240–244.

13. J. Holloway et al., "Comparison and Evaluation of Cesium Atomic Beam Frequency Standards," *Proceedings of the IRE*, Vol. 47 (1959), pp. 1730–1736.

14. W. E. Montgomery, "Application of Integrated Electronics to Military Communications and Radar Systems," *Proceedings of the IEEE*, Vol. 52 (1964), pp. 1721–1731.

15. J. Gerhold, "Dekadischer HF-Messender SMDH," *Neues von Rohde und Schwarz*, Vol. 8 (January 1968), pp. 5–12.

16. B. M. Wojciechowski, "Theory of a Frequency-Synthesizing Network," *Bell System Technical Journal*, Vol. 39 (May 1960), pp. 649–673.

17. M. Colas, "Le Stabilidyne," *L'Onde Electrique*, Vol. 36 (February 1956), pp. 83–93.

18. H. Flicker, "Stand der Frequenzmesstechnik nach dem Überlagerungsverfahren," *Handbuch fur Hochfrequenz- und Elektro-Techniker*, Vol. 6, Verlag fur Radio-Foto-Kinotechnik GMBH, Berlin, 1960, pp. 349–392.

19. The Marconi Company, "Hydrus HF Receiver," *Telecommunications*, Vol. 2 (July 1968), pp. 40–41.

20. M. Boella, "Generatore di frequenze campione per misure di alta precisione," *Alta Frequenza*, Vol. 14 (September–December 1945), pp. 183–194.

21. R. Leonhardt and H. Flicker, "Eine Neuentwicklung: Dekadische Frequenzmessanlage 10 Hz bis 30 MHz mit Absolutkontrolle," *Rohde und Schwarz-Mitteilungen*, August 1952, p. 69.

22. R. J. Breiding and C. Vammen, "RADA Frequency Synthesizer," *Proceedings of the 21st Annual Frequency Control Symposium*, Fort Monmouth, NJ, 1967, pp. 308–330.

23. J. K. Clapp and F. D. Lewis, "A Unique Standard-Frequency Multiplier," *IRE National Convention Record*, 1957, Part 5, pp. 131–136.

24. M. L. Stitch, N. O. Robinson, and W. Silvey, "Parametric Diodes in a Maser Phase-locked Frequency Divider," *IRE Transactions on Microwave Theory and Technique*, Vol. MTT-8 (March 1960), pp. 218–221.

25. R. Vessot et al., "An Intercomparison of Hydrogen and Caesium Frequency Standards," *IEEE Transactions on Instrumentation and Measurement*, Vol. IM-15 (December 1966), pp. 165–176.

26. H. Valdorf and R. Klinger, "Die Entwicklung einer hochkonstanten dekadischen Kurzwellensteuerstufe fur den Bereich 1,5 . . . 30 MHz," *Frequenz*, Vol. 14 (October 1960), pp. 335–343.

27. L. Mooser, "Precision Offset Exciter Equipment XZO for Suppression of TV Common Channel Interference," *News from Rohde-Schwarz*, Vol. 7 (May 1967), pp. 40–43.

28. R. J. Hughes and R. J. Sacha, "The LOHAP Frequency Synthesizer," *Frequency*, Vol. 6 (August 1968), pp. 12–21.

29. J. Noordanus, "Frequency Synthesizers—A Survey of Techniques," *IEEE Transactions on Communication Technology*, Vol. COM-17 (April 1969), pp. 257–271.

30. J. R. Woodbury, "Phase-Locked Loop Pull-In Range," *IEEE Transactions on Communication Technology*, Vol. COM-16 (February 1968), pp. 184–186.

31. L. Sokoloff, "IC Voltage Variable Capacitors (VVC)," *IEEE Transactions on Broadcast and Television Receivers*, Vol. BTR-15 (February 1969), pp. 33–40.

32. A. Noyes, Jr., W. F. Byers, and G. H. Lohrer, "Coherent Decade Frequency Synthesizers," a set of articles in *General Radio Experimenter*, September 1964, May 1965, November–December 1965, September 1966 (summarized in the G.R. Company reprint E119), May–June 1969, January–February 1970.

33. Adret-Electronique, "2 MHz Signal Generator-Synthesizer," Codasyn 201, Instruction Manual, Trappes, July 1969.

34. G. A. G. Rowlandson, "Frequency Synthesis Techniques," *Industrial Electronics*, Vol. 6 (August 1968), pp. 320–323; and (September 1968), pp. 355–359.

35. G. C. Gillette, "The Digiphase Synthesizer," *Frequency Technology*, Vol. 7 (August 1969), pp. 25–29.

36. J. C. Shanahan, "Uniting Signal Generation and Signal Synthesis," *Hewlett-Packard Journal*, Vol. 23 (December 1971), pp. 2–13.

37. R. L. Allen, "Frequency Divider Extends Automatic Digital Frequency Measurements to 12.4 GHz," *Hewlett-Packard Journal*, Vol. 18 (April 1967), pp. 2–7.

38. A. Noyes, Jr., "The Use of Frequency Synthesizer for Precision Measurements of Frequency Stability and Phase Noise," *General Radio Experimenter*, Vol. 41 (January 1967), pp. 15–21.

39. D. E. Maxwell, "A 5 to 50 MHz Direct-Reading Phase Meter with Hundredth-Degree Precision," *IEEE Transactions on Instrumentation and Measurement*, Vol. IM-15 (December 1966), pp. 304–310.

40. R. L. Moynihan, "A Sweeper for GR Synthesizers," *General Radio Experimenter*, Vol. 41 (January 1967), pp. 15–21.

41. Adret-Electronique, "Nouveuax générateurs de signaux électriques programmables," *Note d'information 03*.

42. V. Kroupa, "An All-band 'Single-frequency' Synthesizer," *International Broadcasting Convention, London, IEE Conference Publication No. 69*, September 1970, pp. 117–119.

43. G. J. McDonald and C. S. Burnham, "Review of Progress in Mercantile-Marine Radio-communication," *Proceedings of the IEE*, Vol. 116 (1969), pp. 1807–1820.

44. A. Ruhrmann, "The Remotely Controlled Transmitter Center at Elmshorn," *Telefunken-Zeitung*, Vol. 35 (December 1962), pp. 284–298.

45. D. E. Watt-Carter et al., "The New Leafield Radio Station," set of articles in *The Post Office Electrical Engineers' Journal*, Vol. 59 (1966), pp. 130–134, 178–181, 196–198, 267–270, 283–287.

46. "Unconventional Communications Receiver," *Wireless World*, Vol. 63 (August 1957), pp. 388–389.

47. J. J. Muller and J. Lisimaque, "Portable Single-Sideband High-Frequency Transceiver with Military Applications," *Electrical Communication*, Vol. 43 (December 1968), pp. 360–368.

48. J. Gerhold and G. Pilz, "The EK 47—A Communications Receiver with Digital Tuning Facilities for the Range 10 kHz to 30 MHz," *News from Rohde-Schwarz*, Vol. 9 (October–November 1969), pp. 8–12.

49. D. H. Throne, "A Report of the Performance Characteristics of a New Rubidium Vapor Frequency Standard," *Frequency Technology*, Vol. 8 (January 1970), pp. 16–19.

50. Y. Yasuda, K. Yoshimura, and Y. Saito, "One of the Methods of Frequency Offsetting," *Journal of the Radio Research Laboratories (Tokyo)*, Vol. 13 (July–September 1966), pp. 211–225.

51. V. Kroupa, "Single-Frequency Synthesis and Frequency-Coherent Communication Systems," *Conference on Frequency Generation and Control for Radio Systems, London, IEE Conference Publication No. 31*, May 1967, pp. 96–99.

52. R. Morrison, *Grounding and Shielding Techniques in Instrumentation*, Wiley, New York 1967.

53. H. Ott, *Noise Reduction Techniques in Electronic Systems*, Wiley, New York, 1976.

54. H. P. Westman, ed., *Reference Data for Radio Engineers*, 5th ed., Howard W. Sams, Indianapolis, IN, 1968.

55. D. White, *Electromagnetic Interference and Compatibility*, Vol. 3, Don White Consultants Inc., 14800 Springfield Rd., Germantown, MA 20267, 1973, pp. 4.1–8.30, 10.1–12.14.

56. Rohde and Schwarz Operating and Repair Manual for the SMS Synthesizer.

57. Rohde and Schwarz Operating and Repair Manual for the EK070 Shortwave Receiver.

58. Operating Manual for the Model CV3594, California Microwave.

59. U.S. Patent 3,588,732, Robert D. Tollefson, Richardson, TX., June 28, 1971.

60. K. Fukui et al., "A Portable All-Band Radio Receiver using Microcomputer Controlled PLL Synthesizer," *IEEE Transactions on Consumer Electronics*, Vol. CE-26 (October 1980).

61. M. E. Peterson, "The Design and Performance of an Ultra Low-noise Digital Frequency Synthesizer for Use in VLF Receivers," *Proceedings of the 26th Frequency Control Symposium*, 1972, pp. 55–70.

62. J. Tierney, C. M. Rader, and B. Gold, "A Digital Frequency Synthesizer," *IEEE Transactions on Audio and Electroacoustics*, Vol. AU-19 (1971), pp. 48–57.

63. B. E. Bjerede and G. D. Fisher, "A New Phase Accumulator Approach for Frequency Synthesis," *Proceedings of the IEEE NAECON '76*, May 1976, pp. 928–932.

64. J. Stinehelfer and J. Nichols, "A Digital Frequency Synthesizer for an AM and FM Receiver," *IEEE Transactions on Broadcast and Television Receivers*, Vol. BTR-15 (1969), pp. 235–243.

65. L. F. Blachowicz, "Dial Any Channel to 500 MHz," *Electronics*, May 2, 1966, pp. 60–69.

66. U. L. Rohde, "Modern Design of Frequency Synthesizer," *Ham Radio*, July 1976, pp. 10–22.

67. B. Bjerede and G. Fisher, "An Efficient Hardware Implementation for High Resolution Frequency Synthesis," *Proceedings of the 31st Frequency Control Symposium*, 1977, pp. 318–321.

68. J. Gibbs and R. Temple, "Frequency Domain Yields its Data to Phase-Locked Synthesizer," *Electronics*, April 27, 1978, pp. 107–113.

69. J. Gorski-Popiel, *Frequency Synthesis: Techniques and Applications*, IEEE, New York, 1975.

70. V. F. Kroupa, *Frequency Synthesis: Theory, Design and Applications*, Wiley, New York, 1973.

71. V. Manassewitsch, *Frequency Synthesizers: Theory and Design*, Wiley, New York, 1976.

72. W. F. Egan, *Frequency Synthesis by Phase Lock*, Wiley, New York, 1981.

73. L. Sample, "A Linear CB Synthesizer," *IEEE Transactions on Consumer Electronics*, Vol. CE-23, No. 3 (August 1977), pp. 200–206.

74. I. Dayoff and B. Kirschner, "A Bulk CMOS 40-Channel CB Frequency Synthesizer," *IEEE Transactions on Consumer Electronics*, Vol. CE-23, No. 4 (November 1977), pp. 440–446.

75. G. W. M. Yuen, "An Analog-Tuned Digital Frequency Synthesizer Tuning System for AM/FM Tuner," *IEEE Transactions on Consumer Electronics*, Vol. CE-23, No. 4 (November 1977), pp. 440–446.

76. B. E. Beyers, "Frequency Synthesis Tuning Systems with Automatic Offset Tuning," *IEEE Transactions on Consumer Electronics*, Vol. CE-24, No. 3 (August 1978), pp. 419–428.

77. T. B. Mills, "An AM/FM Digital Tuning System," *IEEE Transactions on Consumer Electronics*, CE-24, No. 4 (November 1978), pp. 507–513.

78. K. Ichinose, "One Chip AM/FM Digital Tuning System," *IEEE Transactions on Consumer Electronics*, Vol. CE-26 (August 1980), pp. 282–288.

79. T. Yamada, "A High Speed NMOS PLL-Synthesizer LSI with On-Chip Prescaler for AM/FM Receivers," *IEEE Transactions on Consumer Electronics*, Vol. CE-26 (August 1980), pp. 289–298.

80. T. Rzezewski and T. Kawasaki, "A Microcomputer Controlled Frequency Synthesizer for TV," *IEEE Transactions on Consumer Electronics*, Vol. CE-24, No. 2 (May 1978), pp. 145–153.

81. K. J. Mueller and C. P. Wu, "A Monolithic ECL/I²L Phase-Locked Loop Frequency Synthesizer for AM/FM TV," *IEEE Transactions on Consumer Electronics*, Vol. CE-25, No. 3 (August 1979), pp. 670–676.

82. G. d'Andrea, V. Libal, and G. Weil, "Frequency Synthesis for Color TV-Receivers with a New Dedicated μ-Computer," *IEEE Transactions on Consumer Electronics*, Vol. 27 (1981), pp. 272–283.

83. B. Apetz, B. Scheckel, and G. Weil, "A 120 MHz AM/FM PLL-IC with Dual On-Chip Programmable Charge Pump/Filter Op-Amp," *IEEE Transactions on Consumer Electronics*, Vol. 27 (1981), pp. 234–242.

84. K. Tanaka, S. IkeGuchi, Y. Nakayama, and Osamu Ikeda, "New Digital Synthesizer LSI for FM/AM Receivers," *IEEE Transactions on Consumer Electronics*, Vol. 27 (1981), pp. 210–219.

6

Practical Circuits

The previous chapters have dealt with the design principles of frequency synthesizers and the effect that parameters have on the loop performance. It is impossible to show all details relevant to the design of frequency synthesizers, especially regarding the selection of components, PC board layouts, and which principle to use over another, as sometimes they are equally good and the choice is very difficult. Engineers typically want to reinvent everything themselves. This is not a very economical way to do research, and inasmuch as one relies on literature, it is also good to take a look at proven designs. A nonworking novel approach is more difficult to digest than looking at a reliable and working approach and trying to improve this and also to understand why it has been done the way it has been done.

In this chapter we take a look at the design and the schematics of three synthesizers:

1. A single-loop 1-kHz reference synthesizer operating from 41 to 71 MHz designed for a simple shortwave receiver.

2. A single-loop 25-kHz synthesizer operating in a similar frequency range that is optimized for speed.

3. A multiloop synthesizer covering 75 to 105 MHz in 100-Hz increments as a multiloop synthesizer approach which is optimized for low-noise sideband performance. This synthesizer can be extended to finer resolution by decreasing the steps of the fine-resolution loop, which could use either the HEF4750/51 series PLL ICs or the fractional division N principle as the output of this stage is divided down, and therefore the noise sideband performance is improved.

6-1 SINGLE-LOOP 41–71 MHz FREQUENCY SYNTHESIZER

The following frequency synthesizer was developed for a low-cost general coverage receiver. Its requirements were:

Settling time	Less than 1 s
Noise sideband performance	Better than 125 dB/Hz
	25 kHz off the carrier
Power consumption	Vicinity of 2 W or less

Figure 6-1 shows the schematic of this one-loop synthesizer. It has the following interesting features. The frequency range is split into three ranges, each using 10-MHz-range oscillators using field-effect transistors. The frequency synthesizer being addressed in parallel BCD decodes the appropriate frequency information, and each oscillator is selected by NPN/PNP transistor switches.

The oscillator output is fed to a high-isolation cascode amplifier of unity gain which drives two independent output stages. The top 2N918 output is used to drive an amplifier, which in turn drives a receiver mixer, and the lower 2N918 transistor drives the Plessey SP8690 10/11 swallow counter.

The frequency synthesizer is based on the swallow counter principle, and it toggles between a division ratio of 100:101. The drawback is that the minimum division ratio for the swallow counter is about 10,000, but as the division ratio is never less than 41,000, this is sufficient for the purpose.

Low-power Schottky clamped integrated circuits together with ECL devices interface with the CMOS. Some speed-up techniques or delay compensation techniques were used in this design. To make the reset pulse longer, 120 pF is attached to the reset line to stretch the pulse. This is a reliable method, although it is not found very often. The loop filter has several time constants. The output of the phase/frequency capacitor CD4046 operates into a 0.1-μF capacitor acting as a spike suppressor and reducing the loop bandwidth to below 1 kHz.

As the reference frequency of 1 kHz requires a loop bandwidth of around 10 Hz or smaller, this is permissible. Under locked condition, the output of the CD 4046 is a very high impedance source, its impedance depending on the spikes coming out of the device as a function of finite reference suppression and balancing of the output MOS switches. For higher frequencies, the 2.2 kΩ/2.2 μF sets the output impedance to 2.2 kΩ. In the case of this particular frequency synthesizer, the loop filter was found experimentally because of our inability to predict the amount of the pulses coming from the phase/frequency comparator. A second low-pass filter of five times the time constants follows at the output of the series resistor of 150 kΩ with the two antiparallel diodes. Initially, as the synthesizer is not in lock, the two diodes will conduct and short-circuit the 150-kΩ resistor. In addition, the output impedance of the 4046 is then fairly low, and therefore fairly rapid frequency acquisition by the

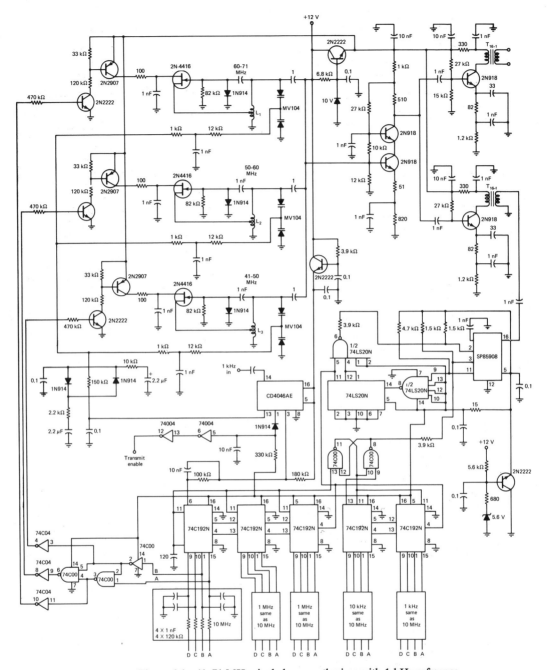

Figure 6-1 41–71 MHz single-loop synthesizer with 1-kHz reference.

pull-in method is possible. The 10 kΩ/2.2 μF loop filter then determines, together with the drive impedance, the frequency lock, while the entire filter arrangement determines the phase-lock time requirements.

In addition, information regarding the locking of the synthesizer is given by an output called "transmit enable," as this synthesizer was also used later in a transceiver application, and it was necessary to prevent transmitting before frequency lock was reached. When experimenting with this synthesizer, this output can be monitored on the scope and will give good information regarding timing when frequency and phase lock is accomplished.

6-2 SINGLE-LOOP 72–92 MHz 25-kHz STEP SYNTHESIZER

The following frequency synthesizer was developed for a fast frequency hopping receiver, and one of the requirements was that the final phase had to be reached within about 3 ms.

This synthesizer has several interesting features, as we will discover, and is a good example of the design criteria and trade-offs. The basic requirements are as follows:

Frequency range	72.725 to 92.225 MHz
Frequency increments	25 kHz
Lock-in time for phase error	Less than 20°; less than 3 ms
Reference frequency suppression	60 dB or better

Figure 6-2 shows the block diagram of this synthesizer. It follows the design rules of previously established swallow counter principles whereby the transfer characteristic

$$f_{\text{VCO}} = f_{\text{Ref}}[(P_M - P_F) \times 40 + P_F \times 41] \tag{6-1}$$

The lock time of the synthesizer is fairly rapid relative to the reference suppression, as both reference frequency suppression and lock-up time are combined through the bandwidth of the loop filter.

Using the familiar equations shown in Chapter 1, it can be shown that, while a single-loop synthesizer can handle general requirements, a second-order loop filter is unable to suppress the reference frequency components to the required level. It was,

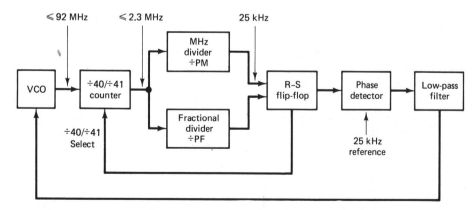

Figure 6-2 Block diagram of the 72–92 MHz synthesizer with 25-kHz step size using the swallow counter principle.

therefore, decided to use a fourth-order low-pass filter. This low-pass filter has to be designed to introduce negligible additional phase delay in the range below and up to the natural loop frequency in order to preserve loop stability and lock-in time. From the block diagram, Figure 6-2, it can be seen that two counters are used. The megahertz information is programmed in the megahertz counter, while the kilohertz information is supplied to the fractional counter. Program steps from 0 to 39 are required for the fractional counter and from 0 to 20 for the megahertz counter. To minimize power consumption, CMOS logic, where possible, is used. A swallow counter minimizes the need for high-speed logic. The algorithm allows direct step down from the approximately 92-MHz VCO frequency to $f_{\mathrm{VCO}}/40$ MHz equals 2.3 MHz, which is in the range of CMOS logic. This algorithm is implemented by hardware in the following manner. Assume that both counters are reset to their lowest division ratio, which is 64 for the megahertz counter and 0 for the fractional counter. Also assume that the programming input to the megahertz counter is 10 and to the fractional counter also 10 and the $\div 40/\div 41$ counter is set to the divide-by-41 mode. Attached to the megahertz counter is a toggle circuit which extends the division ratio of the megahertz counter by 8 to make a total of $64 + 8 + 10 = 82$. Both dividers are now clocked with < 2.3 MHz and count down from their programmed values. The fractional counter reaches zero first after dividing the VCO frequency 10 times by 41. When this happens, the RS flip-flop is triggered and puts the swallow counter into the divide-by-40 mode. The megahertz counter has been decremented by 10 and will now continue to divide by 40 ($82 - 10$ times). Upon reaching zero, both counters are reset and the flip-flop puts the $\div 40/\div 41$ counter back into the divide-by-41 mode. The described procedure can now start again and the total count is $N = 10 \times 41 + 72 \times 40 = 3290$ and multiplied by the reference frequency

$$f_{\mathrm{VCO}} = Nf_{\mathrm{Ref}} = 3290 \times 25 = 82{,}250 \text{ kHz}$$

Since P_M is 82 and P_F is 10, taking the algorithm given above,

$$N = (P_M - P_F)40 + P_F \times 41 = (82 - 10)40 + 10 \times 41 = 3290$$

Figure 6-3 shows the schematic of the VCO together with the dividers and other logics.

The control of the $\div 40/\div 41$ counter is shown in Figure 6-4. The toggle circuit used to bring the minimum count of the megahertz divider to 72 is shown in the overall circuit diagram and consists of AR15 and AR21. The megahertz counter AR16/17, upon reaching zero, delivers carry out which through flip-flop AR21 resets the octal counter AR15. After eight clock pulses, AR15's "0" outpulse resets the flip-flop, which in turn resets all counters to their initial values. The megahertz counter has divide by 64 hard-wired to make its total minimum count 72.

Only if S1 and S2 are logic low does the MC12513 two-module counter divide by 11. This is shown in the timing diagram in Figure 6-4. With a third control input at logic high, the two inputs S1 and S2 are overridden and the MC12513 remains in the divide-by-10 mode, making the total count 40. This third control input is accessed through pin 12 of the MC12513, as shown in the overall circuit diagram.

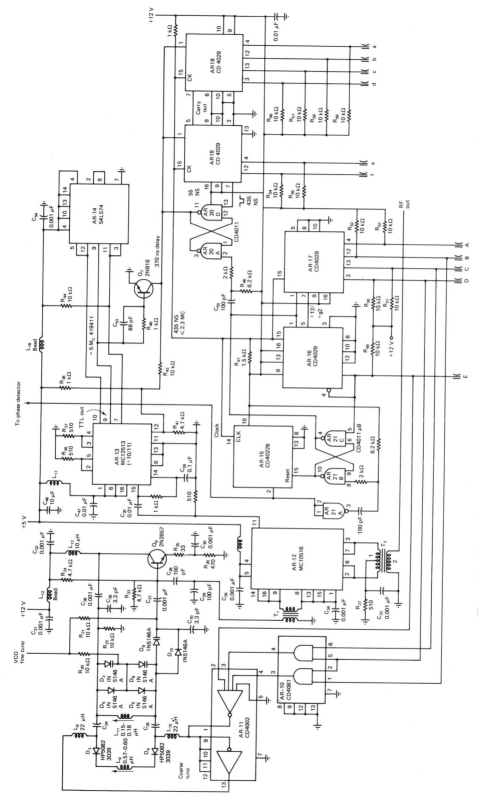

Figure 6-3 Schematic of the VCO and digital divider chain of the 72–92 MHz frequency synthesizer as shown in the block diagram, Figure 6-2.

357

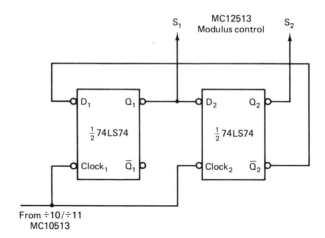

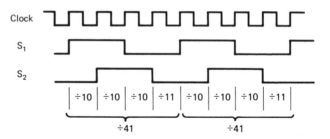

Figure 6-4 Block diagram and timing information for the 40/41 divider system.

The timing circuit (Figure 6-5) shows the three phases of the synthesizer operation. The left side shows the phase where the two-module counter divides by 40 while the megahertz counter is decrementing. The middle part shows the eight toggle pulses still in the ÷40 mode and the right-hand section shows the ÷41 mode while the fractional counter is operative.

The switching-time delays referred to the positive-going clock edges are given in nanoseconds and are worst-case values as far as available from the data books. The only critical transition (toggle to $P_F \times 41$) has a somewhat marginal time space (70 ns) for resetting AR18 and AR19. However, it is unlikely that all four adding delay times are worst-case (maximum) values, so that a more comfortable time margin should be available when reduced to practice.

The interested reader can calculate the propagation delays as shown in Figure 6-5 by using the same analysis as made in Chapter 5 dealing with delay compensation.

Some comments on the design: The VCO covering the frequency range of 72.725

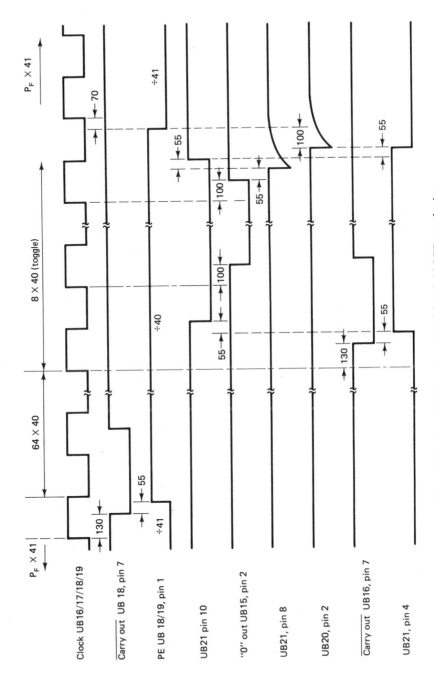

Figure 6-5 Overall timing diagram of the 72–92 MHz synthesizer.

359

to 92.225 MHz is split into two ranges. Range switching is achieved by shunting the oscillator inductance with another one in parallel. The changeover frequency, for reasons of loop stability, is set at 82 MHz. Figure 6-6 shows the phase comparator, the loop filter, and the active low-pass filter.

The RCA CD4046 is well suited for the phase comparator function. Note that the loop of the operational amplifier responsible for the loop filter has a spike suppression filter, and an optional 1 MΩ at the output of the CD4046 cures some of the problems as described previously, where the CD4046 under locked condition enters an area of reduced gain and therefore can cause low-frequency loop instability. This, in return, shows high close-in noise. The loop filter calculation in itself requires the highest attention since stability and FM noise suppression depend strongly on its characteristic. Highest priority should be given to the stability criteria, while lock-in time and reference suppression should follow, in that order. The phase comparator gain constant of the CD4046 was determined to be 1.6 V/rad. The next important parameter to be determined is the VCO gain. It is found by applying voltage to the VCO and making point-to-point measurements. Figure 6-7 shows the resulting transfer characteristic measured from 69 to 82 MHz. The slope on this curve taken at the lowest used VCO frequency determines the value of K_v, which is the highest value encountered in normal operation. The reason for taking the highest value is the fact that the loop gain reaches a maximum, and therefore the stability, a minimum. As K_v decreases, stability is no more a problem; however, the lock-in time will increase. The next input required is the divider ratio N. Since K_v is chosen for the lowest used frequency, the corresponding N is also the smallest used (i.e., 72.725 MHz/25 kHz; $N = 2909$). The last input needed is the natural loop bandwidth, which is the 3-dB-down frequency of the loop filter's magnitude response. Its choice is dictated by the lock-in time allowed. Since the maximum lock-in time is 3 ms, which must be met at the top end of the frequency range, and since the lock-in time is a strong function of K_v and a weaker function of N, one may use the relation for the lock-in time t_ℓ:

$$t_{\ell_{min}} \approx t_{\ell_{max}} \frac{K_{v_{min}}}{K_{v_{max}}} \frac{N_{min}}{N_{max}} \tag{6-2}$$

t_ℓ for our case is roughly 1.1 ms. It is quite difficult to relate the lock-in time to the natural loop frequency with a simple mathematical expression. Using the relation

$$f_o \approx \frac{1}{t_{\ell_{min}}} \tag{6-3}$$

we get $f_o \approx 900$ Hz.

6-2-1 Reference Frequency Filter

The open-loop gain $A(s)$ in this design shows that the reference frequency suppression at 25 kHz amounts to only 44 dB. To reach the target value of 60 dB, additional filtering is required. This is a very delicate task since stability must be maintained, while additional attenuation is needed in the region of the first and higher reference frequency sidebands. The phase margin in the vicinity of the natural loop frequency

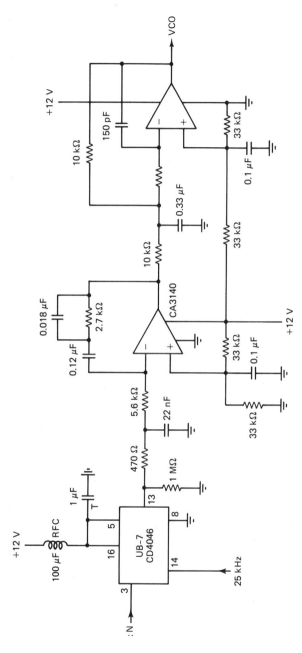

Figure 6-6 Phase/frequency comparator and loop filters for the 72–92 MHz frequency synthesizer.

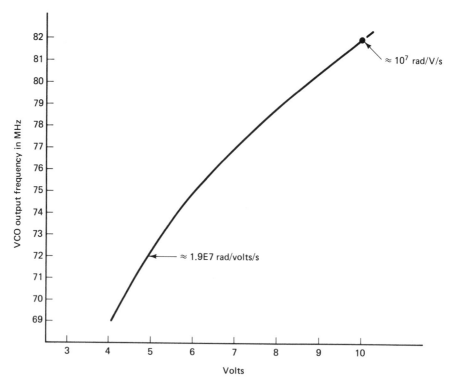

Figure 6-7   VCO transfer characteristic of the VCO used in the 72–92 MHz oscillator.

must not be changed appreciably. To conserve power, a passive parallel T-network was used first, with its attenuation zero placed at 25 kHz. However, stable loop operation could not be achieved together with sufficient reference frequency suppression, even though calculations showed that the solution is feasible. The reason for this disagreement probably lies in the nonlinear transfer characteristic of the varactor diodes, which in the calculation was assumed to be "piecewise linear" and which, through its higher-order terms, may introduce enough disturbance of the loop behavior to cause instabilities, particularly at the low end of the tuning range, where the loop gain is highest.

An active low-pass filter of second-order response was then applied. Its cutoff frequency was first set to 6 kHz, but a slight instability was still observed at the low end, still indicating small phase margin. The cutoff frequency was then moved to 7 kHz and its input resistance trimmed to a somewhat lower value than calculated; this resulted in stable loop operation and an additional 16-dB attenuation at 25 kHz, cutting the reference frequency sideband to the target value of -60 dB. The reduction in input resistance value is a convenient way to reduce the detrimental phase delay near ω_0 of the loop filter, while a reduction in attenuation of the 25-kHz reference signal has to be tolerated. The peak in magnitude near the filter cutoff frequency should be checked for a gain margin of ≈ -10 dB, since the phase margin goes to zero in that frequency range.

It is recommended to use > 10-kΩ resistors in the reference frequency filter in order to "swamp" the badly controlled output resistance of the loop filter op-amp.

To measure the lock-in time of the loop with good resolution (i.e., a few degrees of phase error), the test circuit shown in Figure 6-8 was built. The free-running square-wave generator is connected to the synthesizer programming input, which initiates the

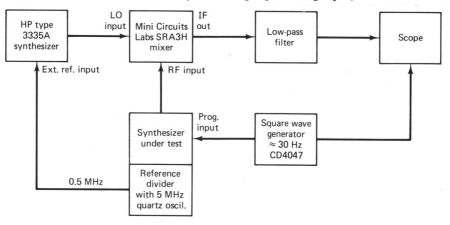

Figure 6-8   Test setup to determine the settling time of the 72–92 MHz synthesizer.

desired frequency step (in our tests, 200 kHz and 8 MHz). It also serves to trigger the oscilloscope. A second synthesizer, the HP3335A, is phase locked to the same reference quartz oscillator used in the synthesizer under test. Both synthesizer output signals are then fed to a mixer (SRA3H). With both synthesizers operating at the same frequency, the mixer output is a dc voltage whose ripple depends on phase noise. Cyclic frequency stepping of the synthesizer under test causes the mixer output to alternate between dc and 200 kHz (8 MHz). A low-pass filter following the mixer is a single RC network with a 3-dB frequency of ≈ 400 kHz.

When stepping the synthesizer under test in increments of 200 kHz, it was found that the beat note disappeared after 1.5 ms operating at 72 MHz, which is at the low end of the tuning range, and after about 3 ms when operating near 81 MHz, the high end of the tuning range. The calibration of the phase error can be done by using the amplitude of the 200-kHz difference frequency, which corresponds to 2π radians. With the steady-state dc output centered on the difference frequency amplitude, ripples of this output amplitude are related by the sine function to the phase deviation.

$$\text{Phase error} = \arcsin \frac{R}{A} \tag{6-4}$$

where R = ripple amplitude

A = difference frequency amplitude

The measurements were limited by the highest available frequency on the HP3335A synthesizer, which is 80.99 MHz. However, one finds that stability and lock-in time are only weakly affected when operating in the range 81 to 92 MHz (by means of shunting only the VCO tank inductance to achieve band switching). A strong influence on the lock-in behavior, however, has to be expected from changes in phase margin. The plot of calculated values of phase margin versus lock-in time illustrates this fact (Figure 6-9).

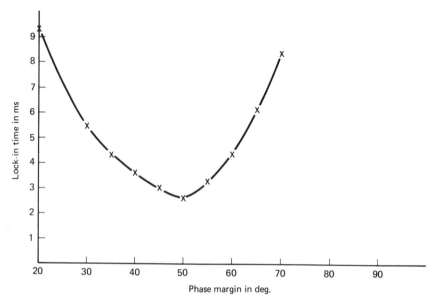

Figure 6-9   Lock-in time as a function of phase margin determined for the 72–92 MHz frequency synthesizer.

Very large frequency steps (i.e., of the order of megahertz) cannot be handled by the mathematical approach since K_v changes strongly and nonlinearly over the switched frequency range.

Experimentally, it was found that an 8-MHz frequency step required 4.5 ms for lock-in.

6-3 75–105 MHz MULTILOOP SYNTHESIZER WITH 100-Hz RESOLUTION

This final synthesizer of the three examples is a multiloop synthesizer designed for a shortwave receiver and generates 75 to 104.9999 MHz in 100-Hz increments. This particular instrument, the Rohde & Schwarz ESH2 receiver, is also designed for battery operation, and therefore the requirement was for the lowest possible power consumption. Figure 6-10 shows the block diagram of this synthesizer. As the sche-

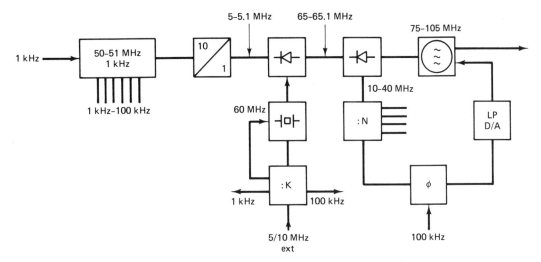

Figure 6-10   Block diagram of the 75–105 MHz synthesizer.

matics are fairly involved, the synthesizer has been split up into several modules. Figures 6-11 to 6-14 show the complete schematic whereby the adjoining points are marked accordingly. The segments were chosen the same way the building blocks were formed and where shielding is required.

The fine-resolution synthesizer (Figure 6-11) covers the range from 50 to 55 MHz. The oscillator is a familiar low-noise design, and two isolation stages are used to drive the divider chain and the divide-by-10 output stage. In addition, the synthesizer provides out-of-lock information. Note the heavy filtering for the input, which assures spurious-free operation.

This fine-resolution synthesizer provides a signal of 5 to 5.09999 MHz, which, in turn, is mixed with 50 MHz from the frequency standard, as seen in Figure 6-12. The 50-MHz crystal oscillator, which can be locked against an external frequency standard, uses a crystal in a cold-well case and has a monolithic heater built in. Therefore, the frequency stability is better than for a temperature-compensated crystal oscillator, and the oscillator can be designed for low-noise operation.

The output of this translation stage covers the range 65.0 to 65.9999 MHz. The output from the double-balanced mixer is taken via a series tuned circuit to reduce spurious output.

A two-stage amplifier of basically unity gain, and several tuned circuits provide the necessary selectivity for a clean signal, as seen in Figure 6-13. The output loop covering 75 to 104.9999 MHz is mixed with this signal, resulting in an IF between 10 and 40 MHz at the output of the mixer.

A diplexer at the output of the mixer, as seen in Figure 6-14, is used to avoid harmonics and feedthrough of the inputs to the double-balanced mixer. The following three-stage amplifier increases the level to the required ECL voltage, which then drive a Plessey swallow counter. The output loop decodes the 100-kHz and 1-MHz

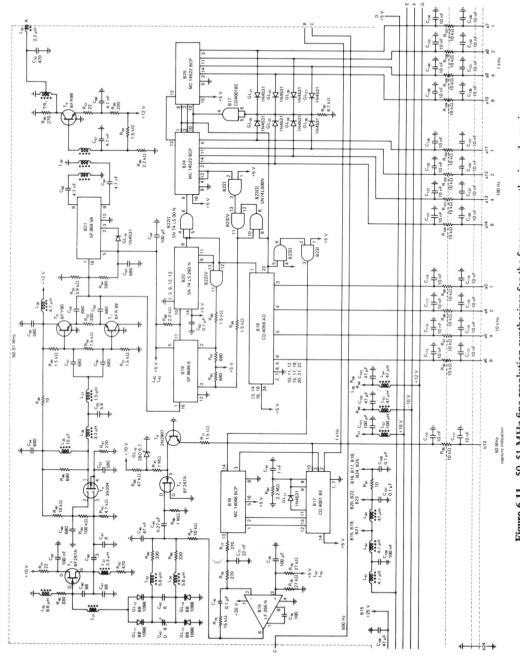

Figure 6-11 50–51 MHz fine-resolution synthesizer for the frequency synthesizer shown in Figure 6-10. (Courtesy of Rohde & Schwarz.)

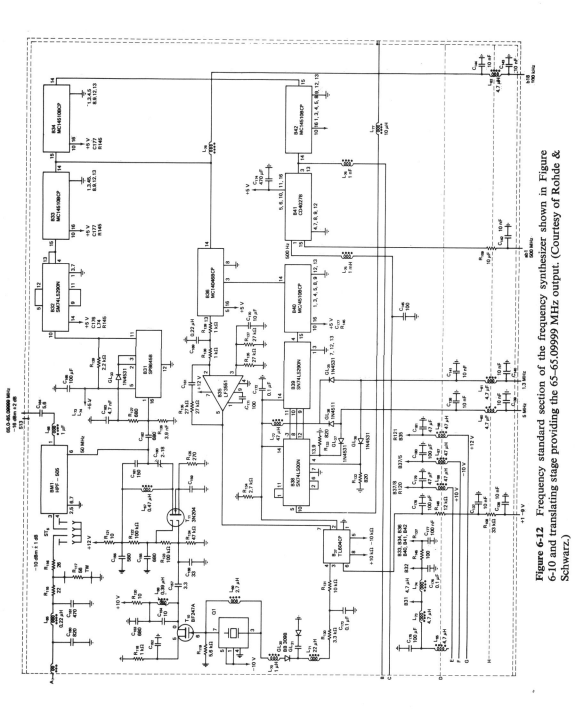

Figure 6-12 Frequency standard section of the frequency synthesizer shown in Figure 6-10 and translating stage providing the 65–65.09999 MHz output. (Courtesy of Rohde & Schwarz.)

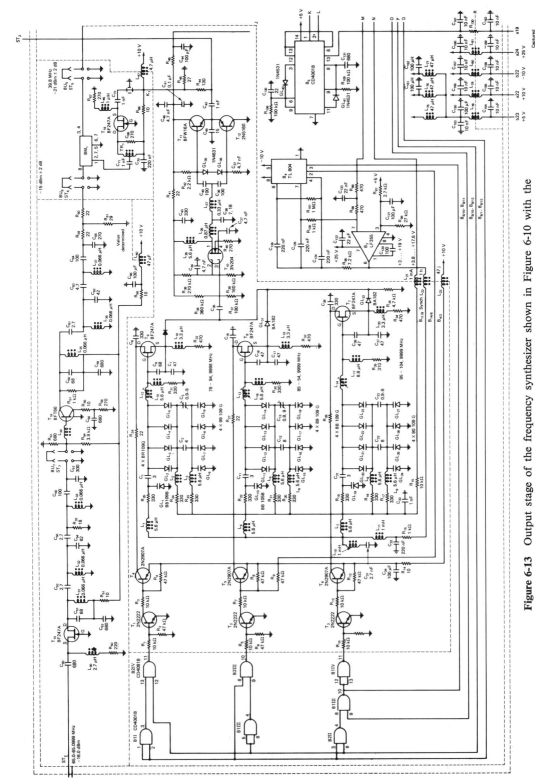

Figure 6-13 Output stage of the frequency synthesizer shown in Figure 6-10 with the down-converter section that drives the programmable dividers for the output loop. (Courtesy of Rohde & Schwarz.)

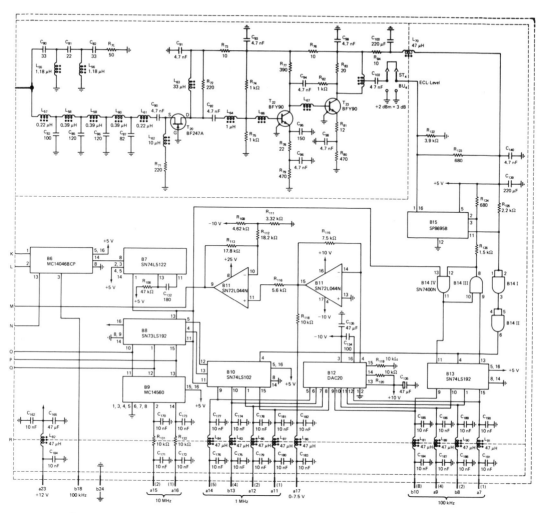

Figure 6-14 Preamplifier and programmable dividers and D/A converter for the output loop of the frequency synthesizer shown in Figure 6-10. (Courtesy of Rohde & Schwarz.)

settings and provides the information to a digital-to-analog converter. The analog voltage is filtered and properly set to coarse tune the three oscillators in Figure 6-13 that are being selected by the logic. As the loop gain changes as a function of the tuning sensitivity of the oscillator stages, the loop filter bandwidth is being adjusted accordingly to provide perfect performance.

This synthesizer has a switching speed in the vicinity of 100 ms because of the heavy filtering in the coarse tuning. As a result of this, the reference suppression for both references is in the vicinity of 100 dB. The synthesizer can be made to switch within 20 to 30 ms at the expense of relaxed reference suppression.

The noise sideband performance was measured to be $-80\,\mathrm{dB/Hz}$ at $10\,\mathrm{Hz}$ and 100 Hz off the carrier, about $-100\,\mathrm{dB/Hz}$ $1\,\mathrm{kHz}$ off the carrier, and about $-140\,\mathrm{dB/Hz}$ $25\,\mathrm{kHz}$ off the carrier. These are typical specifications and vary slightly as a function of frequency. If this schematic were compared with synthesizers designed 5 to 10 years ago, we would notice a vast improvement in performance, fewer components, and somewhat reduced filtering at the expense of more stringent analysis of the individual loops. The particular circuits shown here, the shielding techniques, filtering techniques, and termination techniques for mixers are consistent with recommendations made earlier, and the synthesizer can be used by designers as a starting point for similar projects.

REFERENCES

1. U. L. Rohde, "Modern Design of Frequency Synthesizers," *Ham Radio*, July 1976.
2. Rohde & Schwarz Operating and Repair Manual for the ESH2 Test Receiver.

Appendix

A-1 MATHEMATICAL REVIEW

A-1-1 Functions of a Complex Variable

Definition:

$$\sqrt{-1} = i \text{ or } j \qquad i^2 = -1 \qquad j^2 = -1$$

i or j is also used to indicate reactive components in electrical circuits; i is used in nonelectrical work. A complex number such as

$$p = x + jy \tag{A-1}$$

or

$$p = 4 + j5$$

can be shown in the complex plane as in Figure A-1. This is called the *rectangular form*. The magnitude M, as well as the direction or angle θ, can be computed from

$$M = \sqrt{x^2 + y^2} \tag{A-2}$$

or

$$M = \sqrt{16 + 25} = 6.40$$

and

$$\theta = \arctan \frac{y}{x} \tag{A-3}$$

or

$$\theta = \arctan \tfrac{5}{4} = 51.34°$$

This is called the *polar form*. The conversion from one form to the other is achieved by

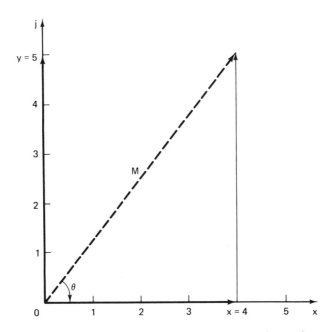

Figure A-1 Complex plane showing a complex number as the sum of two components.

$$x = M \cos \theta \tag{A-4}$$

$$y = M \sin \theta \tag{A-5}$$

and

$$p = M (\cos \theta + j \sin \theta) \tag{A-6}$$

This is the same as

$$p = M \exp (j\theta) \tag{A-7}$$

As

$$p = M (\cos \theta + j \sin \theta)$$

We can expand both $\sin \theta$ and $\cos \theta$ into a series.

$$\sin \theta = \theta - \frac{\theta^3}{3!} + \frac{\theta^5}{5!} - \frac{\theta^7}{7!} + \cdots \qquad |x| < \infty, \quad x = \text{radians} \tag{A-8}$$

$$\cos \theta = 1 - \frac{\theta^2}{2!} + \frac{\theta^4}{4!} - \frac{\theta^6}{6!} + \cdots \qquad |x| < \infty, \quad x = \text{radians} \tag{A-9}$$

Using Euler's theorem, it can be shown that adding the power series together results in the expansion series for e^θ.

Some other useful conversion equations are

$$\sin \theta = \frac{y}{\sqrt{x^2 + y^2}} = \frac{\exp(j\theta) - \exp(-j\theta)}{2j} = \text{Im}\{\exp [j(\theta)]\} \tag{A-10}$$

$$\cos \theta = \frac{x}{\sqrt{x^2 + y^2}} = \frac{\exp(j\theta) + \exp(-j\theta)}{2} = \text{Re}\{\exp [j(\theta)]\} \tag{A-11}$$

The FORTRAN computer language allows the use of complex mathematics, whereas the BASIC language does not permit such easy conversions.

Table A-1 lists operations that are useful in dealing with complex mathematics.

TABLE A-1

RECTANGULAR TO POLAR

```
100 R = SQR(A*A+B*B)     Note: X,Y are positional parameters
                                X - A
110 S = 0                       Y - B
                                A/B⟶Input
120 IF R = 0 Then 170           R/S⟶Output⟶A/B
130 S = ACS(A/R)
140 IF B<0 Then 170
150 B = S
160 Go to 180
170 B = -S
180 A = R
190 Return
```

POLAR TO RECTANGULAR

```
100 A = R*COS(S)     Note: R,S are positional
110 B = R*SIN(S)           parameters
120 R = A                  R - R
130 S = B                  S - S
140 Return
```

MULTIPLICATION

```
100 A3 = A1*A2-B1*B2     Arrays A(1,2)B(1,2)C(1,2)
110 B3 = A1*B2+A2*B1
120 Return

                        Note: A,B,C are positional
                                    parameters
                              A(1,1) - A1  R
                              A(1,2) - B1  I  rect.
                              B(1,1) - A2  R
                              B(1,2) - B2  I  rect.
                              C(1,1) - A3  Real ⎫ Product
                              C(1,2) - B3  Imag ⎭ rect.
```

DIVISION

```
100 B3 = A2*A2+B2*B2     Arrays A(1,2)B(1,2)C(1,2)
110 IF B3<>0 Then 140
120 Print "Error-Denominator = 0"
130 End                 Note: A,B,C are positional
140 A3 = (A1*A2+B1*B2)/B3          parameters
150 B3 = (A2*B1-A1*B2)/B3    A(1,1) - A1 ⎫
160 Return                   A(1,2) - B1 ⎪ both inputs
                             B(1,1) - A2 ⎬ rectangular
                             B(1,2) - B2 ⎭
                             C(1,1) - A3 ⎫ output
                             C(1,2) - B3 ⎭ rectangular
```

TABLE-1 (cont'd)

COMPLEX NUMBER RAISED TO A COMPLEX POWER

```
100 A = A1                      Arrays A(1,2) B(1,2) C(1,2)
110 B = B1
120 GOSUB 240           Note: A,B,C are positional
130 IF R = 0 Then 210            parameters
140 R = LOG(R)                A(1,1) − A1 ⎫
150 Z1 = A2*R−B2*S            A(1,2) − B1 ⎪ both inputs
160 Z2 = A2*S+B2*R            B(1,1) − A2 ⎬ rectangular
170 Z1 = Exp(Z1)             B(1,2) − B2 ⎭
180 A3 = Z1*COS(Z2)
190 B3 = Z1*SIN(Z2)          C(1,1) − A3 ⎫ output
200 Return                   C(1,2) − B3 ⎭ rectangular
210 A3 = 0
220 B3 = 0
230 Return
240 R = SQR(A*A+B*B)
250 S = 0
260 IF R = 0 Then 300
270 S = ACS(A/R)
280 IF>B = >0 Then 300
290 S = −S
300 Return
```

LOGARITHM OF A COMPLEX NUMBER TO A COMPLEX BASE

```
100 GOSUB 190                Arrays A(1,2) B(1,2)
110 IF R1<>0 or R2<>0 Then 140
120 Print "Error−Complex No. = 0"
130 End                 Note: A,B,X,Y are positional
140 R1 = LOG(R1)               parameters
150 R2 = LOG(R2)            A(1,1) − A1    X − R3
160 R3 = R1/R2             A(1,2) − B1    Y − S3
170 S3 = S1−S2             B(1,1) − A2
180 Return                 B(1,2) − B2
190 R1 = SQR(A1*A1+B1*B1)
200 R2 = SQR(A2*A2+B2*B2)   Both inputs: rectangular
210 S1 = 0                  Output:     polar
220 S2 = 0
230 IF R1 = 0 or R2 = 0 Then 290
240 S1 = ACS(A1/R1)
250 S2 = ACS(A2/R2)
260 IF B1 = >0 or B2 = >0 Then 290
270 S1 = −S1
280 S2 = −S2
290 Return
```

SINH

```
100 B2 = Exp(−A1)           Arrays A(1,2) B(1,2)
110 A2 = −0.5*COS(B1)*(B2−1/B2)
120 B2 = 0.5*SIN(B1)*(B2+1/B2)
```

TABLE-1 (cont'd)

130 Return	Note: A,B are positional
	parameters
	A(1,1) − A1
	A(1,2) − B1
	B(1,1) − A2
	B(1,2) − B2

COSH

100 B2 = Exp (A1)	Arrays A(1,2) B(1,2)
110 A2 = 0.5*COS(B1)*(1/B2+B2)	
120 B2 = −0.5*SIN(B1)*(1/B2−B2)	
130 Return	Note: A,B are positional
	parameters
	A(1,1) − A1
	A(1,2) − B1
	B(1,1) − A2
	B(1,2) − B2

TANH

100 Z1 = Exp(2*A1)	Arrays A(1,2) B(1,2)
110 Z2 = 1/Z1	
120 B2 = (Z1+Z2)*0.5+COS(2*B1)	
130 IF ABS(B2)>1.0E−12 Then 160	
140 Print "Error−TANH is infinite"	
150 End	Note: A,B are positional
160 A2 = (Z1−Z2)*0.5/B2	parameters
170 B2 = SIN(2*B1)/B2	A(1,1) − A1 Input
180 Return	A(1,2) − B1 rectangular
	B(1,1) − A2 Output
	B(1,2) − B2 rectangular

ARC SINH

100 A2 = (1−B1)*(1−B1)+A1*A1	Arrays A(1,2) B(1,2)
110 B2 = SQR(A2+4*B1)	
120 A2 = SQR(A2)	Note: A,B are positional
130 Z1 = 0.5*(A2+B2)	parameters
140 Z2 = 0.5*(A2−B2)	A(1,1) − A1
150 B2 = −ASN(Z2)	A(1,2) − B1
160 A2 = LOG(Z1+SQR(ABS(Z1*Z1−1)))	
170 Return	B(1,1) − A2
	B(1,2) − B2

ARC COSH

100 GOSUB 150	Arrays A(1,2) B(1,2)
110 Z2 = A2	
120 A2 = −B2	Note: A,B are positional
130 B2 = Z2	parameters
140 Return	A(1,1) − A1
150 A2 = (A1+1)*(A1+1)+B1*B1	A(1,2) − B1
160 B2 = SQR(A2−4*A1)	B(1,1) − A2

TABLE-1 (cont'd)

170 A2 = SQR(A2)	B(1,2) — B2
180 Z1 = 0.5*(A2+B2)	
190 Z2 = 0.5*(A2−B2)	
200 A2 = ACS(Z2)	
210 B2 = −LOG(Z1+SQR(ABS(Z1*Z4−1)))	
220 Return	

ARC TANH

100 A2 = A1*A1+B1*B1	Arrays A(1,2) B(1,2)
110 IF A2<>1 Then 170	
120 IF ABS(A1)<>1 Then 150	
Note:	A,B are positional
130 Print "Error−ARCTANH not	parameters
defined for Complex No.=1	A(1,1) — A1
or −1"	A(1,2) — B1
140 End	B(1,1) — A2
150 B2 = PI/4	B(1,2) — B2
160 Go to 180	
170 B2 = 0.5*ATN(2*B1/(1−A2))	
180 A2 = −0.25*LOG((A2−2*A1+1)/	
(A2+2*A1+1))	
190 Return	

A-1-2 Complex Planes

The complex number

$$p = x + jy$$

was pictured as a point located x units to the right and y units up from the zero point. Any complex number whose real and imaginary parts are given can be located as a point in the xy-plane. It has become conventional in mathematics to call the variables x and y and call z the resulting complex number. As this book deals mainly with engineering problems rather than mathematics, we have substituted p for z.

Any complex number z consists of a real part x and an imaginary part y and occupies a definite point in the complex plane. The particular plane used to plot z values will, therefore, be called the *z-plane* or *complex impedance plane*. If we had chosen to stay with the previously used p, we could have called this the p-plane.

As we have more values of x's and y's as they are connected together with a mathematical function, we will see that any line in the z-plane is actually a chain of connective points. If the function $F(x, y)$ is known, the graph of the function can be presented.

In generating maps, several methods of projections are used, some of which are to show the real distance between any given points and some of which are chosen to give the correct surface of an area. Depending on the projection used, the resulting image looks different while still providing the same basic information. If one is not familiar with a particular area because of the difference in projection methods, it will be seen that there may not be any similarity, and the same area can look so different that it is hard to think of them as being the same.

Apparently, it is desirable to have more than one particular projection or plane. We can now use this assumption in mathematics, and we will create an additional plane, the *s-plane*. The *s*-plane will be drawn with vertical and horizontal lines in the same way as is done for the *z*-plane, but the coordinates of the point locations will be given as σ units to the right or left and ω units up or down from the zero reference. In mathematics, the letters u and v are used at times, but since we want to solve engineering problems rather than mathematics, and since this is only a question of whether or not one agrees to a certain abbreviation, we will use the term "*s*-plane" and stay with the nomenclature, since this technique will be used for the Laplace transformation, where it is used this way. We therefore define

$$s = \sigma + j\omega \tag{A-12}$$

By using the identity

$$s = f(z) \tag{A-13}$$

we can transform one plane to the other once we know the particular function.

Let us try a simple example. If

$$s = \frac{1}{z} \tag{A-14}$$

or

$$s = \frac{1}{x + jy} = \frac{x - jy}{(x + jy)(x - jy)} \tag{A-15}$$

and

$$s = \sigma + j\omega = \frac{x - jy}{x^2 + y^2} \tag{A-16}$$

then

$$\sigma = \frac{x}{x^2 + y^2} \qquad \omega = \frac{-y}{x^2 + y^2} \tag{A-17}$$

This transform was fairly simple and straightforward and for any given pair of values for x and y we can find the corresponding σ and ω values.

An example using an *LC* oscillator is given below.

Functions in the complex frequency plane.   The frequency response of a network or the steady-state response to a sinusoidal input is directly related to the transfer function of the network. It is important to make sure that the waveform of the signal applied to the electrical circuit is really sinusoidal. The steady-state response assumes sinusoidal waveforms, and an analysis of the response to a nonsinusoidal waveform is better analyzed with the mathematical aid of the Fourier series and integral, which then leads to the Laplace transformation and the inverse Laplace transformation. The following table shows the transfer function of several useful networks with $s = j\omega$ and $\sigma = 0$. Probably the most interesting transfer characteristics for our phase-locked loop applications are the one of the simple *RC* network and the one of the compensated RC network. The simple RC network shown in Figure A-2 is described by

$$F(s) = \frac{1}{sCR + 1} \tag{A-18}$$

Figure A-2   Simple RC network.

The magnitude of the frequency response is

$$|F(j\omega)| = \frac{1}{\sqrt{(1 + \omega^2 R^2 C^2)}} \tag{A-19}$$

and the phase is

$$\theta(\omega) = -\arctan(\omega CR) \tag{A-20}$$

For the type 2 second-order loop with an active filter, the RC lag network shown in Figure A-3 is commonly used. Its frequency response is

$$F(j\omega) = \frac{1 + j\omega R_2 C}{1 + j\omega C(R_1 + R_2)} \tag{A-21}$$

and the magnitude of the frequency response is

$$|F(j\omega)|^2 = \frac{1 + \omega^2 R_2^2 C^2}{1 + \omega^2 C^2 (R_1 + R_2)^2} \tag{A-22}$$

$$\theta(\omega) = \arctan(\omega R_2 C) - \arctan[\omega C(R_1 + R_2)] \tag{A-23}$$

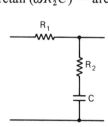

Figure A-3 RC lag filter.

The phase and frequency response are sketched in Figure A-4.

The general transfer characteristics of the networks we are dealing with are defined as

$$F(s) = \frac{A(s)}{B(s)} \tag{A-24}$$

and $F(s)$ is the ratio of two polynomials in s. In an expanded form this reads

$$F(s) = \frac{a_m s^m + a_{m-1} s^{m-1} + \cdots + a_0}{b_n s^n + b_{n-1} s^{n-1} + \cdots + b_0} \tag{A-25}$$

$m < n$ is a practical network. A polynomial may be factored and expressed as a product of binomials.

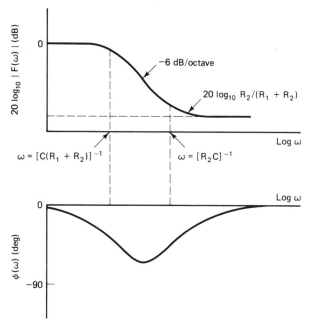

Figure A-4 Phase and frequency response of the lag filter, Figure A-3.

$$F(s) = \frac{a_m(s - z_m)(s - z_{m-1})\cdots(s - z_1)}{b_n(s - p_n)(s - p_{n-1})\cdots(s - p_1)} \tag{A-26}$$

Roots of the numerator are called *zeros*, whereas roots of the denominator are called *poles*. A zero occurs at a frequency where no power is transmitted through the complex network; a pole occurs at a frequency where no power is absorbed by the network. There are m zeros and n poles. The network is said to be of nth *order*; the order is equal to the number of poles, which is the same as the degree of the denominator.

Now let us try an example. Figure A-5 shows a tuned parallel circuit consisting of the capacitor C, the inductance L, the loss resistor R, and the negative resistor R_n, which is generated by an amplifier as dealt with in Chapter 4. The equation for this can be written

$$I = V \frac{1 + sCR + s^2LC}{R - R_n + s(L - CRR_n) - s^2R_nCL} \tag{A-27}$$

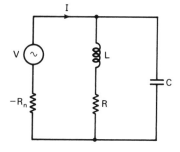

Figure A-5 Tuned circuit with negative resistor.

The denominator provides us with the characteristic equation, which will be set to zero.

$$R - R_n + s(L - CRR_n) - s^2 R_n CL = 0 \qquad (A-28)$$

This is a quadratic equation, and its roots are

$$p_{1,2} = \frac{L - CRR_n}{2R_n CL} \pm \sqrt{\left(\frac{L - CRR_n}{2R_n CL}\right)^2 + \frac{R - R_n}{R_n CL}} \qquad (A-29)$$

and as $s = \sigma \pm j\omega$, we finally obtain

$$\sigma = -\frac{R}{2L} + \frac{1}{2R_n C} \qquad (A-30)$$

and

$$\omega_0 = \sqrt{\frac{1}{LC} - \frac{R}{R_n LC} + \sigma^2} \qquad (A-31)$$

We can define this result in three cases:

1. $\sigma > 1$; any initial oscillation will cease rapidly.
2. $\sigma = 0$; this is the case of a lossless circuit, in which the losses generated by R are exactly compensated by R_n.
3. $\sigma < 1$; in this case we have oscillation that will grow in amplitude until some saturation or limiting effect occurs in the device that produces the negative resistance. Circuits of this kind are called *negative resistance oscillators*.

Let us return now to the general transfer characteristic of the system and determine the stability from the Bode diagram as a graphical method rather than from the characteristic equation of the system under closed-loop conditions, because in complicated systems this will become very difficult. In Chapter 1 we analyzed higher-order loops. However, we will now think what the transfer characteristic of a network in the form of a polynomial expression can be. For phase-locked-loop circuits this function would describe an nth-order PLL.

To review: roots of the numerator are called zeros and roots of the denominator are called poles. There are m zeros and n poles. The network is said to be of nth order. The order is equal to the number of poles, which is the same as the degree of the denominator. What does this mean for phase-locked-loop circuits? Phase-locked-loop circuits are generally categorized into systems of a certain type and of a certain order. The type of phase-locked loop indicates the number of integrators, and as we have seen before, a type 1 first-order loop is a loop in which the filter is omitted and the loop therefore has only one integrator, the VCO. For good tracking, a large dc gain is needed and as the type 1 first-order loop has no filter, the bandwidth also must be large. It is apparent that narrow bandwidth and good tracking are incompatible for first-order loops—the principal reason why they are not used very often.

This network has only one pole. If we use a phase-locked loop with an active integrator, we now cascade two integrators, the VCO and the active integrator, and the loop automatically becomes a type 2 loop. Depending on the filter, we will have a type 2 second-order, third-order, or up to nth-order system. The consequences of the higher order are explained in the next section, where we deal with stability and use the Bode diagram to analyze the stability. On very rare occasions, loops with three integrators have been built, but since they find no application in frequency synthesizers, they are not dealt with here.

A-1-3 Bode Diagram

In Chapter 1, in dealing with the question of stability, the Bode diagram was used. It is an aid to determining loop stability by plotting the amplitude and phase characteristic of the transfer function of a system and applying several criteria.

There are several ways in which stability can be analyzed. The Nyquist stability analysis requires a fairly large amount of calculation, and as most of the information available about phase-locked loops is based on an approximation, it is difficult to obtain all the necessary information.

Considerable information about the behavior of a phase lock can be obtained by determining the location of poles in the closed-loop response. These poles change their locations as the loop gain changes. The path that the pole traces in its migrations in the s-plane is known as the root-locus plot. This method again requires substantial mathematical effort because the roots of the denominator have to be determined with a digital computer. We will see that applying the Bode diagram is a fairly easy and convenient way of forecasting the stability of a loop by analyzing the open-loop gain.

First let us take a look at Figure A-6, which contains all the necessary loop components. We will find this figure again in our high-order PLL analysis program, and we will use this program here to gain knowledge about the use of the Bode plot.

The loop, according to this block diagram, consists of the VCO, a dc amplifier with gain K_2, two lag filters called F_3 and F_4, which are determining τ_1 and τ_2, and the two cutoff frequencies F_6 and F_7. F_6 refers to the cutoff frequency of the operational amplifier used for the active filter, and F_7 is the 3-dB bandwidth that is generated by possible series resistors and bypass capacitors in the system. These various frequencies allow the simulation of influences as they actually occur. In addition, we saw in Chapter 1 that it is possible to use elliptic LC filters for high attenuation, and we also dealt with them in Section 4-7. The Cauer or elliptic low-pass filter can be described by providing the poles and zeros, the order, and the cutoff frequency of the filter. M refers to the order, F_5 refers to the cutoff frequency, and ω and σ refer to the transfer function of the filter. In order to be able to describe a complex system, we will allow for a mixer, and we also have the divider and the phase detector included.

In our first example, we are trying to simulate a first-order loop. The first-order loop has no active integrator and the loop bandwidth is determined by $K_0 K_\theta / N$; all other values, F_1 to F_7, are set so high that they will have no influence. Therefore, our next drawing, Figure A-7, shows the ideal first-order open-loop frequency response. The phase is $-90°$ and constant as a function of frequency, the gain marked V on the plot has a slope of -6 dB/octave, and our open-loop bandwidth is 1 kHz. Note that the frequency display on the X-axis is logarithmic, and the gain is expressed in decibels.

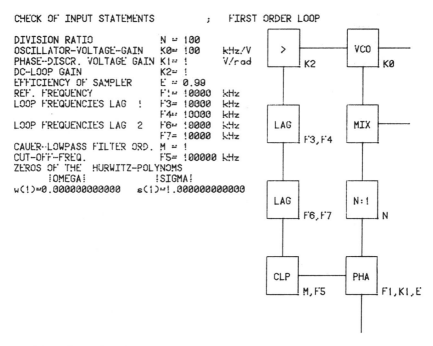

```
CHECK OF INPUT STATEMENTS          ;   FIRST ORDER LOOP

DIVISION RATIO              N = 100
OSCILLATOR-VOLTAGE-GAIN     K0= 100     kHz/V
PHASE-DISCR. VOLTAGE GAIN   K1= 1       V/rad
DC-LOOP GAIN                K2= 1
EFFICIENCY OF SAMPLER       E = 0.99
REF. FREQUENCY              F1= 10000   kHz
LOOP FREQUENCIES LAG  1     F3= 10000   kHz
                           F4= 10000   kHz
LOOP FREQUENCIES LAG  2     F6= 10000   kHz
                           F7= 10000   kHz
CAUER-LOWPASS FILTER ORD. M = 1
CUT-OFF-FREQ.               F5= 100000 kHz
ZEROS OF THE  HURWITZ-POLYNOMS
        !OMEGA!             !SIGMA!
 w(1)=0.000000000000   s(1)=1.000000000000
```

Figure A-6 Block diagram of a universal phase-locked loop system used in the computer program for high-order phase-locked loops.

This is an ideal situation, and there is no question of stability, as there is only 90° phase shift. The very moment we add a simple filter to the first-order loop, it becomes a type 1 second-order loop, which refers to one integrator and a simple *RC* network. As long as the following requirements are fulfilled, there is no problem with stability.

1. The open-loop gain $A(s)$ as plotted must fall below 0 dB before the phase shift reaches 180°. A typical gain margin of $+10$ dB is desirable for $-180°$.
2. A phase shift of less than 180° must be provided at the gain crossover frequency for $A(s)$. This is called *phase margin*. A typical phase margin of 45° is desirable.

It is possible that a loop is conditionally stable and violates the Bode criteria. However, once it meets the Bode criteria, the loop is unconditionally stable. As the type 1 first-order loop phase stays at $-90°$, it will always remain stable. The type 1 second-order loop has only one element for phase shifting, as seen in Figure A-8, and the phase margin at $A(s) = 0$ is sufficient. The gain margin at $-180°$ phase is about 35 dB. Therefore, the type 1 second-order loop, as plotted, is unconditionally stable.

Next we look at a type 1 second-order loop that has phase compensation. In the block diagram of the loop, we made allowance to indicate the phase shift introduced by various components. Rather than use the simple *RC* network, we now use a lag filter corresponding to the two time constants τ_1 and τ_2. The cutoff frequency

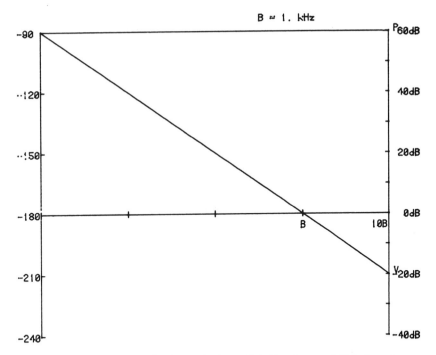

Figure A-7 Bode plot of a first-order loop; P is for phase and V is for gain.

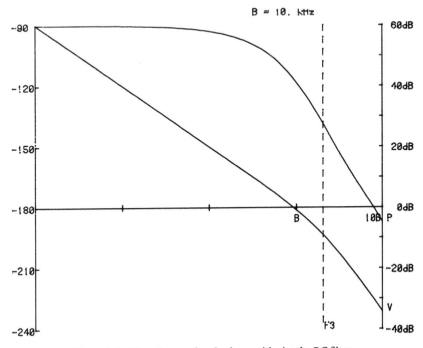

Figure A-8 Type 1 second-order loop with simple *RC* filter.

383

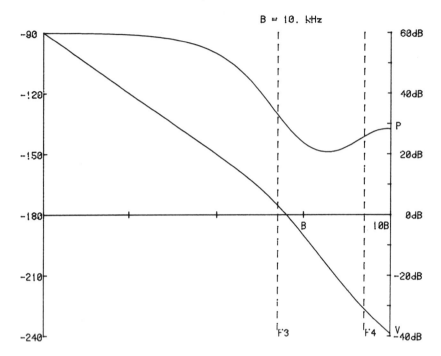

Figure A-9 Type 1 second-order loop taking the phase shift of an operational
amplifier into consideration.

determined by F_3 is set below the open-loop bandwidth of 10 kHz, and it is evident
that the phase is being compensated by the introduction of the time constant calculated
from F_4. This lag filter, therefore, increases the phase margin. At the point of 0-dB
gain, we have sufficient phase margin, and even at -40-dB gain, the phase is still at
about $-130°$. This is equal to a phase margin of about $50°$ (see Figure A-9).

Next we take into consideration the finite cutoff frequency of the operational
amplifier. Figure A-10 shows the Bode diagram in which the operational amplifier,
used as a dc amplifier (gain $K_2 = 1$), introduces considerable phase shift. The system
is still stable, and for $-180°$ phase, the gain is about -20 dB, resulting in a 20-dB
gain margin. At 0 dB, about $45°$ phase margin is available. The operational amplifier
is responsible for a $180°$ phase shift.

We will now look at the influence of more parameters and will plot a type 2
second-order loop. Figure A-11 shows a type 2 high-order loop with an open-loop
bandwidth of 200 kHz using the lag filter with the two cutoff frequencies F_3 and F_4
(note that F_4 is smaller than F_3). F_6 describes the cutoff frequency of the operational
amplifier used for the active filter.

The gain curve marked V starts off with 12 dB/octave due to two integrators and
then, because of the effect of the lag filter, decays with 6 dB/octave. The phase margin
at 0 dB gain is about $30°$, and the gain margin at $-180°$ of phase is about 7 or 8 dB.
This is a stable loop.

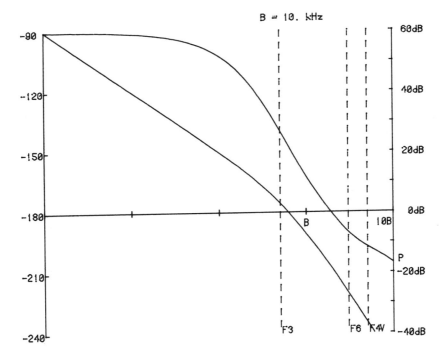

Figure A-10 Type 1 second-order loop with the time constants expressed in frequencies F_3 and F_4, as well as the additional phase shift caused by an operational amplifier.

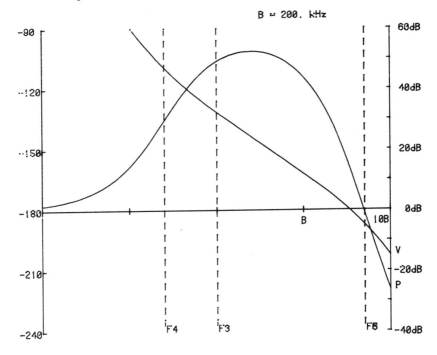

Figure A-11 Type 2 second-order loop showing the influence of the operational amplifier (F_6).

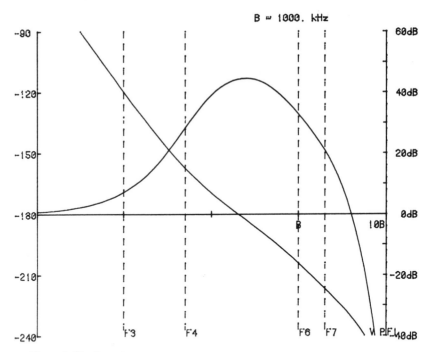

Figure A-12 Type 2 second-order loop in which the two cutoff frequencies F_3 and F_4, the phase shift and cutoff frequencies of the operational amplifier F_6, and an additional *RC* network (F_7) are incorporated.

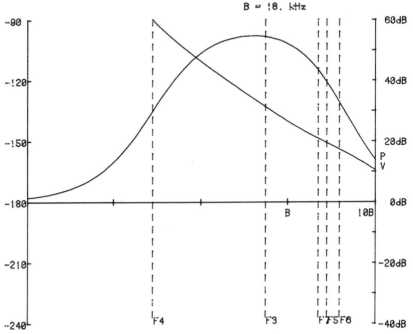

Figure A-13 Type 2 *N*th-order loop in which several elements are incorporated. This is an unstable loop.

Next we make allowance for the low-pass filter action of the *RC* network generated by bypass capacitors, cutoff frequency F_7. This loop, by choosing the right F_3
and F_4 values, is stable as the phase margin at 0 dB gain is 60° and the gain margin
at $-180°$ of phase is about 40 dB (see Figure A-12).

Finally, let us take a look at Figure A-13, which shows the open-loop performance of a type 2 *n*th-order loop that contains allowance for the phase shift of the
operational amplifier *RC* filtering and shows the effect of a first-order elliptic filter.
This loop is no longer stable, as the gain does not fall to 0 dB while the phase is still
less than $-180°$. It is very convenient to use a digital computer to generate these
plots because once all the parameters are known, the Bode diagram instantaneously
reveals whether a loop is stable and what parameters have to be changed to obtain
the necessary phase and gain margins.

A-1-4 Laplace Transformation

Introduction.   The Laplace transformation is a convenient mathematical way
to analyze and synthesize electronic circuitry with much less effort and far more
accuracy than the conventional method by solving differential equations. The Laplace
transformation is based on a method described by Pierre Simon de Laplace, a great
French mathematician who developed the foundation of potential theory and made
important contributions to celestial mechanics and probability theory. The word
"transformation" in this case means that functions in time are converted to functions
in frequency, and vice versa. Let us look at Figure A-14.

Figure A-14 shows a square wave generated by a suitable generator. We all
know that square waves contain harmonics up to very high orders and that the Fourier
analysis can be used to synthesize the square waveform. The Laplace transformation
allows the direct transformation of the square wave into the Fourier spectrum. This
method is used in engineering to analyze the performance of an electrical circuit where
an electrical short pulse, a single event, or a periodic event which is not merely a sine
or cosine function excites this circuit. Therefore, the Laplace transformation is used
as a final method of solving differential equations and will provide an algebraic method
of obtaining a *particular* solution of a differential equation from stated initial conditions. Since this is often what is desired in practice, the Laplace transformation is
preferred for the solution of differential equations for engineering in electronics.

Let us assume that $f(t)$ is a given function like the one shown in Figure A-15
and is defined for all $t \geq 0$. This function $f(t)$ is multiplied by e^{-st} and integrated with
respect to t from 0 to infinity. Provided that the resulting integral exists, we can write

$$F(s) = \int_0^\infty e^{-st} f(t)\, dt \tag{A-32}$$

The function $F(s)$ is called the *Laplace transform* of the original function $f(s)$ and will
be written

$$F(s) = \mathcal{L}(f) = \int_0^\infty e^{-st} f(t)\, dt \tag{A-33}$$

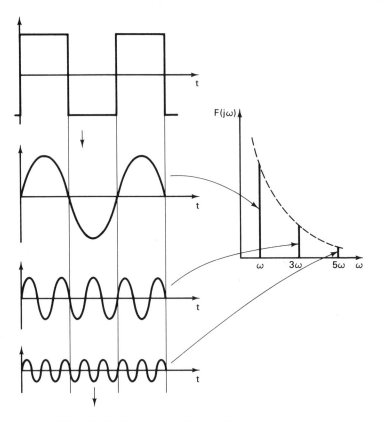

Figure A-14 Square wave showing its sine-wave contents.

Let us assume that we start with the Laplace transform and want to get the resulting time function. Mathematically this would be done with the inverse Laplace transformation and will be denoted by $\mathcal{L}^{-1}\{F(s)\}$. We shall write

$$f(t) = \mathcal{L}^{-1}[F(s)] \tag{A-34}$$

Rather than get scared, it may be nice to use it.

The step function. Let us assume that we have a step function

$$f(t) = 0 \qquad \text{for } t < 1$$

and

$$f(t) = 1 \qquad \text{for } t \geq 0$$

We want to determine $F(s)$.

We obtain by integration

$$\mathcal{L}(f) = \mathcal{L}(1) = \int_0^\infty e^{-st}\, dt = -\frac{1}{s} e^{-st}\Big|_0^\infty \tag{A-35}$$

Hence, when $s > 0$,

$$\mathcal{L}(1) = \frac{1}{s} \tag{A-36}$$

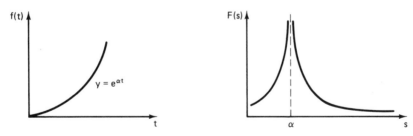

Figure A-15   Function $f(t)$ to be transformed into $F(s)$.

The ramp.   Accordingly, for a ramp

$$\mathcal{L}(f') = \int_0^\infty te^{-st}\,dt = \lim_{c\to\infty}\int_0^c te^{-st}\,dt$$

$$= \lim_{c\to\infty}\frac{e^{-st}(-st-1)}{s^2}\Big|_0^c = \frac{1}{s^2} \tag{A-37}$$

We will use the ramp function as well as the step function in analyzing the loop performance of initial disturbance. In using actual Laplace transformation, the linearity theorem is important.

Linearity theorem.   As the Laplace transformation is a linear operation, we can state that for any given functions $f(t)$ and $g(t)$ whose Laplace transform exists, and any constants a and b, we have

$$\mathcal{L}[af(t) + bg(t)] = a\mathcal{L}[f(t)] + b\mathcal{L}[g(t)] \tag{A-38}$$

In addition, we have to know about the derivatives and integrals.

Differentiation and integration.   The differentiation is made very simple by the fact that differentiation of a function $f(t)$ corresponds simply to multiplication of the transform $F(s)$ by s. This permits replacing operations of calculus by simple algebraic operations on transforms. Furthermore, since integration is the inverse operation of differentiation, we expect it to correspond to division of transforms by s. This means that

$$\mathcal{L}(f') = s\mathcal{L}(f) - f(0) \tag{A-39}$$

and

$$\mathcal{L}\left[\int_0^t f(\tau)\,d\tau\right] = \frac{1}{s}\mathcal{L}[f(t)] \tag{A-40}$$

Table A-2 shows some functions $f(t)$ and their Laplace transforms.

Initial value theorem.   If we apply a nonsinusoidal signal to an electrical circuit, we are interested in obtaining the value of $f(t)$ at the time $t = 0$, and this can be determined from the Laplace transform by

$$\lim_{t\to 0} f(t) = \lim_{s\to\infty} sF(s) \tag{A-41}$$

TABLE A-2 FUNCTIONS $f(t)$ AND THEIR LAPLACE TRANSFORMS $F(s)$

	$F(s)$	$f(t)$
1	$sF(s) - f(0)$	$\dfrac{df(t)}{dt}$
2	$\dfrac{F(s)}{s} + \dfrac{f^{(-1)}(0)}{s}$	$\displaystyle\int_0^t f(t)\,dt$
3	$F(s)c^{-s\tau}$	$f(t - \tau)$
4	$kF(s)$	$kf(t)$
5	$F_1(s)*F_2(s)$	$f_1(t)f_2(t)$
6	$F_1(s)F_2(s)$	$f_1(t)*f_2(t)$
7	0	0
8	$\dfrac{1}{s}$	$u(t)$
9	1	$\delta(t)$
10	$\dfrac{1}{s^2}$	t
11	$\dfrac{1}{s^3}$	$\dfrac{t^2}{2}$
12	$\dfrac{1}{s^n}\quad n>0$	$\dfrac{t^{n-1}}{(n-1)!}$
13	$\dfrac{1}{s - \alpha}$	$e^{\alpha t}$
14	$\dfrac{1}{s(s - \alpha)}$	$\dfrac{1}{\alpha}\dfrac{1}{(e^{\alpha t} - 1)}$
15	$\dfrac{1}{s(s + \alpha)}$	$\dfrac{1}{\alpha}(1 - e^{-\alpha t})$
16	$\dfrac{1}{(s - \alpha)^n}\quad n>0$	$\dfrac{t^n - 1}{(n - 1)!\,e^{\alpha t}}$
17	$\dfrac{1}{s^2 + \alpha^2}$	$\dfrac{1}{\alpha}\sin \alpha t$
18	$\dfrac{s}{s^2 + \alpha^2}$	$\cos \alpha t$
19	$\dfrac{1}{s(s^2 + \alpha^2)}$	$\dfrac{1}{\alpha^2}(1 - \cos \alpha t)$
20	$\dfrac{1}{s^2 - \alpha^2}$	$\dfrac{1}{\alpha}\sinh \alpha t$
21	$\dfrac{s}{s^2 - \alpha^2}$	$\cosh \alpha t$
22	$\dfrac{1}{s(s^2 - \alpha^2)}$	$\dfrac{1}{\alpha^2}(\cosh \alpha t - 1)$
23	$\dfrac{1}{(s - \alpha)(s - \beta)}$	$\dfrac{e^{\beta t} - e^{\alpha t}}{\beta - \alpha}$
24	$\dfrac{s}{(s - \alpha)(s - \beta)}$	$\dfrac{\beta e^{\beta t} - \alpha e^{\alpha t}}{\beta - \alpha}$
25	$\dfrac{1}{s(s - \alpha)(s - \beta)}$	$\dfrac{\beta e^{\alpha t} - \alpha e^{\beta t}}{\alpha\beta(\alpha - \beta)} + \dfrac{1}{\alpha\beta}$
26	$\dfrac{1}{s^2 + 2s\zeta\omega_n + \omega_n^2}$	$\dfrac{e^{-\zeta\omega_n t}\sin\sqrt{1 - \zeta^2}\,\omega_n}{\sqrt{1 - \zeta^2}\,\omega_n}$
27	$\dfrac{s}{s^2 + 2s\zeta\omega_n + \omega_n^2}$	$\left[\cos\sqrt{1 - \zeta^2}\,\omega_n t - \dfrac{\zeta}{\sqrt{1 - \zeta^2}}\sin\sqrt{1 - \zeta^2}\,\omega_n t\right]e^{-\zeta\omega_n t}$
28	$\dfrac{1}{s(s^2 + 2s\zeta\omega_n + \omega_n^2)}$	$\dfrac{1}{\omega_n^2}\left[1 - \left(\cos\sqrt{1 - \zeta^2}\,\omega_n t + \dfrac{\zeta}{\sqrt{1 - \zeta^2}}\sin\sqrt{1 - \zeta^2}\,\omega_n t\right)e^{-\zeta\omega_n t}\right]$

TABLE A-2 (cont'd)

	$F(s)$	$f(t)$
29	$\dfrac{1}{(s-\alpha)(s-\beta)^2}$	$\dfrac{e^{\alpha t}-[1+(\alpha-\beta)t]e^{\beta t}}{(\alpha-\beta)^2}$
30	$\dfrac{s}{(s-\alpha)(s-\beta)^2}$	$\dfrac{\alpha e^{\alpha t}-[\alpha+\beta(\alpha-\beta)t]e^{\beta t}}{(\alpha-\beta)^2}$
31	$\dfrac{s^2}{(s-\alpha)(s-\beta)^2}$	$\dfrac{\alpha^2 e^{\alpha t}-[2\alpha-\beta+\beta(\alpha-\beta)t]\beta e^{\beta t}}{(\alpha-\beta)^2}$
32	$\dfrac{1}{(s-\alpha)(s-\beta)(s-\gamma)}$	$\dfrac{(\beta-\gamma)e^{\alpha t}+(\gamma-\alpha)e^{\beta t}+(\alpha-\beta)e^{\gamma t}}{(\alpha-\beta)(\beta-\gamma)(\gamma-\alpha)}$
33	$\dfrac{1}{(s^2+\alpha^2)(s^2+\beta^2)}$	$\dfrac{\alpha\sin\beta t-\beta\sin\alpha t}{\alpha\beta(\alpha^2-\beta^2)}$
34	$\dfrac{s}{(s^2+\alpha^2)(s^2+\beta^2)}$	$\dfrac{\cos\beta t-\cos\alpha t}{\alpha^2-\beta^2}$
35	$\dfrac{1}{\sqrt{s}}$	$\dfrac{1}{\sqrt{\pi t}}$
36	$\dfrac{1}{s\sqrt{s}}$	$2\sqrt{\dfrac{t}{\pi}}$
37	$\dfrac{1}{s^n\sqrt{s}}$	$\dfrac{n!}{(2n)!}\dfrac{4^n}{\sqrt{\pi}}t^{n-1/2}$
38	$\dfrac{1}{\sqrt{s-\alpha}}$	$\dfrac{1}{\sqrt{\pi t}}e^{\alpha t}$
39	$\dfrac{1}{s\sqrt{s+\alpha}}$	$\dfrac{2}{\sqrt{\alpha\pi}}\displaystyle\int_0^{\sqrt{\alpha t}}e^{-\zeta^2}\,d\xi$
40	$\dfrac{1}{(s+\alpha)\sqrt{s+\beta}}$	$\dfrac{2e^{-\alpha t}}{\sqrt{\pi(\beta-\alpha)}}\displaystyle\int_0^{\sqrt{(\beta-\alpha)t}}e^{-\varsigma^2}\,d\xi$
41	$\dfrac{\sqrt{s+\alpha}}{s}$	$\dfrac{e^{-\alpha t}}{\sqrt{\pi t}}+2\sqrt{\dfrac{\alpha}{\pi}}\displaystyle\int_0^{\sqrt{\alpha t}}e^{-\varsigma^2}\,d\xi$
42	$\dfrac{1}{\sqrt{s^2+\alpha^2}}$	$I_0(\alpha t)$
43	$\dfrac{1}{\sqrt{s^2-\alpha^2}}$	$J_0(\alpha t)$

After the initial start condition, we are interested in determining the final value.

Final value theorem. The final value can be determined accordingly,

$$\lim_{t\to\infty} f(t) = \lim_{s\to 0} sF(s) \qquad \text{(provided that such a limit exists)}$$

Let us use now our knowledge and the integration table for one particular case, the active integrator.

The active integrator. Figure A-16 shows the circuit of an active RC integrator being driven with a step; because of the integration, the output voltage has to be a ramp. Let us prove this. The differential equation can be written

$$v_2(t) = -\frac{1}{C}\int_0^t i\,dt = \frac{-1}{RC}\int_0^t v_1\,dt \qquad \text{(A-42)}$$

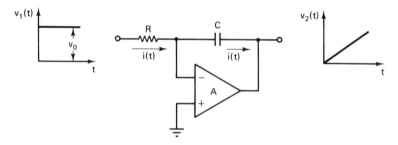

Figure A-16 Active RC integrator being driven with a step function.

Using $\tau = RC$, we obtain in Laplace notation

$$V_2(s) = \frac{-1}{s\tau} V_1(s) \tag{A-43}$$

We assume that the capacitor at $t = 0$ has no charge. The step function $v_1(t)$ rises to the value v_o and

$$V_1(s) = \frac{v_0}{s} \tag{A-44}$$

Therefore,

$$V_2(s) = \frac{-v_0}{\tau} \frac{1}{s^2} \tag{A-45}$$

According to Table A-2,

$$v_2(t) = \mathcal{L}^{-1}[V_2(s)] = -v_0 \frac{t}{\tau} \tag{A-46}$$

This is the equation of a linear ramp.

Let us now become more challenging and determine the locking behavior of a phase-locked loop, using a lag filter as shown in Figure A-17.

Locking behavior of the PLL. The transfer function of the lag filter

$$F(s) = \frac{1 + s\tau_2}{s\tau_1} \tag{A-47}$$

and the phase detector voltage

$$v_\phi(t) = K_\theta \theta \tag{A-48}$$

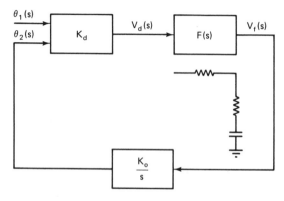

Figure A-17 PLL with lag filter.

and in Laplace notation

$$V_\phi(s) = K_\theta \theta(s). \tag{A-49}$$

The output frequency of the VCO

$$\omega_o = K_o v(t) \tag{A-50}$$

$$\theta_o = K_o \int_0^t v(t)\, dt \tag{A-51}$$

and in Laplace notation

$$\theta(s) = K_o \frac{V(s)}{s} \tag{A-52}$$

There are three building blocks for which we define the following functions:

1. Phase comparator

$$\frac{V_\phi(s)}{\theta_e(s)} = K_o \tag{A-53}$$

2. Low-pass filter

$$\frac{V(s)}{\theta(s)} = F(s) = \frac{1 + s\tau_2}{s\tau_1} \tag{A-54}$$

3. VCO

$$\theta_2(s) = \theta_1(s) - \theta_e(s) = K_o \frac{V(s)}{s} \tag{A-55}$$

This can be rearranged

$$\theta_2(s) = \theta_1(s) \frac{s^2}{s^2 + sK_oK_\theta(\tau_2/\tau_1) + (K_oK_\theta/\tau_1)} \tag{A-56}$$

Using the similar abbreviation

$$\omega_n = \left(\frac{K_oK_\theta}{\tau_1}\right)^{1/2} \tag{A-57}$$

$$\zeta = \frac{\tau_2}{2}\left(\frac{K_oK_\theta}{\tau_1}\right)^{1/2} \tag{A-58}$$

we can rearrange the equation above in the form

$$\theta_e(s) = \theta_1(s) \frac{s^2}{s^2 + 2s\zeta\omega_n + \omega_n^2} \tag{A-59}$$

Applying a step to the input,

$$\theta_1(s) = \frac{\Delta\phi}{s} \tag{A-60}$$

we obtain

$$\theta_e(s) = \frac{s\Delta\phi}{s^2 + 2s\zeta\omega_n + \omega_n^2} \tag{A-61}$$

We apply the initial value theorem,

$$\lim_{t\to 0}\theta_e(t) = \lim_{s\to\infty} s\theta_e(s) = \frac{s^2\,\Delta\phi}{s^2 + 2s\zeta\omega_n + \omega_n^2} = \Delta\phi \tag{A-62}$$

This means that the initial phase error is equal to the step in phase $\Delta\phi$.

Using the final value theorem,

$$\lim_{t \to \infty} \theta_e(t) = \lim_{s \to 0} s\theta_e(s) = \frac{s^2 \, \Delta\phi}{s^2 + 2s\zeta\omega_n + \omega_n^2} = 0 \qquad (A-63)$$

This means that, if we wait long enough, the phase error will be zero. The final remaining task is to look up the equation above in our table of Laplace transform functions, and we find the required transform in No. 27.

$$f(t) = \theta_e(t)$$

$$= \Delta\phi \left[\cos \sqrt{1 - \zeta^2} \, \omega_n t - \frac{\zeta}{\sqrt{1 - \zeta^2}} \sin \sqrt{1 - \zeta^2} \, \omega_n t \right] e^{-\zeta\omega_n t} \qquad (A-64)$$

A-1-5 Low-Noise Oscillator Design

The design of low-noise oscillators is based on various principles.

1. We have learned that one way of reducing the noise is to keep as much energy storage in the capacitor as possible. We can assign for any tuned circuit an equivalent transmission impedance $C_o = \sqrt{L/C}$. This would indicate that the larger the C, the lower the transmission impedance. In addition, such a circuit is less sensitive to circuit board capacitance and should provide better performance.

2. We have learned that the noise outside the loop bandwidth of an oscillator is determined by the Q of the LC network—the highest possible Q that can be obtained in an LC circuit when the losses are minimized. High-Q tuned circuits can be built with transmission lines, and quarter-wavelength transmission lines are specifically used for this purpose. The easiest way of accomplishing this is to take a mechanical cavity that is adjusted to odd numbers of quarter-wavelengths, whereby any material inside the cavity has to be taken into consideration. The wavelengths of a quarter-wave transmission line can be determined from $\lambda_0 = 300/f_0$. If the frequency is inserted in megahertz, the resulting wavelength is in meters. In the event that a dielectric material is used, as in the case of coaxial cable as a cavity oscillator, the wavelengths electrically and mechanically differ:

$$\lambda = \frac{\lambda_o}{\sqrt{\epsilon_r}} \qquad (A-65)$$

For Teflon, $\epsilon_r = 2$.

This principle is used in the Hewlett-Packard HP8940 signal generator, where a cavity is mechanically tuned. This cavity has a high Q of about 600 to 800, and therefore the noise sideband is very low.

Let us design such an oscillator.

Example

A quarter-wavelength oscillator using a rigid coaxial line will be built covering the frequency range from 250 to 450 MHz. We have to use the equation

$$\frac{dz}{\lambda} = \frac{1}{2\pi} \arctan \omega CZ \tag{A-66}$$

where dz is the amount by which the cavity is reduced in size relative to quarter-wavelength. The highest frequency of our oscillator is 450 MHz, and therefore $\lambda_o = 66.6$ cm. Quarter-wavelength $\lambda_o/4 = 16.66$ cm. For reasons of available mechanical space, we have decided to make the transmission line quarter-wavelength cable 5 cm long. Therefore,

$$L = \frac{\lambda_o}{4} - dz = 16.66 - 5 = 11.66$$

We now rearrange the equation above and solve it for C.

$$C = \frac{1}{\omega Z} \tan \frac{2\pi dz}{\lambda_0} \tag{A-67}$$

or

$$C_1 = \frac{1}{2\pi \times 450 \times 10^6 \times 50} \tan \frac{2\pi \times 11.66}{66.6}$$

$$C_1 = 7.736 \times 10^{-12} \times \tan 1.1 \text{ (rad)}$$

$$C_1 = 7.736 \times 10^{-12} \times 1.9649$$

$$C_1 = 13.899 \times 10^{-12} = 13.899 \text{ pF}$$

Electrically, the transmission line, which is now operating as a quarter-wavelength resonator, is an inductance that requires an external capacitor of about 14 pF to be in resonance for 450 MHz. For 250 MHz we will get a new value for the capacitance. First, we determine λ. $\lambda_o = 1.2$ m and $\lambda_o/4 = 30$ cm. Because the mechanical length of our quarter-wavelength is 5 cm,

$$L = \frac{\lambda_o}{4} - dz = 30 - 5 = 25 \text{ cm}$$

We now compute

$$C_2 = \frac{1}{2\pi \times 250 \times 10^6 \times 50} \tan \frac{2\pi \times 25}{120}$$

$$C_1 = 12.732 \times 10^{-12} \tan 1.309$$

$$= 12.732 \times 10^{-12} \times 3.7321 = 47.516 \text{ pF}$$

These are the two values required for the oscillator to cover the frequency range. If one compares these two capacitance values with values obtained with conventional high-Q inductors, it is apparent that those values are substantially larger. This is due to the fact that we have chosen a 50-Ω transmission line. The use of a low-impedance transmission line has several advantages.

1. It can be shown mathematically that the optimum Q of a coaxial transmission line occurs at about 70 Ω. All higher impedances exhibit more losses and lower Q.

2. If a rigid line or its equivalent mechanical arrangement is used, the low-impedance version will have fewer microphonic effects due to mechanical vibration than a high-impedance transmission line and is, therefore, electrically much more stable.

Figure A-18 shows an analysis of this done on a digital computer. We find that, as the impedance increases, the external shunt capacitance goes down in value. In this figure, the computer has plotted the curves from 50 to 300 Ω, and the necessary capacitance can be read from this drawing as a function of frequency and characteristic impedance. For a 300-Ω transmission line and 500 MHz, an external capacitance of about 2.5 pF is required. Most likely, circuit board and other stray capacitances will be in that magnitude. For a 100-Ω oscillator, about 7 pF is required. It is evident that the oscillator we have just calculated, which requires about 14 pF, is a better choice. Another interesting relationship is the required capacitance as a function of increase of resonator length. Figure A-19 shows a diagram in which the capacitance is plotted as a function of frequency and resonator length with a 50-Ω transmission line. If we use a 10-cm resonator, we need about 3.5 pF at 500 MHz and about 25 pF at 250 MHz. Again, this gives some interesting insight in the mechanism. Conventional *LC* circuits theoretically could be built using such low inductances. However, the stray field of this unconfined resonator would result in losses, consequently lowering the magnetic *Q* of the circuit. A similar principle is used in helical resonators, and the Rohde & Schwarz SMDU signal generator uses this principle. There is really no difference

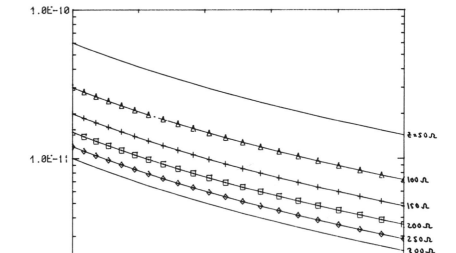

Figure A-18 Capacitance required to tune a quarter-wavelength resonator oscillator from 250 to 500 MHz as a function of the impedance of the quarter-wavelength.

between the two approaches. In the case of Hewlett-Packard, the quarter-wave transmission line is mechanically adjusted in its length. As a result of this, a mechanically more elaborate system is required, whereas in the Rohde & Schwarz SMDU signal generator the helical resonator is loaded with a very large, low microphonic air-variable capacitor of large diameter. Both arrangements are electrically excellent. The air-variable capacitor has the advantage that there is no mechanical abrasion, and therefore the lifetime will be longer. The cavity, on the other hand, provides a somewhat more linear frequency versus tuning curve.

Figure A-20 shows the schematic of such an oscillator. It becomes apparent that a switching technique is used to coarse steer the oscillator within certain ranges. Since we have learned that the tuning diodes will introduce more noise than fixed capacitors switched in by diodes which are not sensitive to noise pickup and other radiation effects, this technique is used. Let us take a look at the possible resolution. The minimum additional capacitor that can be added is 1 pF. At 450 MHz, 1 pF will result in the following detuning:

$$\frac{f_1}{f_2} = \sqrt{\frac{13.951}{14.951}} = \frac{450}{434.69}$$

QUARTER WAVE LENGTH RESONATOR OSCILLATOR
Cp=f(F)

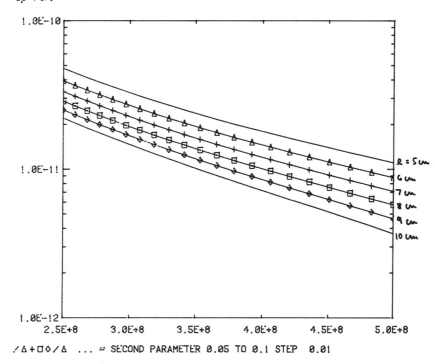

∠△+□◇∠△ ... = SECOND PARAMETER 0.05 TO 0.1 STEP 0.01

Figure A-19   Rigid cable used as a quarter-wave resonator at various lengths showing the external capacitance value required to tune it from 250 to 500 MHz as a function of length.

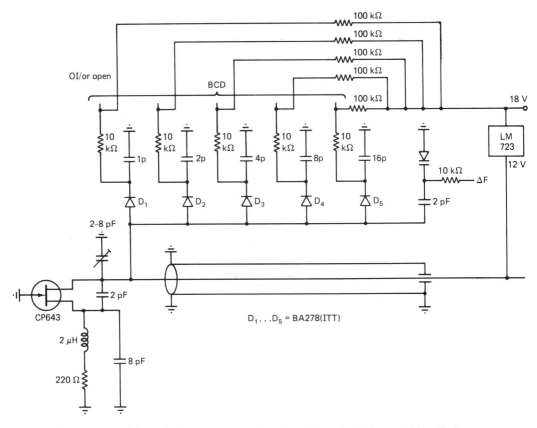

Figure A-20 Schematic of a quarter-wavelength oscillator, including switching diodes.

or a change of 15.3 MHz. At the low end of 225 MHz, this will result in

$$\frac{f_1}{f_2} = \sqrt{\frac{47.517}{48.517}} = \frac{250}{247.47}$$

or we obtain a frequency shift of 2.6 MHz.

Our highest resolution at the top, therefore, is about 15 MHz, with 2.6 MHz at the low frequency end. Therefore, we have to use a decoding circuit that selects the proper capacitor for the same step at the lower frequency range. In order to get 15.3 MHz, we calculate

$$\sqrt{\frac{265}{250}} = 1.0296$$

or

$$\frac{C_1^*}{C_1} = 1.06$$

Our starting value at the low end is 47.517 pF, which has to be reduced to 44.827 for a 15-MHz shift. The difference is about 2.7 pF. Therefore, following the first 1-pF capacitor, we must be able to switch in 2 pF, resulting in a total of 3 pF, which is the close approximation to the required 2.7 pF for the required 15-MHz step. We now follow this binary system, and therefore our next capacitances are 4, 8, 16 pF.

Our binary switch requires 5-bit data command. If we add all the capacitors together, we obtain a total capacitance of 31 pF. As the initial starting capacitance at 500 MHz was set to be about 14 pF, which is found by the feedback network as well as the stray capacitance and a coarse-tuning capacitor, the additional 30 pF, if all five capacitors are switched in, will result in 43 pF. We have to take into consideration the fact that these capacitors have some tolerances and therefore, by selecting the proper values with slightly larger amounts, we can easily make the total 33 pF to obtain the 47.5 pF required. This oscillator exhibits superior performance relative to the normal LC oscillator.

Some authors have found it useful to build a $\lambda/2$ oscillator which then has twice the mechanical length we have currently used, and this may be helpful at higher frequencies. In addition, because of the transmission properties of a half-wavelength cable, a capacitor used at the output of the cable is transformed into an inductor. The drawback of this method, however, is that the resonant impedance for constant Q at the transistor varies as a function of frequency, whereby for higher frequencies where the gain is lower, the impedance gets lower. This is opposite of the quarter-wavelength system, and in my opinion, less desirable.

The tuning diode in the quarter-wave oscillator is responsible for the fine tuning and will cover about 20 MHz of range. At 250 MHz, this is less than 10%, and as we have seen previously, the noise influence under these circumstances is extremely small.

As this oscillator is highly useful, in the next section we will analyze the feedback circuit to determine the amplitude stabilization and harmonic contents with the aid of some nonlinear analysis. Figure A-21 shows a picture of the Rohde & Schwarz SMDU oscillator.

Figure A-21   Photograph of the Rohde & Schwarz SMDU oscillator. (Courtesy of Rohde & Schwarz.)

A-1-6 Oscillator Amplitude Stabilization

In Chapter 4 we mentioned briefly that the oscillator amplitude stabilizes due to some nonlinear performance of the transistor. There are various mechanisms involved, and depending on the circuit, several of them are simultaneously responsible for the performance of an oscillator. Under most circumstances, the transistor is operated in an area where the dc bias voltages are substantially larger than the ac voltages. Therefore, the theory describing the transistor performance under these conditions is called *small-signal theory*. In a transistor oscillator, however, we are dealing with a feedback circuit that applies positive feedback. The energy that is being generated by the initial switch-on of the circuit is being fed back to the input of the circuit, amplified, and returned to the input again until oscillation starts. The oscillation would theoretically increase in value indefinitely unless some limiting or stabilization occurs. In transistor circuits, we have two basic phenomena responsible for limiting the amplitude of oscillation.

1. Limiting because of gain saturation and reduction of open-loop gain.
2. Automatic bias generated by the rectifying mechanism of either the diode in the bipolar transistor or in the junction field-effect transistor. In MOSFETs an external diode is sometimes used for this biasing.
3. A third one would be external AGC, but it will not be considered here.

The oscillators we discuss here are self-limiting oscillators.

The self-limiting process, which by generating a dc offset bias moves the operating point into a region of less gain, is generally noisy. For very low noise oscillators, this operation is not recommended. After dealing with the quarter-wavelength oscillator in the preceding section, we will deal here only with the negative resistance oscillator, in which, through a mechanism explained in Chapter 4, a negative resistance is generated due to feedback and is used to start oscillation with the passive device. Here we look at what is happening inside the transistor that is responsible for amplitude stabilization, and we will thus be in a position to make a prediction regarding the available energy and the harmonic contents.

Figure A-22 shows the quarter-wavelength oscillator redrawn in such a way that the source electrode is now at ground potential while the gate and drain electrode are electrically hot. The reason for doing this is because we will look at the gate-to-source transfer characteristic and use its nonlinearities as a tool to describe what is happening. The same analysis can be applied to a transistor circuit, provided that the resistors used for dc bias are small enough not to cause any dc offset. The field-effect transistor characteristic follows a square law and, therefore, can be expressed as

$$i_2 = I_{DSS}\left(1 - \frac{v_1}{V_p}\right)^2 \tag{A-68}$$

For any other device, we have to take the necessary transfer characteristic into consideration, and this could theoretically be done by changing the square law into nth order. The voltage v_1 will be in the form

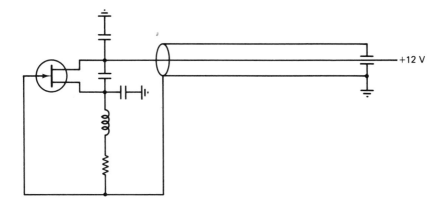

Figure A-22   Quarter-wavelength oscillator with grounded source electrode.

$$v_1 = V_b + V_1 \cos \omega t \tag{A-69}$$

This is the voltage that is being generated due to the selectivity of the tuned circuit at which there is a resonant frequency. Inserting this into the above equation and using

$$V_x = V_p - V_b \tag{A-70}$$

we obtain

$$i_2 = \frac{I_{DSS}}{V_p^2}(V_x^2 - 2V_xV_1 \cos \omega t + V_1^2 \cos^2 \omega t) \tag{A-71}$$

Once we know the peak value of i_2, we can expand this into a Fourier series. In this case a Fourier series expansion for i_2 has only three terms; that is,

$$i_2(t) = I_o + I_1 \cos \omega t + I_2 \cos 2\omega t \tag{A-72}$$

$$I_o = \frac{I_{DSS}}{V_p^2}V_x^2 + \frac{V_1^2}{2} \tag{A-73}$$

$$I_1 = -2\frac{I_{DSS}}{V_p^2}V_xV_1 \tag{A-74}$$

$$I_2 = \frac{I_{DSS}}{V_p^2}\frac{V_1^2}{2} \tag{A-75}$$

Because of the square-law characteristic, I_1 is a linear function of V_1 and we can define a large-signal average transconductance G_m,

$$G_m = \frac{I_1}{V_1} = -2\frac{I_{DSS}}{V_p^2}V_x \tag{A-76}$$

In the case of the square-law characteristic, we find the interesting property that the small-signal transconductance g_m at any particular point is equal to the large-signal average transconductance G_m at the same point. The second harmonic distortion in the output current is given by

$$\frac{I_2}{I_1} = \frac{V_1}{4V_x} = \frac{V_1}{4V_p}\frac{g_{mo}}{g_m} \tag{A-77}$$

The transconductance G_m can be defined in such a way that it indicates the gain for a particular frequency relative to the fundamental, which means that there is a certain G_m for the fundamental frequency and one for the second harmonic, and in the general case, a G_{mn} for the nth-order harmonic. In the more general form, we rewrite our equation

$$i_d = C_n(-V_b + V_1 \cos x)^n \tag{A-78}$$

As this current will exist only during the period from $-\alpha$ to $+\alpha$, the equation

$$-\alpha < x < +\alpha$$

exists only for

$$i_2 = 0$$

$$x = \pm\alpha$$

$$\cos \alpha = \frac{V_b}{V_1}$$

We can rewrite our equation for the drain current or collector current of a transistor:

$$i_d = C_n V_1^n (\cos x - \cos \omega)^n \tag{A-79}$$

The dc value of the current

$$I_d = \frac{1}{\pi} \int_0^\alpha i_d \, dx \tag{A-80}$$

or

$$I_d = \frac{C_n V_1}{\pi} \int_0^\alpha (\cos x - \cos \alpha)^n \, dx \tag{A-81}$$

The amplitude of the fundamental frequency

$$I_1 = \frac{2}{\pi} \int_0^\alpha i_d \cos x \, dx \tag{A-82}$$

or

$$I_1 = \frac{2C_n V_1^n}{\pi} \int_0^\alpha (\cos x - \cos \alpha)^n \cos x \, dx \tag{A-83}$$

For $n = 1$, the collector current

$$I_d = C_1 V_1 A_1 \tag{A-84}$$

and the amplitude of the fundamental frequency

$$I_1 = C_1 V_1 B_1 \tag{A-85}$$

For $n = 2$, the collector current is therefore

$$I_d = C_2 V_1^2 A_2 \tag{A-86}$$

and the amplitude of the fundamental frequency

$$I_1 = C_2 V_1^2 B_2 \tag{A-87}$$

With the definition of the conduction angle,

$$\alpha = \text{arc} \frac{V_b}{V_1} \tag{A-88}$$

These values are listed in Table A-3.

TABLE A-3 NORMALIZED FOURIER COEFFICIENTS

$\dfrac{V_b}{V_1}$	A_1	B_1	$\dfrac{B_1}{A_1}$	A_2	B_2	$\dfrac{B_2}{A_2}$
0	0.318	0.500	1.57	0.250	0.425	1.7
0.1	0.269	0.436	1.62	0.191	0.331	1.73
0.2	0.225	0.373	1.66	0.141	0.251	1.78
0.3	0.185	0.312	1.69	0.101	0.181	1.79
0.4	0.144	0.251	1.74	0.0674	0.126	1.87
0.5	0.109	0.195	1.79	0.0422	0.0802	1.90
0.6	0.077	0.141	1.83	0.0244	0.0458	~1.95
0.7	0.050	0.093	1.86	0.0118	0.0236	~2
0.8	0.027	0.052	1.92	0.0043	0.0082	~2
0.9	0.010	0.020	2	0.00074	0.00148	2
1.0	0	0	2	0	0	2

These are the normalized Fourier coefficients as a function of n and the conduction angle. Theoretically, this has to be expanded to the order n of 3 or 4, depending on the particular device, and can be found from tables or by a digital computer.

For simplifications, let us go back to the case of our square-law device, where our transconductance

$$G_m = \frac{I_1}{V_1} = -2\frac{I_{DSS}}{V_p^2}V_x \tag{A-89}$$

This can be rewritten in the form

$$G_m = -\frac{2I_{DSS}}{V_p^2}(V_p - V_b + V_1 \cos \omega t) \tag{A-90}$$

V_p is the pinch-off voltage of the field-effect transistor, V_b is the bias voltage that is measured between source and ground, and V_1 is the peak value of the voltage of the fundamental frequency. Figure A-23 shows the effect where the sine wave is driving the transfer characteristic, and the resulting output currents are narrow pulses. Based on the duration, the mutual conductance g_m becomes a fraction of the dc transconductance G_m, and therefore the gain is reduced. For small conduction angles I_n/I_d, the mutual conductance can take very small values, and therefore the gain gets very small; this is the cause for stabilizing the amplitude in the oscillator. We note that the gain is being reduced as the amplitude causing the small conduction angle is increased.

Fourier analysis indicates that, for a small harmonic distortion, the RF voltage at the source or gate (depending on where it is grounded) has to be less than 80 mV. Now we can design the oscillator performance.

Let us assume that the saturation voltage of the active device is 2 V, battery voltage applied to the transistor is 12 V, and the transistor starts at a dc current of 10 mA with a source resistor of 200 Ω. This results in a voltage drop of 1 V at the

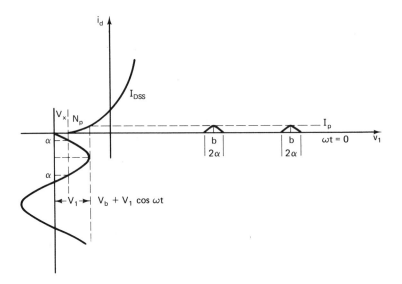

Figure A-23 Current tips as a function of narrow conduction angles in a square-wave transfer characteristic.

source and 2 V in the device; therefore, 9 V is available. It can be assumed that the maximum voltage at the drain will be $9 \times \sqrt{2}$. The capacitor voltage divider from drain to voltage now depends on the gain. If we assume an I_n/I_d of 0.15 for about 50° conduction angle, 2α, and the dc conductance of the transistor at the starting dc operating point is 20 mA/V, the resulting transconductance is 3 mA/V.

Next we need the output impedance the quarter-wave resonator provides,

$$R_L = Q\frac{1}{\omega C}(250 \text{ MHz})$$

or

$$R_L = 600\frac{1}{2\pi \times 47 \times 10^{-12} \times 250 \times 10^6} = 8127 \ \Omega$$

As we want 9 V rms at the output, we have to use the equation

$$\frac{V_{\text{out}}}{V_{\text{in}}} = A(\text{voltage gain}) = g_m R_L = 3 \times 10^{-3} \times 8.127 \times 10^3$$

$$A = 24.38$$

or

$$V_{\text{in}} = \frac{8V}{A} = 328 \text{ mV}$$

This would mean that the capacitance ratio of the feedback capacitors C_1 and C_2 would be $1:24.38$. In practice we will find that this is incorrect, and we need a $1:4$ or $1:5$ ratio. The reason for this is that the equations we have used so far are not accurate enough to represent the actual dc shifts and harmonic occurrences. As mentioned in Sections 4-1 and A-1-5 a certain amount of experimentation is required to obtain the proper value. To determine the actual ratio, it is recommended that one obtain from the transistor manufacturer the device with the lowest gain and build an oscillator testing it over the necessary temperature range. As the gain of the transistor changes as a function of temperature (gain increases as temperature decreases for field-effect transistors and acts in reverse for bipolar transistors), a voltage divider has to be chosen that is, on the one hand, high enough to prevent the device from going into saturation which will cause noise, and on the other hand, small enough to allow oscillation under worst-case conditions. Suitable values were determined for the CP643 transistor and shown in the circuit for the field-effect quarter-wavelength transistor.

A-2 COMPUTER PROGRAMS

A-2-1 Calculations of High-Order Phase-Locked Loops for Frequency Synthesis

The advantages of a third-order type 2 loop for frequency generation were described in Chapter 1. In the literature the third-order loop is usually restricted to circuit constants which permit the use of well-established second-order calculations. A better approach is the exact calculation of an ideal third-order loop.* Even this approach can lead to problems when the ideal loop is reduced to hardware. The solution of a third-order loop using available components, presented herein, takes into account the finite dc gain of the integrator, the main low-frequency pole of the integrator operational amplifier, and the finite high modulation frequency limit of the VTO. Thus if no additional poles are introduced below the VTO modulation input pole, the calculated performance reflects the actual data very accurately. The stray poles can usually be moved outside the range of interest by careful physical layout of the circuit, using good RF techniques. On the other hand, if a fixed known pole exists below the VTO pole frequency, it can be used in the calculations in its place.

The open-loop response (see Figure A-24)

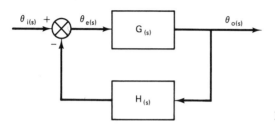

Figure A-24   Feedback system.

---

*This program was developed by Andrzej B. Przedpelski of A.R.F. Products, Inc., Boulder, Colorado, and is reprinted with his permission. His notations differ slightly from the ones used elsewhere in this book.

$$A_{(s)} = G_{(s)}H_{(s)} \qquad \text{(A-91)}$$

determines the loop performance. The loop stability can be determined directly from the Bode diagram phase margin, since the damping factor concept, as commonly used in the second-order loop, is not applicable for the higher-order loops.

The loop reduction of the VTO noise (see Figure A-25) can be expressed as

$$F_{(s)} = \frac{\theta_{e(s)}}{\theta_{i(s)}} = \frac{1}{1 + G_{(s)}H_{(s)}} \qquad \text{(A-92)}$$

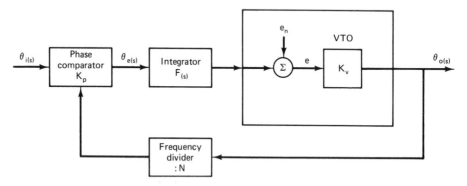

Figure A-25 Noise reduction in third-order type 2 PLL.

and the closed-loop characteristics can also be calculated:

$$B_{(s)} = \frac{\theta_{o(s)}}{\theta_{i(s)}} = \frac{G_{(s)}}{1 + G_{(s)}H_{(s)}} \qquad \text{(A-93)}$$

Using the typical loop of Figure A-25, the feedforward function is

$$G_{(s)} = \frac{K_p F_{(s)} K_v}{s} \qquad \text{(A-94)}$$

and the feedback transfer function is

$$H_{(s)} = \frac{1}{N} \qquad \text{(A-95)}$$

Thus the open-loop response becomes

$$G_{(s)}H_{(s)} = \frac{K_p F_{(s)} K_v}{sN} \qquad \text{(A-96)}$$

The integrator transfer function $F_{(s)}$ determines the basic order of the PLL. For the third-order loop $F_{(s)}$ is

$$F_{(s)} = -\frac{sT_2 + 1}{sT_1(sT_3 + 1)} \qquad \text{(A-97)}$$

with time constants T_1, T_2, and T_3 defined in Figure A-26. However, the operational amplifier has neither infinite gain nor infinite bandwidth. Thus the actual transfer function becomes

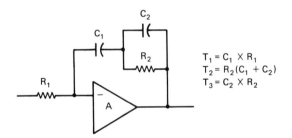

$T_1 = C_1 \times R_1$
$T_2 = R_2(C_1 + C_2)$
$T_3 = C_2 \times R_2$

Figure A-26 Third-order loop integrator.

$$F_{(s)} = \frac{sA_0 + A_0}{s^3(T_oT_1T_3) + s^2(A_oT_1T_3 + T_1T_3 + T_oT_1 + T_oT_2) + s(A_oT_1 + T_1 + T_2 + T_o) + 1}$$

$$(A-98)$$

with A_0 being the dc operational amplifier gain and T_0 the time constant of its first predominant pole, as shown in Figure A-27.

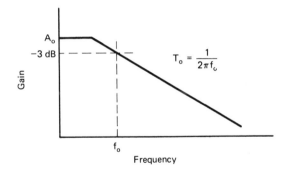

Figure A-27 Typical operational amplifier response.

The ideal VTO transfer function, K_v/s, also has to be modified to include the effect of the modulation frequency response, shown in Figure A-28. The complete VTO transfer function becomes

$$\frac{K_v}{s} = \frac{K_o}{s(1 + sT_v)} \qquad (A-99)$$

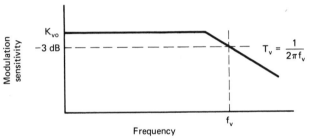

Figure A-28 Cutoff frequency of a VTO to modulation.

where K_o is the dc VTO sensitivity. Using the modified transfer functions of the integrator (A-97) and the VTO (A-99) in Eq. (A-100), we obtain

$$G_{(s)}H_{(s)} = \frac{sBC + B}{s^5D + s^4E + s^3F + s^2L + s}$$ (A-100)

where $\quad B = \dfrac{A_oK_pK_o}{N}$

$C = T_2$

$D = T_oT_vT_1T_3$

$E = T_v\{T_o(T_1 + T_2) + T_1T_3(A_o + 1)\} + T_oT_1T_3$

$F = T_v(A_oT_1 + T_o + T_1 + T_2) + T_o(T_1 + T_2) + T_1T_3(A_o + 1)$

$L = A_oT_1 + T_o + T_v + T_1 + T_2$

showing that the basic third-order loop is actually a fifth-order loop when the limited gain and frequency response of the integrator operational amplifier and the VTO modulation pole are considered. For the final solution, Eq. (A-100) can be rewritten

$$G_{(s)}H_{(s)} = \frac{sBC + B}{s(s^4D + s^2F + 1) + (s^4E + s^2L)}$$ (A-101)

In addition, if

$$A \gg 1$$

and

$$T_o, T_v, T_1, T_2, T_3 < 1$$

some of the coefficients can be simplified:

$$E = A_oT_vT_1T_3$$

$$F = A_oT_1(T_3 + T_v)$$

$$L = A_oT_1$$

Eq. (A-101) becoming, then, in terms of frequency,

$$G_{(j\omega)}H_{(j\omega)} = \frac{j\omega(K_oK_p/N)T_2 + (K_oK_p/N)}{j\omega\left[\omega^2T_1\left(\omega^2\dfrac{T_o}{A_o}T_vT_3 - T_3 - T_v\right) + \dfrac{1}{A_o}\right] + \omega^2(\omega^2T_1T_vT_3 - T_1)}$$ (A-102)

which can be further rearranged for a calculator program:

$$A_{(j\omega)} = G_{(j\omega)}H_{(j\omega)}$$

$$= \frac{K_oK_p}{N\omega T_1}\frac{j\omega T_2 + 1}{j\left[\omega^2\left(\omega^2\dfrac{T_o}{A_o}T_vT_3 - T_3 - T_v\right) + \dfrac{1}{A_oT_1}\right] + \omega(\omega^2T_vT_3 - 1)}$$ (A-103)

A calculator program to solve the absolute value of $G_{(s)}H_{(s)}$ and its phase margin is shown in Table A-4. To obtain the actual phase angle of $G_{(s)}H_{(s)}$, 180° should be

TABLE A-4 INSTRUCTION SET AND LISTING OF PROGRAM FOR HP19C/29C FOR TYPE 2 THIRD-ORDER LOOP

Step	Instruction	Input data units	Keys	Output data units
1	Enter program			
2	Store	T_0	STO 0	
		T_1	STO 1	
		T_2	STO 2	
		T_3	STO 3	
		T_v	STO 4	
		K_p	STO 5	
		K_0	STO 6	
		N	STO 7	
		A_0	STO 8	
3	Key in f, start program	f_1(Hz)	GSB 0	Phase margin (degrees) Open-loop gain (dB) Noise $A\pi$ (dB)
4	Repeat step 3 for other frequencies	f_n(Hz)	GSB 0	Phase margin (degrees) Open-loop gain (dB) Noise $A\pi$ (dB)

Step	Key entry	Key code	Step	Key entry	Key code
001	(g) LBL 0	25 14 00		$\times$	51
	PRX	65		1	01
	(g) π	25 63		(g) $\longrightarrow$ P	25 34
	$\times$	51		R$\downarrow$	12
	2	02		$+$	41
	$\times$	51		PRX	65
	STO 1.0	45.0	050	1	01
	(g) X²	25 53		8	08
	RCL 0	55 00		0	00
010	$\times$	51		$-$	31
	RCL 8	55 08		STO .1	45.1
	$+$	61		R$\downarrow$	12
	RCL 4	55 04		$+$	61
	$\times$	51		RCL 5	55 05
	RCL 3	55 03		$\times$	51
	$\times$	51		RCL 6	55 06
	RCL 3	55 03	060	$\times$	51
	$-$	31		RCL 7	55 07
020	RCL 4	55 04		$+$	61
	$-$	31		RCL 1	55 01
	RCL .0	55.0		$+$	61
	(g) X²	25 53		RCL .0	55.0
	$\times$	51		$+$	61
	RCL 8	55 08		STO .2	45.2
	RCL 1	55 01		(f) log	16 33

TABLE A-4   (cont'd)

Step	Key entry	Key code	Step	Key entry	Key code
	×	51		2	02
	(g) 1/x	25 64	070	0	00
	+	41		×	51
030	RCL .0	55.0		PRX	65
	(g) X²	25 53		RCL .1	55.1
	RCL 3	55 03		RCL .2	55.2
	×	51		(f) → R	16 34
	RCL 4	55 04		1	01
	×	51		+	41
	1	00		(g) → P	25 34
	−	31		(g) 1/x	25 64
	RCL .0	55.0	080	(f) log	16 33
	×	51		2	02
040	CHS	22		0	00
	(g) → P	25 34		×	51
	X ≠ Y	11		PRX	65
	RCL 2	55 02		(g) SPC	25 65
	RCL .0	55.0		(g) RTN	25 13

subtracted from the answer in step 42. The VTO noise reduction can then be calculated using Eq. (A-92). This program was written for a 98-step RPN calculator such as the HP19C/29C.

The refinement of incorporating the additional poles and finite gain into the ideal third-order solution shows up mainly at very low and very high values of frequency. However, in critical applications, it may be worthwhile. A numerical example of this difference is shown in Table A-5 using a frequency synthesizer loop with typical values.

TABLE A-5   COMPARISON OF EXACT AND THIRD-ORDER APPROXIMATION CALCULATED DATA[a]

Frequency (Hz)	Exact calculation			Third-order approximation		
	$G_{(s)}H_{(s)}$ (dB)	Degrees	e/e_n (dB)	$G_{(s)}H_{(s)}$ (dB)	Degrees	e/e_n (dB)
0.01	229.59	−141.63	−229.59	231.70	−179.99	−231.70
0.1	191.67	−175.47	−191.67	191.70	−179.99	−191.70
1.0	151.70	−179.53	−151.70	151.70	−179.53	−151.70
10	111.70	−179.75	−111.70	111.70	−179.79	−111.70
100	71.71	−177.99	−71.71	71.71	−177.94	−71.70
1,000	32.34	−161.06	−32.14	32.34	−160.49	−32.14
10,000	3.33	−131.48	−0.82	3.36	−125.93	−1.58

TABLE A-5 (cont'd)

Frequency (Hz)	Exact calculation $G_{(s)}H_{(s)}$ (dB)	Degrees	e/e_n (dB)	Third-order approximation $G_{(s)}H_{(s)}$ (dB)	Degrees	e/e_n (dB)
13,700	0	−136.61	2.64	0	−129.19	1.33
100,000	−26.33	−253.88	0.11	−28.60	−167.47	0.32
1,000,000	−108.37	−354.41	0	−68.34	−178.72	0
Phase margin		43.39°			50.81°	

$^aT_0 = 0.016$ $\quad T_3 = 6.40 \times 10^{-6}$ $\quad K_p = 0.25$
$T_1 = 2.01 \times 10^{-3}$ $\quad T_v = 1.6 \times 10^{-6}$ $\quad K_o = 10 \times 10^{10}$
$T_2 = 5.73 \times 10^{-5}$ $\quad N = 8192$ $\quad A_o = 10,000$

A-2-2 Phase Noise-to-Residual FM Conversion

The program given in Table A-6 fits straight-line segments from a plot of oscillator phase noise to a power-law model and computes accurate values for integrated phase jitter and residual FM.* It can be used on an HP67/97 calculator and, with some minor modifications, on the later HP41C calculator.

The purity of a frequency source is frequently defined by converting a plot of phase-noise spectral density $[S_{\Delta\theta}(f_m)$ or $\mathcal{L}(f_m)]$ to either an integrated phase-jitter or residual FM value. The HP67/97 calculator program presented here eases the labor of conversions because it only requires the entry of a few selected points of either $S_{\Delta\theta}(f_m)$ or $\mathcal{L}(f_m)$.

The definitions and basic theory of phase noise were described in Chapter 2. Therefore, only the specific procedures that are required for running the program are described here.

The power-law model for phase-noise spectral density is

$$S_{\Delta\theta}(f_m) = Kf_m^x \tag{A-104}$$

which represents a straight-line segment on a plot of $S_{\Delta\theta}(f_m)$ is decibels relative to 1 radian²/Hz versus $\log f_m$ in hertz. Given two points on the plot (f_1, dB_1) and (f_2, dB_2), the values of x and K may be determined by

$$x = \frac{dB_1 - dB_2}{10(\log f_1 - \log f_2)} \tag{A-105}$$

and

$$K = 10^{(dB_1/10) - x \log f_1} \tag{A-106}$$

*This program was developed by William J. Riley, Jr., and reproduced by permission of *Microwaves*, August 1979.

TABLE A-6 PROGRAM LISTING PHASE NOISE-TO-RESIDUAL FM CONVERSION

Step	Key	Code	Comments
001	*LBLA	21 11	
002	CF0	16 22 00	Set up for $\mathcal{L}(f_m)$
003	GTO0	22 00	
004	*LBLa	21 16 11	Set up for $S_{\Delta\phi}(f_m)$
005	SF0	16 21 00	
006	*LBL0	21 00	
007	0	00	
008	STOI	35 46	Initialize
009	STO7	35 07	
010	STO9	35 09	
011	*LBL1	21 01	
012	RCLI	36 46	
013	FIX	−11	Get Entry
014	DSP0	−63 00	
015	*LBL9	21 09	
016	R/S	51	
017	CHS	−22	
018	F0?	16 23 00	
019	GTO2	22 02	
020	3	03	
021	+	−55	Store Entry
022	*LBL2	21 02	
023	STO1	35 01	
024	R↓	−31	
025	STO0	35 00	
026	RCLI	36 46	
027	X≠0?	16−42	Do Calc if not first entry
028	GSB3	23 03	
029	RCL0	36 00	
030	STO2	35 02	
031	RCL1	36 01	Shift Data, Increment Index, & Iterate
032	STO3	35 03	
033	ISZI	16 26 46	
034	GTO1	22 01	
035	*LBL3	21 03	
036	RCL3	36 03	
037	RCL1	36 01	
038	−	−45	
039	1	01	
040	0	00	
041	÷	−24	
042	RCL2	36 02	
043	LOG	16 32	Calc X_i
044	RCL0	36 00	
045	LOG	16 32	
046	−	−45	

TABLE A-6 (cont'd)

Step	Key	Code	Comments
047	÷	−24	
048	STO4	35 04	
049	1	01	
050	+	−55	
051	STO6	35 06	
052	RCL3	36 03	
053	1	01	
054	0	00	
055	÷	−24	
056	RCL2	36 02	
057	LOG	16 32	Calc K_t
058	RCL4	36 04	
059	×	−35	
060	−	−45	
061	10^x	16 33	
062	STO5	35 05	
063	RCL6	36 06	
064	X=0?	16−43	Test Exponent
065	GTO6	22 06	
066	GSB4	23 04	
067	STO8	35 08	
068	ST+7	35−55 07	Calc & Save $\Delta\phi_i^2$ for $X \neq -1$
069	GTO7	22 07	
070	*LBL6	21 06	
071	GSB5	23 05	
072	STO8	35 08	Calc & Save $\Delta\phi_i^2$ for $X = -1$
073	ST+7	35−55 07	
074	*LBL7	21 07	
075	2	02	
076	ST+6	35−55 06	Add 2 to Exponent & Test It
077	RCL6	36 06	
078	X=0?	16−43	
079	GTO8	22 08	
080	GSB4	23 04	
081	STOA	35 11	Calc & Save Δf_i^2 for $X \neq -3$
082	ST+9	35−55 09	
083	RTN	24	
084	*LBL8	21 08	
085	GSB5	23 05	
086	STOA	35 11	Calc & Save Δf_i^2 for $X = -3$
087	ST+9	35−55 09	
088	RTN	24	
089	*LBL4	21 04	
090	RCL0	36 00	
091	RCL6	36 06	
092	Y^x	31	
093	RCL2	36 02	

Step	Key	Code	Comments
094	RCL6	36 06	Subroutine to Calc $\int$ for Exponent $\neq$ -1
095	Y^x	31	
096	−	−45	
097	RCL5	36 05	
098	×	−35	
099	RCL6	36 06	
100	÷	−24	
101	RTN	24	
102	*LBL5	21 05	Subroutine to Calc $\int$ for Exponent $=$ -1
103	RCL0	36 00	
104	LOG	16 32	
105	RCL2	36 02	
106	LOG	16 32	
107	−	−45	
108	RCL5	36 05	
109	×	−35	
110	RTN	24	
111	*LBLB	21 12	Display X_t
112	FIX	−11	
113	DSP2	−63 02	
114	RCL4	36 04	
115	GTO9	22 09	
116	*LBLC	21 13	Display K_t
117	SCI	−12	
118	DSP3	−63 03	
119	RCL5	36 05	
120	GTO9	22 09	
121	*LBLD	21 14	Display Δf_i^2
122	SCI	−12	
123	DSP3	−63 03	
124	RCLA	36 11	
125	GTO9	22 09	
126	*LBLd	21 16 14	Display $\Delta \phi_i^2$
127	SCI	−12	
128	DSP3	−63 03	
129	RCL8	36 08	
130	RTN	24	
131	GTO9	22 09	
132	*LBLE	21 15	Display Δf
133	RCL9	36 09	
134	ENT↑	−21	
135	√X	54	
136	SCI	−12	
137	DSP3	−63 03	
138	GTO9	22 09	
139	*LBLe	21 16 15	

TABLE A-6   (cont'd)

Step	Key	Code	Comments
140	RCL7	36 07	
141	ENT↑	−21	
142	√X	54	Display $\Delta\phi$
143	SCI	−12	
144	DSP3	−63 03	
145	GTO9	22 09	
146	R/S	51	

0	1	2	3	4	5
f_2	dB_2	f_1	dB_1	X_I	K_I

6	7	8	9	A
$X_I + 1$ or $+3$	$\Delta\phi^2$	$\Delta\phi_i^2$	Δf^2	Δf_i^2

The integrated phase jitter ($\Delta\theta$) can then be found over this interval by

$$\Delta\theta^2 = \int_{f_1}^{f_2} S_{\Delta\theta}(f_m)\, df_m$$

$$= \int_{f_1}^{f_2} K f_m^x\, df_m \tag{A-107}$$

$$= \frac{K}{x+1}(f_2^{x+1} - f_1^{x+1}) \qquad \text{for } x \neq -1$$

$$= K(\log f_2 - \log f_1) \qquad \text{for } x = -1 \tag{A-108}$$

The spectral density of frequency fluctuations is given by

$$S_{\Delta f}(f_m) = f_m^2 S_{\Delta\theta}(f_m) = K f_m^{x+2} \tag{A-109}$$

The integrated frequency jitter or residual FM is therefore

$$\Delta f^2 = \int_{f_1}^{f_2} S_{\Delta f}(f_m)\, df_m$$

$$= \int_{f_1}^{f_2} K f_m^{x+2}\, df_m \tag{A-110}$$

$$= \frac{K}{x+3}(f_2^{x+3} - f_1^{x+3}) \qquad \text{for } x \neq -3$$

$$= K(\log f_2 - \log f_1) \qquad \text{for } x = -3 \tag{A-111}$$

The value of phase jitter ($\Delta\theta$) is usually expressed in rms radians and the residual FM (Δf) in rms Hz. These values are the square root of the respective quantities given by Eqs. (A-107), (A-108), (A-110), and (A-111). The phase noise is commonly expressed as $\mathcal{L}(f_m)$, the SSB phase noise-to-carrier power ratio in a 1-Hz bandwidth using units of dBc/Hz. This quantity can be converted to $S_{\Delta\theta}(f_m)$ by adding 3 dB before calculating the power-law fit.

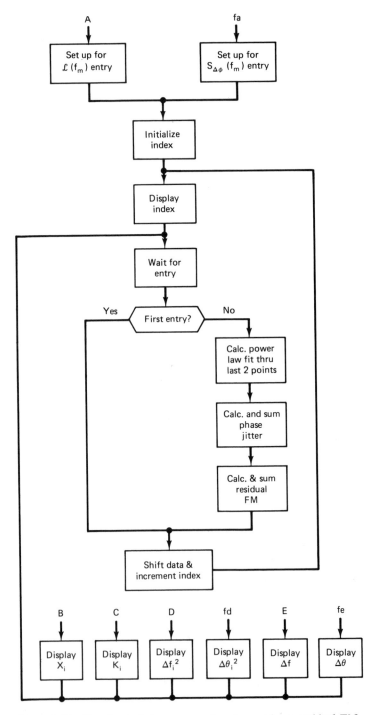

Figure A-29 Flowchart of the program for phase noise-to-residual FM conversion.

How the program operates. A flowchart of the program is shown in Figure A-29 and program operation is indicated by the markings on the magnetic program storage card shown in Figure A-30.

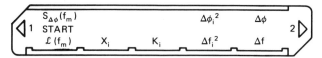

Figure A-30   Marking of the magnetic card.

To run the program, use A or fa keystrokes to start entry of $\mathcal{L}(f_m)$ or $S_{\Delta\theta}(f_m)$, respectively. Then enter pairs of sideband frequency (Hz) and phase noise (dB) data starting at the lowest frequency. The dB values are assumed to be "dB down" or negative, so that keying CHS is not required. Terminate each entry pair with R/S.

The calculator displays a prompt that indicates the number of the next line segment that is to be entered. Choose data points that correspond to good straight-line approximations of the phase-noise plot. Calculations are made after each point is entered (except the first), and the results for the current segment (i) are available after each calculation.

Key B displays x_i and key C displays K_i for the power-law fit. Key D displays Δf_i^2 and fd displays $\Delta\theta_i^2$. These latter quantities are also summed and are available after the last entry.

Key E displays Δf, the residual FM in rms Hz. Keys fe display $\Delta\theta$, the integrated phase jitter in rms radians. Use the $X \leftrightarrows Y$ key to display the corresponding mean-squared value, Δf^2 or $\Delta\theta^2$. The latter quantity represents the total sideband phase noise-to-signal power ratio.

As an example of the use of the program, consider the plot of phase noise shown in Figure A-31. Calculate the integrated phase jitter and residual FM for this source over the range of sideband frequencies from 1 Hz to 30 kHz.

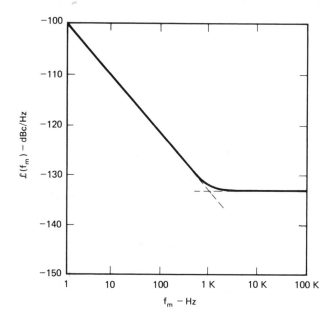

Figure A-31   Phase noise plot generated by the program.

It is apparent from the plot that two line segments give a good approximation to the curve; therefore, use the following three data points:

f_m (Hz)	$\mathcal{L}(f_m)$ (dBc/Hz)
1	-100
1 k	-132
30 k	-132

Load the program into the calculator and depress key A to start the entry of $\mathcal{L}(f_m)$ data. Then make the following entries:

1   ENTER   100   R/S

1   EEX   3   ENTER   132   R/S

The results for the first line segment can be examined:

key B displays $x_1 = -1.07$

key C displays $K_1 = 1.995 \times 10^{-10}$

Enter the third data point,

3   EEX   4   ENTER   132   R/S

to obtain the second x and K values:

key B displays $x_2 = 0.00$

key C displays $K_2 = 1.259 \times 10^{-13}$

Find residual FM by hitting key E: $\Delta f = 1.064$ Hz rms. The integrated phase jitter is found by pressing

fe (displays $\Delta\theta = 6.896 \times 10^{-5}$ radian rms)

$X \leftrightarrows Y$ (displays $\Delta\theta^2 = 4.755 \times 10^{-9}$ radian^2)

The final result can be expressed in dB by hitting

f log 10 × (displays -83.2 dB)

which is the total phase noise-to-signal power ratio.

A-2-3 Mini RC Network Analysis Program

It is important to be able to analyze the frequency response of a system; although this can be done easily for simple circuits, more complex circuits can be handled equally easily with the aid of a computer.

There are numerous computer programs available that can be run on large machines. The following program in BASIC is a useful aid that can be executed on practically all computers capable of BASIC language.

The program, as we will see later, contains an allowance for the Tektronix 4051/52/54 series, where it uses one matrix function of a special ROM which is determined in lines 130 and 140. In the case of a standard BASIC computer, line 140 has to be changed into M0 = 0.

This computer program handles 14 nodes and 51 elements. Depending on the initial dimension statements, it can use up to 32K of memory.

As can be shown in Table A-7, it accepts resistors, capacitors, inductors, operational amplifiers, field-effect transistors, and NPN transistors. For the active devices, various information has to be supplied, such as current-gain output impedance and other items, as seen in Table A-7.

TABLE A-7 LISTING OF INSTRUCTIONS FOR THE MINI *RC* NETWORK ANALYSIS PROGRAM

GENERAL

```
THIS PROGRAM WILL CALCULATE THE VOLTAGE GAIN AND PHASE OF CIRCUITS WITH
UP TO 14 CIRCUIT NODES. ALL CIRCUIT NODES MUST BE NUMBERED CONSECUTIVELY
STARTING AT NODE #1. THE REFERENCE NODE IS 0. ALL ELEMENTS MUST BE IDEN-
TIFIED BY UNIQUE NUMBERS FROM 1 THRU 50, WHERE ANY NUMBER IS ALLOWED TO
BE USED ONLY ONCE. EVERY COMPONENT OR CONTROL (EXCEPT "END") IS DEFINED
BY A LETTER AND THE ELEMENT NUMBER FOLLOWED BY A "," (EXCEPT FOR K# AND
D#). NODE NUMBERS AND ELEMENT VALUES ARE DEFINED BELOW AND MUST BE SEPA-
RATED BY A ",". THE ELEMENT NUMBER OF THE G# COMMAND IS A DUMMY NUMBER
(E.G. 0).
```

COMPONENTS AND CONTROL

```
R#,  RESISTOR   : NODE1,NODE2,R/OHM
L#,  INDUCTOR   : NODE1,NODE2,L/HENRY
C#,  CAPACITOR  : NODE1,NODE2,C/FARAD
F#,  FET        : GATE,SOURCE,DRAIN,GAIN/MHOS
T#,  TRANSISTOR : BASE,EMITTER,COLLECTOR,IC/IB,FT/MHZ,IC/A
A#,  OPAMP      : +IN,-IN,+OUT,-OUT,V-OUT/V-IN,R-OUT/OHM
G#,  GEN.INFORM : IN-NODE,OUT-NODE,FIRST FREQ.,LAST FREQ.,INCR. OR -STEPS/
                  DECADE (STEPS/DEC. MUST BE INDENTED BY A MINUS SIGN)
K#   KILL       : INDICATED ELEMENT IS KILLED
D#   DISPLAY    : INDICATED ELEMENT IS DISPLAYED
E    END        : STOP DESCRIPTION
```

NEW DESCRIPTION (Y/N) ?

The program is really easy to use, and we will become acquainted with it very quickly by using it.

Let us take a look at Figure A-32. This shows an active amplifier with an open-loop gain of 1,000,000 and a feedback network consisting of the series configuration of a 1000-Ω resistor and a 1-μF capacitor, and at the output an additional *RC* network with 1000 Ω and 0.1 μF is added. Such a network would be found in a type 2 third-order loop with a perfect integrator, and this program allows the analysis of the performance very easily.

After loading the program, the information has to be entered in the proper sequence, but it is important to remember that, starting with the first element that

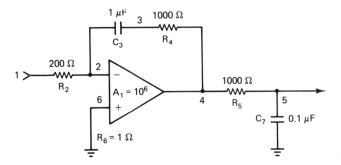

Figure A-32 Active amplifier forming a third-order filter.

receives the number 1, each consecutive element has the next higher number (see Table A-8). Each number can only be used once, and a maximum of 51 elements is

TABLE A-8 DESCRIPTION OF THE THIRD-ORDER LOOP FILTER

A1	6	2	4	0	1000000	50
R2	1	2			200	
C3	2	3			1.0E-6	
R4	3	4			1000	
R5	4	5			1000	
R6	6	0			1	
C7	5	0			1.0E-7	
G51	1	5			1	100000

allowed. As can be seen, the input and output nodes, as well as the nodes in between, have to be determined; in our case, the input node has the number 1 and the output node has the number 5. The number 0 is always assigned to ground. As we are not familiar with the circuit, node 6 has been used, which really is grounded, but the reason for using it is to show that for a change of circuitry or change of ground, this method of using a small resistor to ground is permitted.

After all the elements from A1 to C7 have been entered, the program is ended by an "E". The frequency range and resolution have to be determined. There are two possibilities:

1. A linear frequency range can be used.
2. A logarithmic range can be used.

First, however, the program has to be told that the input node has number 1 and the output node number 5, and then, in our case, the frequency range of interest is from 1 Hz to 100 kHz in four logarithmic steps, as can be verified by the printout (Table A-9).

We will notice that each frequency has four values and that four pieces of information are given simultaneously: the absolute frequency, the amplitude involved under the assumption of 1 V at the input, the gain in decibels, and the phase in degrees. Tables A-8 and A-9, therefore, together with the first table, are the perfect tool to use to draw the Bode plot. This can be done for much more complex circuits, and I am

TABLE A-9 PRINTOUT OF RESULTS OF THE THIRD-ORDER
LOOP FILTER

```
---- FREQUENCY RESPONSE ANALYSIS ----
FREQUENCY/HZ        AMPLITUDE/V     AMPL/DB    PHASE/DEG
1                   795.795008      58.02       90.3
1.77827941004       447.527424      53.02       90.6
3.16227766017       251.696803      48.02       91.0
5.6234132519        141.599287      43.02       91.8
10                  .79.733323      38.03       93.2
17.7827941004       45.025638       33.07       95.7
31.6227766017       25.651626       28.18      100.1
56.234132519        14.999185       23.52      107.4
100                 9.379740        19.44      118.5
177.827941004       6.668639        16.48      131.8
316.227766017       5.490262        14.79      142.0
562.34132519        4.899585        13.80      144.7
1000                4.286977        12.64      138.8
1778.27941004       3.347856        10.50      126.7
3162.27766017       2.250683         7.05      113.8
5623.4132519        1.362180         2.68      104.2
10000               0.785988        -2.09       98.1
17782.7941004       0.445736        -7.02       94.6
31622.7766017       0.251333       -12.00       92.6
56234.132519        0.141456       -16.99       91.5
99999.9999999       0.079568       -21.99       90.8
```

sure the interested reader who uses this program will find all kinds of useful applications for it.

We will, however, go through another circuit, as it is not limited to *RC* networks.

Figure A-33 shows a crystal filter that might be used to reduce the noise from a crystal oscillator. Such devices are mentioned in the literature from time to time, and it should be repeated that the major drawback of such a circuit is the possible ringing due to mechanical vibration, especially the effects of a fan or other rotating devices inside the instrument.

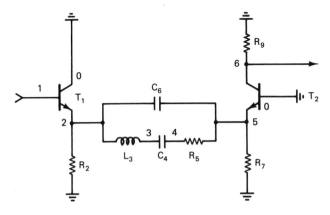

$T_1 = T_2$; $\beta = 10$, $f_T = 100$ MHz ; $I_C = 10$ mA
$R_2 = R_7 = R_9 = 1$ kΩ
$L_3 = 2$ H ; $C_4 = 5.066059182E-16F$;
$R_5 = 50$ Ω ; $C_6 = 2$ pF

Figure A-33 Active crystal filter circuit.

Figure A-33 is a source follower with a 5-MHz third-overtone crystal in series being terminated into a grounded base amplifier, and the output is taken from the collector of the second transistor. Because of the loss resistor R5 of the circuit of 50 Ω and the input impedance of the second transistor in the vicinity of 3 Ω, there is a voltage divider and therefore a lossy circuit. The loss is approximately 17 and has to be compensated by the gain of the second transistor.

As in our earlier example, we entered the elements starting with T1 through R9 (Table A-10), and we have a total of six nodes. This time we are using a linear frequency

TABLE A-10 DESCRIPTION OF THE CRYSTAL FILTER

T1	1	2	0	10	1. 0E+8	0. 01
R2	2	0		1000		
L3	2	3		2		
C4	3	4		5. 066059182E-16		
R5	4	5		50		
C6	2	5		2. 0E-12		
R7	5	0		1000		
T8	0	5	6	10	1. 0E+8	0. 01
R9	6	0		1000		
G01	1	6		4998500	5001000	100

range between 4.9985 and 5.001 MHz in steps of 100 Hz.

The crystal has a parallel and a series resonant frequency, and the frequency-response analysis provides us with this information (Table A-11). The highest gain of

TABLE A-11 PRINTOUT OF THE RESULTS CALCULATED FOR THE CRYSTAL FILTER

```
---- FREQUENCY RESPONSE ANALYSIS ----
FREQUENCY/HZ      AMPLITUDE/V     AMPL/DB     PHASE/DEG
4998500           0. 080747       -21. 86     87. 4
4998600           0. 082460       -21. 68     87. 4
4998700           0. 084438       -21. 47     87. 4
4998800           0. 086744       -21. 24     87. 4
4998900           0. 089470       -20. 97     87. 3
4999000           0. 092740       -20. 65     87. 3
4999100           0. 096737       -20. 29     87. 3
4999200           0. 101733       -19. 85     87. 3
4999300           0. 108156       -19. 32     87. 3
4999400           0. 116719       -18. 66     87. 3
4999500           0. 128707       -17. 81     87. 2
4999600           0. 146689       -16. 67     87. 2
4999700           0. 176655       -15. 06     87. 1
4999800           0. 236582       -12. 52     86. 9
4999900           0. 416294       -7. 61      86. 3
5000000           16. 522212      24. 36      -2. 2
5000100           0. 302806       -10. 38     -91. 1
5000200           0. 123028       -18. 20     -91. 7
5000300           0. 063089       -24. 00     -91. 8
5000400           0. 033118       -29. 60     -91. 8
5000500           0. 015136       -36. 40     -91. 5
5000600           0. 003150       -50. 03     -89. 0
5000700           0. 005422       -45. 32     85. 9
5000800           0. 011843       -38. 53     86. 9
5000900           0. 016839       -35. 47     87. 1
5001000           0. 020836       -33. 62     87. 2
4500000           0. 051191       -25. 82     87. 7
```

this circuit is at 5.000 MHz in the amount of 24 dB, and the highest attenuation occurs at the parallel resonant frequency of the crystal, which is about 5.0006 MHz.

Because of the step size of 100 Hz, the actual parallel frequency may be slightly higher or lower. To determine this, the step size has to be narrowed and the program rerun.

These two examples show the flexibility of this sample program, and it should be mentioned that most simple programs of this nature do not allow the use of an inductance, which is a special feature in this case. Table A-12 is a complete listing of

TABLE A-12 LISTING OF THE COMPUTER PROGRAM FOR THE MINI *RC* CIRCUIT ANALYSIS PROGRAM

```
4 GO TO 100
8 GO TO 1960
12 PRINT "ENTER LISTING DEVICE # (PRINTER=41, SCREEN=RETURN): ";
13 INPUT Z$
14 Z$=Z$&",32"
15 GO TO 49
16 GO TO 730
49 V5=VAL(Z$)
50 RETURN
80 PRI "L_GENERALJ___THIS PROGRAM WILL CALCULATE THE VOLTAGE GAIN AND PHA";
81 PRI "SE OF CIRCUITS WITH__UP TO ";M1;" CIRCUIT NODES. ALL CIRCUIT NO";
82 PRI "DES MUST BE NUMBERED CONSECUTIVELY__STARTING AT NODE #1. THE RE";
83 PRI "FERENCE NODE IS 0. ALL ELEMENTS MUST BE IDEN-__TIFIED BY UNIQUE";
84 PRINT " NUMBERS FROM 1 THRU ";M2-1;", WHERE ANY NUMBER IS ALLOWED TO"
85 PRI "BE USED ONLY ONCE. EVERY COMPONENT OR CONTROL (EXCEPT ""END"")";
86 PRI " IS DEFINED__BY A LETTER AND THE ELEMENT NUMBER FOLLOWED BY A ";
87 PRI """,""" (EXCEPT FOR K# AND__D#). NODE NUMBERS AND ELEMENT VAL";
88 PRI "UES ARE DEFINED BELOW AND MUST BE SEPA-__RATED BY A "","". THE ";
89 PRINT "ELEMENT NUMBER OF THE G# COMMAND IS A DUMMY NUMBER__(E.G. 0).J_"
90 PRINT "COMPONENTS AND CONTROLJ___R#, RESISTOR   : NODE1,NODE2,R/OHM"
91 PRI "L#, INDUCTOR    : NODE1,NODE2,L/HENRY__C#, CAPACITOR  : NODE1,";
92 PRINT "NODE2,C/FARAD__F#, FET         : GATE,SOURCE,DRAIN,GAIN/MHOS"
93 PRINT "T#, TRANSISTOR: BASE,EMITTER,COLLECTOR,IC/IB,FT/ HZ,IC/A"
94 PRINT "A#, OPAMP      : +IN,-IN,+OUT,-OUT,V-OUT/V-IN,R-OUT/OHM__G#, ";
95 PRI "GEN. INFORM: IN-NODE, OUT-NODE,FIRST FREQ.,LAST FREQ. INCR. OR ";
96 PRI "-STEPS/__I_H_H_DECADE (STEPS/DEC. MUST BE INDENTED BY A MINUS SIGN)"
97 PRI "K#  KILL      : INDICATED ELEMENT IS KILLED__D#  DISPLAY    : IN";
98 PRI "DICATED ELEMENT IS DISPLAYED__E    END          : STOP DESCRIPTIONJ_"
99 RETURN
100 INIT
110 SET KEY

120 REM SCRATCH: D1,D2 F0,F1,F2,F3 I,J,K,L M0,M1,M2,M3 N,N1,N2 P2 V5 W
130 REM USE MAT-FCTN: M0=0=NO, M0=1=YES. M1=# OF NODES. 42=# OF ELEM. +1

140 M0=1
150 M1=14
160 M2=51
170 GOSUB 80
180 DIM G(9,2),Z(M1),M(M2,8),Y$(1),Z$(72),M$(10)
190 M$="GKRLCFTADE"
200 DATA 2,3,0,0,2,1,2,1,2,1,3,1,3,3,4,2,0,0,0,0
210 READ G
220 IF M0=1 THEN 240
230 DIM A(M1-1,M1-1),B(M1-1,M1-1)
240 P2=8*ATN(1)
250 M=0
260 PRINT "NEW DESCRIPTION (Y/N) ? ";
```

```
270 INPUT Y$
280 IF Y$="Y" THEN 370
290 PRINT "ENTER FILE # (1 TO 25) : ";
300 INPUT N1
310 IF N1<1 OR N1>25 THEN 260
320 FIND N1+1
330 READ @33:M
340 GO TO 740

350 REM ENTER & EDIT DESCRIPTION

360 PRINT "ERROR.  REPEAT INPUTG_"
370 INPUT Z$
380 B$=SEG(Z$,1,1)
390 N1=POS(M$,B$,1)
400 IF N1=0 THEN 360
410 IF B$="E" THEN 740

420 REM EVALUATE DATA STRING

430 Z$=Z$&",1E174,0,0,0,0,0,0,0,0,"
440 N=1
450 V=0
460 IF N>5+G(N1,2) OR (N<=5 AND N>1+G(N1,1)) THEN 590
470 N2=POS(Z$,",",1)
480 IF N2>1 THEN 510
490 Z$=REP("",1,1)
500 GO TO 470
510 B$=SEG(Z$,1,N2)
520 Z$=REP("",1,N2)
530 B$=B$&",1E174"
540 V=VAL(B$)
550 IF N>1 OR N1>1 THEN 580
560 V=M2
570 GO TO 590
580 IF V=1.0E+174 OR (V=>M2 AND N=1) OR (V>M1 AND N>1 AND N<6) THEN 360
590 Z(N)=V
600 N=N+1
610 IF N<9 THEN 450
620 IF N1=9 THEN 700

630 REM STORE OR KILL ELEMENT Z(1)

640 FOR N=2 TO 8
650   M(Z(1),N)=Z(N)
660 NEXT N
670 M(Z(1),1)=N1-2
680 GO TO 370

690 REM DISPLAY ELEMENT Z(1)

700 N1=Z(1)
710 GOSUB 1030
720 GO TO 370

730 REM DISPLAY DESCRIPTION

740 PRINT "LIST DESCRIPTION (Y/N) ? ";
750 INPUT Y$
760 IF Y$<>"Y" THEN 840
770 GOSUB 12
780 PRINT @V5:"L_";
790 FOR N1=1 TO M2
800   IF M(N1,1)=0 THEN 820
```

```
810    GOSUB 1030
820 NEXT N1
830 PRINT @V5:
840 PRINT "EDIT DESCRIPTION (Y/N) ? ";
850 INPUT Z$
860 IF Z$="Y" THEN 370
870 PRINT "STORE DESCRIPTION (Y/N) ? ";
880 INPUT Y$
890 IF Y$<>"Y" THEN 960
900 PRINT "ENTER FILE # (1 TO 25) : ";
910 INPUT N1
920 IF N1<1 OR N1>25 THEN 840
930 FIND N1+1
940 WRITE M
950 CLOSE
960 PRINT "RUN ANALYSIS (Y/N) ? ";
970 INPUT Y$
980 IF Y$="Y" THEN 1230
990 PRINT "STOP (Y/N) ? ";
1000 INPUT Y$
1010 IF Y$<>"Y" THEN 740
1020 END
1030 Z$=SEG(M$,M(N1,1)+2,1)
1040 PRINT @V5:Z$;N1;
1050 IF N1=>10 THEN 1070
1060 PRINT @V5:" ";
1070 PRINT @V5: USING "3D3DS":M(N1,2),M(N1,3)
1080 IF G(M(N1,1)+2,1)<=2 THEN 1130
1090 PRINT @V5: USING "3DS":M(N1,4)
1100 IF G(M(N1,1)+2,1)<=3 THEN 1140
1110 PRINT @V5: USING "3DS":M(N1,5)
1120 GO TO 1150
1130 PRINT @V5:"     ";
1140 PRINT @V5:"     ";
1150 PRINT @V5:"    ";M(N1,6)," ";
1160 IF G(M(N1,1)+2,2)=1 THEN 1200
1170 PRINT @V5:M(N1,7)," ";
1180 IF G(M(N1,1)+2,2)=2 THEN 1200
1190 PRINT @V5:M(N1,8);
1200 PRINT @V5:" "
1210 RETURN

1220 REM EXEC.

1230 GOSUB 12
1240 PRINT @V5:"L_---- FREQUENCY RESPONSE ANALYSIS ----J_"
1250 N=0
1260 Z=0
1270 FOR N1=1 TO M2
1280    IF M(N1,1)=0 THEN 1370
1290    FOR N2=2 TO 5
1300      IF M(N1,N2)<N THEN 1320
1310      N=M(N1,N2)
1320      IF M(N1,N2)=0 THEN 1340
1330      Z(M(N1,N2))=Z(M(N1,N2))+1
1340    NEXT N2
1350    IF N1=M2 THEN 1370
1360    M5=N1
1370 NEXT N1
1380 PRINT "NODES=",N
1390 N2=0
1400 FOR N1=1 TO N
1410    IF Z(N1)=>2 THEN 1440
1420    N2=1
```

```
1430    PRINT "CONNECTION MISSING AT NODE # G_",N1
1440 NEXT N1
1450 IF N2=1 THEN 740
1460 IF M0=1 THEN 1490
1470 N=N-1
1480 GO TO 1500
1490 DIM A(N+N,N+N),B(N+N,N+N)
1500 IF M(M2,1)<0 THEN 1560
1510 PRINT "I/0-NODES: ";
1520 INPUT M(M2,2),M(M2,3)
1530 PRINT "ENTER FREQUENCIES: FROM,TO,INCR.  OR -STEP/DEC. : ";
1540 INPUT M(M2,6),M(M2,7),M(M2,8)
1550 M(M2,1)=-1
1560 F1=M(M2,6)
1570 F2=M(M2,7)
1580 F3=M(M2,8)
1590 PRINT @V5:" FREQUENCY/HZ","AMPLITUDE/V  AMPL/DB  PHASE/DEG"
1600 PRINT @V5:
1610 F0=F1
1620 FOR M3=0 TO F3*LGT(F2/F1)*(SGN(F3)-1)/2+(SGN(F3)+1)/2*(F2-F1)/F3
1630    IF F3>0 THEN 1660
1640    F0=F1*EXP(-LOG(10)/F3)^M3
1650    GO TO 1670
1660    F0=F1+F3*M3
1670    W=P2*F2/1.0E+12
1680    IF F0=0 THEN 1700
1690    W=2*PI*F0
1700    D1=M(M2,2)
1710    D2=M(M2,3)
1720    GOSUB 2010
1730    IF M0=1 THEN 1840
1740    V1=D1*-1^(M(M2,2)+M(M2,3))
1750    V2=D2*D1/V1
1760    D1=M(M2,2)
1770    D2=M(M2,2)
1780    GOSUB 2010
1790    N2=D1^2+D2^2
1800    N1=D1/N2
1810    N2=-D2/N2
1820    D1=V1*N1-V2*N2
1830    D2=V1*N2+V2*N1
1840    V=90*SGN(D2)
1850    IF D1=0 THEN 1880
1860    V=180*ATN(D2/D1)/PI
1870    V=V+(D1<0)*360*((V<0)-0.5)
1880    D1=SQR(D1^2+D2^2)
1890    D2=20*LGT(D1+1.0E-9)
1900    PRINT @V5:F0," ";
1910    PRINT @V5: USING "3D.6D,6D.2D,6D.1D":D1,D2,V
1920 NEXT M3
1930 PRINT "J_CONTINUE WITH NEW FREQUENCY RANGE (Y/N) ? ";
1940 INPUT Y$
1950 IF Y$<>"Y" THEN 990
1960 PRINT "ENTER FREQUENCIES: FROM,TO,INCR.  OR -STEP/DEC. : ";
1970 INPUT F1,F2,F3
1980 GO TO 1600
1990 END

2000 REM SET UP NODAL MATRIX A +IB AND CALC. DET.  OR INV.

2010 A=0
2020 B=0
2030 FOR N1=1 TO M5
2040    IF M(N1,1)<=0 THEN 2440
```

```
2050   IF M(N1,1)=1 THEN 2410
2060   IF M(N1,1)=2 THEN 2130
2070   IF M(N1,1)=3 THEN 2160
2080   IF M(N1,1)=4 THEN 2210
2090   IF M(N1,1)=5 THEN 2250
2100   IF M(N1,1)=6 THEN 2340
2110   STOP

2120   REM L

2130   V=-1/(W*M(N1,6))
2140   GO TO 2170

2150   REM C

2160   V=W*M(N1,6)
2170   GOSUB 2720
2180   GOSUB 3090
2190   GO TO 2440

2200   REM F

2210   V=M(N1,6)
2220   GOSUB 2630
2230   GO TO 2430

2240   REM T

2250   V=M(N1,8)/0.026
2260   GOSUB 2630
2270   GOSUB 2960
2280   V=V/M(N1,6)
2290   GOSUB 2720
2300   GOSUB 2960
2310   V=V*W*M(N1,6)/(P2*M(N1,7))
2320   GO TO 2180

2330   REM A

2340   V=1/M(N1,7)
2350   GOSUB 2680
2360   GOSUB 2960
2370   V=V*M(N1,6)
2380   GOSUB 2570
2390   GO TO 2430

2400   REM R

2410   V=1/M(N1,6)
2420    GOSUB 2720
2430    GOSUB 2960
2440 NEXT N1
2450 IF M0=1 THEN 2480
2460 GOSUB 3560
2470 RETURN
2480 B=INV(A)
2490 N1=M(M2,2)
2500 N2=M(M2,3)
2510 V2=B(N1,N1)^2+B(N1+N,N1)^2
2520 V1=B(N1,N1)/V2
2530 V2=-B(N1+N,N1)/V2
2540 D1=B(N2,N1)*V1-B(N2+N,N1)*V2
2550 D2=B(N2,N1)*V2+B(N2+N,N1)*V1
2560 RETURN
```

```
2570 REM 4-NODE-INDEX

2580 K=M(N1,2)
2590 L=M(N1,3)
2600 I=M(N1,4)
2610 J=M(N1,5)
2620 GO TO 2770

2630 REM 3-NODE-INDEX

2640 K=M(N1,2)
2650 L=M(N1,3)
2660 I=M(N1,4)
2670 GO TO 2760

2680 REM 2-NODE-INDEX (OUT)

2690 K=M(N1,4)
2700 L=M(N1,5)
2710 GO TO 2750

2720 REM 2-NODE-INDEX (IN)

2730 K=M(N1,2)
2740 L=M(N1,3)
2750 I=K
2760 J=L

2770 REM SORT

2780 IF M0=1 THEN 2950
2790 IF I<D1 THEN 2830
2800 IF I>D1 THEN 2820
2810 I=1
2820 I=I-1
2830 IF J<D1 THEN 2870
2840 IF J>D1 THEN 2860
2850 J=1
2860 J=J-1
2870 IF K<D2 THEN 2910
2880 IF K>D2 THEN 2900
2890 K=1
2900 K=K-1
2910 IF L<D2 THEN 2950
2920 IF L>D2 THEN 2940
2930 L=1
2940 L=L-1
2950 RETURN

2960 REM INSERT REAL

2970 IF M0=1 THEN 3220
2980 IF I=0 THEN 3030
2990 IF K=0 THEN 3010
3000 A(I,K)=A(I,K)+V

3010 IF L=0 THEN 3030
3020 A(I,L)=A(I,L)-V
3030 IF J=0 THEN 3080
3040 IF L=0 THEN 3060
3050 A(J,L)=A(J,L)+V
3060 IF K=0 THEN 3080
```

```
3070 A(J,K)=A(J,K)-V
3080 RETURN

3090 REM INSERT IMAG

3100 IF M0=1 THEN 3390
3110 IF I=0 THEN 3160
3120 IF K=0 THEN 3140
3130 B(I,K)=B(I,K)+V
3140 IF L=0 THEN 3160
3150 B(I,L)=B(I,L)-V
3160 IF J=0 THEN 3210
3170 IF L=0 THEN 3190
3180 B(J,L)=B(J,L)+V
3190 IF K=0 THEN 3210
3200 B(J,K)=B(J,K)-V
3210 RETURN

3220 REM INSERT REAL
3230 REM IF F0<>F1 THEN 4110

3240 IF I=0 THEN 3310
3250 IF K=0 THEN 3280
3260 A(I,K)=A(I,K)+V
3270 A(I+N,K+N)=A(I,K)
3280 IF L=0 THEN 3310
3290 A(I,L)=A(I,L)-V
3300 A(I+N,L+N)=A(I,L)
3310 IF J=0 THEN 3380
3320 IF L=0 THEN 3350
3330 A(J,L)=A(J,L)+V
3340 A(J+N,L+N)=A(J,L)
3350 IF K=0 THEN 3380
3360 A(J,K)=A(J,K)-V
3370 A(J+N,K+N)=A(J,K)
3380 RETURN

3390 REM INSERT IMAG

3400 IF I=0 THEN 3470
3410 IF K=0 THEN 3440
3420 A(I+N,K)=A(I+N,K)+V
3430 A(I,K+N)=-A(I+N,K)
3440 IF L=0 THEN 3470
3450 A(I+N,L)=A(I+N,L)-V
3460 A(I,L+N)=-A(I+N,L)
3470 IF J=0 THEN 3540
3480 IF L=0 THEN 3510
3490 A(J+N,L)=A(J+N,L)+V
3500 A(J,L+N)=-A(J+N,L)
3510 IF K=0 THEN 3540
3520 A(J+N,K)=A(J+N,K)-V
3530 A(J,K+N)=-A(J+N,K)
3540 RETURN

3550 REM D1,D2-DET.COMP. S,L,I,T,S1,J,J2,K

3560 IF N>1 THEN 3600
3570 D1=A(N,N)
3580 D2=B(N,N)
3590 RETURN
3600 D1=1
```

TABLE A-12 (cont'd)

```
3610 D2=0
3620 K=1
3630 L=K
3640 S=ABS(A(K,K))+ABS(B(K,K))
3650 FOR I=K TO N
3660   T=ABS(A(I,K))+ABS(B(I,K))
3670   IF S=>T THEN 3700
3680   L=I
3690   S=T
3700 NEXT I
3710 IF L=K THEN 3800
3720 FOR J=1 TO N
3730   S=A(K,J)
3740   A(K,J)=A(L,J)
3750   A(L,J)=S
3760   S1=B(K,J)
3770   B(K,J)=B(L,J)
3780   B(L,J)=S1
3790 NEXT J
3800 L=K+1
3810 FOR I=L TO N
3820   S1=A(K,K)*A(K,K)+B(K,K)*B(K,K)
3830   S=(A(I,K)*A(K,K)+B(I,K)*B(K,K))/S1
3840   B(I,K)=(A(K,K)*B(I,K)-A(I,K)*B(K,K))/S1
3850   A(I,K)=S
3860 NEXT I
3870 J2=K-1
3880 IF J2=0 THEN 3950
3890 FOR J=L TO N
3900   FOR I=1 TO J2
3910     A(K,J)=A(K,J)-A(K,I)*A(I,J)+B(K,I)*B(I,J)
3920     B(K,J)=B(K,J)-B(K,I)*A(I,J)-A(K,I)*B(I,J)
3930   NEXT I
3940 NEXT J
3950 J2=K
3960 K=K+1
3970 FOR I=K TO N
3980   FOR J=1 TO J2
3990     A(I,K)=A(I,K)-A(I,J)*A(J,K)+B(I,J)*B(J,K)
4000     B(I,K)=B(I,K)-B(I,J)*A(J,K)-A(I,J)*B(J,K)
4010   NEXT J
4020 NEXT I
4030 IF K<>N THEN 3630
4040 L=1
4050 J2=INT(N/2)
4060 IF N=2*J2 THEN 4100
4070 L=0
4080 D1=A(N,N)
4090 D2=B(N,N)
4100 FOR I=1 TO J2
4110   J=N-I+L
4120   S=A(I,I)*A(J,J)-B(I,I)*B(J,J)
4130   S1=A(I,I)*B(J,J)+A(J,J)*B(I,I)
4140   T=D1*S-D2*S1
4150   D2=D2*S+D1*S1
4160   D1=T
4170 NEXT I
4180 RETURN
```

this program as it can be entered into the Tektronix computer. For non-Tektronix computers, the usual input/output statement modification may be required.

A-2-4 Second-Order Type 2 Loop Program with a Computation of Lock-in Time (TEK4051/52/54)

The second-order type 2 loop traditionally has been the most important loop. The reason for this is the fact that if an active filter is used, it combines the most flexibility with the easiest design. The second-order type 2 loop was treated mathematically in Chapter 1, and the following program is designed to determine automatically all the values for such a loop. The program is simple to use and highly interactive. Let us take a look at Table A-13, which is the input statement taken off the Tektronix screen.

TABLE A-13 TYPE 2 SECOND-ORDER PROGRAM FOR TEKTRONIX 4051/52/54 SERIES, INSTRUCTION SET

```
TO MODIFY INPUT DATA STOP PROG.AND USE UDK#1

       *** SECOND ORDER PLL TYPE 1 AND 2 ***

Program calculates filter circuit components of 2nd order PLL
Type 1(Passive filter),Type 2(Active filter),then Bode plots
and finds transient response to step disturbance in frequency
and phase.

ENTER VCO GAIN CONSTANT IN Hz/V =1E6
ENTER PHASE DETECTOR GAIN CONSTANT IN V/rad =1.1
ENTER NATURAL LOOP FREQUENCY IN Hz =300
ENTER REFERENCE FREQUENCY IN Hz =1000
ENTER DAMPING CONSTANT ZETA =.7
ENTER DIVIDER RATIO N1=45000
ENTER PHASE DETECTOR SUPPLY VOLTAGE=12
FILTER ACTIVE OR PASSIVE? (A OR P)A
INPUT PARAMETER TO PRINTER ?(Y OR RETURN)
CHOOSE A FILTER CAPACITANCE IN F =1E-6
RESISTORS ARE:
R1=43.2272684941   R2=742.723067762
IF R1 AND/OR R2 ARE INCONVENIENT CHANGE C?(Y OR RETURN)
FILTER COMPONENT VALUES TO PRINTER ?(Y OR RETURN)
C=1.0E-6             R1=43.2272684941   R2=742.723067762

BODE PLOT TO PLOTTER,SKIP OR SCREEN ?(P,S OR RETURN
```

The example given here is for a VCO with 1-MHz/V VCO gain constant, 1.1-V/rad phase detector gain, a natural loop frequency of 300 Hz, a reference frequency of 1000 Hz, a damping constant $\zeta = 0.7$, a division ratio of 45,000, and a power supply voltage of 12 V. An active filter is used, and a filter capacitor of 1 μF is selected. It is obvious that the VCO frequency is 45 MHz.

The program determines the two resistors in the lag filter to be 43.2 and 743 Ω.

This is a particularly interesting loop which can be used in application where the output frequency is divided by at least 20 or, better, by 100. The closeness of the natural loop frequency to the reference frequency indicates a fairly bad reference suppression of about 14 dB. If the output frequency is divided by 100, equal to 40 dB in improvement, the 1-kHz reference is then 54-dB suppressed. If a loop has to be designed that is optimized for speed, such a configuration will be chosen, and one has to live with the limited reference suppression.

We learned in Chapter 1 that a loop using a digital phase/frequency comparator has two operating ranges as far as acquisition is concerned. We first have the pull-in range, which provides frequency lock, and then the lock-in range, which provides phase lock. The accuracy of these statements is found to be pretty high if actual measurements are made, although the mathematical analysis of the area where frequency lock is achieved and phase lock is being started is not always very precise.

The program determines the pull-in time to be 5.6 ms and the time required for phase lock is, at worst, 14 ms, resulting in a total acquisition time, worst case, of 20 ms. These data are generated in the form of printouts, and the way the mathematical calculations are done was described in Chapter 1. The Bode diagram, Figure A-34, indicates the required phase and gain margins for perfect stability.

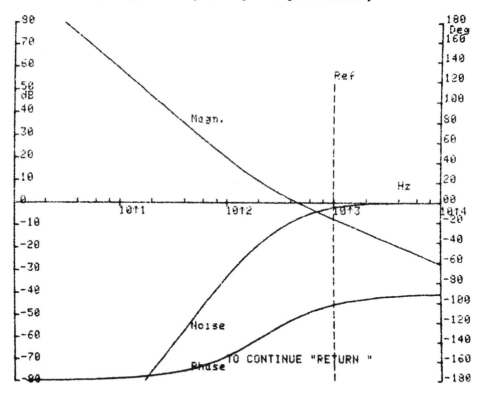

Figure A-34   Bode diagram of a type 2 second-order loop.

Table A-14 is a printout of the calculation of the pull-in time, and Table A-15 is a calculation of the lock-in time.

We remember that the inherent drawback of the second-order type 2 loop where the reference frequency and the natural frequency are that close together is the poor reference suppression, which has been accomplished in favor of fast acquisition.

TABLE A-14 PRINTOUT OF PULL-IN TIME

TIME IN SEC.	INPUT FREQU. DEVIATION IN RAD/S	Frequency step of 20 MHz
0	2.251304182E+7	
4.0E-4	1.446917467E+7	
8.0E-4	9299366.00416	
0.0012	5976720.16768	
0.0016	3841249.38697	
0.002	2468778.26616	
0.0024	1586688.47385	
0.0028	1019767.69139	
0.0032	655406.629307	
0.0036	421231.083674	
0.004	270726.016367	
0.0044	173996.124167	
0.0048	111827.638996	
0.0052	71871.8356705	
0.0056	46192.1650947	
0.006	29687.7921125	

PULL-IN TIME=0.0064 SEC

TABLE A-15 PRINTOUT OF CALCULATION OF LOCK-IN TIME

TIME IN SEC.	VCO PHASE DEVIATION IN DEG.	
0	1.62E+7	
4.0E-4	3400714.84456	
8.0E-4	-2192963.0647	Lock-in time after pull-in
0.0012	-3404628.26727	is completed
0.0016	-2685338.0554	
0.002	-1535135.49166	
0.0024	-620428.095634	
0.0028	-94202.7088136	
0.0032	120488.31022	
0.0036	154821.761633	
0.004	114886.550931	
0.0044	62489.2828415	
0.0048	23314.3890067	
0.0052	1868.84544808	
0.0056	-6220.31386275	
0.006	-6950.76236389	
0.0064	-4875.65296016	
0.0068	-2519.6300269	
0.0072	-855.388324706	
0.0076	10.4077063027	
0.008	308.210225359	
0.0084	308.557536269	
0.0088	205.276357593	
0.0092	100.544268924	
0.0096	30.4044945502	
0.01	-4.19258248581	
0.0104	-14.8271021106	
0.0108	-13.5590584732	
0.0112	-8.57395486759	
0.0116	-3.96592274368	
0.012	-1.03332598564	
0.0124	0.333477200851	
0.0128	0.697361111605	
0.0132	0.590294209713	
0.0136	0.355219734033	
0.014	0.154376433879	
0.0144	0.0327507770234	
0.0148	-0.0205492597781	

In Section A-2-5 we will deal with a fifth-order type 2 loop that combines improved performance. The fifth-order type 2 loop maintains the same total acquisition time but offers increased reference suppression at the expense of additional circuitry. The fifth-order type 2 loop consists of a third-order type 2 loop and an active low-pass filter. The drawback of this high-order loop is the possible introduction of additional noise very close to the center frequency if a medium-performance operational amplifier is used.

Table A-16 is a listing of the computer program that has been written for a TEK4051/52/54 system. The graphic portion, which makes it very attractive, can be deleted if it is of interest to use it on any other BASIC computer. With some minor modification, this can become a very useful tool.

TABLE A-16 LISTING OF THE TYPE 2 SECOND-ORDER LOOP, INCLUDING LOCK-IN TIME AND PULL-IN TIME

```
1 GO TO 100
4 PAGE
5 GO TO 5880
6 RETURN
8 GO TO 1140
100 INIT
101 SET KEY
110 PAGE
120 PRINT "J_"
130 FOR I=1 TO 20
140   PRINT "TO MODIFY INPUT DATA STOP PROG. AND USE UDK#1__K_K_"
150 NEXT I
160 DIM R1(99),R2(99),R3(99),R4(99),Q1(3),P1(2),P2(2)

170 REM VARIABLES USED:A,A1,A5,A6,A7,A8,A$,B,B1,B2,B3,B4,B5,B6,B7,B8,B$
180 REM C,C$,D,D1,D2,E9,E$,F,F3,F4,F6,F7,F$,G1,G2,G3,G4,G5,I,I1,I9,K,K0
190 REM K1,K2,K5,L,L5,L6,M0,M1,M2,M3,M4,M5,M6,M7,M8,M9,N,N1,O,O4,O5,O6
200 REM P,P0,P1,P2,P3,P4,P5,P6,P7,P8,P9,Q0,Q1,Q2,Q3,Q4,Q5,Q6,Q7,Q8,R,R1
210 REM R2,R3,R4,R8,R9,S,S1,S2,S3,S4,S5,S6,S7,S8,T,T1,T2,T5,T6,T7,T8,V5
220 REM V6,V7,W1,W2,Z,Z1,Z2,Z$

230 V5=32
240 V6=32
250 PRINT "J_J_        *** SECOND ORDER PLL TYPE 1 AND 2 ***"
260 PRI "J_PROGRAM CALCULATES FILTER CIRCUIT COMPONENTS OF 2ND ORDER PLL"
270 PRI " TYPE 1(PASSIVE FILTER),TYPE 2(ACTIVE FILTER),THEN BODE PLOTS"
280 PRI " AND FINDS TRANSIENT RESPONSE TO STEP DISTURBANCE IN FREQUENCY"
290 PRINT " AND PHASE. "

300 REM
310 REM    *** PARAMETER INPUT ***
320 REM

330 PRINT "J_J_ENTER VCO GAIN CONSTANT IN HZ/V =";
340 INPUT K0
350 K0=2*PI*K0
360 PRINT "ENTER PHASE DETECTOR GAIN CONSTANT IN V/RAD =";
370 INPUT K1
380 PRINT "ENTER NATURAL LOOP FREQUENCY IN HZ =";
390 INPUT O1
400 O=O1*2*PI
410 PRINT "ENTER REFERENCE FREQUENCY IN HZ =";
420 INPUT F4
430 PRINT "ENTER DAMPING CONSTANT ZETA =";
```

```
440 INPUT Z
450 PRINT "ENTER DIVIDER RATIO N1=";
460 INPUT N1
470 K2=K0*K1/N1
480 PRINT "ENTER PHASE DETECTOR SUPPLY VOLTAGE=";
490 INPUT V7
500 K5=V7/F4/2/PI
510 IF Z<=1 THEN 560

520 REM    *** CALCULATION OF WP0 ***

530 06=SQR(Z^2-1)/Z
540 05=2*PI*0*EXP(Z/SQR(Z^2-1)*0.5*LOG((1+06)/(1-06)))
550 GO TO 570
560 05=2*PI*0*EXP(Z/SQR(1-Z^2)*ATN(SQR(1-Z^2)/Z))
570 PRINT "FILTER ACTIVE OR PASSIVE? (A OR P)";

580 INPUT B$
590 PRINT "INPUT PARAMETER TO PRINTER ?(Y OR RETURN)";
600 INPUT E$
610 IF E$<>"Y" THEN 700
620 PRINT @41;"VCO GAIN CONSTANT IN HZ/V =";K0/2/PI
630 PRINT @41;"PHASE DETECTOR GAIN CONSTANT IN V/RAD =";K1
640 PRINT @41;"NATURAL LOOP FREQUENCY IN HZ =";0/2/PI
650 PRINT @41;"REFERENCE FREQUENCY IN HZ =";F4
660 PRINT @41;"DAMPING CONSTANT ZETA =";Z
670 PRINT @41;"DIVIDER RATIO N1=";N1
680 PRINT @41;"PHASE DETECTOR SUPPLY VOLTAGE =";V7
690 PRINT @41;"FILTER ACTIVE OR PASSIVE? (A OR P)";B$
700 IF B$="A" THEN 920
710 IF B$<>"P" THEN 570

720 REM ***PASSIVE FILTER TIME CONST. ***

730 A=K2*K2
740 B=2*K2
750 C=1-4*Z*Z*K2*K2/0/0
760 D=SQR(B*B-4*A*C)
770 T2=(-B+D)/2/A
780 IF T2<0 THEN 810
790 GO TO 870
800 PRINT "G_G_G_ AUTOMATIC REDUCTION OF NATURAL LOOP FREQ. "
810 0=0-0/100
820 C=1-4*Z*Z*K2*K2/0/0
830 D=SQR(B*B-4*A*C)
840 T2=(-B+D)/2/A
850 IF T2>0 THEN 870
860 GO TO 810

870 PRINT "G_G_G_ NEW NATURAL LOOP FREQ. IS ";0/2/PI;" HZ"
880 T1=K2/0/0-T2
890 GOSUB 970
900 GO TO 1080

910 REM *** ACTIVE FILTER TIME CONST. ***

920 T1=K2/0/0
930 T2=2*Z/0
940 GOSUB 970
950 GO TO 1080

960 REM *** MODIFIE FILTER COMPONENTS ***

970 PRINT "CHOOSE A FILTER CAPACITANCE IN F =";
980 INPUT C
```

```
 990 R8=T1/C
1000 R9=T2/C
1010 PRINT "RESISTORS ARE:"
1020 PRINT "R1=";R8,"R2=";R9
1030 PRINT "G_G_IF R1 AND/OR R2 ARE INCONVENIENT CHANGE C?(Y OR RETURN)";
1040 INPUT A$
1050 IF A$<>"Y" THEN 1080
1060 GO TO 970
1070 RETURN
1080 PRINT "FILTER COMPONENT VALUES TO PRINTER ?(Y OR RETURN)";
1090 INPUT F$
1100 IF F$<>"Y" THEN 1120
1110 PRINT @41:"C=";C,"R1=";R8,"R2=";R9

1120 PRINT "C=";C,"R1=";R8,"R2=";R9
1130 K3=K2*N1

1140 REM
1150 REM *** BODE PLOT ***
1160 REM

1170 PRINT "G_G_J_BODE PLOT TO PLOTTER,SKIP OR SCREEN ?(P,S OR RETURN)";
1180 INPUT C$
1190 IF C$="S" THEN 2340
1200 IF C$="P" THEN 1220
1210 GO TO 1230
1220 V6=1
1230 L5=INT(LGT(F4))+2
1240 FOR I=1 TO 10*L5
1250    I1=I/10
1260    F3=10^I1*2*PI
1270    IF B$="A" THEN 1450

1280    REM *** BODE FUNCTIONS WITH PASSIVE FILTER ***

1290    T=T1+T2
1300    L=1+F3*F3*T*T
1310    A=-T1/L*K2
1320    B=-(1+F3*F3*T2*T)/L*K2/F3
1330    R9=A
1340    I9=B
1350    GOSUB 2370
1360    R3(I)=20*LGT(A)*5/8
1370    R4(I)=B/180*50
1380    A=1-R9
1390    B=I9
1400    R2(I)=20*LGT(1/SQR(A*A+B*B))
1410    GO TO 1560

1420    REM
1430    REM *** BODE-FUNCTIONS WITH ACTIVE FILTER ***
1440    REM

1450    A=-K3/F3/F3/N1/T1
1460    B=-K3*T2/F3/N1/T1
1470    R9=A
1480    I9=B
1490    GOSUB 2370
1500    R3(I)=20*LGT(A)*5/8
1510    R4(I)=B/180*50
1520    REM   *** ERROR FUNCTION ***

1530    A=1-R9
1540    B=I9
```

```
1550    R2(I)=20*LGT(1/SQR(A*A+B*B))
1560    R1(I)=F3/2/PI
1570 NEXT I

1580 REM    *** BODE PLOT GRAPH. ***

1590 PAGE
1600 VIEWPORT 10,120,5,95
1610 WINDOW 0,L5,-50,50
1620 AXIS @V6:1,50/8
1630 FOR I=0 TO L5
1640    FOR K=10 TO 50 STEP 10
1650       I1=LGT(K/5)
1660       MOVE @V6:I+I1,0
1670       RDRAW @V6:0,1
1680       RMOVE @V6:0,-1
1690    NEXT K
1700 NEXT I
1710 MOVE @V6:L5,-50
1720 FOR I=-9 TO 9
1730    RDRAW @V6:-L5/100,0
1740    PRINT @V6:2*I;"0"
1750    IF I=9 THEN 1790
1760    RMOVE @V6:L5/100,0
1770    RDRAW @V6:0,50/9
1780 NEXT I
1790 MOVE @V6:L5,47
1800 PRINT @V6:" DEG"
1810 FOR I=1 TO L5
1820    MOVE @V6:I,-3.5
1830.   PRINT @V6:"10^";I
1840    IMAGE 5D
1850 NEXT I
1860 MOVE @V6:0.9*L5,-3.5
1870 PRINT @V6:"HZ"
1880 FOR I=-80 TO 80 STEP 10
1890    MOVE @V6:0,(I-1)*5/8
1900    PRINT @V6:I
1910 NEXT I
1920 MOVE @V6:0,45*5/8
1930 PRINT @V6:" DB"
1940 MOVE @V6:L5/2,45
1950 PRINT @V6:"BODE PLOT"
1960 MOVE @V6:LGT(1.25),R2(1)
1970 FOR I=2 TO 10*L5
1980    I1=I/10
1990    DRAW @V6:I1,R2(I)
2000    IF I<>4*L5 THEN 2030
2010    PRINT @V6:" NOISE"
2020    MOVE @V6:I1,R2(I)
2030 NEXT I
2040 MOVE @V6:LGT(1.25),R3(1)
2050 FOR I=2 TO 10*L5
2060    I1=I/10
2070    DRAW @V6:I1,R3(I)
2080    IF I<>4*L5 THEN 2110
2090    PRINT @V6:" MAGN. "
2100    MOVE @V6:I1,R3(I)
2110 NEXT I
2120 MOVE @V6:LGT(1.25),R4(1)/2/PI*360
2130 FOR I=2 TO 10*L5
2140    I1=I/10
2150    DRAW @V6:I1,R4(I)/2/PI*360
```

```
2160    IF I<>4*L5 THEN 2190
2170    PRINT @V6:" PHASE"
2180    MOVE @V6:I1,R4(I)/2/PI*360
2190 NEXT I
2200 MOVE @V6:LGT(F4),-50
2210 FOR I=1 TO 28

2220    RDRAW @V6:0,2
2230    RMOVE @V6:0,1
2240 NEXT I
2250 PRINT @V6:"REF"
2260 IF V6=1 THEN 2340
2270 FOR I=1 TO 20
2280    MOVE @V6:L5/2,-45
2290    PRINT @V6:"TO CONTINUE ""RETURN """;
2300 NEXT I
2310 INPUT E$
2320 IF E$="" THEN 2340

2330 REM    *** END BODE PLOT ***

2340 PAGE
2350 GOSUB 5670

2360 REM *** RECT TO POLAR CONVERSION ROUTINE ***

2370 R=SQR(A*A+B*B)
2380 S=0
2390 IF R=0 THEN 2440
2400 S=ACS(A/R)
2410 IF B<0 THEN 2440
2420 B=S
2430 GO TO 2450
2440 B=-S
2450 A=R
2460 RETURN

2470 REM *** POLAR TO RECT. CONVERSION ROUTINE ***

2480 A=R*COS(S)
2490 B=R*SIN(S)
2500 R=A
2510 S=B
2520 RETURN
2530 PAGE

2540 REM    *** PASSIVE FILTER POLYNOMIAL COEFF. AND ROOTS ***

2550 Q1(3)=1
2560 Q1(2)=(N1+K3*T2)/(T1+T2)/N1
2570 Q1(1)=K2/(T1+T2)
2580 GOSUB 2700
2590 GOSUB 3990
2600 RETURN

2610 REM    *** ACTIVE FILTER POLYNOMIAL COEFF. AND ROOTS ***

2620 Q1(3)=1
2630 Q1(2)=K2*T2/T1
2640 Q1(1)=K2/T1
2650 GOSUB 2700
2660 GOSUB 3990
```

```
2670 RETURN
2680 REM  DRIVER FOR POLRT - FIND THE ROOTS OF A REAL POLY.
2690 REM

2700 N=2
2710 E9=6
2720 E9=10^-E9
2730 GOSUB 2880
2740 PRINT "J_J_COMPLETION FLAG = ";F;"J_J_"
2750 PRINT "THE ROOTS ARE :"
2760 PRINT P1(1),P2(1)
2770 PRINT P1(2),P2(2)
2780 RETURN

2790 REM  END OF DRIVER FOR POLRT.
2800 REM    F - (OUTPUT)  ERROR CODE WITH THE MEANINGS:
2810 REM        0 - NO ERROR
2820 REM        1 - ERROR: N<1
2830 REM        3 - ERROR: UNABLE TO DETERMINE A ROOT AFTER
2840 REM            500 ITERATIONS ON 5 STARTING VALUES.
2850 REM        4 - HIGH ORDER COEFFICIENT IS 0
2860 REM    E - (INPUT)  DESIRED ACCURACY (EG. 1E-6)
2870 REM

2880 DELETE Q2
2890 DIM Q2(N+1),P(14)
2900 P(9)=0
2910 P7=N
2920 F=0
2930 IF Q1(P7+1)=0 THEN 2970
2940 IF P7>0 THEN 2990
2950 F=1
2960 RETURN
2970 F=4
2980 RETURN
2990 P(7)=P7
3000 P(8)=P7+1
3010 P(6)=1
3020 Q7=P7+2
3030 FOR Q0=1 TO P7+1
3040   Q2(Q7-Q0)=Q1(Q0)
3050 NEXT Q0
3060 P(11)=0.00500101
3070 P(12)=0.010000101
3080 P(4)=0
3090 P8=P(11)
3100 P(11)=-10*P(12)
3110 P(12)=-10*P8
3120 P8=P(11)
3130 P9=P(12)
3140 P(4)=P(4)+1
3150 GO TO 3190
3160 P(9)=1
3170 P(13)=P8
3180 P(14)=P9
3190 P(5)=0
3200 P3=0
3210 P4=0
3220 P6=0
3230 Q3=1
3240 Q4=0
3250 P5=Q2(P7+1)
```

```
3260 IF P5=0 THEN 3730
3270 FOR P0=1 TO P7
3280    Q0=P7+1-P0
3290    Q8=Q2(Q0)
3300    Q5=P8*Q3-P9*Q4
3310    Q6=P8*Q4+P9*Q3
3320    P5=P5+Q8*Q5
3330    P6=P6+Q8*Q6
3340    P3=P3+P0*Q3*Q8
3350    P4=P4-P0*Q4*Q8
3360    Q3=Q5
3370    Q4=Q6
3380 NEXT P0
3390 P(10)=P3*P3+P4*P4
3400 IF P(10)=0 THEN 3640
3410 P(2)=(P6*P4-P5*P3)/P(10)
3420 P8=P8+P(2)
3430 P(3)=-(P5*P4+P6*P3)/P(10)
3440 P9=P9+P(3)
3450 IF ABS(P(2))+ABS(P(3))<E9 THEN 3520
3460 P(5)=P(5)+1
3470 IF P(5)<500 THEN 3200
3480 IF P(9)<>0 THEN 3520
3490 IF P(4)<5 THEN 3090
3500 F=3
3510 RETURN
3520 P0=N+2
3530 FOR Q0=1 TO P(8)
3540    Q7=P0-Q0
3550    Q8=Q1(Q7)
3560    Q1(Q7)=Q2(Q0)
3570    Q2(Q0)=Q8
3580 NEXT Q0
3590 Q7=P7
3600 P7=P(7)
3610 P(7)=Q7
3620 IF P(9)=0 THEN 3160
3630 GO TO 3670
3640 IF P(9)=0 THEN 3090
3650 P8=P(13)
3660 P9=P(14)
3670 P(9)=0
3680 IF ABS(P9)<10*E9*ABS(P8) THEN 3760
3690 P(1)=P8+P8
3700 P(10)=P8*P8+P9*P9
3710 P7=P7-2
3720 GO TO 3800
3730 P8=0
3740 P(7)=P(7)-1
3750 P(8)=P(8)-1
3760 P9=0
3770 P(10)=0
3780 P(1)=P8
3790 P7=P7-1
3800 Q2(2)=Q2(2)+P(1)*Q2(1)
3810 Q7=P(1)
3820 Q8=P(10)
3830 FOR Q0=2 TO P7
3840    Q2(Q0+1)=Q2(Q0+1)+Q7*Q2(Q0)-Q8*Q2(Q0-1)
3850 NEXT Q0
3860 P1(P(6))=P8
3870 P2(P(6))=P9
```

440

```
3880 P(6)=P(6)+1
3890 IF P(10)=0 THEN 3930
3900 P9=-P9
3910 P(10)=0
3920 GO TO 3860
3930 IF P7>0 THEN 3060
3940 RETURN

3950 REM   END OF "POLYNOMIAL ROOTS"
3960 REM
3970 REM    *** TRANSIENT RESPONSE ***
3980 REM

3990 P1(1)=-P1(1)
4000 P2(1)=-P2(1)
4010 P1(2)=-P1(2)
4020 P2(2)=-P2(2)
4030 RETURN
4040 PRINT "J_ENTER DESIRED FREQUENCY STEP IN HZ :";
4050 INPUT F6
4060 F7=F6*2*PI
4070 PRINT "ENTER START TIME OF TRANSIENT FUNCTION IN MS:";
4080 INPUT T6
4090 T6=1.0E-3*T6
4100 PRINT "ENTER STOP TIME OF TRANSIENT FUNCTION (50 STEPS) IN MS:";
4110 INPUT T7
4120 T7=1.0E-3*T7
4130 V5=32
4140 PRINT "TRANSIENT FUNCTION TO PRINTER OR SCREEN ?(Y OR RETURN)";
4150 INPUT F$
4160 IF F$<>"Y" THEN 4180
4170 V5=41
4180 PAGE
4190 RETURN
4200 GOSUB L6 OF 5540,5560
4210 T8=(T7-T6)/50
4220 FOR I=1 TO 51
4230   T5=T6+(I-1)*T8
4240   GOSUB 4290
4250   GOSUB L6 OF 5210,5380,5460
4260 NEXT I
4270 RETURN

4280 REM   EXP(-W1T) RECT.

4290 A5=EXP(-P1(1)*T5)*COS(P2(1)*T5)
4300 A6=-EXP(-P1(1)*T5)*SIN(P2(1)*T5)

4310 REM   EXP(-W2T) RECT

4320 B1=EXP(-P1(2)*T5)*COS(P2(2)*T5)
4330 B2=-EXP(-P1(2)*T5)*SIN(P2(2)*T5)

4340 REM    EXP(-W1T)-EXP(-W2T)/(W2-W1) RECT

4350 A7=A5-B1
4360 A8=A6-B2
4370 A=A7
4380 B=A8
4390 GOSUB 2370

4400 A7=A
```

```
4410 A8=B
4420 A=P1(2)-P1(1)
4430 B=P2(2)-P2(1)
4440 GOSUB 2370
4450 B3=A
4460 B4=B
4470 R=A7/B3
4480 S=A8-B4
4490 GOSUB 2480
4500 B5=R
4510 B6=S

4520 REM    EXP(-W1T) POL.

4530 A=A5
4540 B=A6
4550 GOSUB 2370
4560 A7=A
4570 A8=B

4580 REM    EXP(-W2T) POL.

4590 A=B1
4600 B=B2
4610 GOSUB 2370
4620 B7=A
4630 B8=B

4640 REM    W1 POL.

4650 A=P1(1)
4660 B=P2(1)
4670 GOSUB 2370
4680 M1=A
4690 M2=B

4700 REM    W2 POL

4710 A=P1(2)
4720 B=P2(2)
4730 GOSUB 2370
4740 M3=A
4750 M4=B

4760 REM    W1*EXP(-W1T)-W2*EXP(-W2T)/(W1-W2) POL.

4770 M5=P1(1)-P1(2)
4780 M6=P2(1)-P2(2)
4790 A=M5
4800 B=M6
4810 GOSUB 2370
4820 M7=A
4830 M8=B
4840 M9=M1*A7
4850 M0=M2+A8
4860 S1=M3*B7
4870 S2=M4+B8
4880 R=M9
4890 S=M0
4900 GOSUB 2480
4910 M9=R
4920 M0=S
4930 R=S1
```

```
4940 S=S2
4950 GOSUB 2480
4960 S1=R
4970 S2=S
4980 S3=M9-S1
4990 S4=M0-S2
5000 A=S3
5010 B=S4
5020 GOSUB 2370
5030 S3=A
5040 S4=B
5050 S5=S3/M7
5060 S6=S4-M8
5070 RETURN

5080 REM    **** FREQUENCY TRANSIENT ****
5090 REM
5100 REM     *** ACTIVE FILTER ***

5110 A1=1+K0*K5*T2/N1/T1
5120 A1=F7/A1
5130 O4=A1*EXP(-T5/(N1*T1/K0/K5+T2))
5140 IF O4<O5 THEN 5180
5150 PRINT @V5:T5,O4
5160 NEXT I
5170 RETURN
5180 PRINT @V5:"PULL-IN TIME=";T5;" SEC"
5190 GO TO 5830

5200 REM     *** PASSIVE FILTER ***

5210 G1=1/(N1*(T1+T2)+K0*K5*T2)
5220 G2=G1*(N1+K0*K5)
5230 FOR I=1 TO 51
5240    T5=T6+(I-1)*(T7-T6)/50
5250    Z2=EXP(-T5*G2)
5260    G3=1/(N1+K0*K5)*(1-Z2)
5270    G4=G1*Z2
5280    G5=N1*F7*(G3+(T1+T2)*G4)
5290    IF G5<O5 THEN 5330
5300    PRINT @V5:T5,G5
5310 NEXT I
5320 RETURN
5330 PRINT @V5:"PULL-IN TIME=";T5;" SEC"
5340 GO TO 5730

5350 REM    **** PHASE TRANSIENT ****
5360 REM
5370 REM     *** ACTIVE FILTER ***

5380 D1=S5*2*PI*N1
5390 D2=S6
5400 R=D1
5410 S=D2
5420 GOSUB 2480
5430 PRINT @V5:T5,R/2/PI*360
5440 RETURN

5450 REM     *** PASSIVE FILTER ***

5460 R=S5
5470 S=S6
5480 GOSUB 2480
```

```
5490 S7=R
5500 S8=S
5510 D1=2*PI*N1*(S7+B5/(T1+T2))
5520 PRINT @V5;T5,D1/2/PI*360
5530 RETURN
5540 PRINT @V5;"TIME IN SEC.        INPUT FREQU. DEVIATION IN RAD/S"
5550 RETURN
5560 PRINT @V5;"TIME IN SEC.        VCO PHASE DEVIATION IN DEG. "
5570 RETURN
5580 FOR I=1 TO 51
5590    T8=(T7-T6)/50
5600    T5=T6+(I-1)*T8
5610    GOSUB 5110
5620 NEXT I
5630 RETURN

5640 REM
5650 REM    *** DRIVER FOR TRANSIENT ANALYSIS ***
5660 REM

5670 IF B$="A" THEN 5790

5680 REM    *** FREQ. TRANSIENT; PASSIVE FILTER ***

5690 GOSUB 4040
5700 GOSUB 5540
5710 GOSUB 5210

5720 REM    *** PHASE TRANSIENT; PASSIVE FILTER ***

5730 L6=3
5740 GOSUB 2550
5750 GOSUB 4070
5760 GOSUB 4200
5770 GO TO 5880

5780 REM    *** FREQ. TRANSIENT; ACTIVE FILTER ***

5790 GOSUB 4040
5800 GOSUB 5540
5810 GOSUB 5580

5820 REM    *** PHASE TRANSIENT; ACTIVE FILTER ***

5830 L6=2
5840 GOSUB 2620
5850 GOSUB 4070
5860 GOSUB 4200
5870 END

5880 REM    *** INPUT DATA EDITING ***

5890 PRINT "VCO GAIN=";

5900 INPUT Z$
5910 IF Z$="" THEN 5930
5920 K0=VAL(Z$)
5930 PRINT "PHASE DETECTOR GAIN=";
5940 INPUT Z$
5950 IF Z$="" THEN 5970
5960 K1=VAL(Z$)
5970 PRINT "NATURAL LOOP FREQ. =";
5980 INPUT Z$
```

TABLE A-16   (cont'd)

```
5990 IF Z$="" THEN 6020
6000 O1=VAL(Z$)
6010 O=O1*2*PI
6020 PRINT "REF. FREQU. =";
6030 INPUT Z$
6040 IF Z$="" THEN 6060
6050 F4=VAL(Z$)
6060 PRINT "ZETA=";
6070 INPUT Z$
6080 IF Z$="" THEN 6100
6090 Z=VAL(Z$)
6100 PRINT "DIVIDER RATIO=";
6110 INPUT Z$
6120 IF Z$="" THEN 6160
6130 N1=VAL(Z$)
6140 K2=K0*K1/N1
6150 GO TO 570
6160 PRINT "DETECTOR SUPPLY VOLTS=";
6170 INPUT Z$
6180 IF Z$="" THEN 6200
6190 V7=VAL(Z$)
6200 PAGE
6210 GO TO 570
6220 END
```

A-2-5 Fifth-Order Type 2 Loop Program with a Computation of Lock-in Time (TEK4051/52/54)

The fifth-order type 2 loop consists of a third-order type 2 loop and an active filter following the integrator. In practice, there is no such device as a second-order type 2 loop, because any additional phase shifts generated by bypass capacitors or imperfect operational amplifiers introduce enough lag that the ideal second-order type 2 loop cannot be realized.

We learned in Chapter 1 that the third-order type 2 loop combines fast acquisition, stable performance, best possible tracking, and high reference suppression. The penalty that has to be paid is a careful stability analysis, best done with a computer program. In the second-order type 2 loop, the damping factor ζ was chosen for best loop performance to be 0.7, and the phase margin was set at 45° with a gain margin of 10 dB.

In the case of higher-order loops, the damping factor does not exist, and the design criterion is to select the appropriate phase margin values (between 30° and 70°). From my experience in building PLLs, I have to admit that the third-order type 2 loop has become my favorite loop.

If the pole of the active low-pass filter is chosen high enough to have no influence on the loop, this program can be used to analyze the third-order type 2 loop by specifying a very high low-pass cutoff frequency and the influence of the additional low-pass filter can be observed by decreasing the cutoff frequency of this filter.

The active low-pass filter is defined by a damping constant in the range 0.1 to 0.7, depending on the desired response; this damping range would include the Chebyshev filter (damping factor = 0.1) and the Butterworth filter (damping factor = 0.7).

As in previous cases, the best way to get acquainted with the program is to use it.

Let us start with the same basic example that we have used in the second-order type 2 loop program. The values for K_v and K_oN can be seen in Table A-17, and the computer has determined that the values for the circuit are about

$$C1 = 1.8 \times 10^{-8}F$$
$$C2 = 3.7 \times 10^{-9}F$$

The reference frequency is 1 kHz again, and the natural loop frequency is set at 300 Hz. For the active low-pass filter, a damping factor of 0.1, Chebyshev performance, is set, and the cutoff frequency of the low-pass filter is set high on purpose, to 5000 Hz. In effect, that means that the active low-pass filter does not influence the new performance. Figure A-35 shows the Bode plot for this loop.

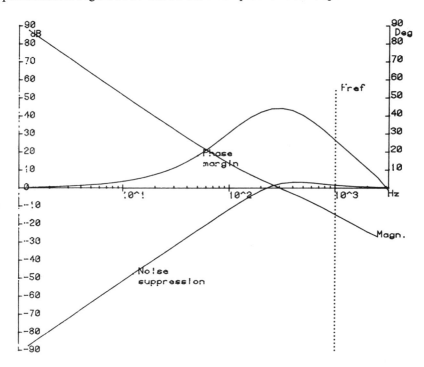

Figure A-35   Bode plot for the loop specified by the components of Table A-17.

It becomes apparent that the reference suppression, stated in Figure A-35 to be 14.7 dB, can be read from the Bode plot. The phase margin is 45 dB, and there is a slight overshoot found in the noise-suppression curve.

Now we are curious to determine the lock-in time of the loop as printed out in Table A-18. If we assume that we want to go to an error of less than 1 Hz, the time in milliseconds for acquisition is 19, which is about the same result as we obtained in the previous example. Some conversion has been made in the program to print out a frequency error rather than a phase error. This was done for reasons of convenience.

TABLE A-17 CIRCUIT COMPONENTS FOR THE SECOND-ORDER TYPE 2 LOOP[a]

```
INTEGRATOR CIRCUIT COMPONENTS ARE :

R1=  5600. 00   R2=  59622. 75   C1= 1. 7796E-008   C2= 3. 6856E-009

K0=1. 1           KV=6000000        DIV=45000        CUTOFF=5000
 T1= 9. 966E-005    T2= 1. 281E-003    T3= 2. 197E-004
 DAMP= 0. 100   NAT. LOOP FREQ. = 3. 000000E+002   REF. FREQ. = 1. 000000E+003

REFERENCE FREQUENCY SUPPRESSION=-14. 6774854947
```

[a]The active low-pass filter cutoff frequency is set too high to have an influence.

TABLE A-18 PRINTOUT OF LOCK-UP PERFORMANCE OF THE LOOP DESCRIBED BY TABLE A-17

```
THE ROOTS ARE :

            1     -1847. 42803358        0

            2     -1340. 36229396    -1363. 97039103

            3     -1340. 36229396     1363. 97039103

            4     -3152. 85902037    -31119. 9298478

            5     -3152. 85902037     31119. 9298478


COMPLETION FLAG = 0

TIME MS           FREQ.  DEVIATION HZ
1                 5. 050545227E+10
2                 -2. 965244896E+9
3                 -6. 547607899E+8
4                 6. 25418558E+8
5                 1. 897611801E+8
6                 -1. 020596805E+7
7                 -1. 216825766E+7
8                 -304614. 741112
9                 848908. 16311
10                119692. 134741
11                -44102. 3566045
12                -12753. 7727193
13                1680. 15436609
14                1059. 09756988
15                -0. 520479747229
16                -72. 5023793303
17                -7. 74030063042
18                4. 13816622111
19                0. 97563670833
20                -0. 178564259242
21                -0. 086029250319
22                0. 00298740254921
23                0. 0062156011
24                4. 635653175E-4
25                -3. 760107015E-4
```

Now let us test another case. Our VCO is operated at the same 45 MHz, the voltage gain of the oscillator is 100 MHz/V, the division ratio is 9000, and the reference frequency is 25 kHz. In order to obtain a good reference suppression and minimize microphonic effects at the same time, the natural loop frequency is set at 500 Hz, and the cutoff frequency of the second-order low-pass filter is set at 5000 Hz. Finally, the damping factor of 0.1 is selected for a Chebyshev response. The Chebyshev response shows slightly more ringing and greater attenuation of the reference.

The computer program as shown in Table A-19 prints the necessary component values and indicates a reference suppression of around 88 dB and a lock-in time of 13 ms. These results also indicate that the lock-in time and the natural loop frequency are closely related, as explained in Chapter 1.

Now let us take a look at the Bode diagram, Figure A-36. Relative to what we are used to, the Bode diagram looks different. The magnitude of the loop gain crosses 0 dB at the required 500-Hz line and shows a peak of 5 kHz, which is the cutoff frequency for the active second-order low-pass filter. In addition, the phase shows a drastic change, but as the gain is already less than -20 dB, the loop remains stable, and because of the fifth-order characteristic, a very high reference suppression is possible.

PLLs are used from time to time to clean up the input frequency, which typically results in a division ratio $N = 1$. The following example shows the case of a high

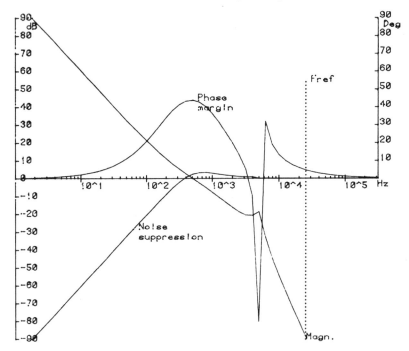

Figure A-36 Bode plot of the type 2 fifth-order loop; note the deep notch in the phase around 5 kHz.

TABLE A-19 COMPUTER PRINTOUT WITH THE COMPONENT VALUES, REFERENCE SUPPRESSION, AND LOCK-UP PERFORMANCE FOR A TYPE 2 FIFTH-ORDER LOOP

R1= INTEGRATOR CIRCUIT COMPONENTS ARE

R1= 5600.00   R2=   1192.46   C1= 5.3387E-007   C2= 1.1057E-007

K0=1.1   KV=1.0E+8   DIV=9000   CUTOFF=5000
 T1= 2.990E-003   T2= 7.685E-004   T3= 1.318E-004
 DAMP= 0.100   NAT. LOOP FREQ. = 5.000000E+002   REF. FREQ. = 2.500000E+004

REFERENCE FREQUENCY SUPPRESSION=-87.9248597865
THE ROOTS ARE :

            1   -3066.42843347   0

            2   -2258.88125194   -2294.20119039

            3   -2258.88125194   2294.20119039

            4   -3141.73498079   -30868.5968595

            5   -3141.73498079   30868.5968595

COMPLETION FLAG = 0

TIME MS	FREQ. DEVIATION HZ
1	2.76558657E+11
2	3.568801007E+10
3	2.209564232E+10
4	-2.042799812E+9
5	1.068376424E+8
6	1.057060465E+7
7	-2485654.90092
8	235033.801247
9	-5070.48845107
10	-1849.41866935
11	311.782683544
12	-22.9057072301
13	-0.233254176448
14	0.28230656 0248
15	-0.0364948986719
16	0.00196654615507
17	1.263129744E-4
18	-3.893078977E-5
19	4.005726393E-6
20	-1.291325829E-7
21	-2.585679046E-8
22	4.985332372E-9
23	-4.072969384E-10
24	1.92310196E-12
25	4.179031297E-12
26	-5.989572113E-13
27	3.722965247E-14
28	1.387722405E-15
29	-5.982278403E-16
30	6.759149108E-17
31	-2.819349421E-18
32	-3.47731511E-19
33	7.886079564E-20
34	-7.111690497E-21
35	1.22922501E-22
36	6.061236673E-23
37	-9.724333545E-24

frequency loop with no dividers. From Table A-20 we learn that the reference frequency is 500 kHz, the natural loop frequency is 2 kHz, damping is 0.1, and the reference suppression is a surprisingly high value, 156 dB. Such a value is not measurable and generally indicates that the reference suppression is high enough, provided that there are no leakages on the printed circuit boards. From the acquisition time printout we can learn that the acquisition time, to be within less than a 1-Hz error, is between 5 and 6 ms. Again, the speed of the loop is determined primarily by the natural loop frequency.

Now let us take a look at the Bode diagram, Figure A-37. The magnitude of the loop gain crosses the 0-dB line at 2 kHz, as required. However, the second-order

TABLE A-20 1:1 LOOP USED AS A "CLEAN-UP" LOOP

```
INTEGRATOR CIRCUIT COMPONENTS ARE

R1=  5600.00    R2=       7.57   C1= 2.1021E-005   C2= 4.3536E-006

K0=1.1           KV=7000000         DIV=1              CUTOFF=10000
 T1= 1.177E-001     T2= 1.921E-004    T3= 3.296E-005
 DAMP= 0.100   NAT. LOOP FREQ. = 2.000000E+003   REF. FREQ. = 5.000000E+005

REFERENCE FREQUENCY SUPPRESSION=-156.217874364
THE ROOTS ARE :

         1      -12566.3706144      0

         2      -9582.88430028     -9130.0692763

         3      -9582.88430028      9130.0692763

         4      -5586.06688322    -59391.2893459

         5      -5586.06688322     59391.2893459


COMPLETION FLAG = 0

    TIME MS              FREQ. DEVIATION HZ
    1                    2.40874457E+10
    2                    -1.620015339E+8
    3                    503007.947789
    4                    -1305.8553883
    5                    2.28513015706
    6                    0.00198404972591
    7                    -4.634963056E-5
    8                    3.042823848E-7
    9                    -1.529032406E-9
    10                   6.679901575E-12
    11                   -2.637451424E-14
    12                   9.509787154E-17
    13                   -3.107074631E-19
    14                   8.896500907E-22
    15                   -2.00722504E-24
    16                   1.876397604E-27
    17                   1.477499666E-29
    18                   -1.322729797E-31
    19                   7.402308757E-34
```

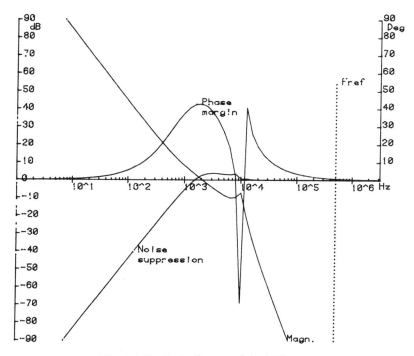

Figure A-37   Bode diagram of the 1:1 loop.

low-pass filter, because of the cutoff frequency of 10 kHz, changes the gain, which then is about −10 dB.

As a result, the total response is influenced, as can be seen by the noise suppression curve, and while stability is maintained, it is advisable to set the cutoff frequency of the second-order low-pass filter slightly higher (i.e., 13 kHz) to avoid any possible instabilities. The program has an automatic recognition of instability feature which we will now test (i.e., testing for pole location with θ70). Table A-21 refers to a loop with a 1-kHz reference, a natural loop frequency of 300 Hz, and a cutoff frequency of the second-order low-pass filter of 800 Hz. This loop is unstable, and the computer requests that the natural loop frequency or other values be changed. If we maintain the same values and change the natural loop frequency to 50 Hz, the component values of the capacitors and the resistors will change, the loop will become stable, and the reference suppression will be 40 dB. Figure A-38 shows the Bode diagram for this particular case. I urge the reader to experiment with this program. While doing this, a certain feeling for designing loops will be generated, and some of the mystery will be taken out.

The following is a printout of the computer program that has been written for a TEK4051/52/54 system. The graphic portion, which makes it very attractive, can be deleted if it is of interest to use it on any other BASIC computer. With some minor modification, this can become a very useful tool (Table A-22).

TABLE A-21 LISTING OF THE COMPONENTS OF AN UNSTABLE LOOP, MADE UNSTABLE BECAUSE OF THE ACTIVE FILTER BEING TOO CLOSE TO THE LOOP CUTOFF AND MADE STABLE BY CHANGING THOSE VALUES

```
INTEGRATOR CIRCUIT COMPONENTS ARE :

R1=  5600.00    R2=  59622.75    C1= 1.7796E-008    C2= 3.6856E-009

K0=1.1           KV=6000000        DIV=45000         CUTOFF=800
 T1= 9.966E-005    T2= 1.281E-003    T3= 2.197E-004
 DAMP= 0.100   NAT.LOOP FREQ. = 3.000000E+002   REF.FREQ. = 1.000000E+003

REFERENCE FREQUENCY SUPPRESSION=-10.8098452261
THE ROOTS ARE :

              1     -2481.76400815      0

              2     -1589.56257481     -1035.43288633

              3     -1589.56257481      1035.43288633

              4      52.447076782      -4352.40276516

              5      52.447076782       4352.40276516


COMPLETION FLAG = 0
*** LOOP UNSTABLE !!! >INCREASE NATURAL LOOP FREQUENCY

AND/OR DAMPING FACTOR,OR MODIFIE R1,R2,C1,C2 ***


 INTEGRATOR CIRCUIT COMPONENTS ARE :

 R1=  5600.00    R2=  9937.13    C1= 6.4065E-007    C2= 1.3268E-007

K0=1.1           KV=6000000        DIV=45000         CUTOFF=800
 T1= 3.588E-003    T2= 7.685E-003    T3= 1.318E-003
 DAMP= 0.100   NAT.LOOP FREQ. = 5.000000E+001   REF.FREQ. = 1.000000E+003

REFERENCE FREQUENCY SUPPRESSION=-40.2319661152
THE ROOTS ARE :

              1     -307.759969228      0

              2     -223.506878017     -227.491598246

              3     -223.506878017      227.491598246

              4     -504.491741531     -4977.27988818

              5     -504.491741531      4977 27988818


COMPLETION FLAG = 0
```

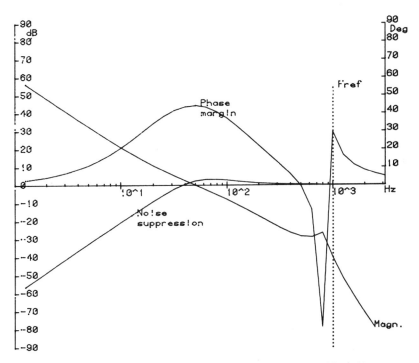

Figure A-38 Bode diagram of the loop described by Table A-21.

TABLE A-22 LISTING OF THE TYPE 2 FIFTH-ORDER PLL PROGRAM

```
1 GO TO 100
4 PAGE
5 GO TO 760
6 RETURN
8 PAGE
9 GO TO 520
10 RETURN
100 INIT
110 PAGE
120 V4=32
130 V5=32
140 V6=32

150 REM*************************************************************
160 REM PROGRAM CALCULATES THE TRANSIENT RESPONSE OF A 5TH ORDER PLL
170 REM WITH AN IDEAL INTEGRATOR OF 2ND ORDER AND AN ACTIVE LOW PASS
180 REM OF 2ND ORDER.  A BODE PLOT OF THE OPEN-LOOP TRANSFER FUNCTION
190 REM IS PROVIDED. USER MAY DEFINE A SAFE PHASE MARGIN(I. E. ^45 DEG.)
200 REM AND A LOWEST NATURAL LOOP FREQUENCY(I. E. ^1/(LOCKING-TIME), OR
210 REM PROVIDE TWO R AND TWO C VALUES FOR THE IDEAL INTEGRATOR CIRCUIT
220 REM THE ACTIVE LOW PASS FILTER IS DEFINED BY A"DAMPING"CONSTANT IN
230 REM RANGE OF 0. 1 TO 1/SQR(2) AND A CUT OFF FREQUENCY LOCATED BETWEEN
240 REM THE NATURAL LOOP FREQUENCY AND THE REFERENCE FREQUENCY.  06. 7. 80
```

```
250 REM*******************************************************************
260 REM NOTE:STEADY STATE VALUE OF STEP TRANSIENT TENDS TOWARD 0 DEG.
270 REM      THE PROGRAM PROVIDES 60 TIME STEPS.
280 REM*******************************************************************
282 REM VARIABLES USED:A,A1,A2,A3,A4,A5,A$,B1,B2,B$,C1,C2,D1,E,E1,E2,E9
284 REM    F,F0,F1,F2,F3,F4,F5,F7,G1,G2,H0,H1,H2,H3,H4,H5,H6,H7,H8,H9,I,I1
286 REM    J,K,K0,K1,K2,K5,K6,K8,L,L1,L5,M,N,N1,N2,N8,O0,O1,O3,P,P0,P1,P2
288 REM    P3,P4,P5,P6,P7,P8,P9,Q0,Q1,Q2,Q3,Q4,Q5,Q6,Q7,Q8,R1,R2,R3,R4,R6
289 REM    R7,R8,R9,S4.

290 PRINT @V4:"REFERENCE FREQ. IN HZ=";
300 INPUT F4
310 PRINT @V4:"PHASE DETECTOR GAIN CONSTANT IN V/RAD=";
320 INPUT K0
330 PRINT @V4:"VCO GAIN CONSTANT IN.RAD/V/S=";
340 INPUT K8
350 PRINT @V4:"DIVIDER RATIO=";
360 INPUT N8
370 PRINT @V4:"DESIRED FREQUENCY STEP IN HZ=";
380 INPUT F5
390 PRINT @V4:"START TIME OF TRANSIENT FUNCTION IN MS=";
400 INPUT T0
410 T0=T0/1000
420 PRINT @V4:"TIME STEP INCREMENT OF TRANSIENT FUNCTION IN MS=";
430 INPUT T7
440 T7=T7/1000
450 N1=60
460 PRINT @V4:"DO YOU WANT TO DEFINE PHASE MARGIN OR R/C VALUES OF"
470 PRINT @V4:"IDEAL INTEGRATOR ? (P OR R)";
480 INPUT A$
490 IF A$="P" THEN 520
500 IF A$="R" THEN 760
510 GO TO 460
520 PRINT @V4:"NATURAL LOOP FREQ. =";
530 INPUT F0
540 PRINT @V4:"PHASE MARGIN(30< MARGIN <70 DEG.)=";
550 INPUT F2
560 DELETE A1,A2,C1,C2

570 REM
580 REM    *** FIND TIME CONSTANTS OF IDEAL INTEGRATOR ***
590 REM

600 F1=2*PI*F2/360
610 O0=2*PI*F0
620 T3=(1/COS(F1)-TAN(F1))/O0
630 T9=K0*K8/N8/O0/O0
640 T2=1/O0/O0/T3
650 A1=1+O0^2*T2^2
660 A2=1+O0^2*T3^2
670 T1=T9*SQR(A1/A2)
680 R8=5600
690 C1=T1/R8
700 R9=(T2-T3)/T1*R8
710 C2=T3/R9
720 PRINT @V5:" INTEGRATOR CIRCUIT COMPONENTS ARE :"
730 PRINT @V5: USING 740:"J_R1=";R8,"R2=";R9,"C1=";C1,"C2=";C2
740 IMAGE 1X,2(4A,6D.2D,3X)2(3A,4E,3X)
750 GO TO 910
760 PRINT @V4:"DEFINE OTHER R/C VALUES FOR IDEAL INTEGRATOR:"
770 DELETE R1,R2,C1,C2
780 PRINT @V4:"R1=";
790 INPUT R1
800 PRINT @V4:"R2=";
```

```
810 INPUT R2
820 PRINT @V4:"C1=";
830 INPUT C1
840 PRINT @V4:"C2=";
850 INPUT C2
860 T1=R1*C1
870 T2=R2*(C1+C2)
880 T3=R2*C2
890 DELETE R2


900 REM ************************************************

910 S4=F5
920 T9=T0
930 T8=T7
940 DELETE A1,A2,C1,C2
950 DIM A1(12,12),A2(12,12),A3(12),A4(12),B1(12,12),B2(12,12),C1(12)
960 DIM C2(12),K1(12),K2(12),E1(12),E2(12),G1(12),G2(12),P1(12),P2(12)
970 DIM Q1(12),R2(150),R3(150),R4(150),A3(12),A4(12)
980 PRINT @V4:"J_DAMPING FACTOR OF ACTIVE 2ND ORDER LOW PASS=";
990 INPUT D1
1000 PRINT @V4:"J_CUT OFF FREQUENCY OF 2ND ORDER LOW PASS IN HZ=";
1010 INPUT F1

1020 REM
1030 REM

1040 O1=F1*2*PI
1050 PRINT @V5:"J_K0=";K0,"KV=";K8,"DIV=";N8,"CUTOFF=";F1
1060 PRINT @V5: USING 1070:"T1=";T1,"T2=";T2,"T3=";T3
1070 IMAGE 1X,3(3A,3E,5X)
1080 PRI @V5: USI 1090:"DAMP=";D1,"NAT. LOOP FREQ. =";F0,"REF FREQ. =";F4
1090 IMAGE 1X,5A,2D.3D,3X,15A,6E,3X,10A,6E
1100 SET DEGREES
1110 L5=INT(LGT(F4))+1.5
1120 FOR I=1 TO 10*L5
1130     I1=I/10
1140     F3=10^I1
1150     IF I=1 THEN 1170
1160     GO TO 1180
1170     F7=LGT(F3)
1180     O3=2*PI*F3
1190     H1=T1*T3/O1/O1
1200     H2=T1/O1*(2*D1*T3+1/O1)
1210     H3=T1*(T3+2*D1/O1)
1220     H4=T1
1230     H5=K0*K8/N8
1240     H6=H4-O3*O3*H2
1250     H7=H3-O3*O3*H1
1260     A5=O3*(T2*H6-H7)/(H6+O3*O3*T2*H7)
1270     R4(I)=ATN(A5)+180
1280     H8=H6+O3*O3*T2*H7
1290     H9=O3*(T2*H6-H7)
1300     H0=H6*H6+O3*O3*H7*H7
1310     R9=H5/O3/O3/H0*SQR(H8*H8+H9*H9)
1320     R3(I)=20*LGT(R9)
1330     IF I=10*L5+1 THEN 1410
1340     R6=R9*COS(R4(I))
1350     R7=R9*SIN(R4(I))
1360     R8=1+R6
1370     R2(I)=20*LGT(1/SQR(R8*R8+R7*R7))
1380 NEXT I
1390 F3=F4
```

```
1400 GO TO 1180
1410 PRINT @V5:"J_REFERENCE FREQUENCY SUPPRESSION=";R3(I)
1420 SET RADIANS
1430 PRINT @V4:"J_G_G_G_ FOR BODE PLOT PRESS RETURN";
1440 INPUT B$
1450 PAGE
1460 VIEWPORT 10,120,5,95
1470 L5=INT(LGT(F4))+1.5
1480 WINDOW 0,L5,-90,90
1490 AXIS 1,10
1500 FOR I=0 TO L5
1510    FOR K=2 TO 9
1520        I1=LGT(K)
1530        MOVE @V6:I+I1,0
1540        RDRAW @V6:0,1
1550        RMOVE @V6:0,-1
1560    NEXT K
1570 NEXT I
1580 MOVE @V6:L5,0
1590 FOR I=1 TO 9
1600    RDRAW @V6:0,10
1610    RDRAW @V6:-L5/100,0
1620    PRINT @V6:I; "0"
1630    IF I=9 THEN 1660
1640    RMOVE @V6:L5/100,0
1650 NEXT I
1660 MOVE @V6:L5,85
1670 PRINT @V6:" DEG"
1680 FOR I=1 TO L5
1690    MOVE @V6:I,-5.5
1700    PRINT @V6:"10'";I
1710    IMAGE 5D
1720 NEXT I
1730 MOVE @V6:L5,-4.5
1740 PRINT @V6:"HZ"
1750 FOR I=-90 TO 90 STEP 10
1760    MOVE @V6:0,I-1
1770    PRINT @V6:I
1780 NEXT I
1790 MOVE @V6:0,84
1800 PRINT @V6:"  DB"
1810 MOVE @V6:L5/2,85
1820 PRINT @V6:"***BODE PLOT***"
1830 MOVE @V6:F7,R3(1)
1840 FOR I=1 TO 10*L5-0.5
1850    I1=I/10
1860    DRAW @V6:I1,R3(I)
1870 NEXT I
1880 PRINT @V6:"MAGN. "
1890 MOVE @V6:F7,R2(1)
1900 FOR I=1 TO 10*L5
1910    I1=I/10
1920    DRAW @V6:I1,R2(I)
1930    IF I=INT(10*L5/3) THEN 1950
1940    GO TO 1970
1950    PRINT @V6:"_NOISEH_H_H_H_H_J_SUPPRESSION"
1960    MOVE @V6:I1,R2(I)
1970 NEXT I
1980 MOVE @V6:F7,R4(1)-180
1990 FOR I=1 TO 10*L5
2000    I1=I/10
2010    DRAW @V6:I1,R4(I)-180
2020    IF I=INT(5*L5) THEN 2040
```

456

```
2030     GO TO 2060
2040     PRINT @V6:" PHASEH_H_H_H_J_MARGIN"
2050     MOVE @V6:I1,R4(I)-180
2060 NEXT I
2070 L1=LGT(F4)
2080 FOR I=-90 TO 55 STEP 2
2090     MOVE @V6:L1,I
2100     DRAW @V6:L1,I
2110 NEXT I
2120 PRINT @V6:" FREF"

2130 REM

2140 SET KEY

2150 REM   *** END BODE PLOT ***

2160 MOVE @V6:0,-79
2170 PRINT @V4:"       TO MODIFY LOW PASS OR"
2180 MOVE @V4:0,-84
2190 PRINT @V4:"       TO MODIFY INTEGRATOR:KEY#2"
2200 MOVE @V4:0,-74
2210 PRINT @V4:"       DEFINE OTHER INTEGRATOR R/C VALUES:KEY#1"
2220 MOVE @V4:0,-89
2230 PRINT @V4:"       FOR LOCKING FUNCT.PRESS:RETURN";
2240 INPUT A$
2250 PAGE
2260 PRINT @V5:"THE ROOTS ARE   "
2270 U=K0*K8/N8
2280 Q1(1)=U*O1*O1/T1/T3
2290 Q1(2)=Q1(1)*T2
2300 Q1(3)=O1*O1/T3
2310 Q1(4)=O1*O1+2*D1*O1/T3
2320 Q1(5)=(2*D1*T3*O1+1)/T3
2330 Q1(6)=1
2340 N1=4
2350 N2=5
2360 E=10^-6
2370 N=N2
2380 GOSUB 2680
2390 PRINT @V5:"J_COMPLETION FLAG = ";F;"J_"
2400 FOR I=1 TO N2
2410     IF SGN(P1(I))=1 THEN 2440
2420 NEXT I
2430 GO TO 3780
2440 PRINT @V5:"*** LOOP UNSTABLE !!! >INCREASE NATURAL LOOP FREQUENCY"
2450 PRINT @V5:"G_G_AND/OR DAMPING FACTOR,OR MODIFIE R1,R2,C1,C2 ***";"J_"
2460 GO TO 460

2470 REM  END OF DRIVER FOR POLRT.
2480 REM  **********************
2490 REM  "POLYNOMIAL ROOTS" - COMPUTES THE REAL AND COMPLEX ROOTS
2500 REM                      OF A REAL POLYNOMIAL.
2510 REM  PARAMETERS
2520 REM     Q1- (INPUT) VECTOR OF N+1  COEFFICENTS OF THE
2530 REM         POLYNOMIAL, ORDERED FROM SMALLEST TO
2540 REM         LARGEST POWER.
2550 REM     N - (INPUT)  ORDER OF POLYNOMIAL
2560 REM     P1- (OUTPUT) VECTOR OF LENGTH N CONTAINING THE
2570 REM         REAL PART OF THE ROOTS OF THE POLNOMIAL
2580 REM     P2- (OUTPUT) VECTOR OF LENGTH N CONTAINING THE
2590 REM         IMAGINARY PART OF THE ROOTS OF THE POLYNOMIAL.
2600 REM     F - (OUTPUT) ERROR CODE WITH THE MEANINGS:
```

```
2610 REM          0 - NO ERROR
2620 REM          1 - ERROR: N<1
2630 REM          3 - ERROR: UNABLE TO DETERMINE A ROOT AFTER
2640 REM             500 ITERATIONS ON 5 STARTING VALUES.
2650 REM          4 - HIGH ORDER COEFFICIENT IS 0.
2660 REM      E - (INPUT)  DESIRED ACCURACY (EG. 1E-6)
2670 REM

2680 DELETE Q2
2690 DIM Q2(N+1),P(14)
2700 P(9)=0
2710 P7=N
2720 F=0
2730 IF Q1(P7+1)=0 THEN 2770
2740 IF P7>0 THEN 2790
2750 F=1
2760 RETURN
2770 F=4
2780 RETURN
2790 P(7)=P7
2800 P(8)=P7+1
2810 P(6)=1
2820 Q7=P7+2
2830 FOR Q0=1 TO P7+1
2840     Q2(Q7-Q0)=Q1(Q0)
2850 NEXT Q0
2860 P(11)=0.00500101
2870 P(12)=0.010000101
2880 P(4)=0
2890 P8=P(11)
2900 P(11)=-10*P(12)
2910 P(12)=-10*P8
2920 P8=P(11)
2930 P9=P(12)
2940 P(4)=P(4)+1
2950 GO TO 2990
2960 P(9)=1
2970 P(13)=P8
2980 P(14)=P9
2990 P(5)=0
3000 P3=0
3010 P4=0
3020 P6=0
3030 Q3=1
3040 Q4=0
3050 P5=Q2(P7+1)
3060 IF P5=0 THEN 3530
3070 FOR P0=1 TO P7
3080     Q0=P7+1-P0
3090     Q8=Q2(Q0)
3100     Q5=P8*Q3-P9*Q4
3110     Q6=P8*Q4+P9*Q3
3120     P5=P5+Q8*Q5
3130     P6=P6+Q8*Q6
3140     P3=P3+P0*Q3*Q8
3150     P4=P4-P0*Q4*Q8
3160     Q3=Q5
3170     Q4=Q6
3180 NEXT P0
3190 P(10)=P3*P3+P4*P4
3200 IF P(10)=0 THEN 3440
3210 P(2)=(P6*P4-P5*P3)/P(10)
3220 P8=P8+P(2)
```

```
3230 P(3)=-(P5*P4+P6*P3)/P(10)
3240 P9=P9+P(3)
3250 IF ABS(P(2))+ABS(P(3))<E THEN 3320
3260 P(5)=P(5)+1
3270 IF P(5)<500 THEN 3000
3280 IF P(9)<>0 THEN 3320
3290 IF P(4)<5 THEN 2890
3300 F=3
3310 RETURN
3320 P0=N+2
3330 FOR Q0=1 TO P(8)
3340    Q7=P0-Q0
3350    Q8=Q1(Q7)
3360    Q1(Q7)=Q2(Q0)
3370    Q2(Q0)=Q8
3380 NEXT Q0
3390 Q7=P7
3400 P7=P(7)
3410 P(7)=Q7
3420 IF P(9)=0 THEN 2960
3430 GO TO 3470
3440 IF P(9)=0 THEN 2890
3450 P8=P(13)
3460 P9=P(14)
3470 P(9)=0
3480 IF ABS(P9)<10*E*ABS(P8) THEN 3560
3490 P(1)=P8+P8
3500 P(10)=P8*P8+P9*P9
3510 P7=P7-2
3520 GO TO 3600
3530 P8=0
3540 P(7)=P(7)-1
3550 P(8)=P(8)-1
3560 P9=0
3570 P(10)=0
3580 P(1)=P8
3590 P7=P7-1
3600 Q2(2)=Q2(2)+P(1)*Q2(1)
3610 Q7=P(1)
3620 Q8=P(10)
3630 FOR Q0=2 TO P7
3640    Q2(Q0+1)=Q2(Q0+1)+Q7*Q2(Q0)-Q8*Q2(Q0-1)
3650 NEXT Q0
3660 P1(P(6))=P8
3670 P2(P(6))=P9
3680 PRINT @V5: USING "L,11X,3D,4X,S":P(6)
3690 PRINT @V5:P8,P9
3700 P(6)=P(6)+1
3710 IF P(10)=0 THEN 3750
3720 P9=-P9
3730 P(10)=0
3740 GO TO 3660
3750 IF P7>0 THEN 2860
3760 RETURN

3770 REM   END OF "POLYNOMIAL ROOTS"
3780 REM   ************************
3790 REM       B-ARRAY (POLAR)

3800 FOR I=1 TO N2
3810    FOR J=1 TO N2
3820       IF I=J THEN 3890
3830       X=P1(I)-P1(J)
```

```
3840        Y=P2(I)-P2(J)
3850        GOSUB 4770
3860        B1(I,J)=M
3870        B2(I,J)=A
3880        GO TO 3910
3890        B1(I,J)=1
3900        B2(I,J)=0
3910     NEXT J
3920 NEXT I

3930 REM       P-ARRAY (POLAR)

3940 FOR I=1 TO N2
3950     X=P1(I)
3960     Y=P2(I)
3970     GOSUB 4770
3980     A3(I)=M
3990     A4(I)=A

4000 NEXT I

4010 REM       A-ARRAY (POLAR)

4020 FOR I=1 TO N2
4030     FOR J=3 TO N2+1
4040         A1(I,J)=A3(I)^(J-2)*Q1(J)
4050         A2(I,J)=A4(I)*(J-2)
4060     NEXT J
4070 NEXT I

4080 REM       A-ARRAY (RECTANGULAR)

4090 FOR I=1 TO N2
4100     FOR J=3 TO N2+1
4110         M=A1(I,J)
4120         A=A2(I,J)
4130         GOSUB 4890
4140         A1(I,J)=X
4150         A2(I,J)=Y
4160     NEXT J
4170 NEXT I

4180 REM       SUM A(I,J)=C1(I),C2(I) (POLAR)

4190 FOR I=1 TO N2
4200     C1(I)=0
4210     C2(I)=0
4220     FOR J=3 TO N2+1
4230         C1(I)=C1(I)+A1(I,J)
4240         C2(I)=C2(I)+A2(I,J)
4250     NEXT J
4260     X=C1(I)
4270     Y=C2(I)
4280     GOSUB 4770
4290     C1(I)=M
4300     C2(I)=A
4310 NEXT I

4320 REM       PRODUCT B(I,J)=G(I) (POLAR)

4330 FOR I=1 TO N2
4340     G1(I)=1
4350     G2(I)=0
4360     FOR J=1 TO N2
```

```
4370       G1(I)=G1(I)*B1(I,J)
4380       G2(I)=G2(I)+B2(I,J)
4390    NEXT J
4400 NEXT I
4410 FOR I=1 TO N2
4420    C1(I)=C1(I)/G1(I)
4430    C2(I)=C2(I)-G2(I)
4440 NEXT I

4450 REM       RESIDUE K(I) (RECTANGULAR)
4460 REM       E-ARRAY (POLAR)

4470 PAGE
4480 PRINT @V5: USING 4490:
4490 IMAGE" TIME MS           FREQ. DEVIATION HZ J_"
4500 FOR L=0 TO 60
4510    T=T9+L*T8
4520    FOR I=1 TO N2
4530       E9=EXP(T*P1(I))
4540       X=E9*COS(T*P2(I))
4550       Y=E9*SIN(T*P2(I))
4560       GOSUB 4770
4570       E1(I)=M
4580       E2(I)=A
4590    NEXT I
4600    FOR I=1 TO N2
4610       M=E1(I)*C1(I)
4620       A=E2(I)+C2(I)
4630       GOSUB 4890
4640       K1(I)=X
4650       K2(I)=Y
4660    NEXT I

4670    REM       SUM OF RESIDUES (RECTANGULAR)

4680    K5=0
4690    K6=0
4700    FOR I=1 TO N2
4710       K5=K5+K1(I)
4720       K6=K6+K2(I)
4730    NEXT I
4740    PRINT @V5:T*1000,360*S4*K5/360*(N8*F4+F5)
4750 NEXT L
4760 END

4770 REM    *** RECTANGULAR TO POLAR CONVERSION ***

4780 M=SQR(X*X+Y*Y)
4790 A=0
4800 IF M=0 THEN 4870
4810 IF Y=0 THEN 4870
4820 A=ACS(X/M)
4830 IF Y=>0 THEN 4870
4840 A=-A
4850 GO TO 4870
4860 A=PI/2-SGN(X)*PI/2
4870 RETURN

4880 REM    *** POLAR TO RECTANGULAR CONVERSION ***

4890 X=M*COS(A)
4900 Y=M*SIN(A)
4910 RETURN
4920 END
```

A-2-6 High-Order Loop Analysis Program with Graphics for TEK4051/52/54

In the various theoretical discussions in the beginning of this book, we have learned that there are no such things as pure first-, second-, or third-order loops. In addition, we have seen that the amplifiers involved have their own phase and frequency response and that feed-through capacitors add additional phase to the system.

It is mathematically very difficult to generate equations that take all of these values into consideration, and for reasons of stability, we generally analyze, as we have seen in the discussions of the Bode diagram, the area at which the open-loop gain is about 10 dB and determine the phase margin at 0-dB gain. Fairly complex filters that do not affect the stability of the loop can be added, as their phase influence is minimal and the reference suppression achieves a prescribed value. Such filters can either be active or passive types, as we have seen.

The following program, which has some limitations in accuracy, allows the analysis of a phase-locked loop with a number of complex elements in it. The example that I have chosen does not incorporate a mixer.

The incorporation of a mixer will change the division ratio N, and depending on the filter used, will add some phase. In this particular program, phase corrections for mixing schemes are not taken into consideration, and the program is really recommended for single-loop synthesizers with LC Cauer low-pass filters.

As it is easier to get acquainted with the program by using it, we will now analyze a phase-locked-loop system with the following parameters:

Oscillator frequency	225 MHz
Division ratio	$N = 9000$
Voltage gain	16 MHz/V
Phase discriminator gain	1.1 V/rad
Dc loop gain	K2 = 1
Efficiency of sampler	$E = 0.99$
Reference frequency	25 kHz
Lag 1 is active filter	
Lag 1 is	0.021 kHz
F4	0.088 kHz
F6	0.16 kHz
F7	5 MHz
Cauer low-pass filter order	$M = 7$
Cutoff frequency	$F = 11.8$ kHz
Zeros of the Hurwitz polynoms	
$\omega(1) = 0$	$\sigma(1) = 0.20363$
$\omega(2) = 0.47012$	$\sigma(2) = 0.17566$
$\omega(3) = 0.81835$	$\sigma(3) = 0.11038$
$\omega(4) = 0.99360$	$\sigma(4) = 0.03650$

The low-pass filter as shown in the loop of Figure A-39 is calculated using the

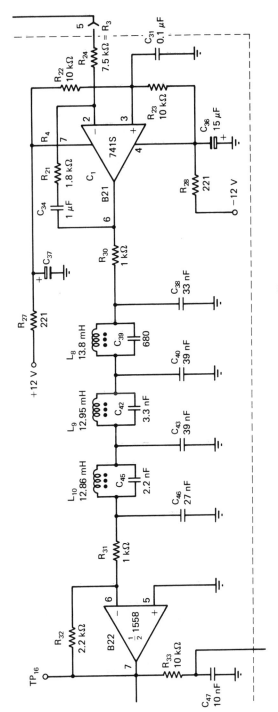

Figure A-39 *LC* type CO75030 filter.

Handbook of Filter Synthesis by Anatol Zverev (page 287) and would properly be called C075030. This means that the reflection coefficient is allowed to be 50% and the angle of 30° determines the suppression. I assume that the reader is familiar with the design of elliptical low-pass filters. Zverev's book (page 137) shows how these filters are being realized. An updated version of this book is the book by Rudolf Saal, *Handbook of Filter Design* (AEG Telefunken, Berlin, 1979). Saal's book provides additional information on digital filters and some complex transformations.

After the program is typed into a Tektronix computer, these values are entered with the user definable key 1. The computer will then respond by reprinting all the information entered, which allows one to check the input. The user-definable key 2 activates the first portion of the program starting in line 1200, in which the block diagram is repeated and corrections can be made by entering new values for the components. For example, if the division ratio should be changed, the same variable as that printed on the display is the one used by the actual program and therefore has to be newly defined (see Figure A-40). User-definable key 3 will generate a printout of the stability of the loop. Table A-23 shows the result which is determined by the computer program starting in line 8000. Even before seeing the Bode diagram, the most important results are already available. The natural frequency of the loop, which is defined by $K_o \times K_\theta/N$, is calculated to be 2.151 kHz and should not be confused with the natural loop frequency described as ω_n, here called loop bandwidth, of 0.507 kHz.

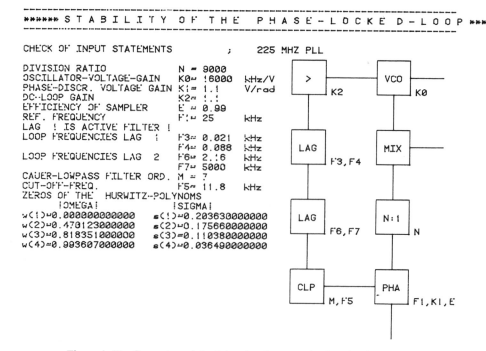

Figure A-40 Computer printout showing the entered values for the components.

TABLE A-23 PRINTOUT OF THE LOOP FREQUENCY AND GAIN AND PHASE MARGINS OF THE LOOP

```
**** S T A B I L I T Y - C R Y T E R I O N *****


   225 MHZ PLL

   LOOP -FREQUENCY          = 2.15111111111 kHz

   GAIN-MARGIN              = 10.3133319262 dB

   AT                       = 1.40522178537 kHz

   PHASE-MARGIN             = 46.8816019297 Deg

   NATURAL LOOP FREQUENCY   = 0.506850554279 kHz

   OVERSHOT                 = 2.0271780845 dB

   AT                       = 0.450533826026 kHz

   ZETA                     = 0.4411802683
```

The gain margin determined by the computer program is 10.3 dB at 1.4 kHz and the phase margin is 46.8°. The overshoot is 2 dB at 0.450 kHz and the damping factor ζ is 0.44. Since this program is highly interactive, I recommend that the reader change values in the input statement and experiment with the loop performance. This loop simulation gives a great insight into the stability and general performance of a loop. Also, one must be aware that this is a simulation, as most of the parameters cannot be changed that easily. Both the VCO gain and the phase detector gain can be changed only within very narrow limits, and the additional amplifier K2 can be inserted to increase the loop gain at the expense of additional noise generated by the amplifier. We must always remember the general rule of keeping the VCO gain as small as possible and make the phase gain as high as possible.

Figure A-41 now shows the Bode diagram, and the two critical points for phase and gain margin can easily be determined. The Bode diagram is initiated with the user-definable key 4, and the portion of the program for the Bode plot starts in line 2000. The Bode diagram in this particular case is only an optical reassurance, as the first printout already indicated the stable performance.

Finally, the computer can calculate the open- and closed-loop transfer characteristic of the phase-locked loop, which can get started with the user-definable key 5 or program starting in line 9000.

The printout in Table A-24 is generated by this program and verifies the previous results.

There is a limitation to this program that should be mentioned. The attenuation calculated at the reference frequency is incorrect and the last two or three readings before this value should be used for extrapolation to determine the reference suppression.

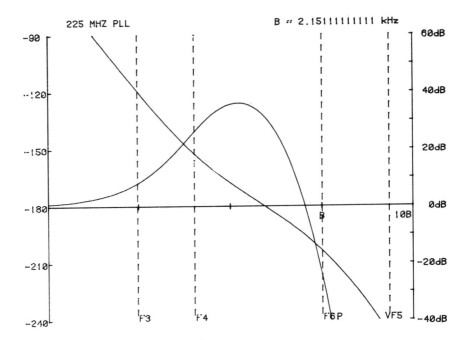

Figure A-41 Bode diagram of the loop described by the block diagram, Figure A-40.

TABLE A-24 PRINTOUT OF THE TRANSFER CHARACTERISTIC OF THE OPEN AND CLOSED LOOPS (225-MHz PLL)

FREQUENCY	OPEN		CLOSED	
kHz	dB	Deg	dB	Deg
0.0010	93.10	-179.42	0.00	-180.00
0.0017	83.67	-178.99	0.00	-180.00
0.0030	74.25	-178.27	0.00	-180.00
0.0051	64.84	-177.03	0.00	-180.00
0.0088	55.44	-174.90	0.01	-180.01
0.0151	46.10	-171.28	0.04	-180.04
0.0259	36.91	-165.30	0.12	-180.21
0.0446	28.11	-156.08	0.32	-180.95
0.0768	20.14	-144.00	0.70	-183.59
0.1321	13.37	-132.44	1.21	-190.48
0.2272	7.64	-126.22	1.66	-203.92
0.3909	2.44	-128.46	2.00	-48.12
0.6724	-2.68	-141.22	1.36	-94.15
1.1569	-8.16	-167.07	-4.08	-159.03
1.9904	-14.53	-208.26	-13.01	-214.34
3.4243	-22.24	-267.99	-22.24	-272.42
5.8912	-31.35	-377.71	-31.57	-377.25
10.1355	-42.18	-586.92	-42.13	-587.25
17.4375	-57.55	-887.74	-57.54	-887.72
30.0000	-74.41	-1002.01	-74.41	-1002.02

Because of the mathematical complexity, the attenuation of the *LC* low-pass filter is not included, and provision has been made only for the influence of phase. As in our example, the cutoff frequency of the low-pass filter is set at 11 kHz, while the natural loop frequency is at about 500 Hz. The influence of the low-pass section on stability is important only as it changes the phase, and the initial reduction in gain is very small. However, if the cutoff frequency is chosen too close to the natural loop frequency, incorrect results may be obtained. This compromise had to be made so as not to make the program too complicated, and it reflects typical design values. Table A-25 shows the printout of the phase-locked-loop analysis program.

TABLE A-25 PRINTOUT OF THE PHASE-LOCKED-LOOP ANALYSIS PROGRAM

```
2 REM**********************************************************************
3 REM************.ANALYSIS OF A PHASE LOCK LOOP ***************************
4 REM**********************************************************************
5 REM**** MAIN-PROGRAMM ***************************************************
6 REM****************************************************' ****************

7 GO TO 1000
8 T=32

9 REM KEY   2 CHECK OF INPUTS

10 GO TO 1200
12 T=32

13 REM KEY 3    STABILITY CRYTERION

14 GO TO 8000
16 T=32

17 REM KEY 4 BODE-PLOT

18 GO TO 2010
20 T=32

21 REM KEY 5 LISTING OF RESULTS

22 GO TO 9000
48 T=1
49 GO TO 1200
52 T=1
53 GO TO 8000
56 T=1
57 GO TO 2010
60 T=1
61 GO TO 9000
1000 SET DEGREES
1010 T=32
1020 DIM A$(7),B$(92),C$(7),D$(92),S(20),W(20)
1030 SET NOKEY
1040 DATA "DIVISION RATIO       ","N ="," "
1050 DATA "OSCILLATOR-VOLTAGE-GAIN","K0=","KHZ/V"
1060 DATA "PHASE-DISCR. VOLTAGE GAIN","K1=","V/RAD"
1070 DATA "DC-LOOP GAIN","K2="," "
1080 DATA "EFFICIENCY OF SAMPLER","E ="," "
1090 DATA "REF. FREQUENCY","F1=","KHZ"
1100 DATA "LOOP FREQUENCIES LAG  1","F3=","KHZ"," ","F4=","KHZ"
1110 DATA "LOOP FREQUENCIES LAG  2","F6=","KHZ"," ","F7=","KHZ"
1120 DATA "CAUER-LOWPASS FILTER ORD. ","M ="," "
1130 DATA "CUT-OFF-FREQ. ","F5=","KHZ"
```

```
1140 DATA "ZEROS OF THE  HURWITZ-POLYNOMS","\OMEGA\","\SIGMA\"

1150 REM CALL BLOCK-DIAGRAMM

1160 GOSUB 4060

1170 REM CALL DATA-INPUT

1180 GOSUB 3000
1190 SET KEY

1200 REM CALL BLOCK-DIAGRAMM

1210 GOSUB 4060

1220 REM CALL CHECK OF INPUT STATEMENTS

1230 GOSUB 6260
1240 END

2000 REM*******************************************************************
2010 REM CALL BODE-PLOT

2020 VIEWPORT 10,120,10,90
2030 WINDOW -3,1,-240,-90
2040 B=ABS(K0*K1*K2/N)
2050 GOSUB 5000

2060 REM PHASE-PLOT

2070 MOVE @T:-3,-90
2080 FOR X=-3 TO 1 STEP 0.05

2090     REM FREQUENCY IN KHZ

2100     F=B*10^X

2110     REM CALL PHASE

2120     GOSUB 6000
2130     DRAW @T:X,P
2140     IF P<-240 THEN 2160
2150 NEXT X
2160 PRINT @T:" P"

2170 REM GAIN-PLOT

2180 WINDOW -3,1,-40,60
2190 MOVE @T:-3,60
2200 FOR X=-3 TO 1 STEP 0.05

2210     REM FREQUENCY IN KHZ

2220     F=B*10^X

2230     REM CALL GAIN

2240     GOSUB 7000
2250     V=20*LGT(V)
2260     DRAW @T:X,V
2270     IF V<-40 THEN 2290
2280 NEXT X
2290 PRINT @T:" V"
2300 END
```

```
3000 REM*********************************************************************
3010 REM**** SUBROUTINE "DATA-INPUT" ****************************************
3020 REM*********************************************************************

3030 RESTORE 1040
3040 PRINT "DATA-INPUT
3050 PRINT "REMARK=";
3060 INPUT D$
3070 GOSUB 4010
3080 INPUT N
3090 GOSUB 4010
3100 INPUT K0
3110 GOSUB 4010
3120 INPUT K1
3130 GOSUB 4010
3140 INPUT K2
3150 GOSUB 4010
3160 INPUT E
3170 E=ABS(E)
3180 IF E<=1 THEN 3210
3190 PRINT "***** E > 1 *****  E=?"
3200 GO TO 3160
3210 GOSUB 4010
3220 INPUT F1
3230 F1=ABS(F1)
3240 GOSUB 4010
3250 INPUT F3
3260 GOSUB 4010
3270 INPUT F4
3280 PRINT "IS AMPLIFIER USED   ? [1/0]";
3290 INPUT A$
3300 IF A$="1" THEN 3370
3310 IF NOT(A$="0") THEN 3280
3320 H=ABS(F3)
3330 F3=H MIN ABS(F4)
3340 F4=H MAX ABS(F4)
3350 A=0
3360 GO TO 3380
3370 A=1
3380 GOSUB 4010
3390 INPUT F6
3400 GOSUB 4010
3410 INPUT F7
3420 H=ABS(F6)
3430 F6=H MIN ABS(F7)
3440 F7=H MAX ABS(F7)
3450 GOSUB 4010
3460 INPUT M
3470 M=INT(ABS(M))
3480 M1=INT((M+1)/2)
3490 GOSUB 4010
3500 INPUT F5
3510 F5=ABS(F5)
3520 READ B$,A$,C$
3530 PRINT B$
3540 PRINT USING "6X,7A,12X,7A":A$,C$
3550 IMAGE"W(",FD,")=",S
3560 IMAGE20T,"K_S(",FD,")=",S
3570 W(1)=0
3580 FOR I=1 TO M1
3590    PRINT USING 3550:I
3600    IF I=1 AND M/2<>M1 THEN 3640
3610    INPUT W(I)
```

```
3620     W(I)=ABS(W(I))
3630     GO TO 3650
3640     PRINT USING "D.10D":W(1)
3650     PRINT USING 3560:I
3660     INPUT S(I)
3670     S(I)=ABS(S(I))
3680 NEXT I
3690 RETURN


4000 REM******************************************************************
4010 REM****** SUBROUTINE STATEMENTS ************************************
4020 REM******************************************************************

4030 READ B$,A$,C$
4040 PRINT @T: USING "26A,27T,3A,8X,5A,13("""H_"")",S":B$,A$,C$
4050 RETURN


4060 REM******************************************************************
4070 REM**** SUBROUTINE "BLOCK-DIAGRAMM" ******************************
4080 REM******************************************************************

4090 VIEWPORT 0,130,0,100
4100 WINDOW 0,130,0,100


4110 REM HEADER

4120 PRINT @T: USING "P,72("""-""")":
4130 PRINT @T:"****** S T A B I L I T Y   O F   T H E";
4140 PRINT @T:"   P H A S E - L O C K - L O O P ***"
4150 PRINT @T: USING "72("""-""")":
4160 DATA " > ","K2","LAG","F3,F4","LAG","F6,F7","CLP","M,F5","VCO","K0"
4170 DATA "MIX"," ","N:1","N","PHA","F1,K1,E",90,80,15,90,20,15
4180 DATA 115,80,10,115,60,10
4190 RESTORE 4160
4200 FOR H=90 TO 115 STEP 25
4210     FOR V=75 TO 15 STEP -20
4220         MOVE @T:H,V
4230         RDRAW @T:0,10
4240         RDRAW @T:-10,0
4250         RDRAW @T:0,-10
4260         RDRAW @T:10,0
4270         READ A$,B$
4280         PRINT @T:" ";B$;
4290         RMOVE @T:-7.5,3.9
4300         PRINT @T:A$
4310         IF H=90 AND V=15 THEN 4340
4320         MOVE @T:H-5,V
4330         RDRAW @T:0,-10
4340     NEXT V
4350 NEXT H
4360 FOR I=1 TO 4
4370     READ H,V,H1
4380     MOVE @T:H,V
4390     RDRAW @T:H1,0
4400 NEXT I
4410 HOME @T:
4420 PRINT @T:"J_J_J_"
4430 RETURN


5000 REM******************************************************************
5010 REM**** BODE - PLOT ************************************************
5020 REM******************************************************************
```

```
5030 PAGE @T:
5040 PRI @T:"          B O D E - P L O T                OPEN LOOP         "
5050 PRINT @T: USING "/,8X,32A,4X,""B = "",FD.FD,"" KHZ""":D$,B
5060 AXIS @T:1,30,-3,-180
5070 AXIS @T:1,15,1,-180
5080 MOVE @T:-0.02,-187
5090 PRINT @T:"B"
5100 MOVE @T:0.8,-187
5110 PRINT @T:"10B"
5120 FOR I=-90 TO -240 STEP -30
5130     MOVE @T:-3,I-2
5140     PRINT @T:"H_H_H_H_"; I
5150     RMOVE @T:4.05,0
5160     PRINT @T: USING "3D,""DB""":120+I/1.5
5170 NEXT I
5180 A$="F1"
5190 H=F1
5200 GOSUB 5370
5210 A$="F3"
5220 H=F3
5230 GOSUB 5370
5240 A$="F4"
5250 H=F4
5260 GOSUB 5370
5270 A$="F5"
5280 H=F5
5290 GOSUB 5370
5300 A$="F6"
5310 H=F6
5320 GOSUB 5370
5330 A$="F7"
5340 H=F7
5350 GOSUB 5370
5360 RETURN

5370 REM*************************************************************************
5380 REM**** SUBROUTINE "VERTICAL-MARKING" **************************
5390 REM*************************************************************************

5400 IF H>10*B OR H<B/1000 THEN 5490
5410 H=LGT(H/B)
5420 MOVE @T:H,-90
5430 FOR I=1 TO 25
5440     RDRAW @T:0,-3
5450     RMOVE @T:0,-3
5460 NEXT I
5470 RMOVE @T:0.02,0
5480 PRINT @T:A$
5490 RETURN

6000 REM*************************************************************************
6010 REM**** SUBROUTINE "PHASE" *************************************
6020 REM*************************************************************************
6030 REM STARTING-VALUES

6040 P=-90

6050 REM SAMPLER
6060 H=360*F/F1
6070 P=P-H/2-ATN(SIN(H)/(1/(1-E+1.0E-7)-COS(H)))

6080 REM LAG  1
```

```
6090 IF A=1 THEN 6130

6100 REM PASSIV

6110 P=P+ATN(F/F4)-ATN(F/F3)
6120 GO TO 6150

6130 REM AKTIV

6140 P=P-ATN(F4/F)

6150 REM LAG  1

6160 P=P+ATN(F/F7)-ATN(F/F6)

6170 REM CAUER-LOW-PASS-FILTER

6180 FOR I=1 TO M1
6190    IF I=1 AND M/2<>M1 THEN 6230
6200    P=P-ATN((F/F5-W(I))/S(I))
6210    P=P-ATN((F/F5+W(I))/S(I))
6220    GO TO 6240
6230    P=P-ATN(F/F5/S(1))
6240 NEXT I
6250 RETURN

6260 REM******************************************************************
6270 REM**** SUBROUTINE "CONTROLL OF  INPUT-STATEMENTS" *****************
6280 REM******************************************************************

6290 PRINT @T:"CHECK OF INPUT STATEMENTS                ";D$,"J_"
6300 RESTORE 1040
6310 GOSUB 4010
6320 PRINT @T:N
6330 GOSUB 4010
6340 PRINT @T:K0
6350 GOSUB 4010
6360 PRINT @T:K1
6370 GOSUB 4010
6380 PRINT @T:K2
6390 GOSUB 4010
6400 PRINT @T:E
6410 GOSUB 4010
6420 PRINT @T:F1
6430 IF A=0 THEN 6450
6440 PRINT @T:"LAG  1 IS ACTIVE FILTER !"
6450 GOSUB 4010
6460 PRINT @T:F
6470 GOSUB 4010
6480 PRINT @T:F4
6490 GOSUB 4010
6500 PRINT @T:F6
6510 GOSUB 4010
6520 PRINT @T:F7
6530 GOSUB 4010
6540 PRINT @T:M
6550 GOSUB 4010
6560 PRINT @T:F5
6570 READ B$,A$,C$
6580 PRINT @T:B$
6590 PRINT @T: USING "6X,7A,12X,7A":A$,C$
6600 FOR I=1 TO M1
6610    PRINT @T: USING "2(2A,FD,"")="",D.12D,3X)":"W(",I,W(I),"S(",I,S(I)
```

472

```
6620 NEXT I
6630 RETURN

7000 REM*****************************************************************
7010 REM**** SUBROUTINE "AMPLIFICATION" ******************************
7020 REM*****************************************************************
7030 REM START-VALUE

7040 V=B/F

7050 REM SAMPLER

7060 H=ABS(SIN(180*F/F1))
7070 V=V*H/(PI*F/F1)/SQR(1+4*(1-E)*(H/E)^2)

7080 REM LAG  1

7090 IF A=1 THEN 7130

7100 REM PASSIV

7110 V=V*SQR((1+F*F/F4/F4)/(1+F*F/F3/F3))
7120 GO TO 7150

7130 REM ACTIVE

7140 V=V*F3*SQR(1/F4/F4+1/F/F)

7150 REM LAG  2

7160 V=V*SQR((1+F*F/F7/F7)/(1+F*F/F6/F6))

7170 REM CAUER-LOW-PASS-FILTER V=1

7180 RETURN

8000 REM*****************************************************************
8010 REM**** SUBROUTINE "STABILITY-CRYTERION   " ************************
8020 REM*****************************************************************

8030 PRINT @T: USING "P,72(""-"")":
8040 PRINT @T:"**** S T A B I L I T Y - C R Y T E R I O N *****"
8050 PRINT @T: USING "72(""-""),//,32A":D$
8060 B=ABS(K0*K1*K2/N)
8070 PRINT @T:"J_NATURAL-FREQUENCY      = ";B;" KHZ"

8080 REM GAIN-MARGIN

8090 B1=B
8100 F=B1

8110 REM CALL PHASE

8120 GOSUB 6000
8130 H1=P+180
8140 F=1.00001*B1

8150 REM CALL PHASE

8160 GOSUB 6000
8170 H2=P+180
8180 B1=B1*(1-1.0E-5/(H2/H1-1))
8190 IF ABS(H1)>0.01 THEN 8100
```

```
8200 REM

8210 F=B1

8220 REM CALL GAIN

8230 GOSUB 7000
8240 V1=-20*LGT(V)
8250 PRINT @T:"J_GAIN-MARGIN               = ";V1;" DB"
8260 PRINT @T:"J_AT                        = ";B1;" KHZ"

8270 REM PHASE-MARGIN

8280 B2=0. 1
8290 F=B*10^B2

8300 REM CALL GAIN

8310 GOSUB 7000
8320 H1=20*LGT(V)
8330 F=B*10^(1.00001*B2)

8340 REM CALL GAIN

8350 GOSUB 7000
8360 H2=20*LGT(V)
8370 B2=B2*(1-1.0E-5/(H2/H1-1))
8380 IF ABS(H1)>0.01 THEN 8290
8390 B2=B*10^B2
8400 F=B2

8410 REM CALL PHASE

8420 GOSUB 6000
8430 P2=180+P
8440 PRINT @T:"J_PHASE-MARGIN             = ";P2;" DEG "
8450 PRINT @T:"J_LOOP-BANDWIDTH           = ";B2;" KHZ"

8460 REM OVERSHOOT

8470 F=B2
8480 H1=0
8490 Q=B2/9

8500 REM CALL GAIN, PHASE

8510 GOSUB 7000
8520 GOSUB 6000
8530 H2=V/SQR(1+V*V+2*V*COS(P))
8540 IF ABS(1-H1/H2)<2.0E-4 THEN 8600
8550 IF H2>H1 THEN 8570
8560 Q=-Q/2
8570 F=F+Q
8580 H1=H2
8590 GO TO 8510
8600 B3=F
8610 V3=20*LGT(H2)
8620 PRINT @T:"J_OVERSHOOT                = ";V3;" DB"
8630 PRINT @T:"J_AT                       = ";B3;" KHZ"
8640 Z=SQR(0.5*(1-SQR(1-1/H2/H2)))
8650 PRINT @T:"J_ZETA                     = ";Z
8660 END
```

```
9000 REM*******************************************************************
9010 REM******** SUBROUTINE RESULTS *************************************
9020 REM*******************************************************************

9030 B$="TRANSFER-CHARACTERISTIC OF THE LOOPI_"
9039 PAGE
9040 HOME @T:
9041 PRINT @T:B$,D$
9050 PRINT "J_J_F MIN (KHZ)= ";
9060 INPUT F9
9070 PRINT "F MAX (KHZ)= ";
9080 INPUT F8
9090 H=ABS(F9)
9100 F9=H MIN ABS(F8)
9110 F8=H MAX ABS(F8)
9120 PRINT "STEPS= ";
9130 INPUT I1

9140 REM HEADER

9141 PAGE
9142 HOME @T:
9150 PRINT @T:B$,D$
9160 PRINT @T: USING "/,6X,""FREQUENCY"",10X,""OPEN "",15X,S":
9170 PRINT @T: USING """CLOSED      "",/":
9180 PRINT @T: USING "9X,""KHZ "",2(8X,""DB"",8X,""DEG ""),/":
9190 I2=(F8/F9)^(1/(I1-1))
9200 B=ABS(K0*K1*K2/N)
9210 F=F9
9220 FOR J=1 TO I1

9230     REM GAIN,PHASE

9240     GOSUB 7000
9250     GOSUB 6000
9260     V4=V/SQR(1+V*V+2*V*COS(P))
9270     V4=20*LGT(V4)
9280     P4=P-ATN(V*SIN(P)/(1+V*COS(P)))
9290     V=20*LGT(V)
9300     PRINT @T: USING "9D.4D,4(8D.2D)":F,V,P,V4,P4
9310     F=I2*F
9320 NEXT J
9330 END

10000 REM LIST THE  PROGRAMM


10010 U=41
10030 LIST @U:1,1999
10040 LIST @U:2000,2999
10050 LIST @U:3000,3999
10060 LIST @U:4000,4999
10070 LIST @U:5000,5999
10080 LIST @U:6000,6999
10090 LIST @U:7000,7999
10100 LIST @U:8000,8999
10110 LIST @U:9000,9999
```

A-2-7 Computer Program for Intermodulation Distortion Products in Mixers (TEK 4051/52/54)

In Chapter 4 a lot of emphasis was put on the possible generation of harmonics at the output due to improper termination. The mixer by itself generates a number of harmonics and products because of its inherent nonlinearities and imperfect matching. The following computer program in BASIC is written for a Tektronix 4051/52/54 computer and uses a lookup table in lines 180 to 260 containing the intermodulation distortion products for a special double-balanced mixer which consists of two rings in push-pull, as shown earlier. This mixer is being driven with $+17$ dBm of LO drive, and the RF input is at 0 dBm. All combination frequencies have been measured, and once the computer program is told what frequency bands and range are being used, the computer program will print out the mixing products. In lines 340 to 550, the computer will ask for the upper and lower input frequency, the upper and lower LO frequency, and the upper and lower output frequency. This is necessary as the frequencies normally are not discrete frequencies but frequency bands. The computer can increment those, and in addition, the computer will ask about the highest intermodulation product.

In practice, it may not be required to look for higher orders than 8 if a high-performance mixer is used. One of the important things is that the isolation of the mixer, which for standard mixers is only 25 to 30 dB, indicates the LO feed-through. This means that if a higher-level mixer is used that has the same isolation, the mixing products may be reduced, but the LO feed-through in the IF part, while at the same attenuation, is now higher in absolute value and can cause problems. The particular model CPC106 mixer, which was designed for the Communications Product Corporation Model HF1030 shortwave receiver, offers 60-dB isolation. The higher-order products, even at an RF level of 0 dBm, are about 100 dB down and were very difficult to measure for orders higher than 8. For this particular mixer, it may be sufficient to limit N to 8. If a different mixer is used, the lookup table may be expanded to higher orders; generally, for higher orders, an attenuation of 100 dB may be assumed. Therefore, it is possible to obtain a printout for orders higher than order N.

The product first considers the $M \times \text{LO} + N \times$ input frequency intermodulation distortion products, and all combinations of M and N are considered. These frequency combinations are then computed and listed with the corresponding M and N values printed, and the level of the intermodulation distortion products indicates the level by referring to 0 dBm input. It can be assumed that for a 10-dB decrease in RF level, second-order intermodulation distortion products are reduced by 20 dB, third order by 30 dB, and Nth order by $N \times 10$ dB.

However, harmonic content is somewhat difficult to determine. That is, as a rough estimate within a certain range, it can be assumed that for any 10-dB reduction, the output will also go down 10 dB. This depends on the particular type of mixer, but for most combinations was found to be fairly accurate.

In addition, the computer program determines the combination of $M \times \text{LO} - N \times$ input frequency intermodulation distortion products and again considers whether these frequencies fall into the range of interest. Table A-26 shows a listing of the program.

TABLE A-26 PRINTOUT OF THE MIXING PRODUCTS GENERATED INSIDE THE CPC106 MIXER

```
LOWER INPUT FREQUENCY =0. 01MHZ
UPPER INPUT FREQUENCY =30MHZ
LOWER LO FREQUENCY=40. 455MHZ
UPPER LO FREQUENCY=70. 455MHZ
LOWER OUTPUT FREQUENCY=40. 45MHZ
UPPER OUTPUT FREQUENCY=40. 46MHZ
FREQUENCY BAND OF M*LO+N*INPUT FREQ. INTERMOD. PROD.
    0*LO +    2*IN    RANGE:     0. 020   TO     60. 000 MHZ;   LEVEL -70DB
    0*LO +    3*IN    RANGE:     0. 030   TO     90. 000 MHZ;   LEVEL -75DB
    0*LO +    4*IN    RANGE:     0. 040   TO    120. 000 MHZ;   LEVEL -90DB
    0*LO +    5*IN    RANGE:     0. 050   TO    150. 000 MHZ;   LEVEL -90DB
    0*LO +    6*IN    RANGE:     0. 060   TO    180. 000 MHZ;   LEVEL-100DB
    0*LO +    7*IN    RANGE:     0. 070   TO    210. 000 MHZ;   LEVEL-100DB
    0*LO +    8*IN    RANGE:     0. 080   TO    240. 000 MHZ;   LEVEL-100DB
    1*LO +    0*IN    RANGE:    40. 455   TO     70. 455 MHZ;   LEVEL -60DB
FREQUENCY BAND OF M*LO-N*INPUT FREQ. INTERMOD. PROD.
    1*LO -    1*IN    RANGE:    10. 455   TO     70. 445 MHZ,   LEVEL   0DB
    1*LO -    2*IN    RANGE:   -19. 545   TO     70. 435 MHZ;   LEVEL -72DB
    1*LO -    3*IN    RANGE:   -49. 545   TO     70. 425 MHZ;   LEVEL -63DB
    1*LO -    4*IN    RANGE:   -79. 545   TO     70. 415 MHZ;   LEVEL -84DB
    1*LO -    5*IN    RANGE:  -109. 545   TO     70. 405 MHZ;   LEVEL -84DB
    1*LO -    6*IN    RANGE:  -139. 545   TO     70. 395 MHZ;   LEVEL -92DB
    1*LO -    7*IN    RANGE:  -169. 545   TO     70. 385 MHZ;   LEVEL -97DB
    2*LO -    2*IN    RANGE:    20. 910   TO    140. 890 MHZ;   LEVEL -72DB
    2*LO -    3*IN    RANGE:    -9. 090   TO    140. 880 MHZ;   LEVEL -66DB
    2*LO -    4*IN    RANGE:   -39. 090   TO    140. 870 MHZ;   LEVEL -97DB
    2*LO -    5*IN    RANGE:   -69. 090   TO    140. 860 MHZ;   LEVEL -86DB
    2*LO -    6*IN    RANGE:   -99. 090   TO    140. 850 MHZ;   LEVEL -97DB
    3*LO -    3*IN    RANGE:    31. 365   TO    211. 335 MHZ;   LEVEL -72DB
    3*LO -    4*IN    RANGE:     1. 365   TO    211. 325 MHZ;   LEVEL -86DB
    3*LO -    5*IN    RANGE:   -28. 635   TO    211. 315 MHZ;   LEVEL -72DB
```

Let us assume an example: Our RF frequency ranges from 10 kHz to 30 MHz for an HF receiver. The LO frequency for an IF of 40.455 MHz, therefore, will range from 40.465 to 70.455 MHz. The IF, having 10-kHz bandwidth, will be 40.455 to 40.460 MHz. Table A-26 shows the combination that results. For reasons of space no steps were printed out, but this table pretty much explains how the results are given. It is always frightening to see how many frequencies are being generated and how difficult it is to avoid spurious outputs. The lowest intermodulation distortion product printed out in this list is 63 dB down and is a product generated by three times the input frequency being mixed with the local oscillator. In practical circumstances, it is not very likely that in a shortwave receiver the input mixer is being driven at 0 dBm; it is more likely that the input level will be −20 dBm. Therefore, all these levels, as printed out here, will go at least 20 dB down if they are only linearly related.

The next interesting run would be two input signals applied simultaneously to the mixer. A corresponding computer program could be generated. Table A-27 is a listing of the computer program for intermodulation distortion products.

TABLE A-27 LISTING OF THE COMPUTER PROGRAM FOR INTERMODULATION
DISTORTION PRODUCTS

```
100 REM *** PROGRAM CALCULATES MIXER INTERMODULATION PRODUCTS
110 REM     WHEN USING THE EMCO TYPE CPC-106 DOUBLE RING MIXER. ***
120 INIT
130 PAGE
140 V4=32
150 V5=32
160 DIM A1(9,9)

170 REM     TABLE OF INTERMOD. PRODUCT LEVELS:

180 DATA 0,60,70,75,90,90,100,100,100
190 DATA 60,0,72,63,84,84,92,97,100
200 DATA 60,35,72,66,97,86,97,102,100
210 DATA 70,15,70,72,86,72,95,95,100
220 DATA 72,37,82,72,97,92,100,100,100
230 DATA 72,37,62,58,90,70,100,100,100
240 DATA 62,45,75,86,100,95,95,100,100
250 DATA 70,40,75,58,90,70,100,90,100
260 DATA 70,50,100,80,92,92,100,100,100

270 REM     ARRAY OF TABLE VALUES:

280 FOR I=1 TO 9
290     FOR J=1 TO 9
300         READ A1(I,J)
310     NEXT J
320 NEXT I

330 REM     INPUT ROUTINE:

340 PRINT @V4:"LOWER INPUT FREQUENCY   =";
350 INPUT F1
360 PRINT @V4:"UPPER INPUT FREQUENCY   =";
370 INPUT F2
380 PRINT @V4:"LOWER LO FREQUENCY=";
390 INPUT F5
400 PRINT @V4:"UPPER LO FREQUENCY=";
410 INPUT F6
420 PRINT @V4:"LOWER OUTPUT FREQUENCY=";
430 INPUT F7
440 PRINT @V4:"UPPER OUTPUT FREQUENCY=";
450 INPUT F8
460 PRINT @V4:"INPUT FREQUENCY INCREMENT(IF NOT USED=0)=";
470 INPUT F9
480 PRINT @V4:"LO FREQUENCY INCREMENT(IF NOT USED=0)=";
490 INPUT F0
500 PRINT @V4:"OUTPUT FREQUENCY INCREMENT(IF NOT USED=0)=";
510 INPUT G1
520 PRINT @V4:"NUMBER OF FREQUENCY INCREMENTS(IF NOT USED=0)=";
530 INPUT G2
540 PRINT @V4:"MAXIMUM INTERMODULATION PRODUCT TESTED(<=8)=";
550 INPUT G3
555 PAGE
560 PRINT @V5:
570 K=G2+1
580 FOR I=1 TO K
590     A=F1+F9*(I-1)
600     B=F2+F9*(I-1)
610     C=A
620     D=B
630     E=F5+F0*(I-1)
640     F=F6+F0*(I-1)
650     G=F7+G1*(I-1)
660     H=F8+G1*(I-1)
665     REM     PRINT-OUT OF INPUT PARAMETERS:
```

```
670      PRINT @V5:"LOWER INPUT FREQUENCY =";A;"MHZ"
680      PRINT @V5:"UPPER INPUT FREQUENCY =";B;"MHZ"
690      PRINT @V5:"LOWER LO FREQUENCY=";E;"MHZ"
700      PRINT @V5:"UPPER LO FREQUENCY=";F;"MHZ"
710      PRINT @V5:"LOWER OUTPUT FREQUENCY=";G;"MHZ"
720      PRINT @V5:"UPPER OUTPUT FREQUENCY=";H;"MHZ"
730      PRINT @V5:
740      PRINT @V5:"FREQUENCY BAND OF M*LO+N*INPUT FREQ. INTERMOD. PROD "
750      G9=G3+1
760      FOR J=1 TO G9
770         I0=G9+1-J
780         FOR K1=1 TO I0
790            I1=J-1
800            I2=K1-1
810            H2=I1*E+I2*A
820            H3=I1*F+I2*D
830            IF H2-H>0 THEN 880
840            IF H3-G=>0 THEN 860
850            GO TO 880
860            PRINT @V5: USING 870:I1,"*LO +",I2,"*IN",H2,H3,-H1(I1+1,I2+1)
870            IMAGE 2(2X,2D,5A)"  RANGE:"6D.3D,3X"TO"2X,6D.3D" MHZ,  LEVEL"4D"DB"
880         NEXT K1
890      NEXT J
900      PRINT @V5:
910      PRINT @V5:"FREQUENCY BAND OF M*LO-N*INPUT FREQ. INTERMOD. PROD. "
920      FOR I1=1 TO G3
930         I0=G3-I1
940         FOR I2=1 TO I0
950            H1=I1*E-I2*A
960            H2=I1*E-I2*B
970            H3=I1*F-I2*C
980            H4=I1*F-I2*D
990            IF H1-H3>0 THEN 1020
1000           H9=H3
1010           GO TO 1030
1020           H9=H1
1030           IF H2-H4>0 THEN 1060
1040           H8=H2
1050           GO TO 1070
1060           H8=H4
1070           IF ABS(H9)-ABS(H8)=0 THEN 1140
1080           IF ABS(H9)-ABS(H8)<0 THEN 1210
1090           IF H8<=0 THEN 1120
1100           IF H8-H>0 THEN 1250
1110           IF H8-H=0 THEN 1260
1120           IF H9-G<0 THEN 1250
1130           IF H9-G=>0 THEN 1260
1140           IF H9-H8=0 THEN 1170
1150           IF H9-G<0 THEN 1250
1160           IF H9-G=>0 THEN 1260
1170           IF ABS(H9)-H=0 THEN 1260
1180           IF ABS(H9)-H>0 THEN 1250
1190           IF ABS(H9)-G<0 THEN 1250
1200           IF ABS(H9)-G=>0 THEN 1260
1210           IF H9=>0 THEN 1240
1220           IF ABS(H9)-H=0 THEN 1260
1230           IF ABS(H9)-H>0 THEN 1250
1240           IF ABS(H8)-G=>0 THEN 1260
1250           GO TO 1280
1260           PRINT @V5: USING 1270:I1,"*LO -",I2,"*IN",H8,H9,-H1(I1+1,I2+1)
1270           IMAGE 2(2X,2D,5A)"  RANGE:"6D.3D,3X"TO"2X,6D.3D" MHZ,  LEVEL"4D"DB
1280        NEXT I2
1290     NEXT I1
1300  NEXT I
1310 END
```

REFERENCES

1. James G. Holbrook, *Laplace Transforms for Electronic Engineers*, Pergamon Press, Elmsford, NY, 1966.

2. Roland Best, *Theorie und Anwendungen des phase-locked Loops*, Fachschriftenverlag Aargauer Tagblatt AG, Aarau, Switzerland, 1976 (Order No. ISBN 3-85502-011-6, 1976).

3. Ing. F. Mohring, *Reception Techniques in the UHF Area* (Empfangstechnik im UHF-Bereich), Loewe Opta AG, 1964.

4. Kenneth K. Clarke and Donald T. Hess, *Communication Circuits: Analysis and Design*, Addison-Wesley, Reading, MA, 1971.

5. J. Kammerloher, *Transistoren*, C. F. Winter'sche Verlagshandlung, Prien, 1963.

Bibliography

DORF, RICHARD C., *Modern Control Systems*. Reading, Mass.: Addison-Wesley Publishing Company, 1980.

GORSKI-POPIEL, JERZY, *Frequency Syntheses: Techniques and Applications*. New York: IEEE Press, 1975.

Phase-Locked Loop Data Book. Phoenix, AZ: Motorola Semiconductor Products, Inc.

PRZEDPELSKI, ANDRZEJ B., "Analyze, Don't Estimate Phase-Locked Loop Performance of Type 2 Third Order Systems," *Electronic Design*, May 10, 1978.

PRZEDPELSKI, ANDRZEJ B., "Optimize Phase-Lock Loops to Meet Your Needs—or Determine Why You Can't," *Electronic Design*, September 13, 1978.

STOUT, DAVID F., and MILTON KAUFMAN. *Handbook of Operational Amplifier Circuit Design*. McGraw-Hill Book Company, 1976.

Index